Intermediate Algebra: A Text/Workbook
Second Edition

SECOND EDITION

INTERMEDIATE ALGEBRA
A Text/Workbook

Charles P. McKeague
Cuesta College

Harcourt Brace Jovanovich, Publishers
and its subsidiary, Academic Press
San Diego   New York   Chicago   Austin
London   Sydney   Tokyo   Toronto

Contents

3 Exponents and Polynomials 113

4 Rational Expressions 183

5 Rational Exponents and Roots 233

6 Quadratic Equations 283

Preface to the Instructor

This second edition of *Intermediate Algebra: A Text/Workbook* retains the same basic format and style of the first edition. The book can be used in traditional lecture classes or in a self-paced situation.

In a lecture-format class, each section of the book can be discussed in a 45–50 minute class session. A successful technique I have used in lecture classes is to have the students work some of the Practice Problems in the margins of their texts after I have done an example on the board or overhead projector.

In a self-paced situation, the Practice Problems in the margins allow the student to become actively involved with the material before starting the Problem Set that follows the section. Since each Practice Problem is similar to the example with the same number, it is fairly easy for the student to work the Practice Problems. To allow for self-evaluation, the answer to each Practice Problem is located at the bottom of the page on which the Practice Problem occurs. In addition, complete solutions to most of the Practice Problems are given in the back of the book.

Organization of the Text   The book begins with a preface to the student explaining what study habits are necessary to ensure success in an intermediate algebra course.

The rest of the book is divided into chapters. Each chapter is organized as follows:

   1. A preface to the student explains in a very general way what he or she can expect to find in the chapter. The preface also includes a list of previous material that is used to develop the concepts in the chapter.

2. The body of the chapter is divided into sections, each containing four main parts:

    a. *Explanations:* The explanations are made as simple and as intuitive as possible. The ideas, properties, and definitions from Chapters 1 and 2 are used continuously throughout the book. The objective is to introduce as few rules and definitions as possible and then refer to them when new situations are encountered.

    b. *Examples:* The examples are chosen to clarify the explanations and preview the problem sets.

    c. *Practice Problems:* In the margin of the text, next to each example, is a Practice Problem with the same number. The Practice Problems are to be worked after the example with the same number has been read.

    d. *Problem Sets:* I have incorporated five main ideas into each problem set.

       i. *Drill:* There are enough problems in each set to ensure student proficiency in the material.

      ii. *Progressive Difficulty:* The problems increase in difficulty as the problem set progresses.

     iii. *Odd-Even Similarities:* Each pair of consecutive problems is similar. The answers to the odd-numbered problems are listed in the back of the book. This gives the students a chance to check their work and then try a similar problem.

     iv. *Application Problems:* Whenever possible I have ended the problem sets with a few application problems. My experience is that students are always curious about how the algebra they are learning can be applied. Also, they are much more likely to put some time and effort into trying application problems if they don't have to work an overwhelming number of them at one time.

      v. *Review Problems:* Beginning with Chapter 2, there are a few review problems at the end of each Problem Set. When possible, these problems review material that will be needed in the next section.

3. The chapter summary and review lists the new properties and definitions found in the chapter. (Often it also contains a list of common mistakes, clearly marked as such, so that the student can learn to recognize and avoid them.) As in the first edition, the margins in the chapter summaries are used for examples. These examples are intended to refresh the student's memory as to the kind of problem that accompanies the topic being reviewed.

4. The chapter test is designed to give the student an idea of how well he or she has mastered the material in the chapter. All answers for these chapter tests are included in the back of the book.

There are a number of changes in this edition that may not be immediately apparent. Many of the sections have been rewritten so that the progression of topics proceeds more smoothly. In some cases, a new example or two has been added or the wording of the explanations rewritten. Although you may not notice these changes, your students will find the book easier to read. The more noticeable changes are included in the following list.

Sequence of Topics   The material on Venn diagrams has been moved from Section 1.1 to Appendix C at the back of the book, while the definition of integer exponents has been added to Section 1.1. Also, more material on fractions has been added to Chapter 1. The material on quadratic inequalities has been moved from Appendix B to the end of Chapter 6.

New Topics   Section 1.7 is new and covers arithmetic with calculators. It is an optional section in that it can be deleted without affecting the material in the rest of the book. Section 2.1 from the first edition has been split into two sections. The new Section 2.1 covers solving linear equations in one variable that do not contain parentheses, while Section 2.2 covers linear equations that do contain parentheses. A few examples and problems on percent have been added to the word problems in Section 2.7 (formerly Section 2.6). Section 2.8 is new and covers word problems that involve sums. Some new material on scientific notation has been added to the material in Sections 3.1 and 3.2. A new section covering factoring in general has been added to the end of Chapter 3. Section 6.5 on equations that are quadratic in form is completely new. Section 9.1 on graphing parabolas has been rewritten to include completing the square as an alternate method of locating the vertex of a parabola.

Review Problems   Starting with Chapter 2, each problem set ends with six to ten review problems. Generally, these review problems cover material that will be used in the next section. I find that assigning the review problems helps prepare my students for the next day's assignment and makes reviewing a part of their daily routine.

Problem Sets   A number of the problem sets have been rewritten. Many now have new problems toward the end that are more challenging. There are also a number of places where I have included problems toward the end of the problem sets that enhance the concepts covered in the previous problems. Many of these problems are more like word problems than drill problems. Finally, the problem sets from the first edition that produced somewhat awkward answers have been rewritten.

Word Problems   The word problems from the first edition have been retained, but the solutions to a number of them are now explained in terms of tables. Also, as in the first edition, the sections labeled ''Word Problems'' contain only three or four different types of problems. I would rather my students have just a few different types of problems to master in a given section than a wide variety of problems. In addition to the problems found in the sections labeled ''Word Problems,'' many of the other problem sets end with one or two word problems as well. Because of this, your students will be working word problems more often than they were in the first edition. You will find that all the different types of word problems you would normally expect in an intermediate algebra book are found here also; however, they are spread throughout the text and are not concentrated in a single section or chapter.

Answers to Odd-Numbered Problems   The answers to the odd-numbered problems in the back of the book have been expanded. Many of the answers for word problems now include the equation necessary to solve the problem as well as the answer to the problem. These equations are shown more often at the beginning of the book. Also, the extraneous solutions to equations involving rational expressions are listed in the answer section along with the actual solutions.

Answers to the Practice Problems The answers to the practice problems have been moved from the back of the book to the page on which the problems occur.

Solutions to the Practice Problems In this edition we have included solutions to most of the Practice Problems. These solutions are given in the back of the book and can be used by students who need extra help with the practice problems.

Supplements to the Text This new edition of *Intermediate Algebra: A Text/Workbook* is accompanied by a number of useful supplements.

1. *Videotape Package* A set of eleven one-hour videotapes is available for duplication to adopters of the text. Each tape covers one chapter of the book and is broken down into ten-minute lectures that cover each section of the chapter.
2. *Computerized Test Bank* This is a program, developed for use on an Apple® II system and almost any dot matrix printer, that provides adopters of the text with an unlimited source of tests on one diskette. The computer program will generate tests written in the format of those found in the Instructor's Resource Manual; however, the computer can provide an infinite number of variations of each type of question in each chapter test.
3. *Instructor's Resource Manual* This manual contains answers to the even-numbered problems in the text. It also contains five additional tests for each chapter of the book, a pretest, and three final exams, one of which is multiple choice. In addition, a list of objectives is given for each chapter of the book, along with a complete set of supplementary problems keyed to these objectives. The answers for the chapter tests in the manual are also keyed to these objectives so that when a student fails a test, it can be quickly determined which objectives he or she needs to work on. The appropriate problems from the supplementary problems can then be assigned.

I have tried to make this book flexible and easy to use. It has been written to assist both you and your students in the classroom.

Acknowledgments

There are many people to thank for their assistance with this revision. Wesley Lawton, my editor at Academic Press, did a fine job of coordinating the reviews of the manuscript and keeping the book on schedule. Frank Gunnip helped check all the examples in the text and solutions to the practice problems, as well as work all the problems in the problem sets. His contribution to this revision was extremely valuable. The production staff at Academic Press went out of their way to implement the changes I had in mind. As always, the people at Kinko's Copies did a very professional job of copying and collating the different parts of this project. My wife Diane has contributed a number of suggestions on different aspects of this revision, and my children Patrick and Amy made sure I didn't spend all my time writing.

Finally, I want to thank the people who reviewed this second edition for their suggestions and contributions. I was very lucky to have such a fine group of instructors contribute their thoughts.

Professor Jean Berdon
Canada College

Professor Frank Gunnip
Macomb and Oakland Community Colleges

Professor Esther Heimer
Southampton Campus of Long Island University

Professor Clifford Hokanson
University of Minnesota Technical College

Professor William T. Long
Broward Community College

Professor Madeline Masterton
Lansing Community College

Professor Rita Parrish
Lamar University

Professor Mark Phillips
Cypress College

Professor Joseph Robbins
Stephen F. Austin University

Professor Jack Rotman
Lansing Community College

Professor R. L. Travis, Senior
Palm Beach Junior College

Professor Will Worthey
Casper College

Professor Yoshi Yamato
Pasadena City College

Preface to the Student

And all this science
I don't understand
It's just my job
five days a week.

Elton John, Bernie Taupin,
*Rocket Man (I Think It's Going
To Be A Long Long Time)*
copyright © 1972, Dick James Music, Ltd.

I have seen a number of students over the last few years for whom this quote really makes sense. They don't enjoy math and science classes because they are always worried about whether they will understand the material. Most of them just try to get by and hope for the best. (Are you like that?)

Then there are other students who just don't worry about it. They know they can become as proficient at algebra as they want (and get whatever grade they want, too). I have people in my class who just can't help but do well on the tests I give. Most of my other students think these people are smart. They may be, but that's not the reason they do well. These successful students have learned that topics in mathematics are not always understandable the first time around. They don't worry about understanding the material; they are successful because they work lots of problems.

That is the key to success in mathematics: working problems. The more problems you work, the better you become at working problems. It's that simple. Don't worry about being successful or understanding the material, just work problems: lots of them. The more problems you work, the better you will understand the material.

That's the answer to the big question of how to master this course. Here are the answers to some other questions that are often asked by students of intermediate algebra.

How much math do I need to know before taking intermediate algebra?
You should have passed a beginning algebra class. If it has been a few years since you took it, you may have to put in some extra time at the beginning of the course to recover some of the skills you have lost.

What is the best way to study?
The best way to study is to study consistently. You must work problems every day. A number of my students spend an hour or so working problems and reading over the new material in the morning, then another hour working problems in the evening. It is often difficult to get into a schedule that is easy to follow if you have been away from school for some time. After a while though, it becomes less difficult, and sometimes almost automatic.

I am in a class that has lectures I attend. If I understand everything that goes on in class, can I take it easy on my homework?

Not necessarily. There is a big difference between understanding a problem someone else is working and working the same problem yourself. There is no substitute for working problems yourself. The concepts and properties are understandable to you only if you yourself work problems involving them.

I'm worried about not understanding the material. I've passed algebra before but I'm not really sure I understood everything that went on.

There will probably be few times when you can understand absolutely everything that goes on in class. This is standard with most math classes. It doesn't mean you will never understand it. As you read through the book and try problems on your own, you will understand more and more of the material. But if you don't try the problems on your own, you are almost guaranteed to remain confused. By the way, reading the book is important, even if it seems difficult. Reading a math book isn't the same as reading a novel. (You'll see what I mean when you start to read this one.) Reading the book through once isn't enough. You will have to read some sections a number of times before they really sink in.

If you have decided to be successful in intermediate algebra, here is a list of things you can do that will help you attain that success.

How To Be Successful in Algebra

1. Read the book and work problems every day. As you read through each section, be sure to work the practice problems in the margin. Each practice problem is similar to the example with the same number. Look over the example and then try the corresponding practice problem. The answers to the practice problems are given on the same page as the problems. If you don't get the correct answer, see if you can rework the problem correctly. If you miss it a second time, check your solution with the solution to the practice problem given in the back of the book. Once you have read through a section and worked the practice problems, you can start on the problems in the problem set. If you get stuck, go back to the examples and the practice problems.

2. Do it on your own. Don't be misled into thinking that someone else's work is your own. Having someone else show you how to work a problem is not the same as working the same problem yourself. It is okay to get help when you are stuck—as a matter of fact it is a good idea, just be sure that you do the work yourself.

3. Don't expect to understand every new topic the first time you see it. Sometimes you will understand everything you are doing, and sometimes you won't. That's just the way things are in mathematics. Expecting to understand each new topic the first time you see it will only lead to disappointment and frustration. Remember, the process of understanding algebra takes time. It requires that you read the book, work problems, and get your questions answered.

4. If you are in a lecture class be sure to attend all class sessions on time. There is no way of knowing exactly what goes on in class unless you are there. Missing class and then getting someone else's

interpretation of what went on in class is not the same as being there yourself.

5. Review every day. After you have finished the assigned problems on a certain day, take at least another 15 minutes and go back and review a section you did previously. You can review by working the practice problems in the margin or by doing some of the problems in the problem set. The more you review, the longer you will retain the material. Also, there are times when material that at first seemed unclear will become understandable when you review it.

6. Spend as much time as it takes for you to master the material. There is no set formula for the exact amount of time you need to spend on algebra to master it. You will find out as you go along what is or isn't enough time for you. Even if you end up having to spend two or more hours on each section to get comfortable with the material, then that's how much time it takes. Trying to get by with less will not work.

7. Relax. It's probably not as difficult as you think.

1 Basic Properties and Definitions

Note: Each chapter will begin with an introduction like this one. These introductions will give a general overview of the chapter, and in succeeding chapters will tell you what previous material you need to know to be successful in the chapter.

To the student:

The material in Chapter 1 is some of the most important material in the book. It is also some of the easiest material to understand. Be sure that you master it. Your success in the following chapters is directly related to how well you understand the material in Chapter 1.

Here is a list of the most essential concepts from Chapter 1 that you will need in order to be successful in the succeeding chapters:

1. You must know how to add, subtract, multiply, and divide positive and negative numbers. You must be consistently accurate in getting correct answers to simple arithmetic problems.
2. You must understand and recognize the commutative, associative, and distributive properties. These are the three most important properties of real numbers. They are used many times throughout the book to justify and explain other rules and properties.
3. You should know the major classifications of numbers. Some rules and properties hold only for specific kinds of numbers. You must therefore know the difference between whole numbers, integers, rational numbers, and real numbers.

Actually, what Chapter 1 is all about is listing the rules of the game. We are playing the game (algebra) with numbers. The properties and definitions in Chapter 1 tell us what we can start with. The rest of the book, then, is simply the playing of the game.

The material in this chapter may seem very familiar to you. You may have a tendency to skip over it lightly because it is familiar. Don't do it. Understanding algebra begins with understanding Chapter 1. Make sure you *understand* Chapter 1, even if you are familiar with it.

Section 1.1 Basic Definitions

This section is, for the most part, simply a list of many of the basic symbols and definitions we will be using throughout the book.

We begin by reviewing the symbols for comparison of numbers and expressions, and then we review the operation symbols.

Comparison Symbols

In symbols	In words
$a = b$	a is equal to b
$a \neq b$	a is not equal to b
$a < b$	a is less than b
$a \leq b$	a is less than or equal to b
$a \geq b$	a is greater than or equal to b
$a > b$	a is greater than b
$a \ngtr b$	a is not greater than b
$a \nless b$	a is not less than b
$a \Leftrightarrow b$	a is equivalent to b
	(This symbol is usually used when accompanying logical statements.)

Operation Symbols

Operation	In symbols	In words
Addition	$a + b$	The sum of a and b
Subtraction	$a - b$	The difference of a and b
Multiplication	ab, $a \cdot b$, $a(b)$, $(a)b$ or $(a)(b)$	The product of a and b
Division	$a \div b$, a/b, or $\frac{a}{b}$	The quotient of a and b

---

The key words are *sum, difference, product,* and *quotient*. They are used frequently in mathematics. For instance, we may say the product of 3 and 4 is 12. We mean both the statements $3 \cdot 4$ and 12 are called the product of 3 and 4. The important idea here is that the word *product* implies multiplication, regardless of whether it is written $3 \cdot 4$, 12, 3(4), or (3)4.

The following is an example of translating expressions written in English into expressions written in symbols.

▼ **Example 1**

In English	In symbols
The sum of x and 5	$x + 5$
The product of 3 and x	$3x$
The quotient of y and 6	$y/6$
Twice the difference of b and 7	$2(b - 7)$
The difference of twice b and 7	$2b - 7$
The quotient of twice x and 3	$2x/3$
The product of x and y is less than the sum of x and y	$xy < x + y$

▲

Note: For each example in the text there is a corresponding practice problem in the margin. After you read through an example in the text, work the practice problem with the same number in the margin.

Practice Problems

1. Write a statement, using symbols, that is equivalent to each English statement.

a. The sum of x and 2
b. The product of 2 and y
c. The quotient of a and 3
d. The difference of x and 4
e. Twice the product of y and z

Answers
1a. $x + 2$ **b.** $2y$ **c.** $\frac{a}{3}$ **d.** $x - 4$
e. $2yz$

Exponents

The next topic we will cover gives us a way to write repeated multiplication in a shorthand form.

Consider the expression 3^4. The 3 is called the base and the 4 is called the exponent. The exponent 4 tells us the number of times the base appears in the product. That is,

$$3^4 = 3 \cdot 3 \cdot 3 \cdot 3 = 81$$

The expression 3^4 is said to be in exponential form, while $3 \cdot 3 \cdot 3 \cdot 3$ is said to be in expanded form.

▼ **Example 2** Expand and multiply.

a. $5^2 = 5 \cdot 5 = 25$ Base 5, exponent 2
b. $2^5 = 2 \cdot 2 \cdot 2 \cdot 2 \cdot 2 = 32$ Base 2, exponent 5
c. $4^3 = 4 \cdot 4 \cdot 4 = 64$ Base 4, exponent 3
d. $9^2 = 9 \cdot 9 = 81$ Base 9, exponent 2   ▲

2. Expand and multiply.
a. 4^2
b. 2^4
c. 3^3
d. 7^2

Order of Operations

Now that we have listed the symbols and notation used to specify addition, subtraction, multiplication, division, and exponents, we need to discuss the order in which we perform these operations when more than one of them is present. It is important when evaluating arithmetic expressions in mathematics that each expression have only one answer in reduced form. Consider the expression

$$3 \cdot 7 + 2$$

If we find the product of 3 and 7 first, then add 2, the answer is 23. On the other hand, if we first combine the 7 and 2, then multiply by 3, we have 27. The problem seems to have two distinct answers depending on whether we multiply first or add first. To avoid this situation we will decide that multiplication in a situation like this will always be done before addition. In this case, only the first answer, 23, is correct.

Here is the complete set of rules for evaluating expressions. It is intended to avoid the type of confusion found in the preceding illustration.

Note: This rule is very important. We will use it many times throughout the book. It is a simple rule to follow. First we evaluate any numbers with exponents; then we multiply and divide; and finally we add and subtract, always working from left to right when more than one of the same operation symbol occurs in a problem.

Rule (Order of Operations)

When evaluating a mathematical expression, we will perform the operations in the following order, beginning with the expression in the innermost parentheses or brackets first and working our way out.

1. Simplify all numbers with exponents, working from left to right if more than one of these expressions is present.
2. Then do all multiplications and divisions left to right.
3. Perform all additions and subtractions left to right.

Here is an example that illustrates the use of this rule.

3. Simplify each expression using the rule for order of operations.

a. $6 + 2(3 + 4)$

b. $5 \cdot 3^2 - 2 \cdot 4^2$

c. $30 - (2 \cdot 3^2 - 8)$

d. $60 + 20 \div 2 - 40$

e. $3 + 5[2 + (7 \cdot 2 - 10)]$

▼ **Example 3** Simplify each expression using the rule for order of operation.

a.
$$
\begin{aligned}
5 + 3(2 + 4) &= 5 + 3(6) &&\text{Simplify inside parentheses} \\
&= 5 + 18 &&\text{Then multiply} \\
&= 23 &&\text{Add}
\end{aligned}
$$

b.
$$
\begin{aligned}
5 \cdot 2^3 - 4 \cdot 3^2 &= 5 \cdot 8 - 4 \cdot 9 &&\text{Simplify exponentials left to right} \\
&= 40 - 36 &&\text{Multiply left to right} \\
&= 4 &&\text{Subtract}
\end{aligned}
$$

c.
$$
\begin{aligned}
20 - (2 \cdot 5^2 - 30) &= 20 - (2 \cdot 25 - 30) \\
&= 20 - (50 - 30) \\
&= 20 - (20) \\
&= 0
\end{aligned}
$$
Simplify inside parentheses, evaluating exponents first, then multiplying, and finally subtracting

d.
$$
\begin{aligned}
40 - 20 \div 5 + 8 &= 40 - 4 + 8 &&\text{Divide first} \\
&= 36 + 8 &&\text{Then add and subtract left} \\
&= 44 &&\text{to right}
\end{aligned}
$$

e.
$$
\begin{aligned}
2 + 4[5 + (3 \cdot 2 - 2)] &= 2 + 4[5 + (6 - 2)] \\
&= 2 + 4(5 + 4) \\
&= 2 + 4(9)
\end{aligned}
$$
Simplify inside innermost parentheses first

$$
\begin{aligned}
&= 2 + 36 &&\text{Then multiply} \\
&= 38 &&\text{Add}
\end{aligned}
$$
▲

Sets

DEFINITION A *set* is a collection of objects or things. The objects in the set are called *elements* or *members* of the set.

Sets are usually denoted by capital letters and elements of sets by lowercase letters. We use braces, { }, to enclose the elements of a set.

To show that an element is contained in a set we use the symbol $\in$. That is,

$x \in A$ is read "*x* is an element (member) of set *A*"
The symbol $\notin$ is read "is *not* a member of"

For example, if *A* is the set $\{1, 2, 3\}$ then $2 \in A$. On the other hand $5 \notin A$, meaning 5 is not an element of set *A*.

DEFINITION Set *A* is a subset of set *B*, written $A \subset B$, if every element in *A* is also an element of *B*. That is,

$A \subset B$ if and only if *A* is contained in *B*

Here are some examples of sets and subsets:

Note: The concept of a set can be considered the starting point for all the branches of mathematics. For instance, most of the important concepts in statistics are based, in one form or another, on probability theory. The basic concept in probability theory is the idea of an event, and an event is nothing more than a set.

▼ **Example 4**

a. The set of numbers used to count things is $\{1, 2, 3, \ldots\}$. The dots mean the set continues indefinitely in the same manner. This is an example of an infinite set.

b. The set of all numbers represented by the dots on the faces of a regular die is $\{1, 2, 3, 4, 5, 6\}$. This set is a subset of the set in part a. It is an example of a *finite* set, since it has a limited number of elements.

c. The set of all Fords is a subset of the set of all cars, since every Ford is also a car. ▲

DEFINITION   The set with no members is called the *empty* or *null set*. It is denoted by the symbol $\varnothing$. (*Note:* a mistake is sometimes made by trying to denote the empty set with the notation $\{\varnothing\}$. The set $\{\varnothing\}$ is not the empty set, since it contains one element, the empty set $\varnothing$.)

The empty set is considered a subset of every set.

Operations with Sets

There are two basic operations used to combine sets. The operations are union and intersection.

DEFINITION   The *union* of two sets A and B, written $A \cup B$, is the set of all elements that are either in A or in B, or in both A and B. The key word here is *or*. For an element to be in $A \cup B$ it must be in A or B. In symbols the definition looks like this:

$$x \in A \cup B \quad \text{if and only if} \quad x \in A \text{ or } x \in B$$

DEFINITION   The *intersection* of two sets A and B, written $A \cap B$, is the set of elements in both A and B. The key word in this definition is the word *and*. For an element to be in $A \cap B$ it must be in both A and B, or

$$x \in A \cap B \quad \text{if and only if} \quad x \in A \text{ and } x \in B$$

▼ **Example 5**   Let $A = \{1, 3, 5\}$, $B = \{0, 2, 4\}$, and $C = \{1, 2, 3, \ldots\}$. Then

a. $A \cup B = \{0, 1, 2, 3, 4, 5\}$

b. $A \cap B = \varnothing$ (A and B have no elements in common)

c. $A \cap C = \{1, 3, 5\} = A$

d. $B \cup C = \{0, 1, 2, 3, \ldots\}$ ▲

Up to this point we have described the sets we have encountered by listing all the elements and then enclosing them with braces $\{\ \ \}$. There is another notation we can use to describe sets. It is called *set-builder* notation. Here is how we would write our definition for the union of two sets A and B using set-builder notation.

$$A \cup B = \{x \mid x \in A \text{ or } x \in B\}$$

The right side of this statement is read "the set of all x such that x is a member of A or x is a member of B." As you can see, the vertical line after the first x is read "such that."

---

4. Identify each statement as either True or False.

a. The set $\{2, 4, 6, \ldots\}$ is an example of an infinite set.

b. The set $\{2, 4, 8\}$ is a subset of $\{2, 4, 6, \ldots\}$.

c. The set of all airplanes is a subset of the set of all 747s.

5. Let $A = \{1, 2, 3\}$, $B = \{0, 3, 7\}$, and $C = \{0, 1, 2, 3 \ldots\}$. Find the following.

a. $A \cup B$

b. $A \cap B$

c. $A \cap C$

d. $B \cap C$

Answers

4a. True   **b.** True   **c.** False

5a. $\{0, 1, 2, 3, 7\}$ **b.** $\{3\}$ **c.** $\{1, 2, 3\}$

d. $\{0, 3, 7\}$

6. Let $A = \{2, 4, 6, 8, 10\}$ and find
$B = \{x \mid x \in A \text{ and } x < 8\}$

▼ **Example 6** Let $A = \{1, 2, 3, 4, 5, 6\}$ and find
$$C = \{x \mid x \in A \text{ and } x \geq 4\}.$$

Solution We are looking for all the elements of A that are also greater than or equal to 4. They are 4, 5, and 6. Using set notation we have

$$C = \{4, 5, 6\} \qquad ▲$$

Answer
6. $\{2, 4, 6\}$

Problem Set 1.1

Translate each of the following statements into symbols. (See Example 1.)

1. The sum of x and 5.

2. The sum of y and -3.

3. The difference of 6 and x.

4. The difference of x and 6.

5. The product of t and 2 is less than y.

6. The product of $5x$ and y is equal to z.

7. The quotient of $3x$ and $2y$ is greater than 6.

8. The quotient of $2y$ and $3x$ is not less than 7.

9. The sum of x and y is less than the difference of x and y.

10. Twice the sum of a and b is 15.

11. Three times the difference of x and 5 is more than y.

12. The product of x and y is greater than or equal to the quotient of x and y.

13. The difference of s and t is not equal to their sum.

14. The quotient of $2x$ and y is less than or equal to the sum of $2x$ and y.

15. Twice the sum of t and 3 is not greater than the difference of t and 6.

16. Three times the product of x and y is equal to the sum of $2y$ and $3z$.

Name _____

Class _____

Date _____

Answers

1. _____

2. _____

3. _____

4. _____

5. _____

6. _____

7. _____

8. _____

9. _____

10. _____

11. _____

12. _____

13. _____

14. _____

15. _____

16. _____

Answers

17. _____   18. _____

19. _____   20. _____

21. _____   22. _____

23. _____   24. _____

25. _____   26. _____

27. _____   28. _____

29. _____   30. _____

31. _____   32. _____

33. _____   34. _____

35. _____   36. _____

37. _____   38. _____

39. _____   40. _____

Expand and multiply.

17. 6^2 **18.** 8^2 **19.** 10^2

20. 10^3 **21.** 2^3 **22.** 5^3

23. 2^4 **24.** 1^4 **25.** 10^4

26. 4^3 **27.** 11^2 **28.** 10^5

Simplify each expression using the rule for order of operations.

29. $3 \cdot 5 + 4$ **30.** $3 \cdot 7 - 6$

31. $2 + 8 \cdot 5$ **32.** $12 - 3 \cdot 3$

33. $3 + 8 \cdot 5 + 4 \cdot 3$ **34.** $6 + 9 \cdot 2 + 7 \cdot 6$

35. $2 \cdot 5 + 3 \cdot 6 + 4 \cdot 7$ **36.** $8 \cdot 5 + 7 \cdot 6 + 6 \cdot 7$

37. $5 \cdot 2^2 + 1$ **38.** $6 \cdot 2^3 + 10$

39. $4 \cdot 2^2 + 5 \cdot 2^3$ **40.** $3 \cdot 4^2 + 2 \cdot 4^3$

41. $2 + 3(2^2 + 3^2)$

42. $3 + 4(4^2 + 5^2)$

43. $20 - 10 \div 5 + 4$

44. $30 - 15 \div 5 + 8$

45. $10 \div 2 - 9 \div 3$

46. $20 \div 5 - 12 \div 6$

47. $5 \cdot 10^3 + 4 \cdot 10^2 + 3 \cdot 10 + 1$

48. $6 \cdot 10^3 + 5 \cdot 10^2 + 4 \cdot 10 + 3$

49. $2^3 + 3(8 + 12 \div 2)$

50. $3^2 + 2(10 + 15 \div 5)$

51. $16 - (4 \cdot 5^2 - 9 \cdot 10)$

52. $18 - (3 \cdot 4^3 - 19 \cdot 10)$

53. $10 - [10 - (4 - 2)]$

54. $20 - [17 - (8 - 3)]$

55. $3 + 2(2 \cdot 3^2 + 1)$

56. $4 + 5(3 \cdot 2^2 - 5)$

57. $3[2 + 4(5 + 2 \cdot 3)]$

58. $2[4 + 2(6 + 3 \cdot 5)]$

Name _____

Class _____

Date _____

Answers

41. _____   **42.** _____

43. _____   **44.** _____

45. _____   **46.** _____

47. _____   **48.** _____

49. _____   **50.** _____

51. _____   **52.** _____

53. _____   **54.** _____

55. _____   **56.** _____

57. _____   **58.** _____

Answers

For the following problems, let $A = \{0, 2, 4, 6\}$, $B = \{1, 2, 3, 4, 5\}$, $C = \{1, 3, 5, 7\}$, and $D = \{-2, -1, 0, 1, 2\}$ and find the following.

59. _____

60. _____

61. _____

62. _____

63. _____

64. _____

65. _____

66. _____

67. _____

68. _____

69. _____

70. _____

71. _____

72. _____

73. _____

74. _____

75. _____

76. _____

77. _____

78. _____

79. _____

80. _____

81. _____

82. _____

59. $A \cup B$

60. $A \cup C$

61. $A \cap B$

62. $A \cap C$

63. $C \cup D$

64. $B \cup D$

65. $C \cap D$

66. $B \cap D$

67. $A \cup D$

68. $B \cup C$

69. $A \cap D$

70. $B \cap C$

71. $A \cup (B \cap C)$

72. $C \cup (A \cap B)$

73. $\{x \mid x \in A \text{ and } x \in B\}$

74. $\{x \mid x \in B \text{ and } x \in C\}$

75. $\{x \mid x \in A \text{ and } x < 4\}$

76. $\{x \mid x \in B \text{ and } x > 3\}$

77. $\{x \mid x \in A \text{ and } x \notin B\}$

78. $\{x \mid x \in B \text{ and } x \notin C\}$

79. $\{x \mid x \in A \text{ or } x \in C\}$

80. $\{x \mid x \in A \text{ or } x \in B\}$

81. $\{x \mid x \in B \text{ and } x \neq 3\}$

82. $\{x \mid x \in C \text{ and } x \neq 5\}$

Section 1.2 The Real Numbers, Opposites, Reciprocals, and Absolute Value

In this section we will give a definition of real numbers in terms of the real number line. We will then classify all pairs of numbers that add to 0, and do the same for all pairs of numbers whose product is 1. We will end the section with two definitions of absolute value and a list of some special sets.

The Real Numbers

The real number line is constructed by drawing a straight line and labeling a convenient point with the number 0. Positive numbers are in increasing order to the right of 0; negative numbers are in decreasing order to the left of 0. The point on the line corresponding to 0 is called the origin.

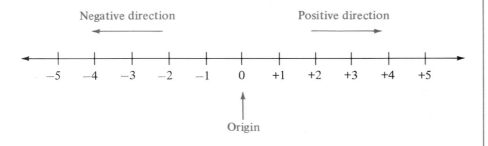

Note: The numbers on the number line increase in size as we move to the right. When we compare the size of two numbers on the number line, the one on the left is always the smaller number.

The numbers associated with the points on the line are called *coordinates* of those points. Every point on the line has a number associated with it. The set of all these numbers makes up the set of real numbers.

DEFINITION   A *real number* is any number that is the coordinate of a point on the real number line.

There are many different sets of numbers contained in the real numbers. We will classify some of them later. Among those numbers contained in the real numbers are all positive and negative fractions and decimals.

▼ **Example 1**   Locate the numbers -4.5, $-.75$, $\frac{1}{2}$, $\sqrt{2}$, π, and 4.1 on the real number line.

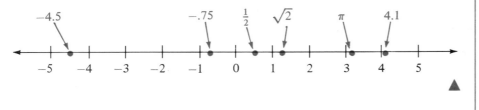

▲

Opposites and Reciprocals

DEFINITION   Any two real numbers, the same distance from 0, but in opposite directions from 0 on the number line, are called *opposites* or *additive inverses.*

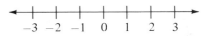

2. Give the opposite of each number.
   a. 5
   b. $\frac{1}{4}$
   c. -3
   d. $-\sqrt{5}$

▼ **Example 2** The numbers -3 and 3 are opposites. So are π and $-\pi$, $\frac{3}{4}$ and $-\frac{3}{4}$, and $\sqrt{2}$ and $-\sqrt{2}$. ▲

The negative sign in front of a number can be read in a number of different ways. It can be read as "negative" or "the opposite of." We say -4 is the opposite of 4 or negative 4. The one we use will depend on the situation. For instance, the expression $-(-3)$ is best read "the opposite of negative 3." Since the opposite of -3 is 3, we have $-(-3) = 3$. In general, if a is any positive real number, then

$$-(-a) = a \qquad \text{(The opposite of a negative is positive)}$$

Before we go further with our study of the number line, we need to review multiplication with fractions. Recall that for the fraction $\frac{a}{b}$, a is called the numerator and b is called the denominator. To multiply two fractions we simply multiply numerators and multiply denominators.

3. Multiply: $\frac{3}{7} \cdot \frac{2}{5}$.

▼ **Example 3** Multiply: $\frac{3}{5} \cdot \frac{7}{8}$.

Solution The product of the numerators is 21 and the product of the denominators is 40:

$$\frac{3}{5} \cdot \frac{7}{8} = \frac{3 \cdot 7}{5 \cdot 8} = \frac{21}{40} \qquad ▲$$

4. Multiply: $9 \cdot \frac{1}{4}$.

▼ **Example 4** Multiply: $8 \cdot \frac{1}{5}$.

Solution The number 8 can be thought of as the fraction $\frac{8}{1}$.

$$8 \cdot \frac{1}{5} = \frac{8}{1} \cdot \frac{1}{5} = \frac{8 \cdot 1}{1 \cdot 5} = \frac{8}{5} \qquad ▲$$

Note: In past math classes you may have written fractions like $\frac{8}{5}$ (improper fractions) as mixed numbers, such as $1\frac{3}{5}$. In algebra, it is usually better to leave them as improper fractions.

The idea of multiplication of fractions is useful in understanding the concept of the reciprocal of a number. Here is the definition.

DEFINITION Any two real numbers whose product is 1 are called *reciprocals* or *multiplicative inverses*.

5. Give the reciprocal of each number.

▼ **Example 5**

	Number	Reciprocal	
a.	3	$\frac{1}{3}$	Because $3 \cdot \frac{1}{3} = \frac{3}{1} \cdot \frac{1}{3} = \frac{3}{3} = 1$
b.	$\frac{1}{6}$	6	Because $\frac{1}{6} \cdot 6 = \frac{1}{6} \cdot \frac{6}{1} = \frac{6}{6} = 1$
c.	$\frac{4}{5}$	$\frac{5}{4}$	Because $\frac{4}{5} \cdot \frac{5}{4} = \frac{20}{20} = 1$
d.	a	$\frac{1}{a}$	Because $a \cdot \frac{1}{a} = \frac{a}{1} \cdot \frac{1}{a} = \frac{a}{a} = 1$ $(a \neq 0)$

a. 5

b. $\frac{1}{4}$

c. $\frac{3}{4}$

d. x

▲

Although we will not develop multiplication with negative numbers until later in this chapter, you should know that the reciprocal of a negative number is also a negative number. For example, the reciprocal of -5 is $-\frac{1}{5}$. Likewise, the reciprocal of $-\frac{3}{4}$ is $-\frac{4}{3}$. We should also note that 0 is the only number without a reciprocal, since multiplying by 0 always results in 0, never 1.

Answers
2a. -5 **b.** $-\frac{1}{4}$ **c.** 3 **d.** $\sqrt{5}$ **3.** $\frac{6}{35}$
4. $\frac{9}{4}$ **5a.** $\frac{1}{5}$ **b.** 4 **c.** $\frac{4}{3}$ **d.** $\frac{1}{x}$ $x \neq 0$

The Absolute Value of a Real Number

Sometimes it is convenient to consider only the distance a number is from 0 and not its direction from 0.

DEFINITION   The *absolute value* of a number (also called its *magnitude*) is the distance the number is from 0 on the number line. If x represents a real number, then the absolute value of x is written $|x|$.

Since distances are always represented by positive numbers or 0, the absolute value of a quantity is always positive or 0; the absolute value of a number is never negative.

The preceding definition of absolute value is geometric in form since it defines absolute value in terms of the number line.

Here is an alternate definition of absolute value that is algebraic since it involves only symbols.

DEFINITION   If x represents a real number, then the *absolute value* (or *magnitude*) of x is written $|x|$, and is given by

$$|x| = \begin{cases} x & \text{if } x \geq 0 \\ -x & \text{if } x < 0 \end{cases}$$

Note: It is important to recognize that if x is a real number, $-x$ is not necessarily negative. For example, if x is 5, then $-x$ is -5. On the other hand, if x were -5, then $-x$ would be $-(-5)$, which is 5.

If the original number is positive or 0, then its absolute value is the number itself. If the number is negative, its absolute value is its opposite (which must be positive). We see that $-x$, as written in this definition, is a positive quantity since x in this case is a negative number.

▼ Example 6

a. $|5| = 5$
b. $|-2| = 2$
c. $\left|-\frac{1}{2}\right| = \frac{1}{2}$
d. $\left|\frac{3}{4}\right| = \frac{3}{4}$

e. $-|-3| = -3$
f. $-|5| = -5$
g. $-|-\sqrt{2}| = -\sqrt{2}$
h. $-\left|\frac{5}{6}\right| = -\frac{5}{6}$

The last four parts of this example do not contradict the statement that the absolute value of a number is always positive or 0. In part e we are asked to find the *opposite* of the absolute value of -3, $-|-3|$. The absolute value of -3 is 3, the opposite of which is -3. If the absolute value of a number is always positive or 0, then the opposite of its absolute value must always be negative or 0.   ▲

6.   Write the following statements as equivalent statements without absolute value symbols.

a. $|7|$
b. $|-4|$
c. $\left|-\frac{2}{3}\right|$
d. $\left|\frac{5}{8}\right|$

e. $-|-6|$
f. $-|7|$
g. $-|-\sqrt{3}|$
h. $-\left|\frac{2}{3}\right|$

Subsets of the Real Numbers

We end this section by listing some of the more important subsets of the real numbers. Each set listed here is a subset of the real numbers.

Counting (or Natural) numbers = $\{1, 2, 3, \ldots\}$
Whole numbers = $\{0, 1, 2, 3, \ldots\}$
Integers = $\{\ldots, -3, -2, -1, 0, 1, 2, 3, \ldots\}$

Rational numbers = $\left\{\dfrac{a}{b} \,\middle|\, a \text{ and } b \text{ are integers, } b \neq 0\right\}$

Note: As you can see, the whole numbers are the counting numbers and 0 together, while the integers are the whole numbers along with the opposites of all the counting numbers. We can say that the counting numbers are a subset of the whole numbers, and the whole numbers are a subset of the integers.

Remember, the notation used to write the rational numbers is read "the set of numbers a/b, such that a and b are integers and b is not equal to 0."

Answers
6a. 7   **b.** 4   **c.** $\frac{2}{3}$ **d.** $\frac{5}{8}$ **e.** -6
f. -7 **g.** $-\sqrt{3}$ **h.** $-\frac{2}{3}$

Any number that can be written in the form

$$\frac{\text{integer}}{\text{integer}}$$

is a rational number. Rational numbers are numbers that can be written as the ratio of two integers. Each of the following is a rational number:

$\frac{3}{4}$ Because it is the ratio of the integers 3 and 4

-8 Because it can be written as the ratio of -8 to 1

0.75   Because it is the ratio of 75 to 100 (or 3 to 4 if you reduce to lowest terms)

0.333 . . .   Because it can be written as the ratio of 1 to 3

There are still other numbers on the number line that are not members of the subsets we have listed so far. They are real numbers, but they cannot be written as the ratio of two integers. That is, they are not rational numbers. For that reason, we call them irrational numbers.

Irrational Numbers $= \{x \mid x \text{ is real, but not rational}\}$

The following are irrational numbers:

$$\sqrt{2}, \quad -\sqrt{3}, \quad 4 + 2\sqrt{3}, \quad \pi, \quad \pi + 5\sqrt{6}$$

▼ **Example 7** For the set $\{-5, -3.5, 0, 3/4, \sqrt{3}, \sqrt{5}, 9\}$, list the numbers that are: a. whole numbers, b. integers, c. rational numbers, d. irrational numbers, and e. real numbers.

Solution

a. whole numbers $= \{0, 9\}$
b. integers $= \{-5, 0, 9\}$
c. rational numbers $= \{-5, -3.5, 0, 3/4, 9\}$
d. irrational numbers $= \{\sqrt{3}, \sqrt{5}\}$
e. They are all real numbers. ▲

Note: We can find decimal approximations to some irrational numbers by using a calculator or a table. For example, on an eight-digit calculator

$$\sqrt{2} = 1.4142135$$

This is not exactly $\sqrt{2}$ but simply an approximation to it. There is no decimal that gives $\sqrt{2}$ exactly.

7. For the set $\left\{-8, -2.1, -\sqrt{2}, 0, \frac{5}{8}, 3\right\}$ choose the following.

a. whole numbers

b. integers

c. rational numbers

d. irrational numbers

e. real numbers

Answers
7a. $\{0, 3\}$ **b.** $\{-8, 0, 3\}$
c. $\{-8, -2.1, 0, \frac{5}{8}, 3\}$
d. $\{-\sqrt{2}\}$ **e.** All of them.

Problem Set 1.2

1. Locate the numbers -3, -1.75, $-\frac{1}{2}$, 0, $\frac{1}{3}$, 1, 1.3, and 4.5 on the number line. (See Example 1.)

2. Locate the numbers -3.25, -3, -2.5, -1, $-\frac{1}{3}$, 0, $\frac{3}{4}$, 1.2, and 2 on the number line.

Complete the following table.

	Number	Opposite	Reciprocal
3.	4		
4.	-3		
5.	$-\frac{1}{2}$		
6.	$\frac{5}{6}$		
7.		-5	
8.		7	
9.		$-\frac{3}{8}$	
10.		$\frac{1}{2}$	
11.			-6
12.			-3
13.			$\frac{1}{3}$
14.			$-\frac{1}{4}$
15.		$-\sqrt{3}$	
16.		$\sqrt{5}$	
17.			$-\sqrt{2}$
18.			$-\frac{3}{5}$
19.	x		
20.	0		

Answers

21. _____ 22. _____

23. _____ 24. _____

25. _____ 26. _____

27. _____ 28. _____

29. _____ 30. _____

31. _____ 32. _____

33. _____ 34. _____

35. _____ 36. _____

37. _____ 38. _____

39. _____ 40. _____

41. _____ 42. _____

43. _____ 44. _____

45. _____ 46. _____

47. _____ 48. _____

49. _____ 50. _____

21. Name two numbers that are their own reciprocals.

22. Give the number that has no reciprocal.

23. Name the number that is its own opposite.

24. The reciprocal of a negative number is negative—true or false?

Write each of the following without absolute value symbols.

25. $|-2|$ **26.** $|-7|$ **27.** $\left|-\frac{3}{4}\right|$ **28.** $\left|\frac{5}{6}\right|$

29. $|\pi|$ **30.** $|-\sqrt{2}|$ **31.** $-|4|$ **32.** $-|5|$

33. $-|-2|$ **34.** $-|-10|$ **35.** $-\left|-\frac{3}{4}\right|$ **36.** $-\left|\frac{7}{8}\right|$

Find the value of each of the following expressions.

37. $-(-2)$ **38.** $-\left(-\frac{3}{4}\right)$ **39.** $-\left[-\left(-\frac{1}{3}\right)\right]$

40. $-[-(-1)]$ **41.** $|2| + |3|$ **42.** $|7| + |4|$

43. $|-3| + |5|$ **44.** $|-1| + |0|$ **45.** $|-8| - |-3|$

46. $|-6| - |-1|$ **47.** $|-10| - |4|$ **48.** $|-3| - |2|$

49. $|-2| + |-3| - |5|$ **50.** $|-6| - |-2| + |-4|$

For the set $\{-6, -5.2, -\sqrt{7}, -\pi, 0, 1, 2, 2.3, \frac{9}{2}, \sqrt{17}\}$ list all the elements that are named in each of the following problems.

51. counting numbers   **52.** whole numbers

53. rational numbers   **54.** integers

55. irrational numbers   **56.** real numbers

57. nonnegative integers   **58.** positive integers

Label the following true or false.

59. Zero has an opposite and a reciprocal.

60. Some irrational numbers are also rational numbers.

61. All whole numbers are integers.

62. Every real number is a rational number.

63. All integers are rational numbers.

64. Some negative numbers are integers.

65. Zero is both rational and irrational.

66. Zero is not considered a real number.

67. The opposite of an integer is also an integer.

68. The reciprocal of an integer is an integer.

69. The counting numbers are a subset of the whole numbers.

70. The rational numbers are a subset of the irrational numbers.

Name _____

Class _____

Date _____

Answers

51. _____

52. _____

53. _____

54. _____

55. _____

56. _____

57. _____

58. _____

59. _____ **60.** _____

61. _____ **62.** _____

63. _____ **64.** _____

65. _____ **66.** _____

67. _____ **68.** _____

69. _____ **70.** _____

Answers

71. _____ 72. _____

73. _____ 74. _____

75. _____ 76. _____

77. _____ 78. _____

79. _____ 80. _____

81. _____ 82. _____

83. _____ 84. _____

85. _____ 86. _____

87. _____ 88. _____

89. _____ 90. _____

91. _____ 92. _____

93. _____ 94. _____

95. _____ 96. _____

97. _____ 98. _____

Multiply the following.

71. $\frac{3}{5} \cdot \frac{7}{8}$

72. $\frac{6}{7} \cdot \frac{9}{5}$

73. $4 \cdot \frac{3}{5}$

74. $9 \cdot \frac{2}{7}$

75. $15 \cdot \frac{8}{17}$

76. $17 \cdot \frac{3}{9}$

77. $\frac{5}{3} \cdot 7 \cdot \frac{8}{3}$

78. $\frac{3}{5} \cdot 6 \cdot \frac{1}{7}$

79. $\frac{3}{5} \cdot \frac{4}{7} \cdot \frac{6}{11}$

80. $\frac{4}{5} \cdot \frac{6}{7} \cdot \frac{3}{11}$

81. $\frac{4}{3} \cdot \frac{3}{4}$

82. $\frac{5}{8} \cdot \frac{8}{5}$

83. $\sqrt{2} \cdot \dfrac{1}{\sqrt{2}}$

84. $\sqrt{3} \cdot \dfrac{1}{\sqrt{3}}$

85. $2 \cdot \dfrac{1}{\sqrt{5}} \cdot \sqrt{5}$

86. $3 \cdot \sqrt{7} \cdot \dfrac{1}{\sqrt{7}}$

87. $\pi \cdot \dfrac{1}{\pi}$

88. $e \cdot \dfrac{1}{e}$

89. Name two numbers that are 5 units from 2 on the number line.

90. Name two numbers that are 6 units from -3 on the number line.

91. If the rational number $\frac{1}{3}$ can be written as the repeating decimal $0.333 \ldots$, what rational number can be written as the repeating decimal $0.999 \ldots$?

92. Write the rational number $\frac{7}{9}$ as a repeating decimal. (*Hint:* Divide 7 by 9 using long division.)

93. Write the rational number $\frac{28}{99}$ as a repeating decimal. (Divide 28 by 99 using long division.)

94. Write the rational number $\frac{123}{999}$ as a repeating decimal.

95. A person has a balance of $25 in a checking account. If the person writes a check for $40, what negative number will give the new balance in the account?

96. A man wins $37 on one hand of cards. On the next hand he loses $57. What negative number can be used to represent his net gain?

97. Name two numbers whose absolute value is 6.

98. Name two numbers whose absolute value is 3/4.

Section 1.3 Simple and Compound Inequalities

In this section we will use some of the ideas developed in the first two sections to graph inequalities. The graph of an inequality uses the real number line to give a visual representation of an algebraic expression.

▼ **Example 1** Graph $\{x \mid x \leq 3\}$.

Solution We want to graph all the real numbers less than or equal to 3—that is, all the real numbers below 3 and including 3. We label 0 on the number line for reference as well as 3 since the latter is what we call the end point. The graph is as follows.

We use a solid circle at 3 since 3 is included in the graph. ▲

▼ **Example 2** Graph $\{x \mid x < 3\}$.

Solution The graph will be identical to the graph in Example 1 except at the end point 3. In this case we will use an open circle since 3 is not included in the graph.

▲

In Section 1.1 we defined the *union* of two sets A and B to be the set of all elements that are in either A or B. The word *or* is the key word in the definition. The *intersection* of two sets A and B is the set of all elements contained in both A and B, the key word here being *and*. We can put the words *and* and *or* together with our methods of graphing inequalities to graph some compound inequalities.

▼ **Example 3** Graph $\{x \mid x \leq -2 \text{ or } x > 3\}$.

Solution The two inequalities connected by the word *or* are referred to as a *compound inequality*. We begin by graphing each inequality separately.

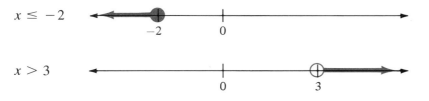

Since the two are connected by the word *or*, we graph their union. That is, we graph all points on either graph.

▲

Practice Problems

1. Graph $\{x \mid x \leq 2\}$.

2. Graph $\{x \mid x < 2\}$.

3. Graph $\{x \mid x \leq -1 \text{ or } x > 2\}$.

Note: It is not absolutely necessary to show these two graphs. It is simply helpful to do so. As you get more practice at this type of graphing you can easily omit them.

Answers
1. For answers to practice problems in this section, see ''Solutions to Selected Practice Problems'' at the back of the book.

4. Graph $\{x|x > -2 \text{ and } x < 3\}$.

▼ **Example 4** Graph $\{x|x > -1 \text{ and } x < 2\}$.

Solution We first graph each inequality separately.

$x > -1$

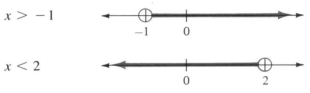

$x < 2$

Since the two inequalities are connected by the word *and,* we graph their intersection—the part they have in common.

Notation Sometimes compound inequalities that use the word *and* as the connecting word can be written in a shorter form. For example, the compound inequality $-3 \le x$ and $x \le 4$ can be written $-3 \le x \le 4$. The word *and* does not appear when an inequality is written in this form. It is implied. Inequalities of the form $-3 \le x \le 4$ are called *continued inequalities*. This new notation is useful because is takes fewer symbols to write it and because if $-3 \le x$ and $x \le 4$, then x must be *between* -3 and 4. With the notation $-3 \le x \le 4$, it "looks" as though x is between -3 and 4. The graph of $-3 \le x \le 4$ is

5. Graph $\{x|-2 < x \le 1\}$.

▼ **Example 5** Graph $\{x|1 \le x < 2\}$.

Solution The word *and* is implied in the continued inequality $1 \le x < 2$. That is, the continued inequality $1 \le x < 2$ is equivalent to $1 \le x$ and $x < 2$. Therefore, we graph all the numbers between 1 and 2 on the number line, including 1 but not including 2.

▲

6. Graph $\{x|x \le -1 \text{ or } 2 \le x \le 4\}$

▼ **Example 6** Graph $\{x|x < -2 \text{ or } 2 < x < 6\}$.

Solution Here we have a combination of compound and continued inequalities. We want to graph all real numbers that are either less than -2 or between 2 and 6.

▲

Problem Set 1.3

Name _____

Class _____

Date _____

Graph the following on the real number line.

1. $\{x \mid x < 1\}$

2. $\{x \mid x > -2\}$

3. $\{x \mid x \leq 1\}$

4. $\{x \mid x \geq -2\}$

5. $\{x \mid x \geq 4\}$

6. $\{x \mid x \leq -3\}$

7. $\{x \mid x > 4\}$

8. $\{x \mid x < -3\}$

9. $\{x \mid x > 0\}$

10. $\{x \mid x < 0\}$

11. $\{x \mid -2 < x\}$

12. $\{x \mid 3 \geq x\}$

13. $\{x \mid 4 \leq x\}$

14. $\{x \mid 2 > x\}$

Graph the following compound inequalities.

15. $\{x \mid x < -3 \text{ or } x > 1\}$

16. $\{x \mid x \leq 1 \text{ or } x \geq 4\}$

17. $\{x \mid x \leq -3 \text{ or } x \geq 1\}$

18. $\{x \mid x < 1 \text{ or } x > 4\}$

19. $\{x \mid -3 \leq x \text{ and } x \leq 1\}$

20. $\{x \mid 1 < x \text{ and } x < 4\}$

21. $\{x \mid -3 < x \text{ and } x < 1\}$

22. $\{x \mid 1 \leq x \text{ and } x \leq 4\}$

Answers

1. ←————————————→

2. ←————————————→

3. ←————————————→

4. ←————————————→

5. ←————————————→

6. ←————————————→

7. ←————————————→

8. ←————————————→

9. ←————————————→

10. ←————————————→

11. ←————————————→

12. ←————————————→

13. ←————————————→

14. ←————————————→

15. ←————————————→

16. ←————————————→

17. ←————————————→

18. ←————————————→

19. ←————————————→

20. ←————————————→

21. ←————————————→

22. ←————————————→

Answers

23. ←———————————————→

24. ←———————————————→

25. ←———————————————→

26. ←———————————————→

27. ←———————————————→

28. ←———————————————→

29. ←———————————————→

30. ←———————————————→

31. ←———————————————→

32. ←———————————————→

33. ←———————————————→

34. ←———————————————→

35. ←———————————————→

36. ←———————————————→

37. ←———————————————→

38. ←———————————————→

39. ←———————————————→

40. ←———————————————→

41. ←———————————————→

42. ←———————————————→

43. ←———————————————→

44. ←———————————————→

23. $\{x \,|\, x < -1 \text{ or } x \geq 3\}$

24. $\{x \,|\, x < 0 \text{ or } x \geq 3\}$

25. $\{x \,|\, x \leq -1 \text{ and } x \geq 3\}$

26. $\{x \,|\, x \leq 0 \text{ and } x \geq 3\}$

27. $\{x \,|\, x > -4 \text{ and } x < 2\}$

28. $\{x \,|\, x > -3 \text{ and } x < 0\}$

Graph the following continued inequalities.

29. $\{x \,|\, -1 \leq x \leq 2\}$

30. $\{x \,|\, -2 \leq x \leq 1\}$

31. $\{x \,|\, -1 < x < 2\}$

32. $\{x \,|\, -2 < x < 1\}$

33. $\{x \,|\, -3 < x < 1\}$

34. $\{x \,|\, 1 \leq x \leq 2\}$

35. $\{x \,|\, -3 \leq x < 0\}$

36. $\{x \,|\, 2 \leq x < 4\}$

37. $\{x \,|\, -4 < x \leq 1\}$

38. $\{x \,|\, -1 < x \leq 5\}$

Graph each of the following.

39. $\{x \,|\, x < -3 \quad \text{or} \quad 2 < x < 4\}$

40. $\{x \,|\, -4 \leq x \leq -2 \quad \text{or} \quad x \geq 3\}$

41. $\{x \,|\, x \leq -5 \quad \text{or} \quad 0 \leq x \leq 3\}$

42. $\{x \,|\, -3 < x < 0 \quad \text{or} \quad x > 5\}$

43. $\{x \,|\, -5 < x < -2 \quad \text{or} \quad 2 < x < 5\}$

44. $\{x \,|\, -3 \leq x \leq -1 \quad \text{or} \quad 1 \leq x \leq 3\}$

Section 1.4   Properties of Real Numbers

In this section we will list all the things we know to be true of real numbers and the operation symbols listed in Section 1.1. Mathematics is a game we play with real numbers. The rules of the game are the properties of real numbers listed in this section. We play the game by taking real numbers and their properties and applying them to as many new situations as possible.

The list of properties given in this section is actually just an organized summary of the things we know from past experience to be true about numbers in general. For instance, we know that adding 3 and 7 gives the same answer as adding 7 and 3. The order of two numbers in an addition problem can be changed without changing the result. This fact about numbers and addition is called the *commutative property of addition*. We say addition is a commutative operation. Likewise, multiplication is a commutative operation.

We now state these properties formally. For all the properties listed in this section, a, b, and c represent real numbers.

Commutative Property of Addition

In symbols: $a + b = b + a$
In words: The *order* of the numbers in a sum does not affect the result.

Commutative Property of Multiplication

In symbols: $a \cdot b = b \cdot a$
In words: The *order* of the numbers in a product does not affect the result.

▼   **Example 1**

a. The statement $3 + 7 = 7 + 3$ is an example of the commutative property of addition.

b. The statement $3 \cdot x = x \cdot 3$ is an example of the commutative property of multiplication.

c. Using the commutative property of addition, the expression $3 + x + 7$ can be simplified:

$$3 + x + 7 = 3 + 7 + x \qquad \text{Commutative property}$$
$$= 10 + x \qquad \text{Addition} \qquad ▲$$

The other two basic operations (subtraction and division) are not commutative. If we change the order in which we are subtracting or dividing two numbers we will change the result.

Another property of numbers you have used many times has to do with grouping. When adding $3 + 5 + 7$ we can add the 3 and 5 first and then the 7, or we can add the 5 and 7 first and then the 3. Mathematically it looks like this: $(3 + 5) + 7 = 3 + (5 + 7)$. Operations that behave in this manner are called *associative* operations. The answers will not change when we change the grouping. Here is the formal definition.

Practice Problems

1. Complete each statement so it is an example of the commutative property.

a. $5 + x = x +$ ____

b. $7 \cdot 3 = 3 \cdot$ ____

c. Simplify $4 + x + 9$ using the commutative property.

Answers
1a. $5 + x = x + 5$ **b.** $7 \cdot 3 = 3 \cdot 7$
c. $x + 13$

Associative Property of Addition

In symbols: $a + (b + c) = (a + b) + c$
In words: The *grouping* of the numbers in a sum does not affect the result.

Associative Property of Multiplication

In symbols: $a(bc) = (ab)c$
In words: The *grouping* of the numbers in a product does not affect the result.

The following examples illustrate how the associative properties can be used to simplify expressions that involve both numbers and variables.

▼ **Example 2**   Simplify by using the associative property.

a. $2 + (3 + y) = (2 + 3) + y$ Associative property
                $= 5 + y$ Addition

b. $5(4x) = (5 \cdot 4)x$ Associative property
          $= 20x$ Multiplication

c. $\frac{1}{4}(4a) = \left(\frac{1}{4} \cdot 4\right)a$ Associative property
          $= 1a$ Multiplication
          $= a$ ▲

Our next property involves both addition and multiplication. It is called the *distributive property* and is stated as follows.

Distributive Property

In symbols: $a(b + c) = ab + ac$
In words: Multiplication *distributes* over addition.

You will see as we progress through the book that the distributive property is used very frequently in algebra. To see that the distributive property works, compare the following:

     $3(4 + 5)$ $3(4) + 3(5)$
     $3(9)$ $12 + 15$
     27 27

In both cases the result is 27. Since the results are the same, the original two expressions must be equal. Or, $3(4 + 5) = 3(4) + 3(5)$.

▼ **Example 3**   Apply the distributive property to the following expressions, then simplify each one.

a. $3(7 + 1) = 3(7) + 3(1) = 21 + 3 = 24$
b. $4(x + 2) = 4(x) + 4(2) = 4x + 8$
c. $5(a + b) = 5a + 5b$ ▲

2. Simplify.

a. $5 + (7 + y)$

b. $3(2x)$

c. $\frac{1}{3}(3a)$

Note: Although the properties we are listing are stated for only two or three real numbers, they hold for as many numbers as needed. For example, the distributive property holds for expressions like $3(x + y + z + 2)$. That is

$3(x + y + z + 2) = 3x + 3y + 3z + 6$

With the distributive property, it is not important how many numbers are contained in the sum, only that it is a sum. Multiplication distributes over addition, whether there are two numbers in the sum or two hundred.

3. Apply the distributive property and then simplify.

a. $2(1 + 5)$
b. $3(a + 4)$
c. $7(x + y)$

Answers
2a. $12 + y$ **b.** $6x$ **c.** a **3a.** 12
b. $3a + 12$ **c.** $7x + 7y$

The distributive property can also be used to combine similar terms. (For now, a term is the product of a number with one or more variables. We will give a precise definition in Chapter 3.) Similar terms are terms with the same variable part. The terms $3x$ and $5x$ are similar, as are $2y$, $7y$, and $-3y$, because the variable parts are the same. To combine similar terms we use the distributive property in the reverse direction from that in Example 3. The following example illustrates.

▼ **Example 4**   Use the distributive property to combine similar terms.

a. $3x + 5x = (3 + 5)x$ Distributive property
$= 8x$ Addition

b. $4a + 7a = (4 + 7)a$ Distributive property
$= 11a$ Addition

c. $3y + y = (3 + 1)y$ Distributive property
$= 4y$ Addition   ▲

The distributive property is also used to add fractions. For example, to add $\frac{3}{7}$ and $\frac{2}{7}$ we first write each as the product of a whole number and $\frac{1}{7}$. Then we apply the distributive property as we did in the preceding example.

$$\frac{3}{7} + \frac{2}{7} = 3 \cdot \frac{1}{7} + 2 \cdot \frac{1}{7}$$

$$= (3 + 2)\frac{1}{7} \qquad \text{Distributive property}$$

$$= 5 \cdot \frac{1}{7}$$

$$= \frac{5}{7}$$

To add fractions using the distributive property, each fraction must have the same denominator. Here are some further examples.

▼ **Example 5**   Add.

a. $\dfrac{3}{9} + \dfrac{4}{9} + \dfrac{1}{9} = 3 \cdot \dfrac{1}{9} + 4 \cdot \dfrac{1}{9} + 1 \cdot \dfrac{1}{9}$

$= (3 + 4 + 1)\dfrac{1}{9} \qquad \text{Distributive property}$

$= 8 \cdot \dfrac{1}{9}$

$= \dfrac{8}{9}$

b. $\dfrac{4}{x} + \dfrac{2}{x} = 4 \cdot \dfrac{1}{x} + 2 \cdot \dfrac{1}{x}$

$= (4 + 2)\dfrac{1}{x} \qquad \text{Distributive property}$

$= 6 \cdot \dfrac{1}{x}$

$= \dfrac{6}{x}$ ▲

4.   Combine similar terms.

a. $4x + 9x$

b. $8a + 2a$

c. $y + 5y$

5.   Add.

a. $\dfrac{2}{7} + \dfrac{1}{7} + \dfrac{3}{7}$

b. $\dfrac{5}{x} + \dfrac{3}{x}$

Note: In actual practice you would probably not show all the steps shown in Example 5. We are showing them simply so you can see that each manipulation we do in algebra can be justified by a property or definition.

Answers

4a. $13x$ **b.** $10a$ **c.** $6y$ **5a.** $\frac{6}{7}$ **b.** $\dfrac{8}{x}$

We can use the commutative, associative, and distributive properties together to simplify expressions such as $3x + 4 + 5x + 8$. We begin by apply the commutative property to change the order of the terms and write:

$$3x + 5x + 4 + 8$$

Next we use the associative property to group similar terms together:

$$(3x + 5x) + (4 + 8)$$

Applying the distributive property to the first two terms we have

$$(3 + 5)x + (4 + 8)$$

Finally, we add 3 and 5, and 4 and 8 to get

$$8x + 12$$

Here are some additional examples.

▼ **Example 6** Simplify.

6. Simplify.

a. $4x + 3 + 5x + 1$

a.
$$
\begin{aligned}
7x + 4 + 6x + 3 &= (7x + 6x) + (4 + 3) && \text{Commutative and} \\
&&& \text{associative} \\
&&& \text{properties} \\
&= (7 + 6)x + (4 + 3) && \text{Distributive} \\
&&& \text{property} \\
&= 13x + 7 && \text{Addition}
\end{aligned}
$$

b. $7a + 2 + a + 4a$

b.
$$
\begin{aligned}
8a + 4 + a + 6a &= (8a + a + 6a) + 4 && \text{Commutative and} \\
&&& \text{associative} \\
&&& \text{properties} \\
&= (8 + 1 + 6)a + 4 && \text{Distributive} \\
&&& \text{property} \\
&= 15a + 4 && \text{Addition} \quad \blacktriangle
\end{aligned}
$$

The remaining properties of real numbers have to do with the numbers 0 and 1.

Note: 0 and 1 are called the *additive identity* and *multiplicative identity,* respectively. Combining 0 with a number, under addition, does not change the identity of the number. Likewise, combining 1 with a number, under multiplication, does not alter the identity of the number. We see that 0 is to addition what 1 is to multiplication.

Additive Identity Property

There exists a unique number 0 such that
In symbols: $a + 0 = a$ and $0 + a = a$
In words: Zero preserves identities under addition. (The identity of the number is unchanged after addition with 0.)

Multiplicative Identity Property

There exists a unique number 1 such that
In symbols: $a(1) = a$ and $1(a) = a$
In words: The number 1 preserves identities under multiplication. (The identity of the number is unchanged after multiplication by 1.)

Answers
6a. $9x + 4$ **b.** $12a + 2$

Additive Inverse Property

For each real number a, there exists a unique number $-a$ such that

In symbols: $a + (-a) = 0$
In words: Opposites add to 0.

Multiplicative Inverse Property

For every real number a, except 0, there exists a unique real number $1/a$ such that

In symbols: $a\left(\dfrac{1}{a}\right) = 1$

In words: Reciprocals multiply to 1.

Of all the basic properties listed, the commutative, associative, and distributive properties are the ones we will use most often. They are important because they are used as justifications or reasons for many of the things we will do in the future.

The following example illustrates how we use the properties listed here. Each line contains an algebraic expression that has been changed in some way. The property that justifies the change is written to the right.

▼ **Example 7**

a. $5(x + 3) = 5x + 15$ — Distributive property

b. $7(1) = 7$ — 1 is the identity element for multiplication

c. $11 + 5 = 5 + 11$ — Commutative property of addition

d. $11 \cdot 5 = 5 \cdot 11$ — Commutative property of multiplication

e. $4 + (-4) = 0$ — Additive inverse property

f. $3 + (x + 1) = (3 + x) + 1$ — Associative property of addition

g. $6(\frac{1}{6}) = 1$ — Multiplicative inverse property

h. $3 + 9 = 9 + 3$ — Commutative property of addition

i. $(2 + 5) + x = 5 + (2 + x)$ — Commutative and associative properties

j. $(1 + y) + 3 = 3 + (1 + y)$ — Commutative property of addition

k. $(5 + 0) + 2 = 5 + 2$ — 0 is the identity element for addition ▲

Notice in part i of Example 7 that both the order and grouping have changed from the left to the right expression, so both the commutative and associative properties were used.

In part j the only change is in the order of the numbers in the expression, not in the grouping, so only the commutative property was used.

7. Identify the property that justifies each of the following.

a. $3 + 9 = 9 + 3$

b. $4(x + 2) = 4x + 8$

c. $3 \cdot y = y \cdot 3$

d. $5(7a) = (5 \cdot 7)a$

e. $2 + 0 = 2$

f. $3(1) = 3$

g. $4 + (-4) = 0$

Answers
7a. Commutative, addition
b. Distributive **c.** Commutative, multiplication **d.** Associative, multiplication **e.** Additive identity
f. Multiplicative identity **g.** Additive inverse

Problem Set 1.4

Name _____

Class _____

Date _____

Use the associative property to rewrite each of the following expressions, and then simplify the result.

1. $4 + (2 + x)$

2. $6 + (5 + 3x)$

3. $(a + 3) + 5$

4. $(4a + 5) + 7$

5. $5(3y)$

6. $7(4y)$

7. $\frac{1}{3}(3x)$

8. $\frac{1}{5}(5x)$

9. $4(\frac{1}{4}a)$

10. $7(\frac{1}{7}a)$

11. $\frac{2}{3}(\frac{3}{2}x)$

12. $\frac{4}{3}(\frac{3}{4}x)$

Answers

1. _____   2. _____

3. _____   4. _____

5. _____   6. _____

7. _____   8. _____

9. _____   10. _____

11. _____   12. _____

13. _____   14. _____

15. _____   16. _____

17. _____   18. _____

19. _____   20. _____

21. _____   22. _____

23. _____   24. _____

Apply the distributive property to each expression. Simplify when possible.

13. $3(x + 6)$

14. $5(x + 9)$

15. $2(6x + 4)$

16. $3(7x + 8)$

17. $5(3a + 2b)$

18. $7(2a + 3b)$

19. $4(7 + 3y)$

20. $8(6 + 2y)$

21. $(5x + 1)8$

22. $(6x + 1)7$

23. $6(3x + 2 + 4y)$

24. $2(5x + 1 + 3y)$

Answers

25. _____	26. _____
27. _____	28. _____
29. _____	30. _____
31. _____	32. _____
33. _____	34. _____
35. _____	36. _____
37. _____	38. _____
39. _____	40. _____
41. _____	42. _____
43. _____	44. _____
45. _____	46. _____
47. _____	48. _____

Use the distributive property to combine similar terms.

25. $5x + 8x$ **26.** $7x + 4x$

27. $8y + 2y + 6y$ **28.** $9y + 3y + 4y$

29. $6a + a + 2a$ **30.** $a + 3a + 4a$

Use the distributive property to add the following fractions.

31. $\dfrac{3}{7} + \dfrac{1}{7} + \dfrac{2}{7}$ **32.** $\dfrac{3}{8} + \dfrac{1}{8} + \dfrac{1}{8}$

33. $\dfrac{4}{\sqrt{3}} + \dfrac{5}{\sqrt{3}}$ **34.** $\dfrac{1}{\sqrt{5}} + \dfrac{8}{\sqrt{5}}$

35. $\dfrac{4}{x} + \dfrac{7}{x}$ **36.** $\dfrac{5}{y} + \dfrac{9}{y}$

37. $\dfrac{3}{a} + \dfrac{5}{a} + \dfrac{1}{a}$ **38.** $\dfrac{4}{x} + \dfrac{1}{x} + \dfrac{3}{x}$

Use the commutative, associative, and distributive properties to simplify the following.

39. $3x + 5 + 4x + 2$ **40.** $5x + 1 + 7x + 8$

41. $x + 3 + 4x + 9$ **42.** $5x + 2 + x + 10$

43. $5a + 7 + 8a + a$ **44.** $6a + 4 + a + 4a$

45. $3y + y + 5 + 2y + 1$ **46.** $4y + 2y + 3 + y + 7$

47. $x + 1 + x + 2 + x + 3$ **48.** $5 + x + 6 + x + 7 + x$

Each of the following problems has a mistake in it. Correct the right-hand side.

49. $5(2x + 4) = 10x + 4$

50. $7(x + 8) = 7x + 15$

51. $3x + 4x = 7(2x)$

52. $3x + 4x = 7x^2$

53. $\frac{3}{5} + \frac{1}{5} = \frac{4}{10}$

54. $\frac{5}{9} + \frac{2}{9} = \frac{7}{18}$

Identify the property of real numbers that justifies each of the following.

55. $3 + 2 = 2 + 3$

56. $3(ab) = (3a)b$

57. $5x = x5$

58. $2 + 0 = 2$

59. $4 + (-4) = 0$

60. $1(6) = 6$

61. $x + (y + 2) = (y + 2) + x$

62. $(a + 3) + 4 = a + (3 + 4)$

63. $4(5 \cdot 7) = 5(4 \cdot 7)$

64. $6(xy) = (xy)6$

65. $4 + (x + y) = (4 + y) + x$

66. $(r + 7) + s = (r + s) + 7$

67. $3(4x + 2) = 12x + 6$

68. $5(\frac{1}{5}) = 1$

Name _____

Class _____

Date _____

Answers

49. _____

50. _____

51. _____

52. _____

53. _____

54. _____

55. _____

56. _____

57. _____

58. _____

59. _____

60. _____

61. _____

62. _____

63. _____

64. _____

65. _____

66. _____

67. _____

68. _____

Answers

Use the given property to complete each of the following.

69. _____

69. $5y = ?$ Commutative property

70. _____

70. $4 + 0 = ?$ Additive identity property

71. _____

72. _____

71. $3 + a = ?$ Commutative property

73. _____

72. $5(x + y) = ?$ Distributive property

74. _____

75. _____

73. $7(1) = ?$ Multiplicative identity property

76. _____

74. $6(\frac{1}{6}) = ?$ Multiplicative inverse property

77. _____

78. _____

75. $2 + (x + 6) = ?$ Associative property

79. _____

76. $5(x \cdot 3) = ?$ Associative property

80. _____

81. _____

77. $(x + 2)y = ?$ Distributive property

82. _____

78. $7a + 7b + 7c = ?$ Distributive property

83. _____

84. _____

79. $11 \cdot 1 = ?$ Multiplicative identity property

80. $-6 + 6 = ?$ Additive inverse property

81. Show that the statement $5x - 5 = x$ is not correct by replacing x with 4 and simplifying both sides.

82. Show that the statement $8x - x = 8$ is not correct by replacing x with 5 and simplifying both sides.

83. Simplify the expressions $15 - (8 - 2)$ and $(15 - 8) - 2$ to show that subtraction is not an associative operation.

84. Simplify the expression $(48 \div 6) \div 2$ and the expression $48 \div (6 \div 2)$ to show that division is not an associative operation.

Section 1.5   Addition and Subtraction of Real Numbers

The purpose of this section is to review the rules for addition and subtraction of real numbers and the justification for those rules. The goal here is the ability to add and subtract positive and negative real numbers quickly and accurately, the latter being the more important.

Addition of Real Numbers

We can justify the rules for addition of real numbers geometrically by use of the real number line. Since real numbers can be thought of as having both a distance from 0 (absolute value) and a direction from 0 (positive or negative), we can visualize addition of two numbers as follows.
   Consider the sum of -5 and 3:

$$-5 + 3$$

We can interpret this expression as meaning "start at the origin and move 5 units in the negative direction and then 3 units in the positive direction." With the aid of a number line we can visualize the process.

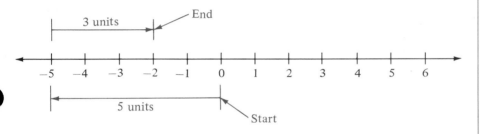

Since the process ends at -2, we say the sum of -5 and 3 is -2:

$$-5 + 3 = -2$$

We can use the real number line in this way to add any combination of positive and negative numbers.
   The sum of -4 and -2, $-4 + (-2)$, can be interpreted as starting at the origin, moving 4 units in the negative direction, and then 2 more units in the negative direction:

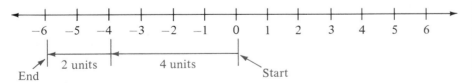

Since the process ends at -6, we say the sum of -4 and -2 is -6:

$$-4 + (-2) = -6$$

We can eliminate actually drawing a number line by simply visualizing it mentally. The following example gives the results of all possible sums of positive and negative 5 and 7.

Note: We are showing addition of real numbers on the number line to justify the rule we will write for addition of positive and negative numbers. You may want to skip ahead and read the rule on the next page first, and then come back and read through this discussion again. The discussion here is the "why" behind the rule.

Practice Problems

1. Add.

   $3 + 5 =$

   $-3 + 5 =$

   $3 + (-5) =$

   $-3 + (-5) =$

Note: This rule is the most important rule we have had so far. It is very important that you use it exactly the way it is written. Your goal is to become fast and accurate at adding positive and negative numbers. When you have finished reading this section and working the problems in the problem set, you should have attained that goal. Almost everything you encounter after this will involve adding positive and negative numbers.

2. Add.

a. $-4 + (-1) + (-3)$

b. $-8 + 4 + (-5)$

c. $-7 + (-2 + 8) + 3$

▼ **Example 1** Add all possible combinations of positive and negative 5 and 7.

Solution

$$5 + 7 = 12$$
$$-5 + 7 = 2$$
$$5 + (-7) = -2$$
$$-5 + (-7) = -12$$ ▲

Looking closely at the relationships in Example 1 (and trying other similar examples if necessary), we can arrive at the following rule for adding two real numbers.

Rule To add two real numbers with

   a. the *same* sign: simply add absolute values and use the common sign. If both numbers are positive, the answer is positive. If both numbers are negative, the answer is negative.
   b. *different* signs: subtract the smaller absolute value from the larger. The answer will have the sign of the number with the larger absolute value.

Here are other examples of addition of real numbers.

▼ **Example 2**

a. $-2 + (-3) + (-4) = -5 + (-4)$
$$= -9$$

b. $-3 + 5 + (-7) = 2 + (-7)$
$$= -5$$

c. $-6 + (-3 + 5) + 4 = -6 + 2 + 4$
$$= -4 + 4$$
$$= 0$$ ▲

Subtraction of Real Numbers

In order to have as few rules as possible, we will not attempt to list new rules for the difference of two real numbers. We will define subtraction in terms of addition and apply the rule for addition.

DEFINITION (SUBTRACTION)   If a and b are any two real numbers, then the difference of a and b is

$$\underbrace{a - b}_{\text{To subtract } b,} = \underbrace{a + (-b)}_{\text{add the opposite of } b.}$$

We define the process of subtracting b from a to be equivalent to adding the opposite of b to a. In short, we say, "subtraction is addition of the opposite."

Here is how it works.

Answers
1. 8, 2, −2, −8   **2a.** −8   **b.** −9
c. 2

▼ **Example 3** Subtract.

a. $5 - 3 = 5 + (-3) = 2$ Subtracting 3 is equivalent to adding -3

b. $-7 - 6 = -7 + (-6) = -13$ Subtracting 6 is equivalent to adding -6

c. $9 - (-2) = 9 + 2 = 11$ Subtracting -2 is equivalent to adding 2

d. $-6 - (-5) = -6 + 5 = -1$ Subtracting -5 is equivalent to adding 5   ▲

3. Subtract

a. $7 - 4$

b. $-6 - 3$

c. $8 - (-2)$

d. $-4 - (-6)$

▼ **Example 4** Subtract -3 from -9.

Solution Since subtraction is not commutative, we must be sure to write the numbers in the correct order. Because we are subtracting -3, the problem looks like this when translated into symbols:

$$-9 - (-3) = -9 + 3 \qquad \text{Change to addition of the opposite.}$$
$$= -6 \qquad \text{Add} \qquad ▲$$

The following example involves combinations of sums and differences. Generally, the differences are first changed to appropriate sums; the additions are then performed left to right.

4. Subtract -5 from 8.

▼ **Example 5** Perform the indicated operations.

a. $9 - 5 + 2 = 9 + (-5) + 2$
$$= 4 + 2$$
$$= 6$$

b. $6 - (-3) + 2 = 6 + 3 + 2$
$$= 9 + 2$$
$$= 11$$

c. $-4 - 2 - (-5) = -4 + (-2) + 5$
$$= -6 + 5$$
$$= -1$$

d. $10 - |-3| + |-2| = 10 - 3 + 2$
$$= 10 + (-3) + 2$$
$$= 9$$

e. $-8 - (-3) - |-7| = -8 - (-3) - 7$
$$= -8 + 3 + (-7)$$
$$= -12 \qquad ▲$$

5. Perform the indicated operations.

a. $2 - 6 + 4$

b. $7 - (-1) + 3$

c. $-9 - 5 - (-7)$

d. $6 - |-2| + |-3|$

e. $-3 - (-9) - |-2|$

Since subtraction is defined in terms of addition, we can state the distributive property in terms of subtraction. That is, if a, b, and c are real numbers, then

$$a(b - c) = ab - ac$$

Here are some examples that use the distributive property and the rules for addition and subtraction of real numbers.

Answers
3a. 3 **b.** -9 **c.** 10 **d.** 2 **4.** 13
5a. 0 **b.** 11 **c.** -7 **d.** 7 **e.** 4

6. Apply the distributive property.

a. $2(x - 5)$

b. $4(y - 2)$

c. $3(a - 1)$

d. $2(x - 7 + y)$

▼ **Example 6** Apply the distributive property.

a. $3(x - 4) = 3x - 12$

b. $2(y - 6) = 2y - 12$

c. $5(a - 3) = 5a - 15$

d. $3(x - 2 + y) = 3x - 6 + 3y$ ▲

We can also use the distributive property to combine similar terms as we did in Section 1.4.

7. Combine similar terms.

a. $5x - 3x$

b. $-5x - 8x$

c. $6y - y$

d. $-8a + 3a$

e. $-4x + 9x - 2x$

▼ **Example 7** Combine similar terms.

a. $8x - 2x = (8 - 2)x$ Distributive property
          $= 6x$ Subtraction

b. $-4x - 7x = (-4 - 7)x$ Distributive property
           $= -11x$ Subtraction

c. $5y - y = (5 - 1)y$ Distributive property
        $= 4y$ Subtraction

(Remember, $y = 1y$. Multiplying by 1 leaves y unchanged.)

d. $-9a + 7a = (-9 + 7)a$ Distributive property
          $= -2a$ Addition

e. $-7x + 5x - 8x = (-7 + 5 - 8)x$ Distributive property
            $= -10x$ Addition and subtraction ▲

We can extend the idea of combining similar terms as shown in Example 7 to some slightly more complicated expressions. Suppose we want to simplify the expression $7x + 4 - 3x$. We can first change the subtraction to addition of the opposite, and then change the order of the terms since addition is a commutative operation.

$$
\begin{aligned}
7x + 4 - 3x &= 7x + 4 + (-3x) &&\text{Definition of subtraction}\\
&= 7x + (-3x) + 4 &&\text{Commutative property}\\
&= 7x - 3x + 4 &&\text{Definition of subtraction}\\
&= 4x + 4 &&\text{Combine similar terms}
\end{aligned}
$$

In actual practice you will not show all the steps we have shown. They are shown here simply so you can see that subtraction can be written in terms of addition, and then the order of the terms rearranged because addition is commutative. The point is, if you move the $3x$ term to another position, you have to take the negative (or subtraction) sign with it. Here are some examples that show only a few of the steps.

8. Simplify by combining similar terms.

a. $7x - 3 - 4x + 8$

b. $10x - x + 5 + 2x$

c. $x - 3 - 4 - 3x$

▼ **Example 8** Simplify by combining similar terms.

a. $8x - 4 - 5x + 9 = 8x - 5x - 4 + 9$
                    $= 3x + 5$

b. $7x - x + 4 - 2x = 7x - x - 2x + 4$
                  $= 4x + 4$

c. $x - 7 + 4 - 6x = x - 6x - 7 + 4$
               $= -5x - 3$ ▲

Answers
6a. $2x - 10$ **b.** $4y - 8$ **c.** $3a - 3$
d. $2x - 14 + 2y$ **7a.** $2x$ **b.** $-13x$
c. $5y$ **d.** $-5a$ **e.** $3x$ **8a.** $3x + 5$
b. $11x + 5$ **c.** $-2x - 7$

Problem Set 1.5

Name _____

Class _____

Date _____

Find each of the following sums.

1. $6 + (-2)$

2. $11 + (-5)$

3. $-6 + 2$

4. $-11 + 5$

5. $-6 + (-2)$

6. $-11 + (-5)$

7. $-3 + 5 + (-7)$

8. $-1 + 4 + (-6)$

9. $3 + (-5) - (-7)$

10. $1 + (-4) + (-7)$

11. $-9 + (-3) + (-1)$

12. $-10 + (-5) + (-2)$

13. $-3 + (-8 + 1) + (-4)$

14. $-2 + (-9 + 2) + (-5)$

Find each of the following differences.

15. $7 - 3$

16. $6 - 9$

17. $-7 - 3$

18. $-6 - 9$

19. $-7 - (-3)$

20. $-6 - (-9)$

21. $7 - (-3)$

22. $6 - (-9)$

23. $-15 - 20$

24. $-11 - 15$

25. $12 - (-4)$

26. $5 - (-2)$

27. $-8 - (-11)$

28. $-4 - (-12)$

Answers

1. _____ 2. _____
3. _____ 4. _____
5. _____ 6. _____
7. _____ 8. _____
9. _____ 10. _____
11. _____ 12. _____
13. _____ 14. _____
15. _____ 16. _____
17. _____ 18. _____
19. _____ 20. _____
21. _____ 22. _____
23. _____ 24. _____
25. _____ 26. _____
27. _____ 28. _____

Answers

29. _____	30. _____
31. _____	32. _____
33. _____	34. _____
35. _____	36. _____
37. _____	38. _____
39. _____	40. _____
41. _____	42. _____
43. _____	44. _____
45. _____	46. _____
47. _____	48. _____
49. _____	50. _____

Perform the indicated operations.

29. $3 + (-2) - 6$

30. $8 + (-3) - 5$

31. $-4 - 3 + 8$

32. $-9 - 5 + 7$

33. $6 - (-2) + 11$

34. $8 - (-3) + 12$

35. $-8 - (-3) - 9$

36. $-1 - (-2) - 3$

37. $4 - (-5) - (-1)$

38. $7 - (-2) - (-6)$

39. $|-2| + |-3| - |-6|$

40. $|-5| + |-2| - |-7|$

41. $|-2| + |-3| - (-6)$

42. $|-5| + |-2| - (-7)$

43. $|-4| - (-2) - |-10|$

44. $|-2| - (-3) - |-12|$

45. $9 - (-2) - 5 - 6 + (-3)$

46. $11 - (-6) - 2 - 4 + (-3)$

47. $|-2| - |-3| - (-8) + |-(-1)|$

48. $|-7| - |-2| - (-4) + |-(-6)|$

49. $-14 - (-20) + |-26| - |-16|$

50. $-11 - (-14) + |-17| - |-20|$

Apply the distributive property.

51. $2(x - 4)$

52. $7(x - 8)$

53. $5(y - 3)$

54. $6(y - 1)$

55. $7(x - 4)$

56. $3(x - 7)$

57. $4(a - 2 + b)$

58. $5(a - 5 + b)$

59. $5(x - y - 4)$

60. $7(a - b - 2)$

Combine similar terms.

61. $5x - 2x$

62. $8x - 2x$

63. $-4x - 9x$

64. $-7x - 10x$

65. $5y - y$

66. $3y - y$

67. $9a - 8a$

68. $3a - 2a$

69. $5x - 3x - 8x$

70. $7x - 3x - 5x$

71. $-4a - 9a + 2a$

72. $-7a - 8a + a$

73. $-3x - x + 6x$

74. $-4x + x - 7x$

Name _____

Class _____

Date _____

Answers

51. _____	**52.** _____
53. _____	**54.** _____
55. _____	**56.** _____
57. _____	**58.** _____
59. _____	**60.** _____
61. _____	**62.** _____
63. _____	**64.** _____
65. _____	**66.** _____
67. _____	**68.** _____
69. _____	**70.** _____
71. _____	**72.** _____
73. _____	**74.** _____

Answers

75. _____ 76. _____

77. _____ 78. _____

79. _____ 80. _____

81. _____ 82. _____

83. _____ 84. _____

85. _____ 86. _____

87. _____ 88. _____

89. _____ 90. _____

91. _____ 92. _____

93. _____ 94. _____

95. _____ 96. _____

Simplify each expression.

75. $3x - 5 + 4x - 9$

76. $7x - 4 - 5x + 8$

77. $8x - 3x + 7 - 4x$

78. $7x - 4x + 3 - 2x$

79. $3a + 2 - a - 5a$

80. $5a + 5 - a - 6a$

81. $6y + 4 - 5y - y + 9$

82. $5y - 3 - 4y - y + 2$

83. $-5t - 3 + 8t + 2 - t$

84. $-9t - 5 + 7t + 3 - t$

85. Subtract 5 from -3.

86. Subtract -3 from 5.

87. Subtract $4x$ from $-3x$.

88. Subtract $-5x$ from $7x$.

89. What number do you subtract from 5 to get -8?

90. What number do you subtract from -3 to get 9?

91. Subtract $3a$ from the sum of $8a$ and a.

92. Subtract $-3a$ from the sum of $3a$ and $5a$.

93. Find five times the sum of $3x$ and -4.

94. Find six times the sum of $3x$ and -5.

95. Add 7 to the difference of $3y$ and -1.

96. Subtract $4a$ from the sum of $-5a$ and 4.

Section 1.6   Multiplication and Division of Real Numbers

Multiplication of Real Numbers

Multiplication with whole numbers is simply a shorthand way of writing repeated addition. That is, the product 3(2) can be interpreted as the sum of three 2s:

$$3(2) = 2 + 2 + 2$$

Although this definition of multiplication does not hold for other kinds of numbers, such as fractions, it does, however, give us ways of interpreting products of positive and negative numbers. For example, $3(-2)$ can be evaluated as follows:

$$3(-2) = -2 + (-2) + (-2)$$
$$= -6$$

We can evaluate the product $-3(2)$ in a similar manner if we first apply the commutative property of multiplication.

$$-3(2) = 2(-3) \qquad \text{Commutative property}$$
$$= -3 + (-3) \qquad \text{Repeated addition}$$
$$= -6$$

From these results it seems reasonable to say that the product of a positive and a negative is a negative number.

The last case we must consider is the product of two negative numbers. For example:

$$-3(-2)$$

To evaluate this product we will look at the expression $-3[2 + (-2)]$ in two different ways. First, since $2 + (-2) = 0$, we have

$$-3[2 + (-2)] = -3(0) = 0$$

So we know this expression is equal to 0. On the other hand, we can apply the distributive property to get

$$-3[2 + (-2)] = -3(2) + (-3)(-2)$$
$$= -6 + ?$$

Since we know the expression is equal to 0, it must be true that our ? is 6, since 6 is the only number we can add to -6 to get 0. Therefore, we have

$$-3(-2) = 6$$

Here is a summary of what we have so far:

$$3(2) = 6$$
$$3(-2) = -6$$
$$-3(2) = -6$$
$$-3(-2) = 6$$

This discussion justifies writing the following rule for multiplication of real numbers.

Note: This discussion is to show why the rule for multiplication of real numbers is written the way it is. Even if you already know how to multiply positive and negative numbers, it is a good idea to review the "why" that is behind it all.

Rule for Multiplying Real Numbers

To multiply two real numbers, simply multiply their absolute values. The product is

    a. *positive* if both numbers have the same sign; that is, both are $+$ or both are $-$; or

    b. *negative* if the two numbers have opposite signs; that is, one $+$ and the other $-$.

The following example illustrates this rule for finding products of positive and negative numbers.

▼ Example 1

a. $(7)(3) = 21$

b. $(7)(-3) = -21$

c. $(-7)(3) = -21$

d. $(-7)(-3) = 21$

e. $(4)(-3)(-2) = -12(-2)$
                   $= 24$

f. $(5)(-3 \cdot 2) = 5(-6)$
                $= -30$

g. $-4(5x) = (-4 \cdot 5)x$ Associative property
             $= -20x$ Multiplication

h. $-2(7a) = (-2 \cdot 7)a$ Associative property
             $= -14a$ Multiplication

i. $-3(x + 4) = -3(x) + (-3)4$ Distributive property
                  $= -3x - 12$ Multiplication

j. $-2(3a + 5) = -2(3a) + (-2)(5)$ Distributive property
                  $= -6a - 10$ Multiplication   ▲

Division of Real Numbers

In order to have as few rules as possible in building our system of algebra, we will now define division for two real numbers in terms of multiplication.

DEFINITION   If a and b are any two real numbers, where $b \neq 0$, then

$$\frac{a}{b} = a \cdot \left(\frac{1}{b}\right)$$

Dividing a by b is equivalent to multiplying a by the reciprocal of b. In short, we say, "division is multiplication by the reciprocal."

Since division is defined in terms of multiplication, the same rules hold for assigning the correct sign to a quotient as held for assigning the correct sign to a product. That is, *the quotient of two numbers with like signs is positive, while the quotient of two numbers with unlike signs is negative.*

Practice Problems

1.   Multiply.

a. $6(2)$

b. $6(-2)$

c. $-6(2)$

d. $-6(-2)$

e. $-2(5)(-1)$

f. $4(-7 \cdot 2)$

g. $-3(2x)$

h. $-5(4a)$

i. $-6(x + 2)$

j. $-3(4a + 1)$

Note: The reason for the restriction $b \neq 0$ in the definition is that division by 0 is not defined. Dividing a number by 0 would have to be equivalent to multiplying the number by the reciprocal of 0. In Section 1.2 we found 0 to be the only real number without a reciprocal. Hence, division by 0 is not defined.

Answers
1a. 12   **b.** -12 **c.** -12 **d.** 12
e. 10   **f.** -56 **g.** $-6x$ **h.** $-20a$
i. $-6x - 12$ **j.** $-12a - 3$

▼ **Example 2** Divide.

a. $\dfrac{6}{3} = 6 \cdot \left(\dfrac{1}{3}\right) = 2$

b. $\dfrac{6}{-3} = 6 \cdot \left(-\dfrac{1}{3}\right) = -2$

c. $\dfrac{-6}{3} = -6 \cdot \left(\dfrac{1}{3}\right) = -2$

d. $\dfrac{-6}{-3} = -6 \cdot \left(-\dfrac{1}{3}\right) = 2$

Notice these examples indicate that if a and b are positive real numbers then

$$\dfrac{-a}{b} = \dfrac{a}{-b} = -\dfrac{a}{b}$$

and

$$\dfrac{-a}{-b} = \dfrac{a}{b}$$ ▲

The second step in the preceding examples is written only to show that each quotient can be written as a product. It is not actually necessary to show this step when working problems.

Review of Division with Fractions

We can also use the definition of division to review division with fractions.

▼ **Example 3** Divide: $\dfrac{3}{5} \div \dfrac{2}{7}$.

Solution To divide by $\frac{2}{7}$, we multiply by its reciprocal, $\frac{7}{2}$:

$$\dfrac{3}{5} \div \dfrac{2}{7} = \dfrac{3}{5} \cdot \dfrac{7}{2}$$

$$= \dfrac{21}{10}$$ ▲

▼ **Example 4** Divide and reduce to lowest terms.

a. $\dfrac{3}{4} \div \dfrac{6}{11} = \dfrac{3}{4} \cdot \dfrac{11}{6}$ Definition of division

$\qquad = \dfrac{33}{24}$ Multiply numerators, multiply denominators

$\qquad = \dfrac{11}{8}$ Divide numerator and denominator by 3

b. $10 \div \dfrac{5}{6} = \dfrac{10}{1} \cdot \dfrac{6}{5}$ Definition of division

$\qquad = \dfrac{60}{5}$ Multiply numerators, multiply denominators

$\qquad = 12$ Divide

c. $-\dfrac{3}{8} \div 6 = -\dfrac{3}{8} \cdot \dfrac{1}{6}$ Definition of division

$\qquad = -\dfrac{3}{48}$ Multiply numerators, multiply denominators

$\qquad = -\dfrac{1}{16}$ Divide numerator and denominator by 3 ▲

Here are some more complicated examples using combinations of the four basic operations and the rule for order of operations from Section 1.1.

---

2. Divide.

a. $\dfrac{12}{4}$

b. $\dfrac{12}{-4}$

c. $\dfrac{-12}{4}$

d. $\dfrac{-12}{-4}$

3. Divide: $\dfrac{3}{4} \div \dfrac{5}{9}$.

4. Divide and reduce to lowest terms.

a. $\dfrac{3}{5} \div \dfrac{6}{7}$

b. $12 \div \dfrac{3}{4}$

c. $-\dfrac{5}{6} \div 10$

Answers
2a. 3 **b.** -3 **c.** -3 **d.** 3 **3.** $\frac{27}{20}$
4a. $\frac{7}{10}$ **b.** 16 **c.** $-\frac{1}{12}$

5. Simplify each expression.

a. $\dfrac{3(-4) - 8}{12 - 2}$

b. $4 - 3(2 - 9) - (-1)$

c. $\dfrac{5(-6) + 3(-2)}{4(-3) + 3}$

6. Simplify $2(5y - 1) - y$.

7. Simplify $6 - 2(5x + 1) + 4x$.

8. Simplify $4(3a + 1) - (7a - 6)$.

▼ **Example 5**   Simplify as much as possible.

a. $\dfrac{5(-3) - 10}{-4 - 1} = \dfrac{-15 - 10}{-4 - 1}$

$\qquad\qquad = \dfrac{-25}{-5}$

$\qquad\qquad = 5$

Notice that the division rule (the line used to separate the numerator from the denominator) is treated like parentheses. It serves to group the numbers on top separately from the numbers on the bottom.

b. $3 - 5(4 - 7) - (-3) = 3 - 5(-3) + 3$

$\qquad\qquad\qquad\qquad\quad = 3 + 15 + 3$

$\qquad\qquad\qquad\qquad\quad = 21$

c. $\dfrac{-5(-4) + 2(-3)}{2(-1) - 5} = \dfrac{20 - 6}{-2 - 5}$

$\qquad\qquad\qquad\quad = \dfrac{14}{-7}$

$\qquad\qquad\qquad\quad = -2$ ▲

▼ **Example 6**   Simplify $3(2y - 1) + y$.

Solution   We begin by multiplying the 3 and $2y - 1$. Then we combine similar terms:

$3(2y - 1) + y = 6y - 3 + y$ $\qquad$ Distributive property

$\qquad\qquad\quad = 7y - 3$ $\qquad$ Combine similar terms   ▲

▼ **Example 7**   Simplify $8 - 3(4x - 2) + 5x$.

Solution   First we distribute the -3 across the $4x - 2$. Then we combine similar terms:

$8 - 3(4x - 2) + 5x = 8 - 12x + 6 + 5x$

$\qquad\qquad\qquad\qquad = -7x + 14$ ▲

▼ **Example 8**   Simplify $5(2a + 3) - (6a - 4)$.

Solution   We begin by applying the distributive property to remove the parentheses. The expression $-(6a - 4)$ can be thought of as $-1(6a - 4)$. Thinking of it in this way allows us to apply the distributive property:

$$-1(6a - 4) = -1(6a) - (-1)(4) = -6a + 4$$

Here is the complete problem:

$5(2a + 3) - (6a - 4) = 10a + 15 - 6a + 4$ $\qquad$ Distributive property

$\qquad\qquad\qquad\qquad\quad = 4a + 19$ $\qquad$ Combine similar terms   ▲

Answers

5a. -2 **b.** 26 **c.** 4 **6.** $9y - 2$

7. $-6x + 4$ **8.** $5a + 10$

Problem Set 1.6

Find the following products.

Name _____

Class _____

Date _____

1. $3(-5)$

2. $-3(5)$

3. $-3(-5)$

4. $4(-6)$

5. $-8(3)$

6. $-7(-6)$

7. $-5(-4)$

8. $-4(0)$

9. $-2(-1)(-6)$

10. $-3(-2)(5)$

11. $2(-3)(4)$

12. $-2(3)(-4)$

13. $-1(-2)(-3)(4)$

14. $-3(-2)(1)(4)$

15. $-2(4)(-3)(1)$

16. $-5(6)(-3)(-2)$

17. $-2(5x)$

18. $-5(4x)$

19. $-7(3a)$

20. $-6(5a)$

21. $4(-8y)$

22. $6(-2y)$

23. $-3(-5x)$

24. $-2(-9x)$

25. $-5(x + 8)$

26. $-7(x + 4)$

27. $-2(4x + 3)$

28. $-6(2x + 1)$

29. $-6(2x - 5)$

30. $-7(3x - 2)$

Answers

1. _____ 2. _____

3. _____ 4. _____

5. _____ 6. _____

7. _____ 8. _____

9. _____ 10. _____

11. _____ 12. _____

13. _____ 14. _____

15. _____ 16. _____

17. _____ 18. _____

19. _____ 20. _____

21. _____ 22. _____

23. _____ 24. _____

25. _____ 26. _____

27. _____ 28. _____

29. _____ 30. _____

Answers

31. _____	32. _____
33. _____	34. _____
35. _____	36. _____
37. _____	38. _____
39. _____	40. _____
41. _____	42. _____
43. _____	44. _____
45. _____	46. _____
47. _____	48. _____
49. _____	50. _____
51. _____	52. _____

Use the definition of division to write each division problem as a multiplication problem, then simplify.

31. $\dfrac{8}{-4}$

32. $\dfrac{-8}{4}$

33. $\dfrac{-8}{-4}$

34. $\dfrac{-12}{-4}$

35. $-\dfrac{3}{4} \div \dfrac{9}{8}$

36. $-\dfrac{2}{3} \div \dfrac{4}{9}$

37. $-8 \div \left(-\dfrac{1}{4}\right)$

38. $-12 \div \left(-\dfrac{2}{3}\right)$

39. $-40 \div \left(-\dfrac{5}{8}\right)$

40. $-30 \div \left(-\dfrac{5}{6}\right)$

41. $\dfrac{4}{9} \div (-8)$

42. $\dfrac{3}{7} \div (-6)$

43. $-\dfrac{7}{12} \div \left(-\dfrac{21}{48}\right)$

44. $\dfrac{-9}{10} \div \left(-\dfrac{27}{40}\right)$

Simplify each expression as much as possible.

45. $3(-4) - 2$

46. $-3(-4) - 2$

47. $5(-2) - (-3)$

48. $-8(-11) - (-1)$

49. $4(-3) - 6(-5)$

50. $-6(-3) - 5(-7)$

51. $-8(4) - (-6)(-2)$

52. $9(-1) - 4(-3)$

Simplify each expression.

53. $2 - 4[3 - 5(-1)]$

54. $6 - 5[2 - 4(-8)]$

55. $(8 - 7)[4 - 7(-2)]$

56. $(6 - 9)[15 - 3(-4)]$

57. $\dfrac{6(-2) - 8}{-15 - (-10)}$

58. $\dfrac{8(-3) - 6}{-7 - (-2)}$

59. $\dfrac{3(-1) - 4(-2)}{8 - 5}$

60. $\dfrac{6(-4) - 5(-2)}{7 - 6}$

61. $8 - (-6)\left[\dfrac{2(-3) - 5(4)}{-8(6) - 4}\right]$

62. $-9 - 5\left[\dfrac{11(-1) - 9}{4(-3) + 2(5)}\right]$

63. $6 - (-3)\left[\dfrac{2 - 4(3 - 8)}{1 - 5(1 - 3)}\right]$

64. $8 - (-7)\left[\dfrac{6 - 1(6 - 10)}{4 - 3(5 - 7)}\right]$

Name _____

Class _____

Date _____

Answers

53. _____   54. _____

55. _____   56. _____

57. _____   58. _____

59. _____   60. _____

61. _____   62. _____

63. _____   64. _____

Answers

65. _____ 66. _____

67. _____ 68. _____

69. _____ 70. _____

71. _____ 72. _____

73. _____ 74. _____

75. _____ 76. _____

77. _____ 78. _____

79. _____ 80. _____

81. _____ 82. _____

83. _____ 84. _____

85. _____ 86. _____

Simplify each expression.

65. $3(5x + 4) - x$ **66.** $4(7x + 3) - x$

67. $3(2a - 4) - 7a$ **68.** $-2(3a - 2) - 7a$

69. $7 + 3(x + 2)$ **70.** $5 + 2(3x - 4)$

71. $6 - 7(m - 3)$ **72.** $3 - 5(2m - 5)$

73. $7 - 2(3x - 1) + 4x$ **74.** $8 - 5(2x - 3) + 4x$

75. $5(y + 2) - 4(y + 1)$ **76.** $6(y - 3) - 5(y + 2)$

77. $5(3y + 1) - (8y - 5)$ **78.** $4(6y + 3) - (6y - 6)$

79. $10 - 4(2x + 1) - (3x - 4)$

80. $7 - 2(3x + 5) - (2x - 3)$

81. Subtract -5 from the product of 12 and $-\frac{2}{3}$.

82. Subtract -3 from the product of -12 and $\frac{3}{4}$.

83. Add -5 to the quotient of -3 and $\frac{1}{2}$.

84. Add -7 to the quotient of 6 and $-\frac{1}{2}$.

85. Add $8x$ to the product of -2 and $3x$.

86. Add $7x$ to the product of -5 and $-2x$.

Section 1.7   Using a Calculator

In this section we will show how a calculator can be used to simplify expressions involving positive and negative numbers. Before we begin, however, we need to say a few words about calculators in general.

Although some of the examples in this section can be worked on any kind of calculator, to work the more complicated examples you will need a scientific calculator. A scientific calculator will contain keys in addition to the keys used for the four basic arithmetic operations, add, subtract, multiply, and divide. To work through the examples and practice problems in this section, and the calculator notes that are shown later in the book, you will need a calculator that has the following keys

Finally, there are two kinds of logic used by scientific calculators, algebraic logic and RPN logic. If your calculator has a key labeled $=$, then it uses algebraic logic. Calculators that use RPN logic do not have an $=$ key. Instead they have a key labeled ENT . The examples in this book are for calculators with algebraic logic.

▼ **Example 1**   Calculate $3 + 4 \cdot 5$.

Solution   If your calculator is operating according to algebraic logic then pressing the following sequence of keys will result in the correct answer of 23

If your calculator gives an answer of 35, then it is not operating according to algebraic logic, but is doing the calculations as they entered, even though it has an $=$ key. If you have this type of calculator, you will have to make some adjustments in the order in which you enter the numbers and the operations. In this case, you would have to use the following sequence in order to obtain the correct answer of 23.

   ▲

▼ **Example 2**   Calculate $12 - 8 \div 4 - 10$.

Solution   Assuming that your calculator is using algebraic logic, you would enter the numbers and operations in the following sequence:

The correct answer is 0.   ▲

Practice Problems

1.   Calculate $7 - 4 \cdot 6$.

2.   Calculate $12 \div 4 - 8 \div 2$.

Note: In a problem like this we could use the $1/x$ key and multiplication instead of the division key to obtain the same result. (Remember, division by a number is the same as multiplication by its reciprocal.) If we did so, the sequence would look like this:

Answers
1. -17 **2.** -1

3. Calculate $8 - (3 - 7 \cdot 6)$.

▼ **Example 3** Calculate $5 - (2 - 8 \cdot 9)$.

Solution Entering the numbers and symbols in the same order as above and then ending the sequence by pressing the = key will get us the correct answer of 75.

To do calculations with negative numbers, you must use the key labeled $\boxed{+/-}$. (On some calculators, this key is labeled $\boxed{\text{CHS}}$.) This is the key that changes the sign of the number showing on the display. For that reason, to enter a negative number on your calculator, you must first enter the numerical part of the number (absolute value) and the change it to a negative number by pressing $\boxed{+/-}$. Here are some examples. ▲

4. Calculate $-3 - (-4)$.

▼ **Example 4** Calculate $4 - (-3)$.

Solution Remember, to enter -3, we first enter 3 and then change it to a negative. The complete problem looks like this.

We should mention here that some calculators will give the correct answer if the numbers are entered in the same sequence as shown in the original expression, using parentheses and a subtraction sign for the -3. To see if your calculator will do this, try this sequence of key strokes:

$$4 \quad \boxed{-} \quad \boxed{(} \quad \boxed{-} \quad 3 \quad \boxed{)} \quad \boxed{=}$$

The correct answer is 7. ▲

Note: If the last key you press during a calculation is the $\boxed{=}$ key, you do not have to clear the calculator by pressing the $\boxed{\text{ON/C}}$ key before you begin the next calculation. The $\boxed{=}$ key automatically clears the calculator after it has performed any operations that were pending.

5. Calculate

$$-342 - 24(-15) - (-12)$$

▼ **Example 5** Calculate $-245 - 65(-25) - (-32)$.

Solution We will continue to use the $\boxed{+/-}$ key to enter negative numbers.

$$245 \quad \boxed{+/-} \quad \boxed{-} \quad 65 \quad \boxed{\times} \quad 25 \quad \boxed{+/-} \quad \boxed{-} \quad 32 \quad \boxed{+/-} \quad \boxed{=}$$

The correct answer is 1412. ▲

Unless we are dividing only one number by another, we must use parentheses to enclose the numerator of the expression we are dividing.

6. Calculate $\dfrac{-34 - (-14)}{-15 - (-5)}$.

▼ **Example 6** Calculate $\dfrac{27 - (-33)}{-17 - 13}$.

Solution We must use parentheses to separate the numerator from the denominator. The correct answer is -2.

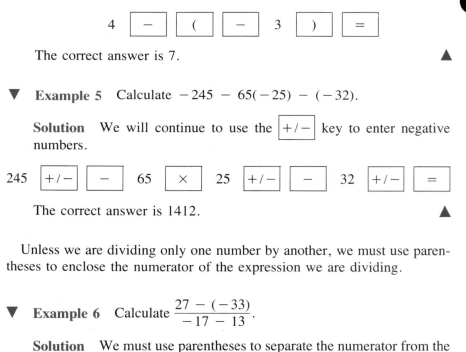

▲

Answers
3. 47 **4.** 1 **5.** 30 **6.** 2

▼ **Example 7** Simplify $9^2 - (6^2 - 5^2)^2$.

Solution We can use the key labeled $\boxed{x^2}$ to do our squaring. The answer is -40.

9 $\boxed{x^2}$ $\boxed{-}$ $\boxed{(}$ 6 $\boxed{x^2}$ $\boxed{-}$ 5 $\boxed{x^2}$ $\boxed{)}$ $\boxed{x^2}$ $\boxed{=}$

▲

To do calculations with exponents larger than 2, we must use the key labeled $\boxed{y^x}$. To calculate 2^3 this way, we would use the sequence

2 $\boxed{y^x}$ 3 $\boxed{=}$

which would give us the correct answer of 8. If you try to simplify $(-2)^3$ using the same sequence, you will get an incorrect answer. The $\boxed{y^x}$ key will not accept negative numbers for the base. It will, however, accept negative numbers for the exponent. To calculate 2^{-3} we would use this sequence:

2 $\boxed{y^x}$ 3 $\boxed{+/-}$ $\boxed{=}$

The answer is 0.125 which is the decimal equivalent of 1/8.

▼ **Example 8** Calculate $2(2.4)^3 - 3(2.4)^2$.

Solution If your calculator has a key labeled $\boxed{STO}$ then you can use it to store the number 2.4 and then recall it by pressing the key labeled $\boxed{RCL}$ each time you need it.

2.4 $\boxed{STO}$ 2 $\boxed{\times}$ $\boxed{RCL}$ $\boxed{y^x}$ 3 $\boxed{=}$ $\boxed{-}$ 3 $\boxed{\times}$ $\boxed{RCL}$ $\boxed{x^2}$ $\boxed{=}$

The answer is 10.368. ▲

---

7. Simplify $8^2 - (4^2 - 2^2)^2$.

8. Calculate $3(1.8)^4 + 2(1.8)^3$.

Note: On some calculators the key for storing a number is labeled $\boxed{M^+}$ or $\boxed{X \rightarrow M}$. The key to recall the stored number is sometimes labeled $\boxed{RM}$. The keys we are interested in are the keys you use to store a number so it can be recalled later, as many times as needed.

Answers
7. -80 **8.** 43.1568

Problem Set 1.7

Use a calculator to simplify each expression.

1. $5 + 4 \cdot 3$

2. $7 + 6 \cdot 8$

3. $4 \cdot 8 - 3 \cdot 6$

4. $7 \cdot 3 - 5 \cdot 4$

5. $18 - 3 + 24 - 2$

6. $27 - 9 + 12 - 6$

7. $7 - (-6)$

8. $9 - (-3)$

9. $-14 - (-26)$

10. $-32 - (-16)$

11. $5 - (3 - 2 \cdot 6)$

12. $7 - (4 - 5 \cdot 3)$

13. $-4(3 - 7) - 6(8 - 5)$

14. $-5(4 - 9) - 4(3 - 6)$

15. $3^2 + 4^2 + 5^2$

16. $9^2 - 8^2 - 7^2$

17. 4^3

18. 6^3

19. 5^4

20. 7^4

21. $2^2 + 2^3 + 2^4$

22. $5^2 + 5^3 + 6^3$

23. 3^{-3}

24. 4^{-2}

25. $\dfrac{-54 - 26}{-24 - 16}$

26. $\dfrac{-57 - (-17)}{-45 + 15}$

27. $\dfrac{-6 - 8(-3)}{-2 - (-7)}$

28. $\dfrac{8 - 6(-2)}{-15 - (-10)}$

29. $2(3.3)^2 + 4(3.3) + 5$

30. $4(2.2)^2 + 3(2.2) + 8$

31. $3(1.7)^4 + 4(1.7)^3$

32. $5(2.8)^4 + 4(2.8)^3$

33. $4.56 - 2(-3.45)$

34. $7.89 - 4(1.23)$

Name _____

Class _____

Date _____

Answers

1. _____   2. _____

3. _____   4. _____

5. _____   6. _____

7. _____   8. _____

9. _____   10. _____

11. _____   12. _____

13. _____   14. _____

15. _____   16. _____

17. _____   18. _____

19. _____   20. _____

21. _____   22. _____

23. _____   24. _____

25. _____   26. _____

27. _____   28. _____

29. _____   30. _____

31. _____   32. _____

33. _____   34. _____

Answers

35. _____   36. _____

37. _____   38. _____

39. _____   40. _____

41. _____   42. _____

43. _____   44. _____

45. _____   46. _____

47. _____   48. _____

49. _____   50. _____

35. $6(7.31) - 4(3.62) - (-2.57)$

36. $8(6.49) - 5(4.53) - (-3.44)$

37. $56.78 \div 37.35 - 3 - 24.56 + (-33.89)$

38. $34.23 - 43.96 \div 7 - 35.22 + (-24.58)$

39. $-324 - 5(24) + 7(-33)$ **40.** $-628 - 4(78) + 6(-45)$

41. $25^2 - 4(379 - 368)^2$ **42.** $17^2 - 2(354 - 347)^3$

43. $[27.4 - (3.4)(4.5)]^2$ **44.** $[78.4 - (2.4)(3.5)]^2$

45. $(318 - 16^2)^2$ **46.** $(752 - 28^2)^2$

47. $\dfrac{34.7(-22.1)}{-383.435}$ **48.** $\dfrac{27.92(-33.05)}{-23.0689}$

49. $\frac{1}{6} + \frac{1}{7} + \frac{1}{8}$ **50.** $\frac{1}{4} + \frac{1}{5} + \frac{1}{6}$

Chapter 1   Summary and Review

The numbers in brackets refer to the section(s) in which the topic can be found.

SYMBOLS [1.1]

$a = b$	a is equal to b
$a \neq b$	a is not equal to b
$a < b$	a is less than b
$a \leq b$	a is less than or equal to b
$a \geq b$	a is greater than or equal to b
$a > b$	a is greater than b
$a \not> b$	a is not greater than b
$a \not< b$	a is not less than b
$a + b$	the sum of a and b
$a - b$	the difference of a and b
$a \cdot b$	the product of a and b
a/b	the quotient of a and b

EXPONENTS [1.1]

Exponents are notation used to indicate repeated multiplication. In the expression 3^4, 3 is the *base* and 4 is the *exponent*.

$$3^4 = 3 \cdot 3 \cdot 3 \cdot 3 = 81$$

The expression 3^4 is said to be in *exponential form,* while the expression $3 \cdot 3 \cdot 3 \cdot 3$ is in *expanded form.*

1. $2^5 = 2 \cdot 2 \cdot 2 \cdot 2 \cdot 2 = 32$

$5^2 = 5 \cdot 5 = 25$

$10^3 = 10 \cdot 10 \cdot 10 = 1000$

$1^4 = 1 \cdot 1 \cdot 1 \cdot 1 = 1$

ORDER OF OPERATIONS [1.1]

When evaluating a mathematical expression, we will perform the operations in the following order, beginning with the expression in the innermost parentheses or brackets and working our way out.

1. Simplify all numbers with exponents, working from left to right if more than one of these numbers is present.
2. Then do all multiplications and divisions left to right.
3. Finally, perform all additions and subtractions left to right.

2. $10 + (2 \cdot 3^2 - 4 \cdot 2)$
$= 10 + (2 \cdot 9 - 4 \cdot 2)$
$= 10 + (18 - 8)$
$= 10 + 10$
$= 20$

SETS [1.1]

A *set* is a collection of objects or things.

   The *union* of two sets A and B, written $A \cup B$, is all the elements that are in A *or* are in B.

   The *intersection* of two sets A and B, written $A \cap B$, is the set consisting of all elements common to both A *and* B.

   Set A is a *subset* of set B, written $A \subset B$, if all elements in set A are also in set B.

3.   If $A = \{0, 1, 2\}$ and $B = \{2, 3\}$ then
$A \cup B = \{0, 1, 2, 3\}$ and
$A \cap B = \{2\}$

4. 5 is a counting number, a whole number, an integer, a rational number, and a real number.

$\frac{3}{4}$ is a rational number and a real number.

$\sqrt{2}$ is an irrational number and a real number.

SPECIAL SETS [1.2]

Counting numbers $= \{1, 2, 3 \ldots\}$
Whole numbers $= \{0, 1, 2, 3, \ldots\}$
Integers $= \{\ldots -3, -2, -1, 0, 1, 2, 3, \ldots\}$
Rational numbers $= \left\{ \dfrac{a}{b} \middle| a \text{ and } b \text{ are integers, } b \neq 0 \right\}$
Irrational numbers $= \{x | x \text{ is a nonrepeating, nonterminating decimal}\}$
Real numbers $= \{x | x \text{ is rational or } x \text{ is irrational}\}$

5. The numbers 5 and -5 are opposites; their sum is 0.

$$5 + (-5) = 0$$

OPPOSITES [1.2, 1.4]

Any two real numbers the same distance from 0 on the number line, but in opposite directions from 0, are called *opposites* or *additive inverses*. Opposites always add to 0.

6. The numbers 3 and $\frac{1}{3}$ are reciprocals; their product is 1.

$$3\left(\frac{1}{3}\right) = 1$$

RECIPROCALS [1.2, 1.4]

Any two real numbers whose product is 1 are called *reciprocals*. Every real number has a reciprocal except 0.

7. $|5| = 5$
$|-5| = 5$

ABSOLUTE VALUE [1.2]

The *absolute value* of a real number is its distance from 0 on the number line. If $|x|$ represents the absolute value of x, then

$$|x| = \begin{cases} x & \text{if } x \geq 0 \\ -x & \text{if } x < 0 \end{cases}$$

The absolute value of a real number is never negative.

8. Graph each inequality.

a. $\{x | x < 2\}$

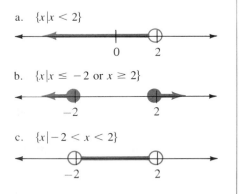

b. $\{x | x \leq -2 \text{ or } x \geq 2\}$

c. $\{x | -2 < x < 2\}$

INEQUALITIES [1.3]

The set $\{x | x < 2\}$ is the set of all real numbers that are less than 2. To graph this set we place an open circle at 2 on the real number line and then draw an arrow that starts at 2 and points to the left.

The set $\{x | x \leq -2 \text{ or } x \geq 2\}$ is the set of all real numbers that are either less than or equal to -2 or greater than or equal to 2.

The set $\{x | -2 < x < 2\}$ is the set of all real numbers that are between -2 and $+2$, that is, the real numbers that are greater than -2 and less than $+2$.

PROPERTIES OF REAL NUMBERS [1.4]

	For Addition	For Multiplication
Commutative	$a + b = b + a$	$a \cdot b = b \cdot a$
Associative	$a + (b + c) = (a + b) + c$	$a \cdot (b \cdot c) = (a \cdot b) \cdot c$
Identity	$a + 0 = a$	$a \cdot 1 = a$
Inverse	$a + (-a) = 0$	$a\left(\dfrac{1}{a}\right) = 1$
Distributive	$a(b + c) = ab + ac$	

ADDITION [1.5]

To add two real numbers with

1. *the same sign:* simply add absolute values and use the common sign.
2. *different signs:* subtract the smaller absolute value from the larger absolute value. The answer has the same sign as the number with the larger absolute value.

9.
$$5 + 3 = 8$$
$$5 + (-3) = 2$$
$$-5 + 3 = -2$$
$$-5 + (-3) = -8$$

SUBTRACTION [1.5]

If a and b are real numbers,

$$a - b = a + (-b)$$

To subtract b, add the opposite of b.

10.
$$6 - 2 = 6 + (-2) = 4$$
$$6 - (-2) = 6 + 2 = 8$$

MULTIPLICATION [1.6]

To multiply two real numbers simply multiply their absolute values. Like signs give a positive answer. Unlike signs give a negative answer.

11.
$$5(4) = 20$$
$$5(-4) = -20$$
$$-5(4) = -20$$
$$-5(-4) = 20$$

DIVISION [1.6]

If a and b are real numbers and $b \neq 0$, then

$$\frac{a}{b} = a \cdot \left(\frac{1}{b}\right)$$

To divide by b, multiply by the reciprocal of b.

12.
$$\frac{12}{-3} = -4$$
$$\frac{-12}{-3} = 4$$

COMMON MISTAKES

1. Interpreting absolute value as changing the sign of the number inside the absolute value symbols. That is, $|-5| = +5$, $|+5| = -5$. To avoid this mistake, remember, absolute value is defined as a distance and distance is always measured in positive units.

2. Confusing $-(-5)$ with $-|-5|$. The first answer is $+5$, while the second answer is -5.

Chapter 1 Test

The numbers in brackets indicate the section to which the problems correspond.

Write each of the following in symbols. [1.1]

1. Twice the sum of $3x$ and $4y$.

2. The difference of $2a$ and $3b$ is less than their sum.

Simplify each expression using the rule for order of operation. [1.1]

3. $3 \cdot 2^2 + 5 \cdot 3^2$

4. $6 + 2(4 \cdot 3 - 10)$

5. $12 - 8 \div 4 + 2 \cdot 3$

6. $20 - 4[3^2 - 2(2^3 - 6)]$

If $A = \{1, 2, 3, 4\}$, $B = \{2, 4, 6\}$, and $C = \{1, 3, 5\}$, find: [1.1]

7. $A \cap C$

8. $\{x | x \in B \text{ and } x \in C\}$

Give the opposite and reciprocal of each of the following. [1.2]

9. -3

10. $\frac{4}{3}$

Simplify each of the following. [1.2]

11. $-(-3)$

12. $-|-2|$

For the set $\{-5, -4.1, -3.75, -\frac{5}{6}, -\sqrt{2}, 0, \sqrt{3}, 1, 1.8, 4\}$, list all the elements belonging to the following sets. [1.2]

13. Integers

14. Rational numbers

15. Irrational numbers

16. Real numbers

Graph each of the following. [1.3]

17. $\{x | x \leq -1 \text{ or } x > 5\}$

18. $\{x | -2 \leq x \leq 4\}$

State the property or properties that justify each of the following. [1.4]

19. $4 + x = x + 4$

20. $5(1) = 5$

21. $3(x \cdot y) = (3y) \cdot x$

22. $(a + 1) + b = (a + b) + 1$

Name _____

Class _____

Date _____

Answers

1. _____
2. _____
3. _____
4. _____
5. _____
6. _____
7. _____
8. _____
9. _____
10. _____
11. _____
12. _____
13. _____
14. _____
15. _____
16. _____
17. ←————————————→
18. ←————————————→
19. _____
20. _____
21. _____
22. _____

Answers

23. _____   24. _____

25. _____   26. _____

27. _____   28. _____

29. _____   30. _____

31. _____   32. _____

33. _____   34. _____

35. _____   36. _____

37. _____   38. _____

39. _____   40. _____

41. _____   42. _____

43. _____   44. _____

45. _____   46. _____

47. _____   48. _____

49. _____   50. _____

Simplify each of the following as much as possible.

23. $5(-4) + 1$ **24.** $-4(-3) + 2$

25. $-3(5) - 4$ **26.** $12 \div \frac{2}{3} - 4$

27. $-5 - 15(\frac{7}{5})$ **28.** $\dfrac{6(-3) - 2}{-6 - 2}$

29. $\dfrac{-4(-1) - (-10)}{5 - (-2)}$ **30.** $-4\left[\dfrac{-3 - (-6)}{2(-4) - 4}\right]$

31. $3 - 2\left[\dfrac{8(-1) - 7}{-3(2) - 4}\right]$ **32.** $(6 - 5)[4 - 3(2 - 1)]$

33. $6(4x)$ **34.** $-5(2x)$

35. $5(x + 3)$ **36.** $-2(x + 9)$

37. $-3(2x + 4)$ **38.** $-4(3x + 2)$

39. $-2(3x - 5y + 4)$ **40.** $2x + 5x$

41. $-3x + 7x$ **42.** $-9x + 2x + 3x$

43. $-x + 7x - 4x$ **44.** $8 - 3(2x + 4)$

45. $5(2y - 3) - (6y - 5)$ **46.** $3 + 4(2x - 5) - 5x$

47. $2 + 5a + 3(2a - 4)$

48. Add $-\frac{2}{3}$ to the product of -2 and $\frac{5}{6}$.

49. Subtract $\frac{3}{4}$ from the product of -4 and $\frac{7}{16}$.

50. Subtract -4 from the quotient of -4 and $-\frac{1}{3}$.

2 First-Degree Equations and Inequalities

To the student:

One of the best-known mathematical formulas is the formula $E = mc^2$ from Einstein's theory of relativity. Einstein viewed the universe as if everything in it were in one of two states, matter or energy. His theory states that matter and energy are constantly being transformed into one another. The amount of energy (E) that can be obtained from an object with mass m is given by the formula $E = mc^2$, where c is the speed of light. Now as far as we are concerned, the theory behind the formula is not important. What is important is that the formula $E = mc^2$ describes a certain characteristic of the universe. The universe has always had this characteristic. The formula simply gives us a way of stating it in symbols. Once this property of matter and energy has been stated in symbols we can apply any of our mathematical knowledge to it, if we need to. The idea behind all of this is that mathematics can be used to describe the world around us symbolically. Mathematics is the language of science.

In this chapter we will begin our work with equations. The information in this chapter is some of the most important information in the book. You will learn the basic steps used in solving equations. Probably the most useful tool in algebra is the ability to solve first-degree equations in one variable. The methods we develop to solve first-degree equations in one variable will be used again and again throughout the rest of the book.

In this chapter we will also consider first-degree inequalities in one variable as well as provide a section on formulas and a section on word problems.

Note: Remember, in these chapter introductions we want to mention some of the ways in which the material in the chapter can be used. Don't worry; you are not going to have to know Einstein's theory of relativity to understand the chapter. The discussion here is just to let you know that there are applications of the material in the chapter.

A large part of your success in this chapter depends on how well you mastered the concepts from Chapter 1. Here is a list of the more important concepts needed to begin this chapter:

1. You must know how to add, subtract, multiply, and divide positive and negative numbers.
2. You should be familiar with the commutative, associative, and distributive properties.
3. You should understand that opposites add to 0 and reciprocals multiply to 1.
4. You must know the definition of absolute value.

Section 2.1   First-Degree Equations

In this section we will solve some first-degree equations. A first-degree equation is any equation that can be put in the form

$$ax + b = c$$

where a, b, and c are constants.

Some examples of first-degree equations are

$$5x + 3 = 2 \qquad 2x = 7 \qquad 2x + 5 = 0$$

Each is a first-degree equation because it can be put in the form $ax + b = c$. In the first equation, $5x$, 3, and 2 are called *terms* of the equation. $5x$ is a variable term; 3 and 2 are constant terms.

DEFINITION   The *solution set* for an equation is the set of all numbers which, when used in place of the variable, make the equation a true statement.

Practice Problems

1. Show that $x = 3$ is a solution to the equation

$$4x - 2 = 10$$

▼   **Example 1**   The solution set for $2x - 3 = 9$ is $\{6\}$, since replacing x with 6 makes the equation a true statement.

$$
\begin{aligned}
\text{If} \qquad\qquad x &= 6 \\
\text{then} \qquad 2x - 3 &= 9 \\
\text{becomes} \qquad 2(6) - 3 &= 9 \\
12 - 3 &= 9 \\
9 &= 9 \qquad \text{A true statement} \quad ▲
\end{aligned}
$$

DEFINITION   Two or more equations with the same solution set are called *equivalent equations*.

2. Show that the equations $3x + 1 = 16$ and $4x - 6 = 14$ both have solution set $\{5\}$.

▼   **Example 2**   The equations $2x - 5 = 9$, $x - 1 = 6$, and $x = 7$ are all equivalent equations since the solution set for each is $\{7\}$.   ▲

In addition to the properties from Chapter 1, we need two new properties—one for addition or subtraction and one for multiplication or division—to assist us in solving first-degree equations.

Properties of Equality

The first property states that adding the same quantity to both sides of an equation preserves equality. Or, more importantly, adding the same amount to both sides of an equation *never changes* the solution set. This property is called the *addition property of equality* and is stated in symbols as follows.

Addition Property of Equality

For any three algebraic expressions A, B, and C,

$$\text{if} \qquad A = B$$
$$\text{then } A + C = B + C$$

In words: Adding the same quantity to both sides of an equation will not change the solution.

Our second new property is called the multiplication property of equality and is stated like this.

Note: Since subtraction is defined in terms of addition, and division is defined in terms of multiplication, we do not need to introduce separate properties for subtraction and division. The solution set for an equation will never be changed by subtracting the same amount from both sides or by dividing both sides by the same nonzero quantity.

Multiplication Property of Equality

For any three algebraic expressions A, B, and C, where $C \neq 0$,

$$\text{if} \qquad A = B$$
$$\text{then } AC = BC$$

In words: Multiplying both sides of an equation by the same nonzero quantity will not change the solution.

The following examples illustrate how we use the properties from Chapter 1 along with the addition property of equality and the multiplication property of equality to solve first-degree equations.

▼   **Example 3**   Solve for x: $2x - 3 = 9$.

Solution   We begin by using the addition property of equality to add $+3$, the opposite of -3, to both sides of the equation:

$$2x - 3 + 3 = 9 + 3$$
$$2x = 12$$

To get x alone on the left side, we use the multiplication property of equality and multiply both sides by $\frac{1}{2}$, the reciprocal of 2:

$$\tfrac{1}{2}(2x) = \tfrac{1}{2}(12)$$
$$x = 6$$

Since the addition and multiplication properties of equality always produce equations equivalent to the original equations, our last equation, $x = 6$, is equivalent to our first equation, $2x - 3 = 9$. The solution set is, therefore, $\{6\}$.   ▲

3.   Solve for x: $5x - 2 = 33$.

Note: Even though we have not shown it, we are using the associative property when we say that $\frac{1}{2}$ times $2x$ is x. Remember, it is the associative property that allows us to change the grouping in a product. If we were to show the associative property, it would look like this:

$$\frac{1}{2}(2x) = \left(\frac{1}{2} \cdot 2\right)x = 1x = x$$

Answer
3. 7

4. Solve $\frac{2}{3}x + 4 = -8$.

Note: In all the examples in this section, we begin our solution process by using the addition property of equality to put all the terms with variables in them (called variable terms, like $3a$ and $-6a$ in Example 5) on one side of the equation, and all the terms without variables in them (called constant terms, like -5 and 1 in Example 5) on the other side. When we get to the next section of the book, we will give a detailed list of the steps that are used in solving a first-degree equation.

5. Find the solution set for

$$3a - 3 = -5a + 9$$

Note: From Chapter 1 we know that multiplication by a number and division by its reciprocal always produce the same result. Because of this fact, instead of multiplying each side of our equation by $\frac{1}{9}$, we could just as easily divide each side by 9. If we did so, the last two lines in our solution would look like this:

$$\frac{9x}{9} = \frac{6}{9}$$

$$x = \frac{2}{3}$$

▼ **Example 4** Solve $\frac{3}{4}x + 5 = -4$.

Solution We begin by adding -5 to both sides of the equation. Once this has been done, we multiply both sides by the reciprocal of $\frac{3}{4}$, which is $\frac{4}{3}$.

$$\frac{3}{4}x + 5 = -4$$

$$\frac{3}{4}x + 5 + (-5) = -4 + (-5) \qquad \text{Add } -5 \text{ to both sides}$$

$$\frac{3}{4}x = -9$$

$$\frac{4}{3}\left(\frac{3}{4}x\right) = \frac{4}{3}(-9) \qquad \text{Multiply both sides by } \frac{4}{3}$$

$$x = -12 \qquad\qquad \frac{4}{3}(-9) = \frac{4}{3}\left(\frac{-9}{1}\right) = \frac{-36}{3}$$
$$= -12 \quad ▲$$

Our next example involves solving an equation that has variable terms on both sides of the equal sign.

▼ **Example 5** Find the solution set for $3a - 5 = -6a + 1$.

Solution To solve for a we must isolate it on one side of the equation. Let's decide to isolate a on the left side. To do this we must remove the $-6a$ from the right side. We accomplish this by adding $6a$ to both sides of the equation.

$$3a - 5 = -6a + 1$$
$$3a + 6a - 5 = -6a + 6a + 1 \qquad \text{Add } 6a \text{ to both sides}$$
$$9a - 5 = 1$$
$$9a - 5 + 5 = 1 + 5 \qquad \text{Add 5 to both sides}$$
$$9a = 6$$

$$\frac{1}{9}(9a) = \frac{1}{9}(6) \qquad \text{Multiply both sides by } \frac{1}{9}$$

$$a = \frac{2}{3} \qquad\qquad \frac{1}{9}(6) = \frac{6}{9} = \frac{2}{3} \quad ▲$$

We can check our solution in Example 5 by replacing a in the original equation with $\frac{2}{3}$.

When $a = \frac{2}{3}$

the equation $3a - 5 = -6a + 1$

becomes $3\left(\frac{2}{3}\right) - 5 = -6\left(\frac{2}{3}\right) + 1$

$$2 - 5 = -4 + 1$$
$$-3 = -3 \quad \text{A true statement}$$

Answers
4. -18 **5.** $\frac{3}{2}$

Problem Set 2.1

Name _____

Class _____

Date _____

Solve each of the following equations.

1. $x - 5 = 3$

2. $x + 2 = 7$

3. $2x - 4 = 6$

4. $3x - 5 = 4$

5. $4a - 1 = 7$

6. $3a - 5 = 10$

7. $3 - y = 10$

8. $5 - 2y = 11$

9. $-5x - 4 = 16$

10. $-6x - 5 = 11$

11. $3 - 4a = -11$

12. $8 - 2a = -13$

13. $9 + 5a = -2$

14. $3 + 7a = -7$

15. $\frac{2}{3}x = 8$

16. $\frac{3}{2}x = 9$

17. $-\frac{3}{5}a + 2 = 8$

18. $-\frac{5}{3}a + 3 = 23$

19. $6 + \frac{2}{7}y = 8$

20. $4 + \frac{3}{7}y = 1$

Answers

1. _____   2. _____

3. _____   4. _____

5. _____   6. _____

7. _____   8. _____

9. _____   10. _____

11. _____   12. _____

13. _____   14. _____

15. _____   16. _____

17. _____   18. _____

19. _____   20. _____

Answers

21._____	22._____
23._____	24._____
25._____	26._____
27._____	28_____
29._____	30._____
31._____	32._____
33._____	34._____
35._____	36._____
37._____	38._____

Solve each equation.

21. $2x - 5 = 3x + 2$

22. $5x - 1 = 4x + 3$

23. $-3a + 2 = -2a - 1$

24. $-4a - 8 = -3a + 7$

25. $7y - 4 = 2y + 11$

26. $8y - 2 = 6y - 10$

27. $5 - 2x = 3x + 1$

28. $7 - 3x = 8x - 4$

29. The equations you have solved so far have had exactly one solution. Because of the absolute value symbols, the equation $|x + 2| = 5$ has two solutions. One of the solutions is $x = -7$. Without showing any work, what do you think is the other solution?

30. One solution to the equation $|x - 3| = 2$ is $x = 5$. Without showing any work, what is the other solution?

31. Is $x = -3$ a solution to $2 - 4x = -x + 17$?

32. Is $x = -3$ a solution to $2 - 4x = -x + 11$?

Review Problems   From here on, each problem set will end with a series of review problems. In mathematics it is very important to review. The more you review, the better you will understand the topics we cover and the longer you will remember them. Also, there are times when material that seemed confusing earlier will be less confusing the second time around.

The following problems review material we covered in Section 1.5. Reviewing these problems will help you understand the next section.

Simplify each expression.

33. $4(3x - 2) + 1$

34. $3(2x + 1) - 5$

35. $3(2y - 1) + y$

36. $2(4y - 3) + y$

37. $8 - 3(4x - 2)$

38. $6 - 2(3x + 1)$

Section 2.2   More First-Degree Equations

In this section we will solve some equations that are somewhat more complicated than the equations we solved in the previous section. In this section,
the equations we will solve all require some simplification of one or both
sides of the equation. In our first example we begin by combining terms of
each side of the equation.

Practice Problems

▼ **Example 1**   Solve for x: $7x - x + 4 - 2x = 4$.

Solution   We begin by simplifying the left side as much as possible.

$$7x - x + 4 - 2x = 4$$
$$4x + 4 = 4 \qquad \text{Simplify the left side}$$
$$4x + 4 - 4 = 4 - 4 \qquad \text{Subtract 4 from both sides}$$
$$\text{(or, add } -4 \text{ to both sides)}$$
$$4x = 0$$
$$\frac{1}{4}(4x) = \frac{1}{4}(0) \qquad \text{Multiply both sides by } \tfrac{1}{4}$$
$$x = 0 \qquad \blacktriangle$$

1. Solve for x:
$$4x - 3 + x - 2 = 17 - 3$$

▼ **Example 2**   Solve $4(2a + 1) + 8 = 5a$.

Solution   We begin by applying the distributive property to multiply
$4(2a + 1)$. Then we collect similar terms and proceed as usual.

$$4(2a + 1) + 8 = 5a$$
$$8a + 4 + 8 = 5a \qquad \text{Distributive property}$$
$$8a + 12 = 5a \qquad \text{Add 4 and 8}$$
$$8a + (-5a) + 12 = 5a + (-5a) \qquad \text{Add } -5a \text{ to each side}$$
$$3a + 12 = 0$$
$$3a + 12 + (-12) = 0 + (-12) \qquad \text{Add } -12 \text{ to each side}$$
$$3a = -12$$
$$\frac{1}{3}(3a) = \frac{1}{3}(-12) \qquad \text{Multiply by } \tfrac{1}{3}$$
$$a = -4$$

2. Solve $3(4a + 2) - 4 = 7a$.

The solution is -4 which we can check if we wish by substituting it for
a in the original equation.

When
the equation
becomes
$$a = -4$$
$$4(2a + 1) + 8 = 5a$$
$$4[2(-4) + 1] + 8 = 5(-4)$$
$$4(-8 + 1) + 8 = -20$$
$$4(-7) + 8 = -20$$
$$-28 + 8 = -20$$
$$-20 = -20 \qquad \text{A true statement}$$
$$\blacktriangle$$

Note: It is always a good idea to practice
checking the solutions to your equations.
There may be times when it is important
to you to check your answers—for
instance, when you are taking a test. If
you haven't practiced doing so, you may
run into trouble.

As the equations become more complicated, it is sometimes helpful to use
the following steps as a guide in solving the equations.

Answers
1. $\frac{19}{5}$ **2.** $-\frac{2}{5}$

To Solve a First-Degree Equation

Step 1: Use the distributive property to separate terms.

Step 2: Use the commutative and associative properties to simplify both sides as much as possible.

Step 3: Use the addition property of equality to get all the terms containing the variable (variable terms) on one side and all other terms (constant terms) on the other side.

Step 4: Use the multiplication property of equality to get x alone on one side of the equal sign.

Step 5: Check your results in the original equation, if necessary.

Let's see how our steps apply by solving another equation

▼ **Example 3**   Solve $3(2y - 1) + y = 5y + 3$.

Solution   We begin by using the distributive property to separate terms.

Step 1 $\begin{cases} 3(2y - 1) + y = 5y + 3 \\ \quad\downarrow \quad\downarrow \\ 6y - 3 + y = 5y + 3 \end{cases}$ Distributive property

Step 2 $\quad 7y - 3 = 5y + 3$ $\qquad 6y + y = 7y$

Step 3 $\begin{cases} 7y + (-5y) - 3 = 5y + (-5y) + 3 & \text{Add } -5y \text{ to both} \\ 2y - 3 = 3 & \text{sides} \\ 2y - 3 + 3 = 3 + 3 & \text{Add } +3 \text{ to both} \\ 2y = 6 & \text{sides} \end{cases}$

Step 4 $\begin{cases} \frac{1}{2}(2y) = \frac{1}{2}(6) \\ y = 3 \end{cases}$

The solution set is {3}. ▲

▼ **Example 4**   Solve the equation $8 - 3(4x - 2) + 5x = 35$.

Solution   We must begin by distributing the -3 across the quantity $4x - 2$. (It would be a mistake to subtract 3 from 8 first, since the rule for order of operation indicates we are to do multiplication before subtraction.)

Step 1 $\begin{cases} 8 - 3(4x - 2) + 5x = 35 \\ \quad\downarrow \quad\downarrow \\ 8 - 12x + 6 + 5x = 35 \end{cases}$ Distributive property

Step 2 $\quad -7x + 14 = 35$

Step 3 $\begin{cases} -7x + 14 - 14 = 35 - 14 & \text{Subtract 14 from both} \\ & \text{sides} \\ -7x = 21 \end{cases}$

Step 4 $\begin{cases} -\frac{1}{7}(-7x) = \left(-\frac{1}{7}\right)21 & \text{Multiply both sides} \\ & \text{by } -\frac{1}{7} \\ x = -3 \end{cases}$ ▲

3. Solve for y:
$$2(5y - 1) - y = 7y + 2$$

Note: After step 2 has been completed, there are, at most, four terms left—two variable terms and two constant terms. After step 3 has been completed, there are two terms left—one variable term and one constant term.

4. Solve for x:
$$6 - 2(5x - 1) + 4x = 20$$

Answers
3. 2 **4.** -2

Problem Set 2.2

Solve each equation.

1. $2x - 3 - x = 3x + 5$

2. $3x - 5 - 2x = 2x - 3$

3. $5y - 2 + 4y = 2y + 12$

4. $7y - 3 + 2y = 7y - 9$

5. $11x - 5 + 4x - 2 = 8x$

6. $2x + 7 - 3x + 4 = -2x$

7. $3(x - 2) = 12$

8. $4(x + 1) = 12$

9. $2(3k - 5) = k$

10. $3(4k - 1) = 9k$

11. $-5(2x + 1) + 5 = 3x$

12. $-3(5x + 7) - 4 = -10x$

13. $5(y + 2) - 4(y + 1) = 3$

14. $6(y - 3) - 5(y + 2) = 8$

Name _____

Class _____

Date _____

Answers

1. _____ 2. _____

3. _____ 4. _____

5. _____ 6. _____

7. _____ 8. _____

9. _____ 10. _____

11. _____ 12. _____

13. _____ 14. _____

15. _____   16. _____

17. _____   18. _____

19. _____   20. _____

21. _____   22. _____

23. _____   24. _____

25. ◄──────────────────────►

26. ◄──────────────────────►

27. ◄──────────────────────►

28. ◄──────────────────────►

29. ◄──────────────────────►

30. ◄──────────────────────►

31. ◄──────────────────────►

32. ◄──────────────────────►

15. $6 - 7(m - 3) = -1$ **16.** $3 - 5(2m - 5) = -2$

17. $4(a - 3) + 5 = 7(3a - 1)$ **18.** $6(a - 4) + 6 = 2(5a + 2)$

19. $7 + 3(x + 2) = 4(x - 1)$ **20.** $5 + 2(2x - 4) = 3(2x - 1)$

21. $7 - 2(3x - 1) + 4x = 5$ **22.** $8 - 5(2x - 3) + 4x = 20$

23. $10 - 4(2x + 1) - (3x - 4) = -9x + 4 - 4x$

24. $7 - 2(3x + 5) - (2x - 3) = -5x + 3 - 2x$

Review Problems   The following review material we covered in Section 1.3. Reviewing these problems will help you with the next section.

Graph each inequality.

25. $\{x \mid x > -5\}$ **26.** $\{x \mid x \le 4\}$

27. $\{x \mid x \le -2 \text{ or } x > 5\}$ **28.** $\{x \mid x < 3 \text{ or } x \ge 5\}$

29. $\{x \mid x > -4 \text{ and } x < 0\}$ **30.** $\{x \mid x \ge 0 \text{ and } x \le 2\}$

31. $\{x \mid 1 \le x \le 4\}$ **32.** $\{x \mid -4 < x < -2\}$

Section 2.3   First-Degree Inequalities

A first-degree inequality is any inequality that can be put in the following form:

$$ax + b < c \qquad (a, b, \text{ and } c \text{ constants}, a \neq 0)$$

where the inequality symbol ($<$) can be replaced with any of the other three inequality symbols ($\leq$, $>$, or $\geq$).

Some examples of first-degree inequalities are

$$3x - 2 \geq 7 \qquad -5y < 25 \qquad 3(x - 4) > 2x$$

Each of these is a first-degree inequality because it can be put in the form $ax + b < c$. They may not be in that form to begin with, but each can be put in the correct form.

Solving first-degree inequalities is similar to solving first-degree equations. We need to develop two new properties to solve inequalities. Here is our first property.

Addition Property for Inequalities

For any algebraic expressions A, B, and C,

$$\text{if} \qquad A < B$$
$$\text{then } A + C < B + C$$

In words: Adding the same quantity to both sides of an inequality will not change the solution set.

Note: Since subtraction is defined as addition of the opposite, our new property holds for subtraction as well as addition. That is, we can subtract the same quantity from each side of an inequality and always be sure that we have not changed the solution.

With the addition property for inequalities, we are free to add any quantity to both sides of an inequality without changing the solution to the inequality. Here is an example that shows how we use the addition property for inequalities.

▼   **Example 1**   Solve $3x + 3 < 2x - 1$ and graph the solution.

Solution   We use the addition property for inequalities to write all the variable terms on one side and all constant terms on the other side.

$$
\begin{aligned}
3x + 3 &< 2x - 1 \\
3x + (-2x) + 3 &< 2x + (-2x) - 1 \qquad \text{Add } -2x \text{ to each side} \\
x + 3 &< -1 \\
x + 3 + (-3) &< -1 + (-3) \qquad \text{Add } -3 \text{ to each side} \\
x &< -4
\end{aligned}
$$

The solution is $x < -4$, the graph of which is as follows:

▲

Practice Problems

1.   Solve $4x - 2 > 3x + 4$ and graph the solution.

Answers
1. See "Solutions to Selected Practice Problems" for this section.

Before we state the multiplication property for inequalities, we will take a look at what happens to an inequality statement when we multiply both sides by a positive number and what happens when we multiply by a negative number.

We begin by writing three true inequality statements:

$$3 < 5 \qquad -3 < 5 \qquad -5 < -3$$

We multiply both sides of each inequality by a positive number—say, 4.

$$4(3) < 4(5) \qquad 4(-3) < 4(5) \qquad 4(-5) < 4(-3)$$
$$12 < 20 \qquad\quad -12 < 20 \qquad\quad -20 < -12$$

Notice in each case that the resulting inequality symbol points in the same direction as the original inequality symbol. Multiplying both sides of an inequality by a positive number preserves the *sense* of the inequality.

Let's take the same three original inequalities and multiply both sides by -4.

$$3 < 5 \qquad\qquad -3 < 5 \qquad\qquad -5 < -3$$
$$\downarrow \qquad\qquad\qquad \downarrow \qquad\qquad\qquad \downarrow$$
$$-4(3) > -4(5) \qquad -4(-3) > -4(5) \qquad -4(-5) > -4(-3)$$
$$-12 > -20 \qquad\quad 12 > -20 \qquad\qquad 20 > 12$$

Notice in this case that the resulting inequality symbol always points in the opposite direction from the original one. Multiplying both sides of an inequality by a negative number *reverses* the sense of the inequality. Keeping this in mind, we will now state the multiplication property for inequalities.

Note: The purpose of this discussion is to justify the multiplication property for inequalities. If you are having trouble understanding it, you may want to read the property itself first and then read through the discussion here. What is important is that you understand, and can use, the multiplication property for inequalities.

Multiplication Property for Inequalities

Let A, B, and C represent algebraic expressions.

$$\text{If} \quad A < B$$
$$\text{then } AC < BC \text{ if } C \text{ is positive } (C > 0)$$
$$\text{or} \quad AC > BC \text{ if } C \text{ is negative } (C < 0)$$

In words: Multiplying both sides of an inequality by a positive number always produces an equivalent inequality. Multiplying both sides of an inequality by a negative number reverses the sense of the inequality.

Note: Since division is defined as multiplication by the reciprocal, we can apply our new property to division as well as multiplication. We can divide both sides of an inequality by any nonzero number as long as we reverse the direction of the inequality when the number we are dividing by is a negative number.

The multiplication property for inequalities does not limit what we can do with inequalities. We are still free to multiply both sides of an inequality by any nonzero number we choose. If the number we multiply by happens to be *negative*, then we *must* also *reverse* the direction of the inequality. That is the only difference between the properties we use to solve equations and the properties we use to solve inequalities. As you read through the examples that follow, watch what happens when we multiply both sides by a negative number.

▼ **Example 2** Solve $3x - 5 \le 7$.

Solution

$$3x - 5 \le 7$$
$$3x - 5 + 5 \le 7 + 5 \qquad \text{Add } +5 \text{ to both sides}$$
$$3x \le 12$$
$$\tfrac{1}{3}(3x) \le \tfrac{1}{3}(12) \qquad \text{Multiply by } \tfrac{1}{3}$$
$$x \le 4$$

The solution set is $\{x \mid x \le 4\}$, the graph of which is

▲

▼ **Example 3** Find the solution set for $-2y - 3 < 7$.

Solution

$$-2y - 3 < 7$$
$$-2y < 10 \qquad \text{Add } +3 \text{ to both sides}$$
$$-\tfrac{1}{2}(-2y) > -\tfrac{1}{2}(10) \qquad \text{Multiply by } -\tfrac{1}{2} \text{ and reverse the}$$
$$y > -5 \qquad\qquad \text{direction of the inequality symbol}$$

The solution set is $\{y \mid y > -5\}$, the graph of which is

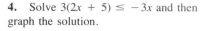

▲

When our inequalities become more complicated, we use the same basic steps we used in Section 2.2 when we were solving equations. That is, we simplify each side of the inequality before we apply the addition property or multiplication property. When we have solved the inequality, we graph the solution on a number line.

▼ **Example 4** Solve $3(2x - 4) - 7x \le -3x$.

Solution We begin by using the distributive property to separate terms. Next, simplify both sides:

$$3(2x - 4) - 7x \le -3x$$
$$6x - 12 - 7x \le -3x$$
$$-x - 12 \le -3x \qquad 6x - 7x = (6 - 7)x = -x$$
$$-12 \le -2x \qquad \text{Add } x \text{ to both sides}$$
$$-\tfrac{1}{2}(-12) \ge -\tfrac{1}{2}(-2x) \qquad \text{Multiply both sides by } -\tfrac{1}{2} \text{ and}$$
$$6 \ge x \qquad\qquad \text{reverse the direction of the}$$
$$\text{inequality symbol}$$

The solution set is $\{x \mid x \le 6\}$, and the graph is

▲

2. Solve $4x + 2 \le -6$ and graph the solution.

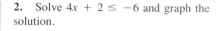

3. Solve $-3y - 2 < 7$ and graph the solution.

4. Solve $3(2x + 5) \le -3x$ and then graph the solution.

Note: In Examples 3 and 4, notice that each time we multiplied both sides of the inequality by a negative number we also reversed the direction of the inequality symbol. Failure to do so would cause our graph to lie on the wrong side of the end point.

In the examples that follow, we extend the work we started in Section 1.3 with continued inequalities and compound inequalities.

5. Solve the continued inequality

$$-5 \le 3k + 1 \le 10$$

Graph the solution.

▼ **Example 5** Solve the continued inequality $-2 \le 5k - 7 \le 18$.

Solution We can extend our properties for addition and multiplication to cover this situation. If we add a number to the middle expression, we must add the same number to the outside expressions. If we multiply the center expression by a number, we must do the same to the outside expressions, remembering to reverse the direction of the inequality symbols if we multiply by a negative number.

$$
\begin{array}{rccl}
-2 \le & 5k - 7 & \le 18 & \\
-2 + 7 \le & 5k - 7 + 7 & \le 18 + 7 & \text{Add 7 to each expression} \\
5 \le & 5k & \le 25 & \\
\tfrac{1}{5}(5) \le & \tfrac{1}{5}(5k) & \le \tfrac{1}{5}(25) & \text{Multiply each expression by } \tfrac{1}{5} \\
1 \le & k & \le 5 &
\end{array}
$$

Note: Recall from Chapter 1 that the continued inequality

$$-1 \le k \le 5$$

is equivalent to the inequalities

$$-1 \le k \text{ and } k \le 5$$

The graph of the solution set is

▼ **Example 6** Solve and graph $-3 < 2x - 5 < 3$.

6. Solve and graph

$$-7 \le 2x + 1 \le 7$$

Solution We begin by adding 5 to all three parts of the inequality.

$$
\begin{array}{rccl}
-3 < & 2x - 5 & < 3 & \\
2 < & 2x & < 8 & \text{Add 5 to all three members} \\
1 < & x & < 4 & \text{Multiply through by } \tfrac{1}{2}
\end{array}
$$

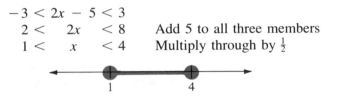

▼ **Example 7** Solve the compound inequality $3t + 7 \le -4 \text{ or } 3t + 7 \ge 4$.

7. Graph the solution for the compound inequality

$$3t - 6 \le -3 \quad \text{or} \quad 3t - 6 \ge 3$$

Solution We solve each half of the compound inequality separately, then graph the solution set:

$$
\begin{array}{rcl}
3t + 7 \le -4 & \text{or} & 3t + 7 \ge 4 \\
3t \le -11 & \text{or} & 3t \ge -3 \\
t \le -\tfrac{11}{3} & \text{or} & t \ge -1
\end{array}
$$

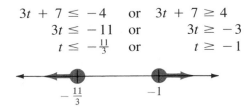

Problem Set 2.3

Solve each of the following inequalities and graph each solution.

1. $2x \le 3$

2. $5x \ge -15$

3. $-5x \le 25$

4. $-7x \ge 35$

5. $-3x + 1 > 10$

6. $-2x - 5 \le 15$

7. $6 - m \le 7$

8. $5 - m > -2$

9. $-3 - 4x \le 9$

10. $-2 - 5x < 18$

11. $3 - 2y \ge -4$

12. $5 - 3y < -2$

Name _____

Class _____

Date _____

Answers

1. <----------------------->

2. <----------------------->

3. <----------------------->

4. <----------------------->

5. <----------------------->

6. <----------------------->

7. <----------------------->

8. <----------------------->

9. <----------------------->

10. <----------------------->

11. <----------------------->

12. <----------------------->

Answers

13. ←———————————→

14. ←———————————→

15. ←———————————→

16. ←———————————→

17. ←———————————→

18. ←———————————→

19. ←———————————→

20. ←———————————→

21. ←———————————→

22. ←———————————→

23. ←———————————→

24. ←———————————→

Simplify each side first, then solve the following inequalities.

13. $2(3y + 1) \leq -10$

14. $3(2y - 4) > 0$

15. $-(a + 1) - 4a \leq 2a - 8$

16. $-(a - 2) - 5a \leq 3a + 7$

17. $2t - 3(5 - t) < 0$

18. $3t - 4(2t - 5) < 0$

19. $5 - 7(2a + 3) \geq -2$

20. $3 - 4(3a - 1) > 1$

21. $-3(x + 5) \leq -2(x - 1)$

22. $-4(2x + 1) \leq -3(x + 2)$

23. $5(y + 3) + 4 < 6y - 1 - 5y$

24. $4(y - 1) + 2 \geq 3y + 8 - 2y$

Solve the following continued inequalities. Be sure to graph the solutions.

25. $-2 \le m - 5 \le 2$

26. $-3 < m + 1 \le 3$

27. $-6 < 2a + 2 < 6$

28. $-6 < 5a - 4 < 6$

29. $5 \le 3a - 7 \le 11$

30. $1 \le 4a + 1 \le 3$

Graph the solution sets for the following compound inequalities.

31. $x + 5 \le -2$ or $x + 5 \ge 2$

32. $3x + 2 < -3$ or $3x + 2 > 3$

33. $5y + 1 \le -4$ or $5y + 1 \ge 4$

34. $7y - 5 \le -2$ or $7y - 5 \ge 2$

35. $2x + 5 > 3x - 1$ or $x - 4 < 2x + 6$

36. $3x - 1 < 2x + 4$ or $5x - 2 > 3x + 4$

Name _____

Class _____

Date _____

Answers

25. $\longleftarrow\!\!\!\longrightarrow$

26. $\longleftarrow\!\!\!\longrightarrow$

27. $\longleftarrow\!\!\!\longrightarrow$

28. $\longleftarrow\!\!\!\longrightarrow$

29. $\longleftarrow\!\!\!\longrightarrow$

30. $\longleftarrow\!\!\!\longrightarrow$

31. $\longleftarrow\!\!\!\longrightarrow$

32. $\longleftarrow\!\!\!\longrightarrow$

33. $\longleftarrow\!\!\!\longrightarrow$

34. $\longleftarrow\!\!\!\longrightarrow$

35. $\longleftarrow\!\!\!\longrightarrow$

36. $\longleftarrow\!\!\!\longrightarrow$

Answers

37. _____

38. _____

39. _____

40. _____

41. _____

42. _____

43. _____

44. _____

45. _____

46. _____

47. _____

48. _____

49. _____

50. _____

51. _____

52. _____

37. Suppose that a number lies somewhere between 2 and 5 on the number line. (If we let x represent this number, then an inequality that describes this situation is $2 < x < 5$.) Between what two numbers does the opposite of the number lie? Write an inequality that shows where the opposite of the number lies.

38. A number lies between -2 and 3 on the number line. Write an inequality that shows where the opposite of the number lies.

39. Is -5 one of the numbers in the solution set for the inequality $|x| < 2$?

40. Is -3 one of the numbers in the solution set for the inequality $|x| > 2$?

41. Checking the solution set for an inequality is not as easy as checking the solution to an equation. You can, however, check to see that the end point for your solution set is correct. (If $x > 5$ is the solution set for an inequality, then 5 is the end point for the solution set.) Suppose you are taking a test and your solution set for the inequality $-3x + 2 > 2x + 12$ is $x < -2$. Check the end point by replacing x in the original inequality with -2 and observing whether both sides simplify to the same number.

42. The solution set for $-7(x - 2) \geq -2x - 1$ is $x \leq 3$. Check the end point of the solution set in the original inequality.

Review Problems   The following problems review some of the material we covered in Sections 1.2 and 1.5.

Simplify each expression.

43. $|-4|$

44. $\left|-\frac{3}{4}\right|$

45. $-\left|-\frac{1}{2}\right|$

46. $-\left(-\frac{1}{2}\right)$

47. $|7| - |-3|$

48. $|8| - |-2|$

49. $|-2| - |-3| - (-2)$

50. $|-4| - (-3) - |-2|$

51. Give a definition for the absolute value of x that involves the number line. (This is the geometric definition.)

52. Give a definition of the absolute value of x that does not involve the number line. (This is the algebraic definition.)

Section 2.4   Equations with Absolute Value

In Chapter 1 we defined the absolute value of x, $|x|$, to be the distance between x and 0 on the number line. The absolute value of a number measures its distance from 0.

▼ **Example 1**   Solve for x: $|x| = 5$.

Solution   Using the definition of absolute value, we can read the equation as, "The distance between x and 0 on the number line is 5." If x is 5 units from 0, then x can be 5 or -5.

$$\text{If } |x| = 5, \qquad \text{then } x = 5 \quad \text{or} \quad x = -5 \qquad \blacktriangle$$

In general, then, we can see that any equation of the form $|a| = b$ is equivalent to the equations $a = b$ or $a = -b$.

▼ **Example 2**   Solve $|2a - 1| = 7$.

Solution   We can read this equation as "$2a - 1$ is 7 units from 0 on the number line." The quantity $2a - 1$ must be equal to 7 or -7.

$$|2a - 1| = 7$$
$$2a - 1 = 7 \quad \text{or} \quad 2a - 1 = -7$$

We have transformed our absolute value equation into two first-degree equations that do not involve absolute value. We can solve each equation using the method in Section 2.1:

$$
\begin{array}{llll}
2a - 1 = 7 & \text{or} & 2a - 1 = -7 & \\
2a = 8 & \text{or} & 2a = -6 & \text{Add } +1 \text{ to both sides} \\
a = 4 & \text{or} & a = -3 & \text{Multiply by } \frac{1}{2}
\end{array}
$$

Our solution set is $\{4, -3\}$.   ▲

To check our solutions, we put them into the original absolute value equation:

When	$a = 4$	When	$a = -3$
the equation	$\|2a - 1\| = 7$	the equation	$\|2a - 1\| = 7$
becomes	$\|2(4) - 1\| = 7$	becomes	$\|2(-3) - 1\| = 7$
	$\|7\| = 7$		$\|-7\| = 7$
	$7 = 7$		$7 = 7$

▼ **Example 3**   Solve $|5x - 3| + 5 = 12$.

Solution   In order to use the definition of absolute value to solve this equation, we must isolate the absolute value on the left side of the equal sign. We can delete the $+5$ from the left side by adding -5 to both sides of the equation.

$$|5x - 3| + 5 + (-5) = 12 + (-5)$$
$$|5x - 3| = 7$$

Now that the equation is in the correct form, we can see that $5x - 3$ is 7 or -7.

$$
\begin{array}{llll}
5x - 3 = 7 & \text{or} & 5x - 3 = -7 & \\
5x = 10 & \text{or} & 5x = -4 & \text{Add } +3 \text{ to both sides} \\
x = 2 & \text{or} & x = -\frac{4}{5} & \text{Multiply by } \frac{1}{5}
\end{array}
$$

The solution set is $\{2, -\frac{4}{5}\}$.   ▲

Practice Problems

1. Solve for x: $|x| = 3$.

2. Solve $|3x - 6| = 9$.

3. Solve $|4x - 3| + 2 = 3$.

Answers
1. $-3, 3$ **2.** $-1, 5$ **3.** $1, \frac{1}{2}$

4. Solve $|7a - 1| = -2$.

Note: Recall from Chapter 1 that $\varnothing$ is the symbol we use to denote the empty set. When we use it to indicate the solutions to an equation, then we are saying the equation has no solution.

5. Solve $|2a + 1| = |4a - 3|$.

▼ **Example 4**   Solve $|3a - 6| = -4$.

Solution   The solution set is $\varnothing$ because the left side cannot be negative and the right side is negative. No matter what we try to substitute for the variable a, the quantity $|3a - 6|$ will always be positive, or zero. It can never be -4. ▲

Consider the statement $|x| = |y|$. What can we say about x and y? We know they are equal in absolute value. By the definition of absolute value, they are the same distance from 0 on the number line. They must be equal to each other or opposites of each other. In symbols we write

$$|x| = |y| \iff x = y \quad \text{or} \quad x = -y$$

Equal in absolute value | Equals | or | Opposites

▼ **Example 5**   Solve $|3a + 2| = |2a + 3|$.

Solution   The quantities $(3a + 2)$ and $(2a + 3)$ have equal absolute values. They are, therefore, the same distance from 0 on the number line. They must be equals or opposites.

$$|3a + 2| = |2a + 3|$$

Equals | *Opposites*

$$3a + 2 = 2a + 3 \quad \text{or} \quad 3a + 2 = -(2a + 3)$$
$$a + 2 = 3 \qquad\qquad 3a + 2 = -2a - 3$$
$$a = 1 \qquad\qquad 5a + 2 = -3$$
$$5a = -5$$
$$a = -1$$

The solution set is $\{1, -1\}$.

It makes no difference in the outcome of the problem if we take the opposite of the first or second expression. It is very important, once we have decided which one to take the opposite of, that we take the opposite of both its terms and not just the first term. That is, the opposite of $2a + 3$ is $-(2a + 3)$, which we can think of as $-1(2a + 3)$. Distributing the -1 across *both* terms, we have

$$-1(2a + 3) = -2a - 3$$

▲

Problem Set 2.4

Name _____

Class _____

Date _____

Use the definition of absolute value to solve each of the following problems.

1. $|x| = 4$ **2.** $|x| = 7$ **3.** $|a| = 2$

4. $|a| = 5$ **5.** $|x| = -3$ **6.** $|x| = -4$

7. $|a| + 2 = 3$ **8.** $|a| - 5 = 2$ **9.** $|y| + 4 = 3$

10. $|y| + 3 = 1$ **11.** $|x| - 2 = 4$ **12.** $|x| - 5 = 3$

13. $|x - 2| = 5$ **14.** $|x + 1| = 2$

15. $|a - 4| = 1$ **16.** $|a + 2| = 7$

17. $|3 - x| = 1$ **18.** $|4 - x| = 2$

19. $|2x + 1| = -3$ **20.** $|2x - 5| = -5$

21. $|3a + 1| = 5$ **22.** $|2x - 3| - 4 = 3$

23. $|3x + 4| + 1 = 7$ **24.** $|5x - 3| - 4 = 3$

25. $|2y - 3| + 4 = 3$ **26.** $|7y - 8| + 9 = 1$

Answers

1. _____   2. _____
3. _____   4. _____
5. _____   6. _____
7. _____   8. _____
9. _____   10. _____
11. _____   12. _____
13. _____   14. _____
15. _____   16. _____
17. _____   18. _____
19. _____   20. _____
21. _____   22. _____
23. _____   24. _____
25. _____   26. _____

Answers

27. _____ 28. _____

29. _____ 30. _____

31. _____ 32. _____

33. _____ 34. _____

35. _____ 36. _____

37. _____ 38. _____

39. _____

40. _____

41. ◄————————————►

42. ◄————————————►

43. ◄————————————►

44. ◄————————————►

Solve the following equations by the method used in Example 5.

27. $|3a + 1| = |2a - 4|$ **28.** $|5a + 2| = |4a + 7|$

29. $|6x - 2| = |3x + 1|$ **30.** $|x - 5| = |2x + 1|$

31. $|y - 2| = |y + 3|$ **32.** $|y - 5| = |y - 4|$

33. $|3x - 1| = |3x + 1|$ **34.** $|5x - 8| = |5x + 8|$

35. $|3 - m| = |m + 4|$ **36.** $|5 - m| = |m + 8|$

37. $|3 - x| = |4 + 5x|$ **38.** $|7 - x| = |8 - 2x|$

39. The statement $|a - b| = |b - a|$ is true, no matter what numbers a and b are. The statement itself is a property of absolute value. Show that the statement is true when $a = 4$ and $b = -7$, as well as when $a = -5$ and $b = -8$.

40. Show that the statement $|ab| = |a||b|$ is true when $a = 3$ and $b = -6$, and when $a = -8$ and $b = -2$.

Review Problems   The following problems review material we covered in Sections 1.3 and 2.3. Reviewing these problems will help you with the next section.

Graph each inequality.

41. $x < -2$ or $x > 8$ **42.** $1 < x < 4$

43. $-3 \le 2x + 1 \le 3$ **44.** $4t - 3 \le -9$ or $4t - 3 \ge 9$

Section 2.5 Inequalities Involving Absolute Value

In this section we will again apply the definition of absolute value to solve inequalities involving absolute value. Again, the absolute value of x, which is $|x|$, represents the distance that x is from 0 on the number line. We will begin by considering three absolute value expressions and their English translations:

Expression	*In Words*
$|x| = 7$	x is exactly 7 units from 0 on the number line
$|a| < 5$	a is less than 5 units from 0 on the number line
$|y| \geq 4$	y is greater than or equal to 4 units from 0 on the number line

Once we have translated the expression into words, we can use the translation to graph the original equation or inequality. The graph is then used to write a final equation or inequality that does not involve absolute value.

Original Expression	*Graph*	*Final Expression*

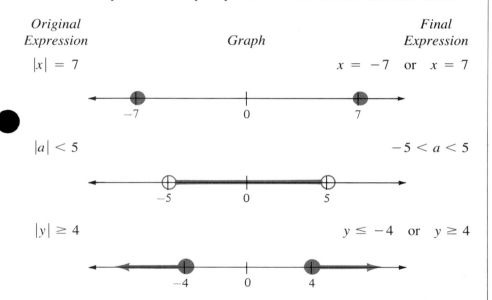

$|x| = 7$ $x = -7$ or $x = 7$

$|a| < 5$ $-5 < a < 5$

$|y| \geq 4$ $y \leq -4$ or $y \geq 4$

Note: Remember, the continued inequality

$$-5 < a < 5$$

is equivalent to

$$-5 < a \text{ and } a < 5$$

That is, it represents all real numbers that are both greater than -5 and less than 5.

Although we will not always write out the English translation of an absolute value inequality, it is important that we understand the translation. Our second expression, $|a| < 5$, means a is within 5 units of 0 on the number line. The graph of this relationship is

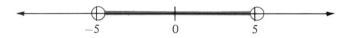

which can be written with the following continued inequality:

$$-5 < a < 5$$

We can follow this same kind of reasoning to solve more complicated absolute value inequalities.

Practice Problems

1.   Graph the solution set

$$|2x + 1| \le 7$$

▼ **Example 1**   Graph the solution set $|2x - 5| < 3$.

Solution   The absolute value of $2x - 5$ is the distance that $2x - 5$ is from 0 on the number line. We can translate the inequality as, "$2x - 5$ is less than 3 units from 0 on the number line." That is, $2x - 5$ must appear between -3 and 3 on the number line.

A picture of this relationship is

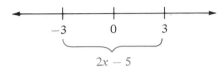

Using the picture, we can write an inequality without absolute value that describes the situation:

$$-3 < 2x - 5 < 3$$

Next, we solve the continued inequality by first adding $+5$ to all three members and then multiplying all three by $\frac{1}{2}$:

$$-3 < 2x - 5 < 3$$
$$2 < \quad 2x \quad < 8 \qquad \text{Add } +5 \text{ to all three members}$$
$$1 < \quad x \quad < 4 \qquad \text{Multiply each member by } \frac{1}{2}$$

The graph of the solution set is

We can see from the solution that in order for the absolute value of $2x - 5$ to be within 3 units of 0 on the number line, x must be between 1 and 4. ▲

2.   Solve and graph $|4a - 3| < 5$.

▼ **Example 2**   Solve and graph $|3a + 7| \le 4$.

Solution   We can read the inequality as, "The distance between $3a + 7$ and 0 is less than or equal to 4." Or, "$3a + 7$ is within 4 units of 0 on the number line." This relationship can be written without absolute value as

$$-4 \le 3a + 7 \le 4$$

Solving as usual, we have

$$-4 \le 3a + 7 \le 4$$
$$-11 \le \quad 3a \quad \le -3 \qquad \text{Add } -7 \text{ to all three members}$$
$$-\frac{11}{3} \le \quad a \quad \le -1 \qquad \text{Multiply each by } \frac{1}{3}$$

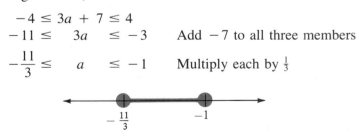

We can see from Examples 1 and 2 that in order to solve an inequality involving absolute value, we must be able to write an equivalent expression that does not involve absolute value.

Answers
1. See "Solutions to Selected Practice Problems."

▼ **Example 3** Solve $|x - 3| > 5$ and graph the solution.

Solution We interpret the absolute value inequality to mean that $x - 3$ is more than 5 units from 0 on the number line. The quantity $x - 3$ must be either above $+5$ or below -5. Here is a picture of the relationship:

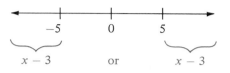

An inequality without absolute value that also describes this situation is

$$x - 3 < -5 \quad \text{or} \quad x - 3 > 5$$

Adding $+3$ to both sides of each inequality we have

$$x < -2 \quad \text{or} \quad x > 8$$

the graph of which is

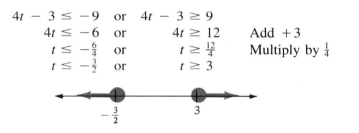 ▲

▼ **Example 4** Graph the solution set $|4t - 3| \geq 9$.

Solution The quantity $4t - 3$ is greater than or equal to 9 units from 0. It must be either above $+9$ or below -9.

$$
\begin{array}{lll}
4t - 3 \leq -9 & \text{or} & 4t - 3 \geq 9 \\
4t \leq -6 & \text{or} & 4t \geq 12 \qquad \text{Add } +3 \\
t \leq -\frac{6}{4} & \text{or} & t \geq \frac{12}{4} \qquad \text{Multiply by } \frac{1}{4} \\
t \leq -\frac{3}{2} & \text{or} & t \geq 3
\end{array}
$$

 ▲

▼ **Example 5** Solve and graph $|2x + 3| + 4 < 9$.

Solution Before we can apply the method of solution we used in the previous examples, we must isolate the absolute value on one side of the inequality. To do so, we add -4 to each side.

$$
\begin{aligned}
|2x + 3| + 4 &< 9 \\
|2x + 3| + 4 + (-4) &< 9 + (-4) \\
|2x + 3| &< 5
\end{aligned}
$$

From this last line we know that $2x + 3$ must be between -5 and $+5$.

$$
\begin{array}{lll}
-5 < 2x + 3 < 5 & & \\
-8 < \quad 2x \quad < 2 & & \text{Add } -3 \text{ to each member} \\
-4 < \quad x \quad < 1 & & \text{Multiply each member by } \frac{1}{2}
\end{array}
$$

The graph is

▲

---

3. Solve $|x + 2| > 7$ and graph the solution.

4. Graph the solution set
$$|3t - 6| \geq 3$$

5. Solve and graph
$$|2x + 5| - 2 < 9$$

6. Solve and graph

$$|5 - 2t| > 3$$

Note: Remember, the multiplication property for inequalities requires that we reverse the direction of the inequality symbol *every* time we multiply both sides of an inequality by a negative number.

7. Solve $|8y + 3| \leq -5$.

8. Solve $|2x - 9| \geq -7$.

▼ **Example 6** Solve and graph $|4 - 2t| > 2$.

Solution The inequality indicates that $4 - 2t$ is less than -2 or greater than $+2$. Writing this without absolute value symbols we have

$$4 - 2t < -2 \quad \text{or} \quad 4 - 2t > 2$$

To solve these inequalities we begin by adding -4 to each side.

$$4 + (-4) - 2t < -2 + (-4) \quad \text{or} \quad 4 + (-4) - 2t > 2 + (-4)$$
$$-2t < -6 \qquad\qquad \text{or} \qquad\qquad -2t > -2$$

Next we must multiply both sides of each inequality by $-\frac{1}{2}$. When we do so, we must also reverse the direction of each inequality symbol.

$$-2t < -6 \qquad\qquad \text{or} \qquad\qquad -2t > -2$$
$$-\tfrac{1}{2}(-2t) > -\tfrac{1}{2}(-6) \quad \text{or} \quad -\tfrac{1}{2}(-2t) < -\tfrac{1}{2}(-2)$$
$$t > 3 \qquad\qquad \text{or} \qquad\qquad t < 1$$

Although in situations like this we are used to seeing the "less than" symbol written first, the meaning of the solution is clear. We want to graph all real numbers that are either greater than 3 or less than 1. Here is the graph.

Since absolute value always results in a nonnegative quantity, we sometimes come across special solution sets when a negative number appears on the right side of an absolute value inequality.

▼ **Example 7** Solve $|7y - 1| < -2$.

Solution The *left* side is never negative because it is an absolute value. The *right* side is negative. We have a positive quantity less than a negative quantity, which is impossible. The solution set is the empty set, $\varnothing$. There is no real number to substitute for y to make the above inequality a true statement. ▲

▼ **Example 8** Solve $|6x + 2| > -5$.

Solution This is the opposite case from that in Example 7. No matter what real number we use for x on the *left* side, the result will always be positive, or zero. The *right* side is negative. We have a positive quantity greater than a negative quantity. Every real number we choose for x gives us a true statement. The solution set is the set of all real numbers. ▲

Problem Set 2.5

Name _____

Class _____

Date _____

Solve each of the following inequalities using the definition of absolute value. Graph the solution set in each case.

1. $|x| < 3$

2. $|x| \leq 7$

3. $|x| \geq 2$

4. $|x| > 4$

5. $|x| + 2 < 5$

6. $|x| - 3 < -1$

7. $|t| - 3 > 4$

8. $|t| + 5 > 8$

9. $|y| < -5$

10. $|y| > -3$

11. $|x| \geq -2$

12. $|x| \leq -4$

Answers

1. ⟵————————————⟶

2. ⟵————————————⟶

3. ⟵————————————⟶

4. ⟵————————————⟶

5. ⟵————————————⟶

6. ⟵————————————⟶

7. ⟵————————————⟶

8. ⟵————————————⟶

9. ⟵————————————⟶

10. ⟵————————————⟶

11. ⟵————————————⟶

12. ⟵————————————⟶

Answers

13. ← ————————————— →

14. ← ————————————— →

15. ← ————————————— →

16. ← ————————————— →

17. ← ————————————— →

18. ← ————————————— →

19. ← ————————————— →

20. ← ————————————— →

21. ← ————————————— →

22. ← ————————————— →

23. ← ————————————— →

24. ← ————————————— →

13. $|x - 3| < 7$

14. $|x + 4| < 2$

15. $|a + 5| \geq 4$

16. $|a - 6| \geq 3$

17. $|a - 1| < -3$

18. $|a + 2| \geq -5$

19. $|2x - 4| < 6$

20. $|2x + 6| < 2$

21. $|3y + 9| \geq 6$

22. $|5y - 1| \geq 4$

23. $|2k + 3| \geq 7$

24. $|2k - 5| \geq 3$

25. $|x - 3| + 2 < 6$

26. $|x + 4| - 3 < -1$

27. $|2a + 1| + 4 \geq 7$

28. $|2a - 6| - 1 \geq 2$

29. $|3x + 5| - 8 < 5$

30. $|6x - 1| - 4 \leq 2$

Solve each inequality and graph the solution set. Keep in mind that if you multiply or divide both sides of an inequality by a negative number you must reverse the sense of the inequality.

31. $|5 - x| > 3$

32. $|7 - x| > 2$

33. $|3 - \frac{2}{3}x| \geq 5$

34. $|3 - \frac{3}{4}x| \geq 9$

35. $|2 - \frac{1}{2}x| > 1$

36. $|3 - \frac{1}{3}x| > 1$

Name _____

Class _____

Date _____

Answers

25. ←————————————————→

26. ←————————————————→

27. ←————————————————→

28. ←————————————————→

29. ←————————————————→

30. ←————————————————→

31. ←————————————————→

32. ←————————————————→

33. ←————————————————→

34. ←————————————————→

35. ←————————————————→

36. ←————————————————→

Answers

37. _____

38. _____

39. _____

40. _____

41. _____

42. _____

43. _____

44. _____

45. _____

46. _____

37. Write the continued inequality $-4 \leq x \leq 4$ as a single inequality involving absolute value.

38. Write the continued inequality $-8 \leq x \leq 8$ as a single inequality involving absolute value.

Review Problems   The following problems review some of the material we covered in Section 1.4.

Identify the property (or properties) that justifies each of the following statements.

39. $ax = xa$

40. $5(\frac{1}{5}) = 1$

41. $3 + (x + y) = (3 + x) + y$

42. $3 + (x + y) = (x + y) + 3$

43. $3 + (x + y) = (3 + y) + x$

44. $7(3x - 5) = 21x - 35$

45. $4(xy) = 4(yx)$

46. $4(xy) = (4y)x$

Section 2.6   Formulas

A formula in mathematics is an equation that contains more than one variable. There are probably some formulas that are already familiar to you—for example, the formula for the area (A) of a rectangle with length l and width w is $A = lw$.

There are some others with which you are probably not as familiar—for example, the formula for the surface area (s) of a closed cylinder with a given height h and radius r as shown in Example 3.

Formulas are very common in the application of algebra to other disciplines. They are found in chemistry, physics, biology, and business, among others.

There are generally two main types of problems associated with formulas. We can solve for one of the variables in a formula if we are given numerical replacements for the other variables. Or we can solve for one of the variables in a formula without being given replacements for the other variables.

▼   **Example 1**   Given the formula $A = \frac{1}{2}(b + B)h$, find B when $A = 20$ sq ft (square feet), $b = 3$ ft (feet), and $h = 4$ ft.

Solution   The formula is for the area of a trapezoid with bases b and B and height h as shown in the figure in the margin.

$$\text{When} \quad A = 20,\ b = 3,\ \text{and}\ h = 4,$$
$$\text{the formula} \quad A = \tfrac{1}{2}(b + B)h$$
$$\text{becomes} \quad 20 = \tfrac{1}{2}(3 + B)4$$

Multiplication is commutative, so we can multiply the $\frac{1}{2}$ and the 4:

$$20 = 2(3 + B)$$
$$10 = 3 + B \qquad \text{Multiply both sides by } \tfrac{1}{2}$$
$$7 = B \qquad \text{Add } -3 \text{ to both sides}$$

The larger base is $B = 7$ ft.   ▲

▼   **Example 2**   Given the formula $P = 2w + 2l$, solve for w.

Solution   The formula represents the relationship between the perimeter P (the distance around the outside), the length l, and the width w of a rectangle.

To solve for w we must isolate it on one side of the equation. We can accomplish this if we delete the $2l$ term and the coefficient 2 from the right side of the equation.

To begin, we add $-2l$ to both sides:

$$P + (-2l) = 2w + 2l + (-2l)$$
$$P - 2l = 2w$$

To delete the 2 from the right side, we can multiply both sides by $\frac{1}{2}$:

$$\tfrac{1}{2}(P - 2l) = \tfrac{1}{2}(2w)$$
$$\frac{P - 2l}{2} = w$$

Practice Problems

1. Given the formula in Example 1, find b when $A = 40$ sq ft, $B = 5$ ft, and $h = 6$ ft.

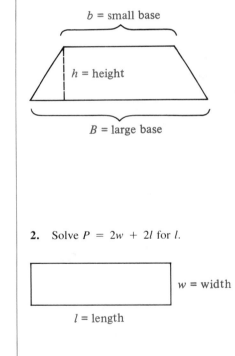

b = small base

h = height

B = large base

2. Solve $P = 2w + 2l$ for l.

w = width

l = length

Note: We know we are finished solving a formula for a specified variable when that variable appears alone on one side of the equal sign and not on the other.

Answers

1. $\frac{25}{3}$ ft   **2.** $l = \dfrac{P - 2w}{2}$

The two formulas

$$P = 2l + 2w \quad \text{and} \quad w = \frac{P - 2l}{2}$$

give the relationship between P, l, and w. They look different, but they both say the same thing about P, l, and w. The first formula gives P in terms of l and w, and the second formula gives w in terms of P and l. ▲

3. Solve $S = 2x^2 + 4xy$ for y.

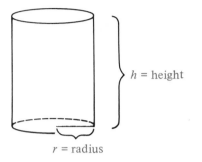

h = height

r = radius

▼ **Example 3** Solve the formula $s = 2\pi rh + \pi r^2$ for h.

Solution This is the formula for the surface area of a right circular cylinder with radius r and height h as shown in the figure in the margin. To isolate h, we first add $-\pi r^2$ to both sides. Then we multiply each side by $\frac{1}{2}\pi r$.

$$s = 2\pi rh + \pi r^2$$
$$s + (-\pi r^2) = 2\pi rh + \pi r^2 + (-\pi r^2) \qquad \text{Add } -\pi r^2$$
$$\text{to both sides}$$
$$s - \pi r^2 = 2\pi rh$$
$$\frac{1}{2\pi r}(s - \pi r^2) = \frac{1}{2\pi r}(2\pi rh) \qquad \text{Multiply by } \frac{1}{2\pi r}$$
$$\frac{s - \pi r^2}{2\pi r} = h$$
$$\text{or} \quad h = \frac{s - \pi r^2}{2\pi r} \qquad \qquad ▲$$

4. Solve for x: $ax + 5 = cx + 3$.

▼ **Example 4** Solve for x: $ax - 3 = bx + 5$.

Solution In this example we must begin by collecting all the variable terms on the left side of the equation and all the constant terms on the other side (just like we did when we were solving first-degree equations in Section 2.2).

$$ax - 3 = bx + 5$$
$$ax - bx - 3 = 5 \qquad \text{Add } -bx \text{ to each side}$$
$$ax - bx = 8 \qquad \text{Add } 3 \text{ to each side}$$

At this point we need to apply the distributive property to write the left side as $(a - b)x$.

$$(a - b)x = 8 \qquad \text{Distributive property}$$
$$\frac{1}{a - b}(a - b)x = \frac{1}{a - b} \cdot 8 \qquad \text{Multiply each side by } \frac{1}{a - b}$$
$$x = \frac{8}{a - b} \qquad ▲$$

Note: We are applying the distributive property in the same way we applied it when we first learned how to simplify $7x - 4x$. Recall that $7x - 4x = 3x$ because

$$7x - 4x = (7 - 4)x = 3x$$

We are using the same type of reasoning when we write

$$ax - bx = (a - b)x$$

Answers

3. $y = \dfrac{S - 2x^2}{4x}$ **4.** $x = \dfrac{-2}{a - c}$

Problem Set 2.6   **93**

Problem Set 2.6

Solve each of the following formulas for the variable that does not have a numerical replacement.

1. $A = lw$;
  $A = 30, l = 5$

2. $A = lw$;
  $A = 16, w = 2$

3. $I = prt$;
  $I = 200, p = 1{,}000, r = .05$

4. $I = prt$;
  $I = 100, p = 2{,}000, t = 2$

5. $P = 2l + 2w$;
  $P = 16, l = 3$

6. $P = 2l + 2w$;
  $P = 40, w = 5$

7. $A = \frac{1}{2}(b + B)h$;
  $A = 9, b = 2, h = 6$

8. $A = \frac{1}{2}(b + B)h$;
  $A = 15, B = 2, h = 8$

9. $y = mx + b$;
  $y = 18, b = 2, m = 2$

10. $y = mx + b$;
  $y = 30, m = 2, x = 5$

11. $s = \frac{1}{2}(a + b + c)$;
  $s = 12, a = 1, b = 2$

12. $s = \frac{1}{2}(a + b + c)$;
  $s = 15, a = 8, c = 4$

Name _____

Class _____

Date _____

Answers

1. _____   2. _____

3. _____   4. _____

5. _____   6. _____

7. _____   8. _____

9. _____   10. _____

11. _____   12. _____

Answers

Solve each of the following formulas for the indicated variables.

13. _____

14. _____

15. _____

16. _____

17. _____

18. _____

19. _____

20. _____

21. _____

22. _____

23. _____

24. _____

13. $A = lw$ for l

14. $A = \frac{1}{2}bh$ for b

15. $I = prt$ for t

16. $I = prt$ for r

17. $PV = nRT$ for T

18. $PV = nRT$ for R

19. $y = mx + b$ for b

20. $y = mx + b$ for x

21. $s = \frac{1}{2}(a + b + c)$ for c

22. $s = \frac{1}{2}(a + b + c)$ for b

23. $A = P + Prt$ for r

24. $A = P + Prt$ for t

25. $C = \frac{5}{9}(F - 32)$ for F

26. $F = \frac{9}{5}C + 32$ for C

27. $A = a + (n - 1)d$ for d

28. $A = a + (n - 1)d$ for n

29. $9x - 3y = 6$ for y

30. $9x + 3y = 15$ for y

31. $z = \frac{x - \mu}{s}$ for x

32. $z = \frac{x - \mu}{s}$ for μ

33. $ax + 4 = bx + 9$ for x

34. $ax - 5 = cx - 2$ for x

35. $A = P + Prt$ for P

36. $s = 2\pi r + \pi r^2 h$ for π

Name _____

Class _____

Date _____

Answers

25. _____

26. _____

27. _____

28. _____

29. _____

30. _____

31. _____

32. _____

33. _____

34. _____

35. _____

36. _____

Answers

37. _____

38. _____

39. _____

40. _____

41. _____

42. _____

43. _____

44. _____

45. _____

46. _____

47. _____

48. _____

37. $ax + b = cx + d$ for x

38. $4x + 2y = 3x + 5y$ for y

39. Solve the inequality $-2.5 < \dfrac{x - \mu}{s} < 2.5$ for x.

40. Solve the absolute value inequality $\left| \dfrac{x - \mu}{s} \right| < 1.96$ for x.

41. The formula $F = \frac{9}{5}C + 32$ gives the relationship between the Celsius and Fahrenheit temperature scales. If the temperature range on a certain day is 86° to 104° Fahrenheit (that is, $86 \le F \le 104$), what is the temperature range in degrees Celsius?

42. If the temperature in degrees Fahrenheit is between 68° and 95°, what is the corresponding temperature range in degrees Celsius?

Review Problems   The following problems review some of the material we covered in Section 1.1. Reviewing these problems will help you with the next section.

Translate each of the following into symbols.

43. Twice the sum of x and 3.

44. Twice the sum of x and 3 is 16.

45. Five times the difference of x and 3.

46. Five times the difference of x and 3 is 10.

47. The sum of $3x$ and 2 is equal to the difference of x and 4.

48. The sum of x and $x + 2$ is 12 more than their difference.

Section 2.7   Word Problems

There are a number of word problems whose solutions depend on solving first-degree equations in one variable. We will begin our study of word problems by considering some simple problems stated in words.

Admittedly, the problems in this section are a bit contrived. That is, the problems themselves are not the kind of problems you would find in the fields of study that require a good background in mathematics, like chemistry or physics (although you may see these problems on entrance exams or aptitude tests). As we progress through the book we will solve word problems of a more realistic nature. In the meantime, the problems in this section will allow you to practice the procedures used in setting up and solving word problems.

Here are some general steps we will follow in solving word problems.

To Solve a Word Problem

Step 1:   Let x represent the quantity asked for in the problem.
Step 2:   Write expressions, using the variable x, that represent any other unknown quantities in the problem.
Step 3:   Write an equation, in x, that describes the situation.
Step 4:   Solve the equation found in step 3.
Step 5:   Check the solution in the original words of the problem.

Step 3 is usually the most difficult step. Step 3 is really what word problems are all about—translating a problem stated in words into an algebraic equation.

As an aid in simplifying step 3, we will look at a number of phrases written in English and the equivalent mathematical expression.

English Phrase	*Algebraic Expression*
The sum of a and b	$a + b$
The difference of a and b	$a - b$
The product of a and b	$a \cdot b$
The quotient of a and b	a/b
4 more than x	$4 + x$
Twice the sum of a and 5	$2(a + 5)$
The sum of twice a and 5	$2a + 5$
8 decreased by y	$8 - y$
3 less than m	$m - 3$
7 times the difference of x and 2	$7(x - 2)$

Note: The word *sum* always indicates addition. The word *difference* always implies subtraction. *Product* indicates multiplication and *quotient* means division.

We could extend the list even more. For every English sentence involving a relationship with numbers, there is an associated mathematical expression.

▼   **Example 1**   Twice the sum of a number and 3 is 16. Find the number.

Solution

Step 1:   Let x = the number asked for.
Step 2:   Twice the sum of x and 3 = $2(x + 3)$.
Step 3:   An equation that describes the situation is

$$2(x + 3) = 16$$

(The word *is* always translates to =.)

Practice Problems

1. Twice the difference of a number and 2 is 28. Find the number.

Answer
1. 16

Step 4: Solving the equation, we have

$$2(x + 3) = 16$$
$$2x + 6 = 16$$
$$2x = 10$$
$$x = 5$$

Step 5: Checking $x = 5$ in the original problem, we see that twice the sum of 5 and 3 is twice 8 or 16. ▲

2. Twice the sum of two consecutive integers is 22. Find the two integers.

▼ **Example 2** The sum of two consecutive even integers is 3 times the smaller integer. Find the two integers.

Solution

Step 1: Let $x =$ the smaller integer.
Step 2: The next consecutive even integer after x is $x + 2$. The sum of the two integers is $x + (x + 2)$, or $2x + 2$. Three times the smaller is $3x$.
Step 3: An equation that describes the situation is

Note: When we ask for consecutive even integers, we mean even integers that are next to each other on the number line—like 6 and 8, 12 and 14, and 20 and 22. Consecutive means following one another in uninterrupted order. To get from one even integer to the next consecutive even integer we must add 2. That is why we let the first one be x and the next consecutive one be $x + 2$.

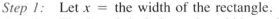

The sum of two consecutive even integers is   three times the smaller

$$x + (x + 2) = 3x$$
$$2x + 2 = 3x \quad \text{Simplify left side}$$
$$2 = x \quad \text{Add } -2x \text{ to each side}$$

The two integers are $x = 2$ and $x + 2 = 4$.

Step 4: Checking these numbers in the original problem we see that their sum is $2 + 4 = 6$ and three times the smaller is $3(2) = 6$. The solutions check. ▲

3. A rectangle is twice as long as it is wide. The perimeter is 36 inches. Find the dimensions.

▼ **Example 3** A rectangle is 3 times as long as it is wide. The perimeter is 40 feet. Find the dimensions.

Solution

Step 1: Let $x =$ the width of the rectangle.
Step 2: The length is 3 times the width, or $3x$.

```
           3x
   ┌──────────────────┐
   │                  │
   │                  │ x
   │                  │
   └──────────────────┘
```

Step 3: The perimeter of a rectangle is twice the width plus twice the length:

$$2x + 2(3x) = 40$$

Step 4: Solve

$$2x + 2(3x) = 40$$
$$2x + 6x = 40$$
$$8x = 40$$
$$x = 5$$

The width is 5 feet. The length is 15 feet.

Step 5: Since the sum of twice 5 plus twice 15 is 40, the solutions check in the original problem. ▲

Answers
2. 5, 6   **3.** Width 6; length 12 inches

In all problems that involve geometric figures (rectangles, triangles, squares, etc.), it is helpful to draw the figure and label the dimensions.

▼ **Example 4**   Diane is 4 years older than JoAnn. In 6 years the sum of their ages will be 68. What are their ages now?

Solution

Step 1:   Let x = JoAnn's age now.
Step 2:   With age problems like this, it is usually helpful to use a table like the following:

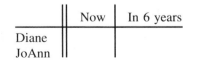

	Now	In 6 years
Diane		
JoAnn		

There is one column for each of the different times given (''Now'' and ''In 6 years'') and a row for each of the people mentioned (Diane and JoAnn).

To fill in the table, we use JoAnn's age as x. In 6 years she will be $x + 6$ years old. Diane is 4 years older than JoAnn or $x + 4$ years old. In 6 years she will be $x + 10$ years old.

	Now	In 6 years
Diane	$x + 4$	$x + 10$
JoAnn	x	$x + 6$

Step 3:   In 6 years the sum of their ages will be 68.

$$(x + 6) + (x + 10) = 68$$

Step 4:   Solve

$$2x + 16 = 68$$
$$2x = 52$$
$$x = 26$$

JoAnn is 26 and Diane is 30.

Step 5:   In 6 years JoAnn will be 32 and Diane will be 36. The sum of their ages will then be $32 + 36 = 68$. The solutions check in the original problem. ▲

The next examples we will do involve percent problems. You have probably worked problems similar to these in other math classes, although you may not have worked them using the method we will show here.

▼ **Example 5**   What number is 15% of 63?

Solution   To solve a problem like this we let x = the number in question and then translate the sentence directly into an equation. Here is how it is done.

What number is 15% of 63?

$$x = 0.15 \cdot 63$$
$$= 9.45$$

The number 9.45 is 15% of 63. ▲

---

4.   Lloyd is 3 years older than Joyce. In 5 years the sum of their ages will be 65. How old are they now?

5.   What number is 25% of 74?

Note: We write 0.15 instead of 15% when we translate the sentence into an equation because we cannot do calculations with the % symbol. Since percent (%) means per hundred, we think of 15% as 15 hundredths, or 0.15.

Answers
4. Joyce is 26; Lloyd is 29.   **5.** 18.5

6. What percent of 84 is 21?

▼ **Example 6** What percent of 42 is 21?

Solution We translate the sentence as follows

$$\underbrace{\text{What percent}}_{x} \quad \underset{\cdot}{\overset{\downarrow}{\text{of}}} \quad \underset{42}{\overset{\downarrow}{\text{42}}} \quad \underset{=}{\overset{\downarrow}{\text{is}}} \quad \underset{21}{\overset{\downarrow}{\text{21?}}}$$

Next we multiply each side by $\frac{1}{42}$ (which gives the same result as dividing each side by 42).

$$\frac{1}{42}(x \cdot 42) = \frac{1}{42}(21)$$

$$x = \frac{21}{42}$$

$$= 0.50 \text{ or } 50\%$$ ▲

7. 35 is 40% of what number?

▼ **Example 7** 25 is 40% of what number?

Solution Again, we translate the sentence directly:

$$\underset{25}{\overset{\downarrow}{\text{25}}} \quad \underset{=}{\overset{\downarrow}{\text{is}}} \quad \underset{0.40}{\overset{\downarrow}{\text{40\%}}} \quad \underset{\cdot}{\overset{\downarrow}{\text{of}}} \quad \underbrace{\text{what number?}}_{x}$$

We solve the equation by dividing both sides by 0.40 (which gives the same result as multiplying both sides by 1/0.40).

$$\frac{25}{0.40} = \frac{0.40 \cdot x}{0.40}$$

$$62.5 = x$$

25 is 40% of 62.5. ▲

Problem Set 2.7

Number Problems

Solve each of the following word problems. Be sure to show the equation used in each case.

1. A number increased by 2 is 5 less than twice the number. Find the number.

2. Twice a number decreased by 3 is equal to the number. Find the number.

3. Three times the sum of a number and 4 is 3. Find the number.

4. Five times the difference of a number and 3 is 10. Find the number.

5. Twice the sum of 2 times a number and 1 is the same as 3 times the difference of the number and 5. Find the number.

6. The sum of 3 times a number and 2 is the same as the difference of the number and 4. Find the number.

7. If 5 times a number is increased by 2, the result is 8 more than 3 times the number. Find the number.

8. If 6 times a number is decreased by 5, the result is 7 more than 4 times the number decreased by 5. Find the number.

Name _____

Class _____

Date _____

Answers

1. _____   2. _____

3. _____   4. _____

5. _____   6. _____

7. _____   8. _____

Answers

Consecutive Integer Problems

9. _____   10. _____

11. _____   12. _____

13. _____   14. _____

15. _____   16. _____

9. The sum of two consecutive even integers is 18. Find the two integers.

10. The sum of two consecutive odd integers is 16. Find the two integers.

11. The sum of two consecutive integers is 1 less than 3 times the smaller. Find the two integers.

12. The sum of two consecutive integers is 5 less than 3 times the larger. Find the integers.

13. If twice the smaller of two consecutive integers is added to the larger, the result is 7. Find the smaller one.

14. If twice the larger of two consecutive integers is added to the smaller, the result is 23. Find the smaller one.

15. If the larger of two consecutive odd integers is subtracted from twice the smaller, the result is 5. Find the two integers.

16. If the smaller of two consecutive even integers is subtracted from twice the larger, the result is 12. Find the two integers.

Geometry Problems

17. A rectangle is twice as long as it is wide. The perimeter is 60 feet. Find the dimensions.

18. The length of a rectangle is 5 times the width. The perimeter is 48 inches. Find the dimensions.

19. A square has a perimeter of 28 feet. Find the length of the side.

20. A square has a perimeter of 36 centimeters. Find the length of the side.

21. A triangle has a perimeter of 23 inches. The medium side is 3 more than the smallest side, and the longest side is twice the shortest side. Find the shortest side.

22. The longest side of a triangle is 3 times the shortest side. While the medium side is twice the shortest side, the perimeter is 18 meters. Find the dimensions.

23. The length of a rectangle is 3 less than twice the width. The perimeter is 18 meters. Find the width.

24. The length of a rectangle is one more than twice the width. The perimeter is 20 feet. Find the dimensions.

Name _____

Class _____

Date _____

Answers

17. _____   18. _____

19. _____   20. _____

21. _____   22. _____

23. _____   24. _____

Answers

25. _____   26. _____

27. _____   28. _____

29. _____   30. _____

31. _____   32. _____

33. _____   34. _____

35. _____   36. _____

37. _____   38. _____

39. _____   40. _____

Age Problems

25. Patrick is 4 years older than Amy. In 10 years the sum of their ages will be 36. How old are they now?

26. Mr. Lloyd is 2 years older than Mrs. Lloyd. Five years ago the sum of their ages was 44. How old are they now?

27. Jane is 3 times as old as Kate. In 5 years Jane's age will be 2 less than twice Kate's. How old are the girls now?

28. Carol is 2 years older than Mike. In 4 years her age will be 8 less than twice his. How old are they now?

Percent Problems

29. What number is 54% of 38?

30. What number is 11% of 67?

31. What percent of 36 is 9?

32. What percent of 50 is 5?

33. 37 is 4% of what number?

34. 8 is 2% of what number?

Review Problems   The following problems review some of the material we covered in Section 1.6.

Simplify each expression as much as possible.

35. $4(-3) - 5(-6)$

36. $-4(-5) - 7(-2)$

37. $-18 \div \left(-\frac{3}{4}\right)$

38. $-14 \div \left(\frac{7}{10}\right)$

39. $4 - (-2)\left[\dfrac{3(-4) - 6}{2 - 2(4)}\right]$

40. $7 - 2\left[\dfrac{6 - 3(5 - 9)}{-3 - 3}\right]$

Section 2.8 Additional Word Problems

Suppose we know that the sum of two numbers is 50. If we let x represent one of the two numbers, how can we represent the other? Let's suppose for a moment that x turns out to be 30. Then the other number will be 20, because their sum is 50. That is, if two numbers add up to 50, and one of them is 30, then the other must be $50 - 30 = 20$. Generalizing this to any number x, we see that, if two numbers have a sum of 50, and one of the numbers is x, then the other must be $50 - x$. The table that follows shows some additional examples.

If two numbers have a sum of	and one of them is	then the other must be
50	x	$50 - x$
10	y	$10 - y$
12	n	$12 - n$

Now let's look at some application problems that include this type of reasoning.

▼ **Example 1** The sum of two numbers is 12. If one of the numbers is twice as large as the other, find the two numbers.

Solution If we let $x =$ one of the numbers, then the other number must be $12 - x$, because their sum is 12. Since one of the numbers is twice the other, the equation that describes the situation is

$$
\begin{aligned}
x &= 2(12 - x) & \\
x &= 24 - 2x & \text{Multiply out the right side} \\
3x &= 24 & \text{Add } 2x \text{ to each side} \\
x &= 8 & \text{Multiply each side by } \tfrac{1}{3}
\end{aligned}
$$

One number is $x = 8$, so the other is $12 - x = 12 - 8 = 4$. The two solutions, 4 and 8, check in the original problem since their sum is $4 + 8 = 12$ and 8 is twice 4. ▲

▼ **Example 2** Suppose Bob has a collection of dimes and nickels that totals \$3.50. If he has a total of 50 coins, how many of each type does he have?

Solution If we let $x =$ the number of dimes, then $50 - x$ is the number of nickels. (The number of coins is 50, so if he has x of one kind, he must have $50 - x$ of the other.) Since each dime is worth 10 cents, the value of the x dimes is $10x$. Likewise, since each nickel is worth 5 cents, the value of the $50 - x$ nickels is $5(50 - x)$. Here is all the information we have summarized in a table.

	Dimes	Nickels	Total
Number	x	$50 - x$	50
Value	$10x$	$5(50 - x)$	350

The second line in our table gives us the equation we need to solve the problem. Since the amount of money he has in dimes, plus the amount of money he has in nickels must total \$3.50, we have

$$10x + 5(50 - x) = 350$$

Practice Problems

1. The sum of two numbers is 20. If one of the numbers is three times as large as the other, find the two numbers.

2. Fred has a collection of dimes and nickels that have a total value of \$2.50. If he has a total of 40 coins, how many of each type does he have?

Note that we have written this equation in terms of cents. Next we solve the equation.

$$10x + 5(50 - x) = 350$$
$$10x + 250 - 5x = 350$$
$$5x + 250 = 350$$
$$5x = 100$$
$$x = 20 \text{ dimes}$$
$$\text{so, } 50 - 20 = 30 \text{ nickels}$$

Bob has 20 dimes (with a value of $2.00) and 30 nickels (with a value of $1.50) that total $3.50. ▲

3. Howard invests a total of $8,000 in two accounts. One account earns 8% annually, and the other earns 10% annually. If the total interest earned from both accounts in a year is $680, how much is invested in each account?

▼ **Example 3** Suppose a person invests a total of $10,000 in two accounts. One account earns 5% annually and the other earns 6% annually. If the total interest earned from both accounts in a year is $560, how much is invested in each account?

Solution The form of the solution to this problem is very similar to that of Example 2. If we let x equal the amount invested at 6%, then $10,000 - x$ is the amount invested at 5%. The total interest earned from both accounts is $560. The amount of interest earned on x dollars at 6% is $0.06x$, while the amount of interest earned on $(10,000 - x)$ dollars at 5% is $0.05(10,000 - x)$.

	Dollars at 6%	Dollars at 5%	Total
Number	x	$10,000 - x$	10,000
Interest	$0.06x$	$0.05(10,000 - x)$	560

Again, the last line gives us the equation we are after.

$$0.06x + 0.05(10,000 - x) = 560$$

To make this equation a little easier to solve, we begin by multiplying both sides by 100 to move the decimal point two places to the right.

$$6x + 5(10,000 - x) = 56,000$$
$$6x + 50,000 - 5x = 56,000$$
$$x + 50,000 = 56,000$$
$$x = 6,000$$

The amount of money invested at 6% is $6,000. The amount of money invested at 5% is $10,000 - $6,000 = $4,000. ▲

Problem Set 2.8

Number Problems

1. The sum of two numbers is 24. If one of the numbers is twice as large as the other, find the two numbers.

2. The sum of two numbers is 16. If one of the numbers is three times as large as the other, find the two numbers.

3. The sum of two numbers is 16. One of the numbers is 2 less than twice the other. Find the two numbers.

4. The sum of two numbers is 21. One of the numbers is 3 more than twice the other. Find the numbers.

Coin Problems

5. Sylvia has a collection of dimes and nickels that have a total value of $2.80. If she has a total of 36 coins, how many of each type does she have?

6. Sharon has a collection of dimes and quarters that have a total value of $2.00. If she has a total of 14 coins, how many of each type does she have?

7. A coin collection consists of nickels and quarters. If there are 26 coins in the collection with a total value of $2.50, how many of each coin are there?

8. A coin collection consists of nickels and quarters. If there are 24 coins in the collection with a total value of $3.00, how many of each coin are there?

Name _____

Class _____

Date _____

Answers

1. _____

2. _____

3. _____

4. _____

5. _____

6. _____

7. _____

8. _____

Answers

9. _____

10. _____

11. _____

12. _____

13. _____

14. _____

15. ←——————————→

16. ←——————————→

17. ←——————————→

18. ←——————————→

19. ←——————————→

20. ←——————————→

Interest Problems

9. A woman has a total of $9,000 to invest. She invests part of the money in an account that pays 8% per year and the rest in an account that pays 9% per year. If the interest earned in the first year is $750, how much did she invest in each account?

10. A man invests $12,000 in two accounts. If one account pays 10% per year, and the other pays 7% per year, how much was invested in each account if the total interest earned in the first year was $960?

11. A total of $15,000 is invested in two accounts. One of the accounts earns 12% per year, while the other earns 10% per year. If the total interest earned in the first year is $1,600, how much was invested in each account?

12. A total of $11,000 is invested in two accounts. One of the two accounts pays 9% per year, and the other account pays 11% per year. If the total interest paid in the first year is $1,150, how much was invested in each account?

13. Stacey has a total of $6,000 in two accounts. The total amount of interest she earns from both accounts in the first year is $500. If one of the accounts earns 8% interest per year and the other earns 9% interest per year, how much did she invest in each account?

14. Travis has a total of $6,000 invested in two accounts. The total amount of interest he earns from the accounts in the first year is $410. If one account pays 6% per year and the other pays 8% per year, how much did he invest in each account?

Review Problems   The following problems review material we covered in Section 2.3.

Solve each inequality and graph the solution.

15. $2x - 3 < 5$

16. $3x - 2 > 7$

17. $-4x \leq 24$

18. $-5x \geq -35$

19. $-3 < 2x + 1 < 3$

20. $2x - 3 \leq -6$ or $2x - 3 \geq 6$

Chapter 2   Summary and Review

ADDITION PROPERTY OF EQUALITY [2.1]

For algebraic expressions A, B, and C,

$$\text{if} \qquad A = B$$
$$\text{then} \qquad A + C = B + C$$

This property states that we can add the same quantity to both sides of an equation without changing the solution set.

1. We can solve $x + 3 = 5$ by adding -3 to both sides:

$$x + 3 + (-3) = 5 + (-3)$$
$$x = 2$$

MULTIPLICATION PROPERTY OF EQUALITY [2.1]

For algebraic expressions A, B, and C,

$$\text{if} \qquad A = B$$
$$\text{then} \qquad AC = BC, \quad C \neq 0$$

Multiplying both sides of an equation by the same nonzero quantity never changes the solution set.

2. We can solve $3x = 12$ by multiplying both sides by $\frac{1}{3}$:

$$3x = 12$$
$$\tfrac{1}{3}(3x) = \tfrac{1}{3}(12)$$
$$x = 4$$

SOLVING A FIRST-DEGREE EQUATION IN ONE VARIABLE [2.2]

Step 1: Use the distributive property to separate terms.

Step 2: Simplify the left and right sides of the equation separately whenever possible.

Step 3: Use the addition property of equality to write all terms containing the variable on one side of the equal sign and all remaining terms on the other.

Step 4: Use the multiplication property of equality in order to get x alone on one side of the equal sign.

Step 5: Check your solution in the original equation, if necessary.

3. Solve $3(2x - 1) = 9$
$$3(2x - 1) = 9$$
$$6x - 3 = 9$$
$$6x - 3 + 3 = 9 + 3$$
$$6x = 12$$
$$x = 2$$

ADDITION PROPERTY FOR INEQUALITIES [2.3]

For expressions A, B, and C,

$$\text{if} \qquad A < B$$
$$\text{then} \qquad A + C < B + C$$

Adding the same quantity to both sides of an inequality never changes the solution set.

4. Adding 5 to both sides of the inequality $x - 5 < -2$ gives

$$x - 5 + 5 < -2 + 5$$
$$x < 3$$

MULTIPLICATION PROPERTY FOR INEQUALITIES [2.3]

For expressions A, B, and C,

$$\text{if} \qquad A < B$$
$$\text{then} \qquad AC < BC \quad \text{if} \quad C > 0, \text{ (C is positive)}$$
$$\text{or} \qquad AC > BC \quad \text{if} \quad C < 0, \text{ (C is negative)}$$

We can multiply both sides of an inequality by the same nonzero number without changing the solution set as long as each time we multiply by a negative number we also reverse the direction of the inequality symbol.

5. Multiplying both sides of $-2x \geq 6$ by $-\frac{1}{2}$ gives

$$-2x \geq 6$$
$$-\tfrac{1}{2}(-2x) \leq -\tfrac{1}{2}(6)$$
$$x \leq -3$$

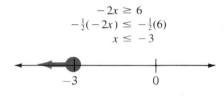

6. $2(3x - 5) > 14$

$\qquad 6x - 10 > 14$

$\qquad 6x > 24$

$\qquad x > 4$

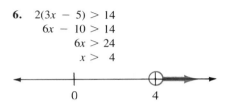

7. To solve $|2x - 1| + 2 = 7$ we first isolate the absolute value on the left side by adding -2 to each side to obtain

$$|2x - 1| = 5$$
$$2x - 1 = 5 \quad \text{or} \quad 2x - 1 = -5$$
$$2x = 6 \quad \text{or} \quad 2x = -4$$
$$x = 3 \quad \text{or} \quad x = -2$$

8. To solve $|x - 3| + 2 < 6$ we first add -2 to obtain

$$|x - 3| < 4$$

which is equivalent to

$$-4 < x - 3 < 4$$
$$-1 < \quad x \quad < 7$$

9. Solve for w:

$$P = 2l + 2w$$
$$P - 2l = 2w$$
$$\frac{P - 2l}{2} = w$$

10. If the perimeter of a rectangle is 32 inches and the length is 3 times the width, we can find the dimensions by letting x be the width and $3x$ the length.

$$x + x + 3x + 3x = 32$$
$$8x = 32$$
$$x = 4$$

Width is 4 inches, length is 12 inches.

SOLVING A FIRST-DEGREE INEQUALITY IN ONE VARIABLE [2.3]

Follow the same first four steps used to solve a first-degree equation—using, of course, the addition and multiplication properties for inequalities. As a fifth step, graph the solution set.

ABSOLUTE VALUE EQUATIONS [2.4]

To solve an equation that involves absolute value we isolate the absolute value on one side of the equation and then rewrite the absolute value equation as two separate equations that do not involve absolute value. In general, if b is a positive number then

$$|a| = b \text{ is equivalent to } a = b \text{ or } a = -b$$

ABSOLUTE VALUE INEQUALITIES [2.5]

To solve an inequality that involves absolute value we first isolate the absolute value on the left side of the inequality symbol. Then we rewrite the absolute value inequality as an equivalent continued or compound inequality that does not contain absolute value symbols. In general, if b is a positive number, then

$$|a| < b \text{ is equivalent to } -b < a < b$$
$$\text{and } |a| > b \text{ is equivalent to } a < -b \text{ or } a > b$$

FORMULAS [2.6]

A formula in algebra is an equation involving more than one variable. To solve a formula for one of its variables, simply isolate that variable on one side of the equation.

SOLVING A PROBLEM STATED IN WORDS [2.7, 2.8]

Step 1: Let x represent the quantity asked for.

Step 2: If possible, write all other unknown quantities in terms of x.

Step 3: Write an equation, using x, that describes the situation.

Step 4: Solve the equation in step 3.

Step 5: Check the solution from step 4 with the original words of the problem.

COMMON MISTAKE

A very common mistake in solving inequalities is to forget to reverse the direction of the inequality symbol when multiplying both sides by a negative number. When this mistake occurs, the graph of the solution set is always to the wrong side of the end point.

Chapter 2 Test

Solve the following equations. [2.1, 2.2]

1. $x - 5 = 7$

2. $3y = -4$

3. $3a - 6 = 11$

4. $2x - 5 - x + 4 = 3x + 5$

5. $5(x - 1) - 2(2x + 3) = 5x - 4$

6. $7 - 2(3x + 1) = -4x + 1$

Solve the following inequalities and then graph the solutions. [2.3]

7. $-5t \leq 30$

8. $8 - 2x \geq 6$

9. $4x - 5 < 2x + 7$

10. $3(2y + 4) \geq 5(y - 8)$

Name _____

Class _____

Date _____

Answers

1. _____   2. _____

3. _____   4. _____

5. _____   6. _____

7. ⟵————————————⟶

8. ⟵————————————⟶

9. ⟵————————————⟶

10. ⟵————————————⟶

Answers

11. _____

12. _____

13. ←——————————→

14. ←——————————→

15. _____

16. _____

17. _____

18. _____

19. _____

20. _____

Solve the following equations. [2.4]

11. $|x - 4| = 2$

12. $|2a + 7| = 5$

Solve the following inequalities and graph the solutions. [2.5]

13. $|6x - 1| > 7$

14. $|3x - 5| - 4 \le 3$

Solve for the indicated variable. [2.6]

15. $A = 2l + 2w$ for w.

16. $A = \frac{1}{2}h(b + B)$ for B

17. Find two consecutive even integers whose sum is 18. (Be sure to write an equation that describes the situation.) [2.7]

18. Patrick is 4 years older than Amy. In 5 years he will be twice as old as she is now. Find their ages now. [2.7]

19. The sum of two numbers is 19. If one of the numbers is 4 more than twice the other, find the numbers. [2.8]

20. Diane has a collection of dimes and nickels worth $1.10. If the total number of coins is 14, how many of each kind does she have? [2.8]

3

Exponents and Polynomials

To the student:

There are many expressions and equations in mathematics that involve exponents. For example, in genetics, the phenotypic variance P^2 of a given trait is the sum of the genetic variance (G^2), the environmental variance (E^2), and the variance due to the interaction between them (I^2), or $P^2 = G^2 + E^2 + I^2$. The 2's in the equation are exponents. Before we get to the point where we can work with equations like this, we must review the properties of exponents and practice working with expressions that involve exponents.

In addition to being able to add, subtract, multiply, and divide real numbers, your success in this chapter depends on your ability to understand and apply the distributive property. The fact that multiplication distributes over addition allows us to add and multiply polynomials. Understanding addition and multiplication of polynomials allows us to understand subtraction and factoring of polynomials. Actually, we could probably rename this chapter "Exponents and Applications of the Distributive Property." Understanding the distributive property is the key to understanding this chapter.

Section 3.1   Properties of Exponents I

In Chapter 1 we defined positive integer exponents in terms of repeated multiplication. That is, $3^4 = 3 \cdot 3 \cdot 3 \cdot 3 = 81$. Also, recall that, for the expression 3^4, the base is 3 and the exponent is 4. The expression 3^4 is written in *exponential form*, while the expression $3 \cdot 3 \cdot 3 \cdot 3$ is in *expanded form*.

113

Practice Problems

1. Expand and multiply, if possible.

a. $(-2)^3$

b. $(-7)^2$

c. -7^2

d. $\left(\dfrac{3}{5}\right)^3$

Here are some more examples of expressions with integer exponents and their expansions.

▼ **Example 1** Expand and multiply, if possible.

a. $(-4)^3 = (-4)(-4)(-4) = -64$ Base -4, exponent 3

b. $(-5)^2 = (-5)(-5) = 25$ Base -5, exponent 2

c. $-5^2 = -5 \cdot 5 = -25$ Base 5, exponent 2

d. $\left(\frac{2}{3}\right)^4 = \frac{2}{3} \cdot \frac{2}{3} \cdot \frac{2}{3} \cdot \frac{2}{3} = \frac{16}{81}$ Base $\frac{2}{3}$, exponent 4 ▲

In this section we will be concerned with the simplification of those products that involve more than one base and more than one exponent. Actually, almost all of the expressions can be simplified by applying the definition of positive integer exponents; that is, by writing all expressions in expanded form and then simplifying by using ordinary arithmetic. This process, however, is usually very time-consuming. We can shorten the process considerably by making some generalizations about exponents and applying the generalizations whenever it is convenient.

2. Write the product $x^5 \cdot x^4$ with a single exponent.

▼ **Example 2** Write the product $x^3 \cdot x^4$ with a single exponent.

Solution
$$
\begin{aligned}
x^3 \cdot x^4 &= (x \cdot x \cdot x)(x \cdot x \cdot x \cdot x) \\
&= (x \cdot x \cdot x \cdot x \cdot x \cdot x \cdot x) \\
&= x^7 \qquad \textit{Notice: } 3 + 4 = 7
\end{aligned}
$$
▲

We can generalize this result into the first property of exponents.

Note: We are stating our properties of exponents for integer exponents instead of just positive integer exponents. As you will see, the definition for negative integer exponents is stated in such a way that we can change any expression with a negative exponent to an equivalent expression with a positive exponent. This allows us to state our properties for all integers, not just for positive ones.

Property 1 for Exponents

If a is a real number, and r and s are integers, then

$$a^r \cdot a^s = a^{r+s}$$

The product of two expressions with the same base is equivalent to the base raised to the sum of the exponents from the original two expressions.

Expressions of the form $(a^r)^s$ occur frequently with exponents. Here is an example:

3. Simplify $(4^5)^2$ by writing an equivalent expression with a single exponent.

▼ **Example 3** Write $(5^3)^2$ with a single exponent.

Solution
$$
\begin{aligned}
(5^3)^2 &= 5^3 \cdot 5^3 \\
&= 5^6 \qquad \textit{Notice: } 3 \cdot 2 = 6
\end{aligned}
$$
▲

Generalizing this result we have a second property of exponents.

Property 2 for Exponents

If a is a real number and r and s are integers, then

$$(a^r)^s = a^{r \cdot s}$$

Answers

1a. -8 **b.** 49 **c.** -49 **d.** $\frac{27}{125}$

2. x^9 **3.** 4^{10}

A third property of exponents arises when we have the product of two or more numbers raised to an integer power. For example:

▼ Example 4 Expand $(3x)^4$ and then multiply.

Solution
$$\begin{aligned}(3x)^4 &= (3x)(3x)(3x)(3x)\\ &= (3 \cdot 3 \cdot 3 \cdot 3)(x \cdot x \cdot x \cdot x)\\ &= 3^4 \cdot x^4 \qquad \textit{Notice}: \text{The exponent 4 distributes}\\ &\qquad\qquad\qquad\qquad \text{over the product } 3x.\\ &= 81x^4\end{aligned}$$ ▲

4. Expand $(2x)^3$ and then multiply.

Generalizing Example 4 we have Property 3 for exponents.

Property 3 for Exponents

If a and b are any two real numbers, and r is an integer, then

$$(ab)^r = a^r \cdot b^r$$

Here are some examples that use combinations of the first three properties of exponents to simplify expressions involving exponents.

▼ Example 5 Simplify each expression using the properties of exponents.

5. Simplify each expression.

a. $\begin{aligned}(-3x^2)(5x^4) &= -3(5)(x^2 \cdot x^4) \quad &\text{Commutative, associative}\\ &\qquad\qquad\qquad\qquad &\text{properties}\\ &= -15x^6 \quad &\text{Property 1 for exponents}\end{aligned}$

a. $(-2x^3)(4x^5)$

b. $\begin{aligned}(-2x^2)^3(4x^5) &= (-2)^3(x^2)^3(4x^5) \quad &\text{Property 3}\\ &= -8x^6 \cdot (4x^5) \quad &\text{Property 2}\\ &= (-8 \cdot 4)(x^6 \cdot x^5) \quad &\text{Commutative and associative}\\ &= -32x^{11} \quad &\text{Property 1}\end{aligned}$

b. $(-3y^3)^3(2y^6)$

c. $\begin{aligned}(x^2)^4(x^2y^3)^2(y^4)^3 &= x^8 \cdot x^4 \cdot y^6 \cdot y^{12} \quad &\text{Properties 2 and 3}\\ &= x^{12}y^{18} \quad &\text{Property 1}\end{aligned}$ ▲

c. $(a^2)^3(a^3b^4)^2(b^5)^2$

The last property of exponents for this section deals with negative integer exponents.

Property 4 for Exponents

If a is any nonzero real number and r is a positive integer, then

$$a^{-r} = \frac{1}{a^r}$$

Note: This property is actually a definition. That is, we are defining negative integer exponents as indicating reciprocals. Doing so gives us a way to write an expression with a negative exponent as an equivalent expression with a positive exponent.

▼ Example 6 Write with positive exponents, then simplify.

6. Write with positive exponents, then simplify.

a. $5^{-2} = \dfrac{1}{5^2} = \dfrac{1}{25}$

a. 3^{-2}

b. $(-2)^{-3} = \dfrac{1}{(-2)^3} = \dfrac{1}{-8} = -\dfrac{1}{8}$

b. $(-5)^{-3}$

c. $\left(\dfrac{3}{4}\right)^{-2} = \dfrac{1}{\left(\frac{3}{4}\right)^2} = \dfrac{1}{\frac{9}{16}} = \dfrac{16}{9}$ ▲

c. $\left(\frac{2}{3}\right)^{-2}$

Answers
4. $8x^3$ **5a.** $-8x^8$ **b.** $-54y^{15}$
c. $a^{12}b^{18}$ **6a.** $\frac{1}{9}$ **b.** $-\frac{1}{125}$ **c.** $\frac{9}{4}$

The next example shows how we simplify expressions that contain both positive and negative exponents.

7. Simplify and write your answers with positive exponents.

a. $(3x^{-4})^2$

b. $(3y^{-3})^2(5y^4)$

▼ **Example 7**   Simplify and write your answers with positive exponents only. (Assume all variables are nonzero.)

a.

$$\begin{aligned}
(2x^{-3})^4 &= 2^4(x^{-3})^4 && \text{Property 3} \\
&= 16x^{-12} && \text{Property 2} \\
&= 16 \cdot \frac{1}{x^{12}} && \text{Property 4} \\
&= \frac{16}{x^{12}} && \text{Multiplication of fractions}
\end{aligned}$$

b.

$$\begin{aligned}
(5y^{-4})^2(2y^5) &= 25y^{-8}(2y^5) && \text{Properties 2 and 3} \\
&= (25 \cdot 2)(y^{-8}y^5) && \text{Commutative and associative} \\
&= 50y^{-3} && \text{Property 1} \\
&= 50 \cdot \frac{1}{y^3} && \text{Property 4} \\
&= \frac{50}{y^3} && \text{Multiplication of fractions} \quad ▲
\end{aligned}$$

Scientific Notation

The last topic we will cover in this section is scientific notation. Scientific notation is a way in which to write very large or very small numbers in a more manageable form. Here is the definition.

DEFINITION   A number is written in *scientific notation* if it is written as the product of a number between 1 and 10 with an integer power of 10. A number written in scientific notation has the form

$$n \times 10^r$$

where $1 \le n < 10$ and $r =$ an integer.

8. Write 27,400 in scientific notation.

▼ **Example 8**   Write 376,000 in scientific notation.

Solution   We must rewrite 376,000 as the product of a number between 1 and 10 and a power of 10. To do so we move the decimal point 5 places to the left so that it appears between the 3 and the 7. Then we multiply this number by 10^5. The number that results has the same value as our original number and is written in scientific notation.

$$376,000 = 3.76 \times 10^5$$

Moved 5 places

Decimal point originally here

Keeps track of the 5 places we moved the decimal point

▲

Answers

7a. $\dfrac{9}{x^8}$ **b.** $\dfrac{45}{y^2}$ **8.** 2.74×10^4

If a number written in expanded form is greater than or equal to 10, then when the number is written in scientific notation the exponent on 10 will be positive. A number that is less than 1 will have a negative exponent when written in scientific notation.

▼ **Example 9**   Write 4.52×10^3 in expanded form.

Solution   Since 10^3 is 1,000, we can think of this as simply a multiplication problem. That is

$$4.52 \times 10^3 = 4.52 \times 1,000 = 4,520$$

On the other hand, we can think of the exponent 3 as indicating the number of places we need to move the decimal point in order to write our number in expanded form. Since our exponent is positive 3, we move the decimal point three places to the right.

$$4.52 \times 10^3 = 4,520 \qquad \blacktriangle$$

The table that follows lists some additional examples of numbers written in expanded form and in scientific notation. In each case, note the relationship between the number of places the decimal point is moved and the exponent on 10.

Number Written in Expanded Form		Number Written Again in Scientific Notation
376,000	=	3.76×10^5
49,500	=	4.95×10^4
3,200	=	3.2×10^3
591	=	5.91×10^2
46	=	4.6×10^1
8	=	8×10^0
0.47	=	4.7×10^{-1}
0.093	=	9.3×10^{-2}
0.00688	=	6.88×10^{-3}
0.0002	=	2×10^{-4}
0.000098	=	9.8×10^{-5}

Calculator Note: Some scientific calculators have a key that allows you to enter numbers in scientific notation. The key is labeled

$$\boxed{\text{EXP}} \quad \text{or} \quad \boxed{\text{EE}} \quad \text{or} \quad \boxed{\text{SCI}}$$

To enter the number 3.45×10^6 you would first enter the decimal number, then press the scientific notation key, and finally, enter the exponent.

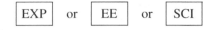

To enter 6.2×10^{-27} you would use the following sequence:

$$6.2 \quad \boxed{\text{EXP}} \quad 27 \quad \boxed{+/-}$$

---

9.   Write 3.91×10^4 in expanded form.

Note: Remember, the key labeled $\boxed{+/-}$ is the key used to change the sign of the number just entered.

Answer
9. 39,100

Problem Set 3.1

Evaluate each of the following.

1. 4^2 **2.** $(-4)^2$ **3.** -4^2 **4.** $-(-4)^2$

5. -3^3 **6.** $(-3)^3$ **7.** 2^5 **8.** 2^4

9. $(\frac{1}{2})^3$ **10.** $(\frac{3}{4})^2$ **11.** $(-\frac{5}{6})^2$ **12.** $(-\frac{7}{8})^2$

Use the properties of exponents to simplify each of the following as much as possible.

13. $x^5 \cdot x^4$ **14.** $x^6 \cdot x^3$ **15.** $(2^3)^2$ **16.** $(3^2)^2$

17. $(-2x^2)^3$ **18.** $(-3x^4)^3$ **19.** $-3a^2(2a^4)$ **20.** $5a^7(-4a^6)$

21. $6x^2(-3x^4)(2x^5)$ **22.** $(5x^3)(-7x^4)(-2x^6)$

23. $(-3n)^4(2n^3)^2(-n^6)^4$ **24.** $(5n^6)^2(-2n^3)^2(-3n^7)^2$

Write each of the following with positive exponents. Then simplify as much as possible.

25. 3^{-2} **26.** $(-5)^{-2}$ **27.** $(-2)^{-5}$ **28.** 2^{-5}

29. $(-3)^{-2}$ **30.** $(-7)^{-2}$ **31.** $(\frac{3}{4})^{-2}$ **32.** $(\frac{3}{5})^{-2}$

33. $(\frac{1}{3})^{-2} + (\frac{1}{2})^{-3}$ **34.** $(\frac{1}{2})^{-2} + (\frac{1}{3})^{-3}$

35. $(\frac{2}{3})^{-2} - (\frac{2}{5})^{-2}$ **36.** $(\frac{3}{2})^{-2} - (\frac{3}{4})^{-2}$

Name _____

Class _____

Date _____

Answers

1. _____ 2. _____

3. _____ 4. _____

5. _____ 6. _____

7. _____ 8. _____

9. _____ 10. _____

11. _____ 12. _____

13. _____ 14. _____

15. _____ 16. _____

17. _____ 18. _____

19. _____ 20. _____

21. _____ 22. _____

23. _____ 24. _____

25. _____ 26. _____

27. _____ 28. _____

29. _____ 30. _____

31. _____ 32. _____

33. _____ 34. _____

35. _____ 36. _____

Answers

37. _____ 38. _____

39. _____ 40. _____

41. _____ 42. _____

43. _____ 44. _____

45. _____ 46. _____

47. _____ 48. _____

49. _____ 50. _____

51. _____ 52. _____

53. _____ 54. _____

55. _____ 56. _____

57. _____ 58. _____

59. _____

60. _____

61. _____

62. _____

63. _____

64. _____

65. _____

66. _____

67. _____ 68. _____

69. _____ 70. _____

71. _____ 72. _____

73. _____ 74. _____

75. _____ 76. _____

77. _____ 78. _____

Simplify each expression. Write all answers with positive exponents only. (Assume all variables are nonzero.)

37. $x^{-4}x^7$ **38.** $x^{-3}x^8$ **39.** $(a^2b^{-5})^3$ **40.** $(a^4b^{-3})^3$

41. $(2x^{-3})^3(6x^4)$ **42.** $(4x^{-4})^3(2x^8)$ **43.** $(5y^4)^{-3}(2y^{-2})^3$

44. $(3y^5)^{-2}(2y^{-4})^3$ **45.** $x^{m+2} \cdot x^{-2m} \cdot x^{m-5}$ **46.** $x^{m-4} \cdot x^{m+9} \cdot x^{-2m}$

47. $(y^m)^2(y^{-3m})(y^{m+3})$ **48.** $(y^m)^{-4}(y^{3m})(y^{m-6})$

Write each number in scientific notation.

49. 378,000   **50.** 3,780,000

51. 4,900   **52.** 490

53. 0.00037   **54.** 0.000037

55. 0.00495   **56.** 0.0495

57. 0.562   **58.** 0.0562

Write each number in expanded form.

59. 5.34×10^3 **60.** 5.34×10^2

61. 7.8×10^6 **62.** 7.8×10^4

63. 3.44×10^{-3} **64.** 3.44×10^{-5}

65. 4.9×10^{-1} **66.** 4.9×10^{-2}

67. The statement $(a + b)^{-1} = a^{-1} + b^{-1}$ is false for all pairs of real numbers a and b. Show that it is false when $a = 2$ and $b = 4$.

68. Is the statement $(a + b)^2 = a^2 + b^2$ true in general? Try it with $a = 2$ and $b = 3$ and see.

69. The mass of the earth is approximately 5.98×10^{24} kilograms. If this number were written in expanded form, how many zeros would it contain?

70. The mass of a single hydrogen atom is approximately 1.67×10^{-27} kilograms. If this number were written in expanded form, how many digits would there be to the right of the decimal point?

Review Problems   The following problems review material we covered in Section 1.5.

Simplify each expression.

71. $6 - (-8)$ **72.** $-6 - (-8)$

73. $8 - (-6)$ **74.** $-8 - (-6)$

75. $-4 - (-3)$ **76.** $4 - (-3)$

77. $-4 - (-9)$ **78.** $4 - (-9)$

Section 3.2 Properties of Exponents II

We begin this section by stating two properties of exponents that show how exponents affect division. The first property shows that exponents distribute over quotients. This is Property 5 in our list of properties.

Property 5 for Exponents

If a and b are any two real numbers with $b \neq 0$, and r is an integer, then

$$\left(\frac{a}{b}\right)^r = \frac{a^r}{b^r}$$

PROOF OF PROPERTY 5

$$\left(\frac{a}{b}\right)^r = \underbrace{\left(\frac{a}{b}\right)\left(\frac{a}{b}\right)\left(\frac{a}{b}\right)\cdots\left(\frac{a}{b}\right)}_{r \text{ factors}}$$

$$= \frac{a \cdot a \cdot a \cdots a \leftarrow r \text{ factors}}{b \cdot b \cdot b \cdots b \leftarrow r \text{ factors}}$$

$$= \frac{a^r}{b^r}$$

Note: Although this is one of the few proofs we will show for the properties of exponents, we could prove all of them. The proofs are all similar. You may want to try to prove some of the other properties on your own.

Since we will be working with quotients in this section, let's assume all our variables represent nonzero numbers.

Practice Problems

▼ **Example 1** Simplify each expression and write all answers with positive exponents only.

a. $\left(\dfrac{x^2}{y^3}\right)^4 = \dfrac{(x^2)^4}{(y^3)^4}$ Property 5

$\qquad\qquad = \dfrac{x^8}{y^{12}}$ Property 2

b. $\left(\dfrac{2x^{-2}}{y^{-1}}\right)^3 = \dfrac{(2x^{-2})^3}{(y^{-1})^3}$ Property 5

$\qquad\qquad = \dfrac{8x^{-6}}{y^{-3}}$ Properties 2 and 3

$\qquad\qquad = \dfrac{\frac{8}{x^6}}{\frac{1}{y^3}}$ Definition of negative exponents (Property 4)

$\qquad\qquad = \dfrac{8}{x^6} \cdot \dfrac{y^3}{1}$ Division of fractions

$\qquad\qquad = \dfrac{8y^3}{x^6}$ ▲

1. Simplify each expression and write all answers with positive exponents only.

a. $\left(\dfrac{x^3}{y^4}\right)^5$

b. $\left(\dfrac{2x^{-3}}{y^{-2}}\right)^4$

We will now consider some examples of the quotient of two expressions involving exponents in which the bases are the same. Since multiplication with the same base resulted in addition of exponents, and since division is

Answers

1a. $\dfrac{x^{15}}{y^{20}}$ **b.** $\dfrac{16y^8}{x^{12}}$

to multiplication as subtraction is to addition, it seems reasonable to expect division with the same base to result in subtraction of exponents.

Let's begin with an example in which the exponent in the numerator is larger than the exponent in the denominator:

$$\frac{6^5}{6^3} = \frac{6 \cdot 6 \cdot 6 \cdot 6 \cdot 6}{6 \cdot 6 \cdot 6}$$

Note: This discussion is the justification for Property 6 of exponents. You may want to look ahead to Property 6 to see what it looks like, and then come back to this discussion.

Dividing out the 6's common to the numerator and denominator, we have

$$\frac{6^5}{6^3} = \frac{\not{6} \cdot \not{6} \cdot \not{6} \cdot 6 \cdot 6}{\not{6} \cdot \not{6} \cdot \not{6}}$$
$$= 6 \cdot 6$$
$$= 6^2 \quad \textit{Notice: } 5 - 3 = 2$$

If we were simply to subtract the exponent in the denominator from the exponent in the numerator, we would obtain the correct result, which is 6^2.

Let's consider an example where the exponent in the denominator is larger than the exponent in the numerator:

$$\frac{5^3}{5^7} = \frac{\not{5} \cdot \not{5} \cdot \not{5}}{\not{5} \cdot \not{5} \cdot \not{5} \cdot 5 \cdot 5 \cdot 5 \cdot 5}$$
$$= \frac{1}{5 \cdot 5 \cdot 5 \cdot 5}$$
$$= \frac{1}{5^4}$$
$$= 5^{-4} \quad \textit{Notice: } 3 - 7 = -4$$

Here again, simply subtracting the exponent in the denominator from the exponent in the numerator would give the correct result.

We summarize this discussion with Property 6 for exponents.

Property 6 for Exponents

If a is any nonzero real number, and r and s are any two integers, then

$$\frac{a^r}{a^s} = a^{r-s}$$

Notice again we have specified r and s to be any integers. Our definition of negative exponents is such that the properties of exponents hold for all integer exponents, whether positive integers or negative.

2. Apply Property 6 to each expression and then simplify. All answers should contain positive exponents only.

a. $\dfrac{3^7}{3^4}$

b. $\dfrac{x^3}{x^{10}}$

c. $\dfrac{a^5}{a^{-7}}$

d. $\dfrac{m^{-3}}{m^{-5}}$

Answers

2a. 27   **b.** $\dfrac{1}{x^7}$ **c.** a^{12} **d.** m^2

▼ **Example 2** Apply Property 6 to each expression and then simplify the result. All answers that contain exponents should contain positive exponents only.

a. $\dfrac{2^8}{2^3} = 2^{8-3} = 2^5 = 32$

b. $\dfrac{x^2}{x^{18}} = x^{2-18} = x^{-16} = \dfrac{1}{x^{16}}$

c. $\dfrac{a^6}{a^{-8}} = a^{6-(-8)} = a^{14}$

d. $\dfrac{m^{-5}}{m^{-7}} = m^{-5-(-7)} = m^2$

▲

In the next example we use more than one property of exponents to simplify an expression.

▼ **Example 3** Simplify $\left(\dfrac{x^{-3}}{x^5}\right)^{-2}$.

3. Simplify $\left(\dfrac{x^{-4}}{x^7}\right)^{-2}$.

Solution Let's begin by apply Property 6 to simplify inside the parentheses.

$$\left(\frac{x^{-3}}{x^5}\right)^{-2} = (x^{-3-5})^{-2} \qquad \text{Property 6}$$

$$= (x^{-8})^{-2}$$

$$= x^{16} \qquad \text{Property 2} \qquad \blacktriangle$$

Note: In Example 3, we could have obtained the same result by applying Property 5 first.

$$\left(\frac{x^{-3}}{x^5}\right)^{-2} = \frac{(x^{-3})^{-2}}{(x^5)^{-2}} \quad \text{Property 5}$$

$$= \frac{x^6}{x^{-10}} \qquad \text{Property 2}$$

$$= x^{6-(-10)} \quad \text{Property 6}$$

$$= x^{16}$$

Let's complete our list of properties by looking at how the numbers 0 and 1 behave when used as exponents.

We can use the original definition for exponents when the number 1 is used as an exponent.

$$a^1 = \underbrace{a}_{\text{1 factor}}$$

For 0 as an exponent, consider the expression $3^4/3^4$. Since $3^4 = 81$, we have

$$\frac{3^4}{3^4} = \frac{81}{81} = 1$$

On the other hand, since we have the quotient of two expressions with the same base, we can subtract exponents.

$$\frac{3^4}{3^4} = 3^{4-4} = 3^0$$

Hence, 3^0 must be the same as 1.

Summarizing these results, we have our last property for exponents.

Property 7 for Exponents

If a is any real number, then

$$\text{and} \quad \begin{array}{l} a^1 = a \\ a^0 = 1 \end{array} \quad \text{(as long as } a \neq 0\text{)}$$

▼ **Example 4** Simplify.

a. $(2x^2y^4)^0 = 1$
b. $(2x^2y^4)^1 = 2x^2y^4$ $\qquad \blacktriangle$

4. Simplify.

a. $(3xy^5)^0$
b. $(3xy^5)^1$

Answers
3. x^{22} **4a.** 1 **b.** $3xy^5$

Here are two examples that use many of the properties of exponents. There are a number of different ways to proceed on problems like these. You should use the method that works best for you.

5. Simplify.

a. $\dfrac{(3x^3)^2(-2x^{-5})^2}{9x^{-3}(4x^{-2})}$

b. $\left(\dfrac{3x^2y^0z^{-1}}{9x^4y^{-2}z^3}\right)^{-2}$

▼ **Example 5** Simplify.

a. $\dfrac{(2x^2)^4(-3x^{-2})^2}{4x^{-6}(9x^{-3})} = \dfrac{16x^8 \cdot 9x^{-4}}{4x^{-6} \cdot 9x^{-3}}$

$\qquad\qquad = \dfrac{144x^4}{36x^{-9}}$ Property 1

$\qquad\qquad = 4x^{13}$ Property 6

b. $\left(\dfrac{2x^0y^4z^{-3}}{8x^5y^{-3}z^{-2}}\right)^{-2} = \left(\dfrac{x^{-5} \cdot y^7 \cdot z^{-1}}{4}\right)^{-2}$ Property 6

$\qquad\qquad = \dfrac{x^{10}y^{-14}z^2}{4^{-2}}$ Properties 2 and 3

$\qquad\qquad = \dfrac{x^{10}\left(\dfrac{1}{y^{14}}\right)z^2}{\frac{1}{16}}$ Property 4

$\qquad\qquad = \dfrac{16x^{10}z^2}{y^{14}}$ ▲

We can use our properties of exponents to do arithmetic with numbers written in scientific notation. Here is an example.

6. Simplify and write all answers in scientific notation.

a. $(3 \times 10^7)(2 \times 10^{-4})$

b. $\dfrac{3.9 \times 10^6}{1.3 \times 10^{-4}}$

c. $\dfrac{(2.4 \times 10^6)(1.8 \times 10^{-4})}{1.2 \times 10^{-3}}$

▼ **Example 6** Simplify each expression and write all answers in scientific notation.

a. $(2 \times 10^8)(3 \times 10^{-3}) = (2)(3) \times (10^8)(10^{-3})$

$\qquad\qquad\qquad\qquad = 6 \times 10^5$

b. $\dfrac{4.8 \times 10^9}{2.4 \times 10^{-3}} = \dfrac{4.8}{2.4} \times \dfrac{10^9}{10^{-3}}$

$\qquad\qquad = 2 \times 10^{9-(-3)}$

$\qquad\qquad = 2 \times 10^{12}$

c. $\dfrac{(6.8 \times 10^5)(3.9 \times 10^{-7})}{7.8 \times 10^{-4}} = \dfrac{(6.8)(3.9)}{7.8} \times \dfrac{(10^5)(10^{-7})}{10^{-4}}$

$\qquad\qquad\qquad = 3.4 \times 10^2$ ▲

Calculator Note: If you have a scientific calculator with a scientific notation key, then the sequence of keys you would use to do part b of Example 6 would look like this.

Note: Remember, on some calculators the scientific notation key may be labeled

EE or SCI .

4.8   EXP   9   ÷   2.4   EXP   3   +/−   =

Problem Set 3.2

Use the properties of exponents to simplify each expression. All answers should contain positive exponents only. Assume all variables are nonzero.

1. $\left(\dfrac{x^3}{y^2}\right)^2$

2. $\left(\dfrac{x^5}{y^2}\right)^3$

3. $\left(\dfrac{2a^{-2}}{b^{-1}}\right)^2$

4. $\left(\dfrac{2a^{-3}}{b^{-2}}\right)^3$

5. $\dfrac{3^4}{3^6}$

6. $\dfrac{3^6}{3^4}$

7. $\dfrac{2^{-2}}{2^{-5}}$

8. $\dfrac{2^{-5}}{2^{-2}}$

9. $\dfrac{x^{-1}}{x^9}$

10. $\dfrac{x^{-3}}{x^5}$

11. $\dfrac{2a^{-5}}{a^{-6}}$

12. $\dfrac{a^{-3}}{3a^{-4}}$

13. $\dfrac{3^5 \cdot 3^2}{3^6 \cdot 3^5}$

14. $\dfrac{2^7 \cdot 2^3}{2^6 \cdot 2^8}$

15. $\left(\dfrac{x^{-2}}{x^4}\right)^{-1}$

16. $\left(\dfrac{x^3}{x^{-2}}\right)^{-2}$

17. $\dfrac{a^{-4}b^5}{a^{-3}b^{-2}}$

18. $\dfrac{a^5b^{-3}}{a^{-2}b^{-1}}$

Answers

19. _____   20. _____

21. _____   22. _____

23. _____   24. _____

25. _____   26. _____

27. _____   28. _____

29. _____   30. _____

31. _____   32. _____

33. _____   34. _____

35. _____   36. _____

19. $\left(\dfrac{x^{-5}y^2}{x^{-3}y^5}\right)^{-2}$

20. $\left(\dfrac{x^{-8}y^{-3}}{x^{-5}y^6}\right)^{-1}$

21. $\dfrac{12m^{-6}n^0}{3m^{-4}n^{-5}}$

22. $\dfrac{18m^8n^{-4}}{6m^0n^{-7}}$

23. $\dfrac{(2x^2)^3(3x^4)^{-1}}{8x^{-3}}$

24. $\dfrac{(3x)^4(2x^2)^{-3}}{9x^{-2}}$

25. $\left(\dfrac{2x^{-3}y^0}{4x^6y^{-5}}\right)^{-2}$

26. $\left(\dfrac{2x^6y^4z^0}{8x^{-3}y^0z^{-5}}\right)^{-1}$

27. $\left(\dfrac{ab^{-3}c^{-2}}{a^{-3}b^0c^{-5}}\right)^{-1}$

28. $\left(\dfrac{a^3b^2c^1}{a^{-1}b^{-2}c^{-3}}\right)^{-2}$

29. $\left(\dfrac{x^{-3}y^2}{x^4y^{-5}}\right)^{-2}\left(\dfrac{x^{-4}y}{x^0y^2}\right)$

30. $\left(\dfrac{x^{-1}y^4}{x^{-5}y^0}\right)^{-1}\left(\dfrac{x^3y^{-1}}{xy^{-3}}\right)$

31. $\dfrac{x^{n+2}}{x^{n-3}}$

32. $\dfrac{x^{n-3}}{x^{n-7}}$

33. $\dfrac{a^{3m}a^{m+1}}{a^{4m}}$

34. $\dfrac{a^{2m}a^{m-5}}{a^{3m-7}}$

35. $\dfrac{(y^r)^{-2}}{y^{-2r}}$

36. $\dfrac{(y^r)^2}{y^{2r-1}}$

Use the properties of exponents to simplify each of the following expressions. Write all answers in scientific notation.

37. $(4 \times 10^{10})(2 \times 10^{-6})$

38. $(3 \times 10^{-12})(3 \times 10^{4})$

39. $(4.5 \times 10^{6})(2 \times 10^{4})$

40. $(4.3 \times 10^{8})(2 \times 10^{5})$

41. $\dfrac{8 \times 10^{14}}{4 \times 10^{5}}$

42. $\dfrac{6 \times 10^{8}}{2 \times 10^{3}}$

43. $\dfrac{6.8 \times 10^{6}}{3.4 \times 10^{10}}$

44. $\dfrac{9.6 \times 10^{11}}{4.8 \times 10^{15}}$

45. $\dfrac{(5 \times 10^{6})(4 \times 10^{-8})}{8 \times 10^{4}}$

46. $\dfrac{(6 \times 10^{-7})(3 \times 10^{9})}{5 \times 10^{6}}$

47. $\dfrac{(2.4 \times 10^{-3})(3.6 \times 10^{-7})}{(4.8 \times 10^{6})(1 \times 10^{-9})}$

48. $\dfrac{(7.5 \times 10^{-6})(1.5 \times 10^{9})}{(1.8 \times 10^{4})(2.5 \times 10^{-2})}$

Convert each number to scientific notation and then simplify. Write all answers in scientific notation.

49. $(2,000,000)(0.0000249)$

50. $(30,000)(0.000192)$

51. $\dfrac{69,800}{0.000349}$

52. $\dfrac{0.000545}{1,090,000}$

53. $\dfrac{(40,000)(0.0007)}{0.0014}$

54. $\dfrac{(800,000)(0.00002)}{4,000}$

Name _____

Class _____

Date _____

Answers

37. _____
38. _____
39. _____
40. _____
41. _____
42. _____
43. _____
44. _____
45. _____
46. _____
47. _____
48. _____
49. _____
50. _____
51. _____
52. _____
53. _____
54. _____

Answers

55. _____

56. _____

57. _____   58. _____

59. _____   60. _____

61. _____   62. _____

63. _____

64. _____

65. _____   66. _____

67. _____   68. _____

69. _____   70. _____

71. _____   72. _____

55. Write the number 278×10^5 in scientific notation.

56. Write the number 278×10^{-5} in scientific notation.

For each expression that follows, find a value of x that makes it a true statement.

57. $4^3 \cdot 4^x = 4^9$

58. $(4^3)^x = 4^9$

59. $\dfrac{3^x}{3^5} = 3^4$

60. $\dfrac{3^x}{3^5} = 3^{-4}$

61. $2^x \cdot 2^3 = \dfrac{1}{16}$

62. $(2^x)^3 = \dfrac{1}{8}$

63. A light-year, the distance light travels in one year, is approximately 5.9×10^{12} miles. The Andromeda Galaxy is approximately 1.7×10^6 light-years from our galaxy. Find the distance in miles between our galaxy and the Andromeda Galaxy.

64. The distance from the earth to the sun is approximately 9.3×10^7 miles. If light travels 1.2×10^7 miles in one minute, how many minutes does it take the light from the sun to reach the earth?

Review Problems   The following problems review some of the material we covered in Section 1.6.

Simplify each expression.

65. $6 + 2(x + 3)$

66. $8 + 3(x + 4)$

67. $3(2a + 1) - 6a$

68. $5(3a + 3) - 8a$

69. $3(4y - 2) - (6y - 3)$

70. $2(5y - 6) - (3y + 4)$

71. $3 - 7(x - 5) + 3x$

72. $4 - 9(x - 3) + 5x$

Section 3.3 Polynomials, Sums, and Differences

We begin this section with the definition of a term around which polynomials are defined. Once we have listed all the terminology associated with polynomials, we will show how the distributive property is used to find sums and differences of polynomials.

Polynomials in General

DEFINITION   A *term* or *monomial* is a constant or the product of a constant and one or more variables raised to whole-number exponents.

The following are monomials or terms:

$$-16, \qquad 3x^2y, \qquad -\tfrac{2}{5}a^3b^2c, \qquad xy^2z$$

The numerical part of each monomial is called the *numerical coefficient,* or just *coefficient* for short. For the preceding terms the coefficients are -16, 3, $-\tfrac{2}{5}$, and 1. Notice that the coefficient for xy^2z is understood to be 1.

DEFINITION   A *polynomial* is any finite sum of terms. Since subtraction can be written in terms of addition, finite differences are also included in this definition.

The following are polynomials:

$$2x^2 - 6x + 3, \qquad -5x^2y + 2xy^2, \qquad 4a - 5b + 6c + 7d$$

Polynomials can be classified further according to the number of terms present. If a polynomial consists of two terms, it is said to be a *binomial*. If it has three terms, it is called a *trinomial*. And as stated above, a polynomial with only one term is said to be a *monomial*.

DEFINITION   The *degree* of a polynomial with one variable is the highest power to which the variable is raised in any one term.

▼ **Example 1**

a. $6x^2 + 2x - 1$ A trinomial of degree 2
b. $5x - 3$ A binomial of degree 1
c. $7x^6 - 5x^3 + 2x - 4$ A polynomial of degree 6
d. $-7x^4$ A monomial of degree 4
e. 15 A monomial of degree 0   ▲

Polynomials in one variable are usually written in decreasing powers of the variable. When this is the case, the coefficient of the first term is called the *leading coefficient*. In part a of Example 1 above, the leading coefficient is 6. In part b it is 5. The leading coefficient in part c is 7.

Practice Problems

1. Identify each expression as a monomial, binomial, or trinomial, and give the degree of each.
a. $3x + 1$
b. $4x^2 + 2x + 5$
c. -17
d. $4x^5 - 7x^3$

Answers
1a. Binomial, 1 **b.** Trinomial, 2
c. Monomial, 0 **d.** Binomial, 5

Addition and Subtraction of Polynomials

Combining polynomials to find sums and differences is a very simple process. For the most part it involves applying the distributive property to combine similar terms.

DEFINITION   Two or more terms that differ only in the numerical coefficients are called *similar* or *like* terms. Since similar terms differ only in their coefficients, they have identical variable parts—that is, the same variables raised to the same power. For example, $3x^2$ and $-5x^2$ are similar terms. So are $15x^2y^3z$, $-27x^2y^3z$ and $\frac{3}{4}x^2y^3z$.

We can use the distributive property to combine the similar terms $6x^2$ and $9x^2$ as follows:

$$6x^2 + 9x^2 = (6 + 9)x^2 \qquad \text{Distributive property}$$
$$= 15x^2 \qquad \text{The sum of 6 and 9 is 15}$$

The distributive property can also be used to combine more than two like terms.

2. Combine similar terms:

$$8a^2b + 6a^2b - 4a^2b$$

▼ **Example 2**   Combine $7x^2y + 4x^2y - 10x^2y + 2x^2y$.

Solution

$$7x^2y + 4x^2y - 10x^2y + 2x^2y = (7 + 4 - 10 + 2)x^2y \qquad \text{Distributive property}$$
$$= 3x^2y \qquad \text{Addition} \;\blacktriangle$$

To add two polynomials, we simply apply the commutative and associative properties to group similar terms together and then use the distributive property as we have in the preceding example.

3. Add $3x^2 + 2x - 5$ and $2x^2 - 7x + 3$.

▼ **Example 3**   Add $5x^2 - 4x + 2$ and $3x^2 + 9x - 6$.

Solution

$$(5x^2 - 4x + 2) + (3x^2 + 9x - 6)$$
$$= (5x^2 + 3x^2) + (-4x + 9x) + (2 - 6) \qquad \text{Commutative and associative properties}$$
$$= (5 + 3)x^2 + (-4 + 9)x + (2 - 6) \qquad \text{Distributive property}$$
$$= 8x^2 + 5x + (-4)$$
$$= 8x^2 + 5x - 4 \qquad\qquad\qquad \blacktriangle$$

Note: In actual practice it is not necessary to show all the steps shown in Example 3. It is important to understand that addition of polynomials is equivalent to combining similar terms.

4. Find the sum of $x^3 + 7x^2 + 3x + 2$ and $-3x^3 - 2x^2 + 3x - 1$.

▼ **Example 4**   Find the sum of $-8x^3 + 7x^2 - 6x + 5$ and $10x^3 + 3x^2 - 2x - 6$.

Solution   We can add the two polynomials using the method of Example 3, or we can arrange similar terms in columns and add vertically. Using the column method, we have

$$
\begin{array}{r}
-8x^3 + 7x^2 - 6x + 5 \\
10x^3 + 3x^2 - 2x - 6 \\
\hline
2x^3 + 10x^2 - 8x - 1
\end{array}
$$

$\blacktriangle$

Answers
2. $10a^2b$ **3.** $5x^2 - 5x - 2$
4. $-2x^3 + 5x^2 + 6x + 1$

It is important to notice that no matter which method is used to combine two polynomials, the variable part of the combined terms never changes. It is sometimes tempting to say $7x^2 + 3x^2 = 10x^4$, which is incorrect. Remember, we combine similar terms by using the distributive property: $7x^2 + 3x^2 = (7 + 3)x^2 = 10x^2$. The variable part common to each term is unchanged.

To find the difference of two polynomials, we need to use the fact that the opposite of a sum is the sum of the opposites. That is,

$$-(a + b) = -a + (-b)$$

One way to remember this is to observe that $-(a + b)$ is equivalent to $-1(a + b) = (-1)a + (-1)b = -a + (-b)$.

If there is a negative sign directly preceding the parentheses surrounding a polynomial, we may remove the parentheses and preceding negative sign by changing the sign of each term within the parentheses.

For example:

$$-(3x + 4) = -3x + (-4) = -3x - 4$$
$$-(5x^2 - 6x + 9) = -5x^2 + 6x - 9$$
$$-(-x^2 + 7x - 3) = x^2 - 7x + 3$$

To find the difference of two or more polynomials, we simply apply this principle and proceed as we did when finding sums.

▼ **Example 5**   Subtract: $(9x^2 - 3x + 5) - (4x^2 + 2x - 3)$.

Solution   First we write the problem in terms of subtraction. Then we subtract by adding the opposite of each term in the polynomial that follows the subtraction sign.

$(9x^2 - 3x + 5) - (4x^2 + 2x - 3)$
$= 9x^2 - 3x + 5 + (-4x^2) + (-2x) + 3$ The opposite of a sum is the sum of the opposites

$= (9x^2 - 4x^2) + (-3x - 2x) + (5 + 3)$ Commutative and associative properties

$= 5x^2 - 5x + 8$ Combine similar terms   ▲

▼ **Example 6**   Subtract $4x^2 - 9x + 1$ from $-3x^2 + 5x - 2$.

Solution   Again, to subtract, we add the opposite.

$(-3x^2 + 5x - 2) - (4x^2 - 9x + 1)$
$= -3x^2 + 5x - 2 - 4x^2 + 9x - 1$
$= (-3x^2 - 4x^2) + (5x + 9x) + (-2 - 1)$
$= -7x^2 + 14x - 3$ ▲

5. Subtract:

$(4x^2 - 2x + 7) - (7x^2 - 3x + 1)$

6. Subtract $3x + 5$ from $7x - 4$.

Answers
5. $-3x^2 + x + 6$ **6.** $4x - 9$

Here is another example involving subtraction. Notice that each time we remove parentheses that are preceded by a subtraction sign, we change the sign of each term contained within the parentheses.

7. Simplify as much as possible:

$(3x^4 + 2x + 1) - (3x^2 - 5)$
$- (2x^3 - 4x^2 + 2x)$

▼ **Example 7** Simplify as much as possible:

$$(2x^3 + 5x^2 + 3) - (4x^2 - 2x - 7) - (6x^3 - 3x + 1)$$

Solution We begin by removing all parentheses. When we do so, we must remember to change the sign of each term that is contained within parentheses that are preceded by a negative (or subtraction) sign.

$$(2x^3 + 5x^2 + 3) - (4x^2 - 2x - 7) - (6x^3 - 3x + 1)$$
$$= 2x^3 + 5x^2 + 3 - 4x^2 + 2x + 7 - 6x^3 + 3x - 1$$
$$= (2x^3 - 6x^3) + (5x^2 - 4x^2) + (2x + 3x) + (3 + 7 - 1)$$
$$= -4x^3 + x^2 + 5x + 9 \qquad ▲$$

When one set of grouping symbols is contained within another, it is best to begin the process of simplification within the innermost grouping symbol and work out from there.

8. Simplify $2x - 4[6 - (5x + 3)]$.

▼ **Example 8** Simplify $4x - 3[2 - (3x + 4)]$.

Solution Removing the innermost parentheses first, we have

$$4x - 3[2 - (3x + 4)] = 4x - 3(2 - 3x - 4)$$
$$= 4x - 3(-3x - 2)$$
$$= 4x + 9x + 6$$
$$= 13x + 6 \qquad ▲$$

9. Simplify:

$(9x - 4) - [(2x + 5) - (x + 3)]$

▼ **Example 9** Simplify $(2x + 3) - [(3x + 1) - (x - 7)]$.

Solution

$$(2x + 3) - [(3x + 1) - (x - 7)] = (2x + 3) - (3x + 1 - x + 7)$$
$$= (2x + 3) - (2x + 8)$$
$$= 2x + 3 - 2x - 8$$
$$= -5 \qquad ▲$$

In the example that follows we will find the value of a polynomial for a given value of the variable.

10. Find the value of
$2x^3 - 3x^2 + 4x - 8$ when x is -2.

▼ **Example 10** Find the value of $5x^3 - 3x^2 + 4x - 5$ when x is 2.

Solution We begin by substituting 2 for x in the original polynomial.

$$\begin{array}{lc} \text{When} & x = 2 \\ \text{the polynomial} & 5x^3 - 3x^2 + 4x - 5 \\ \text{becomes} & 5 \cdot 2^3 - 3 \cdot 2^2 + 4 \cdot 2 - 5 \end{array}$$

When we simplify a numerical term that contains an exponent, like $5 \cdot 2^3$, we evaluate the power first, and then multiply: $5 \cdot 2^3 = 5 \cdot 8 = 40$.

$$5 \cdot 2^3 - 3 \cdot 2^2 + 4 \cdot 2 - 5 = 5 \cdot 8 - 3 \cdot 4 + 4 \cdot 2 - 5$$
$$= 40 - 12 + 8 - 5$$
$$= 31 \qquad ▲$$

Answers
7. $3x^4 - 2x^3 + x^2 + 6$ **8.** $22x - 12$
9. $8x - 6$ **10.** -44

Problem Set 3.3

Identify those of the following that are monomials, binomials, or trinomials. Give the degree of each and name the leading coefficient.

1. $5x^2 - 3x + 2$

2. $2x^2 + 4x - 1$

3. $3x - 5$

4. $5y + 3$

5. $8a^2 + 3a - 5$

6. $9a^2 - 8a - 4$

7. $4x^3 - 6x^2 + 5x - 3$

8. $9x^4 + 4x^3 - 2x^2 + x$

9. $-\frac{3}{4}$

10. -16

11. $4x - 5 + 6x^3$

12. $9x + 2 + 3x^3$

Simplify each of the following by combining similar terms.

13. $(4x + 2) + (3x - 1)$

14. $(8x - 5) + (-5x + 4)$

15. $2x^2 - 3x + 10x - 15$

16. $6x^2 - 4x - 15x + 10$

17. $12a^2 + 8ab - 15ab - 10b^2$

18. $28a^2 - 8ab + 7ab - 2b^2$

19. $(5x^2 - 6x + 1) - (4x^2 + 7x - 2)$

20. $(11x^2 - 8x) - (4x^2 - 2x - 7)$

Name _____

Class _____

Date _____

Answers

1. _____
2. _____
3. _____
4. _____
5. _____
6. _____
7. _____
8. _____
9. _____
10. _____
11. _____
12. _____
13. _____
14. _____
15. _____
16. _____
17. _____
18. _____
19. _____
20. _____

Answers

21. _____

22. _____

23. _____

24. _____

25. _____

26. _____

27. _____

28. _____

29. _____

30. _____

31. _____

32. _____

33. _____

34. _____

35. _____

36. _____

37. _____

38. _____

21. $(6x^2 - 4x - 2) - (3x^2 + 7x) + (4x - 1)$

22. $(8x^2 - 6x) - (3x^2 + 2x + 1) - (6x^2 + 3)$

23. $(y^3 - 2y^2 - 3y + 4) - (2y^3 - y^2 + y - 3)$

24. $(8y^3 - 3y^2 + 7y + 2) - (-4y^3 + 6y^2 - 5y - 8)$

25. $(5x^3 - 4x^2) - (3x + 4) + (5x^2 - 7) - (3x^3 + 6)$

26. $(x^3 - x) - (x^2 + x) + (x^3 - 1) - (-3x + 2)$

27. $(8x^2 - 2xy + y^2) - (7x^2 - 4xy - 9y^2)$

28. $(2x^2 - 5xy + y^2) + (-3x^2 + 4xy - 5)$

29. $(3a^3 + 2a^2b + ab^2 - b^3) - (6a^3 - 4a^2b + 6ab^2 - b^3)$

30. $(a^3 - 3a^2b + 3ab^2 - b^3) - (a^3 + 3a^2b + 3ab^2 + b^3)$

31. Subtract $2x^2 - 4x$ from $2x^2 - 7x$.

32. Subtract $-3x + 6$ from $-3x + 9$.

33. Find the sum of $x^2 - 6xy + y^2$ and $2x^2 - 6xy - y^2$.

34. Find the sum of $9x^3 - 6x^2 + 2$ and $3x^2 - 5x + 4$.

35. Subtract $-8x^5 - 4x^3 + 6$ from $9x^5 - 4x^3 - 6$.

36. Subtract $4x^4 - 3x^3 - 2x^2$ from $2x^4 + 3x^3 + 4x^2$.

37. Find the sum of $11a^2 + 3ab + 2b^2$, $9a^2 - 2ab + b^2$, and $-6a^2 - 3ab + 5b^2$.

38. Find the sum of $a^2 - ab - b^2$, $a^2 + ab - b^2$, and $a^2 + 2ab + b^2$.

Simplify each of the following. Begin by working on the innermost parentheses first.

39. $-[2 - (4 - x)]$

40. $-[-3 - (x - 6)]$

41. $-5[-(x - 3) - (x + 2)]$

42. $-6[(2x - 5) - 3(8x - 2)]$

43. $4x - 5[3 - (x - 4)]$

44. $x - 7[3x - (2 - x)]$

45. $-(3x - 4y) - [(4x + 2y) - (3x + 7y)]$

46. $(8x - y) - [-(2x + y) - (-3x - 6y)]$

47. $4a - \{3a + 2[a - 5(a + 1) + 4]\}$

48. $6a - \{-2a - 6[2a + 3(a - 1) - 6]\}$

49. Find the value of $2x^2 - 3x - 4$ when x is 2.

50. Find the value of $4x^2 + 3x - 2$ when x is -1.

51. Find the value of $x^2 - 6x + 5$ when x is 0.

52. Find the value of $4x^2 - 4x + 4$ when x is 0.

53. Find the value of $x^3 - x^2 + x - 1$ when x is -2.

54. Find the value of $x^3 + x^2 + x + 1$ when x is -2.

Name _____

Class _____

Date _____

Answers

39. _____

40. _____

41. _____

42. _____

43. _____

44. _____

45. _____

46. _____

47. _____

48. _____

49. _____

50. _____

51. _____

52. _____

53. _____

54. _____

Answers

55. _____

56. _____

57. _____

58. _____

59. _____

60. _____

61. _____ 62. _____

63. _____ 64. _____

65. _____ 66. _____

67. _____ 68. _____

55. Let $a = 3$ in each of the following expressions and then simplify each one.

$$(a + 4)^2 \qquad a^2 + 16 \qquad a^2 + 8a + 16$$

56. Let $a = 2$ in each of the following expressions and then simplify each one.

$$(2a - 3)^2 \qquad 4a^2 - 9 \qquad 4a^2 - 12a + 9$$

57. If an object is thrown straight up into the air with a velocity of 128 feet/second, then its height h above the ground t seconds later is given by the formula

$$h = -16t^2 + 128t.$$

Find the height after 3 seconds, and after 5 seconds.

58. The formula for the height of an object that has been thrown straight up with a velocity of 64 feet/second is

$$h = -16t^2 + 64t.$$

Find the height after 1 second and after 3 seconds.

59. There is a surprising relationship between the set of odd whole numbers $\{1, 3, 5, 7, 9, \ldots\}$ and the set of whole number squares $\{1, 4, 9, 16, 25, \ldots\}$. To see this relationship, add the first two odd numbers, then the first three odd numbers, and then the first four odd numbers. See if you can write this relationship in words.

60. If x is a positive integer, then the formula

$$S = \frac{x^2 + x}{2}$$

gives the sum S of all the integers from 1 to x. Use this formula to find the sum of the first 10 positive integers.

Review Problems   The following problems review material we covered in Section 3.1. Reviewing these problems will help you with the next section.

Simplify each expression.

61. $4x^3(5x^2)$

62. $4x^3(-3x)$

63. $2a^2b(ab^2)$

64. $2a^2b(-6a^2b)$

65. $2x(3x^2)$

66. $-3y(4y^2)$

67. $2x(-xy)$

68. $-3y(-xy)$

Section 3.4   Multiplication of Polynomials

The distributive property is the key to multiplying polynomials. The simplest type of multiplication occurs when we multiply a polynomial by a monomial.

▼ **Example 1**   Find the product of $4x^3$ and $5x^2 - 3x + 1$.

Solution

$$4x^3(5x^2 - 3x + 1)$$
$$= 4x^3(5x^2) + 4x^3(-3x) + 4x^3(1) \qquad \text{Distributive property}$$
$$= 20x^5 - 12x^4 + 4x^3$$

Notice we multiply coefficients and add exponents.   ▲

The distributive property can also be applied to multiply a polynomial by a polynomial. Let's consider the case where both polynomials have two terms.

▼ **Example 2**   Multiply $2x - 3$ and $x + 5$.

Solution

$$(2x - 3)(x + 5)$$
$$= (2x - 3)x + (2x - 3)5 \qquad \text{Distributive property}$$
$$= 2x(x) + (-3)x + 2x(5) + (-3)5 \qquad \text{Distributive property}$$
$$= 2x^2 - 3x + 10x - 15$$
$$= 2x^2 + 7x - 15 \qquad \text{Combine like terms}$$

Notice the third line in this example. It consists of all possible products of terms in the first binomial and those of the second binomial. We can generalize this into a rule for multiplying two polynomials.   ▲

Rule   To multiply two polynomials, multiply each term in the first polynomial by each term in the second polynomial.

Multiplying polynomials can be accomplished by a method that looks very similar to long multiplication with whole numbers. We line up the polynomials vertically and then apply our rule for multiplication of polynomials. Here's how it looks using the same two binomials used in the last example:

$$
\begin{array}{r}
2x - 3 \\
x + 5 \\
\hline
10x - 15 \\
2x^2 - 3x \phantom{{}- 15} \\
\hline
2x^2 + 7x - 15
\end{array}
$$

Multiply $+5$ times $2x - 3$
Multiply x times $2x - 3$
Add in columns

Practice Problems

1.   Multiply: $5x^2(3x^2 - 4x + 2)$.

2.   Multiply $4x - 1$ and $x + 3$.

Note: The vertical method of multiplying polynomials does not directly show the use of the distributive property. It is, however, very useful since it always gives the correct result and is easy to remember.

Answers
1. $15x^4 - 20x^3 + 10x^2$
2. $4x^2 + 11x - 3$

3. Multiply using the vertical method:

$$(3x + 2)(x^2 - 5x + 6)$$

▼ **Example 3** Multiply $(2x - 3y)$ and $(3x^2 - xy + 4y^2)$ vertically.

Solution

$$
\begin{array}{r}
3x^2 - xy + 4y^2 \\
2x - 3y \\
\hline
-9x^2y + 3xy^2 - 12y^3 \\
6x^3 - 2x^2y + 8xy^2 \\
\hline
6x^3 - 11x^2y + 11xy^2 - 12y^3
\end{array}
$$

Multiply $(3x^2 - xy + 4y^2)$ by $-3y$
Multiply $(3x^2 - xy + 4y^2)$ by $2x$
Add similar terms ▲

The product of two binomials occurs very frequently in algebra. Since this type of product is so common, we have a special method of multiplication that applies only to products of binomials.

Consider the product of $(2x - 5)$ and $(3x - 2)$. Distributing $(3x - 2)$ over $2x$ and -5 we have

$$
\begin{aligned}
(2x - 5)(3x - 2) &= (2x)(3x - 2) + (-5)(3x - 2) \\
&= (2x)(3x) + (2x)(-2) + (-5)(3x) + (-5)(-2) \\
&= 6x^2 - 4x - 15x + 10 \\
&= 6x^2 - 19x + 10
\end{aligned}
$$

Looking closely at the second and third lines we notice the following relationships:

Note: This method is called the FOIL Method—*F*irst-*O*utside-*I*nside-*L*ast. The FOIL method does not show the properties used in multiplying two binomials. It is simply a way of finding products of binomials quickly. Remember, the FOIL method only applies to products of two binomials. The vertical method applies to all products of polynomials with two or more terms.

1. $6x^2$ comes from multiplying the *first* terms in each binomial:

$$(2x - 5)(3x - 2) \qquad 2x(3x) = 6x^2 \qquad \text{First terms}$$

2. $-4x$ comes from multiplying the *outside* terms in the product:

$$(2x - 5)(3x - 2) \qquad 2x(-2) = -4x \qquad \text{Outside terms}$$

3. $-15x$ comes from multiplying the *inside* terms in the product:

$$(2x - 5)(3x - 2) \qquad -5(3x) = -15x \qquad \text{Inside terms}$$

4. 10 comes from multiplying the *last* two terms in the product:

$$(2x - 5)(3x - 2) \qquad -5(-2) = 10 \qquad \text{Last terms}$$

Once we know where the terms in the answer come from, we can reduce the number of steps used in finding the product:

$$
\begin{aligned}
(2x - 5)(3x - 2) = \underset{\text{First}}{6x^2} \quad - \quad \underset{\text{Outside}}{4x} \quad - \quad \underset{\text{Inside}}{15x} \quad + \quad \underset{\text{Last}}{10} \\
= 6x^2 - 19x + 10
\end{aligned}
$$

4. Multiply using the FOIL method:

$$(2a - 3b)(5a - b)$$

▼ **Example 4** Multiply: $(4a - 5b)(3a + 2b)$.

Solution Applying the FOIL method we have

$$
\begin{aligned}
(4a - 5b)(3a + 2b) &= \underset{F}{12a^2} + \underset{O}{8ab} - \underset{I}{15ab} - \underset{L}{10b^2} \\
&= 12a^2 - 7ab - 10b^2
\end{aligned}
$$
▲

Answers
3. $3x^3 - 13x^2 + 8x + 12$
4. $10a^2 - 17ab + 3b^2$

Problem Set 3.4

Name _____

Class _____

Date _____

Multiply the following by applying the distributive property.

1. $2x(6x^2 - 5x + 4)$

2. $-3x(5x^2 - 6x - 4)$

3. $-3a^2(a^3 - 6a^2 + 7)$

4. $4a^3(3a^2 - a + 1)$

5. $2a^2b(a^3 - ab + b^3)$

6. $-5a^2b^2(8a^2 - 2ab + b^2)$

Multiply the following vertically.

7. $(x - 5)(x + 3)$

8. $(x + 4)(x + 6)$

9. $(2x - 3)(3x - 5)$

10. $(3x + 4)(2x - 5)$

Answers

1. _____

2. _____

3. _____

4. _____

5. _____

6. _____

7. _____

8. _____

9. _____

10. _____

Answers

11. _____

12. _____

13. _____

14. _____

15. _____

16. _____

17. _____

18. _____

19. _____

20. _____

11. $(x + 3)(x^2 + 6x + 5)$

12. $(x - 2)(x^2 - 5x + 7)$

13. $(a - b)(a^2 + ab + b^2)$

14. $(a + b)(a^2 - ab + b^2)$

15. $(2x + y)(4x^2 - 2xy + y^2)$

16. $(x - 3y)(x^2 + 3xy + 9y^2)$

17. $(2a - 3b)(a^2 + ab + b^2)$

18. $(5a - 2b)(a^2 - ab - b^2)$

19. $2x^2(x - 5)(3x - 7)$

20. $-5x^3(3x - 2)(x + 4)$

Multiply the following using the FOIL method.

21. $(x - 2)(x + 3)$

22. $(x + 2)(x - 3)$

23. $(x - 2)(x - 3)$

24. $(x + 2)(x + 3)$

25. $(2a + 3)(3a + 2)$

26. $(5a - 4)(2a + 1)$

27. $(3x - 5)(2x + 4)$

28. $(x - 7)(3x + 6)$

29. $(5x - 4)(x - 5)$

30. $(7x - 5)(3x + 1)$

31. $(4a + 1)(5a + 1)$

32. $(3a - 1)(2a - 1)$

33. $(5x - 6y)(4x + 3y)$

34. $(6x - 5y)(2x - 3y)$

35. $(2x - 3y)(4x - 5y)$

36. $(6x - 2y)(3x + y)$

Name _____

Class _____

Date _____

Answers

21. _____

22. _____

23. _____

24. _____

25. _____

26. _____

27. _____

28. _____

29. _____

30. _____

31. _____

32. _____

33. _____

34. _____

35. _____

36. _____

Answers

37. _____

38. _____

39. _____

40. _____

41. _____

42. _____

43. _____

44. _____

45. _____

46. _____

47. _____

48. _____

49. _____

50. _____

51. _____

52. _____

53. _____   54. _____

55. _____   56. _____

37. $(4a + b)(7a - 2b)$

38. $(3a - 4b)(6a + b)$

39. $(x^2 + 1)(x^2 + 2)$

40. $(x^2 - 3)(x^2 + 1)$

41. $(x^2 + 2)(x^2 - 5)$

42. $(x^2 - 3)(x^2 + 7)$

43. $(x + a)(x + b)$

44. $(x - a)(x - b)$

45. $(x + 5)(x - 5)$

46. $(x + 7)(x - 7)$

47. $(2x + 3y)(2x - 3y)$

48. $(3x + 2y)(3x - 2y)$

49. $(x^2 + 3)(x^2 - 3)$

50. $(x^2 + 4)(x^2 - 4)$

51. Let $a = 2$ and $b = 3$ and evaluate each of the following expressions.

$$(a + b)^2 \qquad a^2 + 2ab + b^2 \qquad a^2 + b^2$$

52. Let $x = 5$ in each of the following expressions and then simplify.

$$(x - 10)^2 \qquad x^2 - 20x + 100 \qquad x^2 - 100$$

Review Problems   The following problems review material we covered in Section 2.2.

Solve each equation.

53. $7x - 4 = 3x + 12$

54. $9x - 10 = 3x + 8$

55. $5 - 2(3a + 1) = -7$

56. $7 - 2(4a - 3) = -11$

Section 3.5 Special Products

● We begin this section by using the FOIL method to find the square of a binomial.

Practice Problems

▼ **Example 1** Find $(4x - 6)^2$.

1. Expand and multiply: $(3x - 2)^2$.

Solution Applying the definition of exponents and then the FOIL method we have

$$
\begin{aligned}
(4x - 6)^2 &= (4x - 6)(4x - 6) \\
&= 16x^2 - 24x - 24x + 36 \\
&\qquad\ \ \text{F}\qquad\ \ \text{O}\qquad\ \ \text{I}\qquad\ \ \text{L} \\
&= 16x^2 - 48x + 36 \qquad\qquad ▲
\end{aligned}
$$

This example is the square of a binomial. This type of product occurs frequently enough in algebra that we have a special formula for it.

Here are the formulas for binomial squares:

$$(a + b)^2 = (a + b)(a + b) = a^2 + ab + ab + b^2 = a^2 + 2ab + b^2$$

$$(a - b)^2 = (a - b)(a - b) = a^2 - ab - ab + b^2 = a^2 - 2ab + b^2$$

Observing the results in both cases we have the following rule.

Rule The square of a binomial is the sum of the square of the first term, twice the product of the two terms, and the square of the last term. Or:

$$
(a + b)^2 = \quad a^2 \quad + \quad 2ab \quad + \quad b^2
$$

	Square of first term	Twice the product of the two terms	Square of last term

$$
(a - b)^2 = \quad a^2 \quad - \quad 2ab \quad + \quad b^2
$$

Note: From the rule and examples that follow it should be obvious that $(a + b)^2 \neq a^2 + b^2$. That is, the square of a sum is not the same as the sum of the squares.

▼ **Example 2** Use the preceding formulas to expand each binomial square.

2. Expand and simplify.

a. $(x + y)^2 = x^2 + 2xy + y^2 = x^2 + 2xy + y^2$

a. $(x - y)^2$

b. $(x + 7)^2 = x^2 + 2(x)(7) + 7^2 = x^2 + 14x + 49$

b. $(x + 5)^2$

c. $(3x - 5)^2 = (3x)^2 + 2(3x)(-5) + (-5)^2 = 9x^2 - 30x + 25$

c. $(2x + 5)^2$

d. $(4x - 2y)^2 = (4x)^2 + 2(4x)(-2y) + (-2y)^2 = 16x^2 - 16xy + 4y^2$

d. $(3x - 4y)^2$

First term squared	Twice their product	Last term squared	Answer

▲

● Another frequently occurring kind of product is found when multiplying two binomials that differ only in the sign between their terms.

Answers
1. $9x^2 - 12x + 4$ **2a.** $x^2 - 2xy + y^2$
b. $x^2 + 10x + 25$
c. $4x^2 + 20x + 25$
d. $9x^2 - 24xy + 16y^2$ **3.** $16x^2 - 9$

3. Multiply $(4x - 3)$ and $(4x + 3)$.

▼ **Example 3** Multiply $(3x - 5)$ and $(3x + 5)$.

Solution Applying the FOIL method we have

$$(3x - 5)(3x + 5) = 9x^2 + 15x - 15x - 25 \quad \text{Two middle terms}$$
$$ \text{F} \quad\quad \text{O} \quad\quad \text{I} \quad\quad \text{L} \quad\quad \text{add to } 0$$
$$= 9x^2 - 25 \quad\quad\quad\quad\quad ▲$$

The outside and inside products in Example 3 are opposites and therefore add to 0.

Here it is in general:

$$(a - b)(a + b) = a^2 + ab - ab + b^2 \quad \text{Two middle terms}$$
$$ \text{add to } 0$$
$$= a^2 - b^2$$

Rule To multiply two binomials that differ only in the sign between their two terms, simply subtract the square of the second term from the square of the first term:

$$(a - b)(a + b) = a^2 - b^2$$

The expression $a^2 - b^2$ is called the *difference of two squares*.

Once we memorize and understand this rule, we can multiply binomials of this form with a minimum of work.

4. Multiply.

a. $(x + 2)(x - 2)$

b. $(3a + 1)(3a - 1)$

c. $(x^2 + 3)(x^2 - 3)$

d. $(5x + 7y)(5x - 7y)$

e. $(x^3 - 4a)(x^3 + 4a)$

▼ **Example 4** Find the following products.

a. $(x - 5)(x + 5) = x^2 - 25$

b. $(2a - 3)(2a + 3) = 4a^2 - 9$

c. $(x^2 + 4)(x^2 - 4) = x^4 - 16$

d. $(3x + 7y)(3x - 7y) = 9x^2 - 49y^2$

e. $(x^3 - 2a)(x^3 + 2a) = x^6 - 4a^2 \quad\quad ▲$

Answers
3. $16x^2 - 9$ **4a.** $x^2 - 4$ **b.** $9a^2 - 1$
c. $x^4 - 9$ **d.** $25x^2 - 49y^2$
e. $x^6 - 16a^2$

Problem Set 3.5

Find the following special products.

1. $(x + 5)^2$

2. $(x - 2)^2$

3. $(x - 3)^2$

4. $(x + 3)^2$

5. $(a - 1)^2$

6. $(a + 1)^2$

7. $(a + 4)^2$

8. $(a - 4)^2$

9. $(y - 6)^2$

10. $(y + 7)^2$

11. $(x + 2)^2$

12. $(x - 5)^2$

13. $(2a - 3)^2$

14. $(3a + 2)^2$

15. $(5x + 2y)^2$

16. $(3x - 4y)^2$

17. $(5x - 2y)^2$

18. $(7x - y)^2$

19. $(x + 3)(x - 3)$

20. $(x + 9)(x - 9)$

21. $(a - 1)(a + 1)$

22. $(a - 2)(a + 2)$

23. $(y - 8)(y + 8)$

24. $(y + 6)(y - 6)$

25. $(x^2 + 6)(x^2 - 6)$

26. $(x^2 + 5)(x^2 - 5)$

Name _____

Class _____

Date _____

Answers

1. _____

2. _____

3. _____

4. _____

5. _____

6. _____

7. _____

8. _____

9. _____

10. _____

11. _____

12. _____

13. _____

14. _____

15. _____

16. _____

17. _____

18. _____

19. _____

20. _____

21. _____

22. _____

23. _____

24. _____

25. _____

26. _____

Answers

27. _____

28. _____

29. _____

30. _____

31. _____

32. _____

33. _____

34. _____

35. _____

36. _____

37. _____

38. _____

39. _____

40. _____

41. _____

42. _____

43. _____

44. _____

45. _____

46. _____

47. _____

48. _____

49. _____

50. _____

27. $(2a + 3b)(2a - 3b)$

28. $(6a - 1)(6a + 1)$

29. $(3r + 7s)(3r - 7s)$

30. $(5r - 2s)(5r + 2s)$

31. $(5x - 4y)(5x + 4y)$

32. $(4x - 5y)(4x + 5y)$

33. $(x^2 + 2)^2$

34. $(x^2 - 3)^2$

35. $(x^2 - y^2)^2$

36. $(x^2 + y^2)^2$

37. $(x + \frac{1}{2})(x - \frac{1}{2})$

38. $(x + \frac{1}{3})(x - \frac{1}{3})$

39. $(a + \frac{1}{2})^2$

40. $(a - \frac{1}{3})^2$

Expand each of the following and then multiply. Remember, $a^3 = a \cdot a \cdot a$, so $(x + 2)^3 = (x + 2)(x + 2)(x + 2)$.

41. $(x + 2)^3$

42. $(x - 2)^3$

43. $(a - 1)^3$

44. $(a + 1)^3$

45. Multiply $(x + 3)(x - 3)(x^2 + 9)$ by first multiplying $(x + 3)$ and $(x - 3)$ and then multiplying that result with $x^2 + 9$.

46. Multiply $(x + 2)(x - 2)(x^2 + 4)$ by multiplying from left to right.

Review Problems　　The following problems review material we covered in Section 2.4.

Solve each equation.

47. $|x + 1| = 3$

48. $|x - 2| = 7$

49. $|x + 7| - 3 = 4$

50. $|x + 2| - 2 = 3$

Section 3.6 Division of Polynomials

We begin this section by considering division of a polynomial by a monomial. This is the simplest kind of polynomial division. The rest of the section is devoted to division of a polynomial by a polynomial. This kind of division is similar to long division with whole numbers.

Dividing a Polynomial by a Monomial

To divide a polynomial by a monomial we use the definition of division and apply the distributive property. The following example illustrates the procedure.

▼ **Example 1** Divide.

$$\frac{10x^5 - 15x^4 + 20x^3}{5x^2}$$

$$= (10x^5 - 15x^4 + 20x^3) \cdot \frac{1}{5x^2} \qquad \text{Dividing by } 5x^2 \text{ is the same as multiplying by } 1/5x^2$$

$$= 10x^5 \cdot \frac{1}{5x^2} - 15x^4 \cdot \frac{1}{5x^2} + 20x^3 \cdot \frac{1}{5x^2} \qquad \text{Distributive property}$$

$$= \frac{10x^5}{5x^2} - \frac{15x^4}{5x^2} + \frac{20x^3}{5x^2} \qquad \text{Multiplying by } 1/5x^2 \text{ is the same as dividing by } 5x^2$$

$$= 2x^3 - 3x^2 + 4x \qquad \text{Divide coefficients, subtract exponents}$$

Notice that division of a polynomial by a monomial is accomplished by dividing each term of the polynomial by the monomial. The first two steps are usually not shown in a problem like this. They are part of Example 1 to justify distributing $5x^2$ under all three terms of the polynomial $10x^5 - 15x^4 + 20x^3$. ▲

Here are some more examples of this kind of division:

▼ **Example 2** Divide. Write all results with positive exponents.

a. $\dfrac{8x^3y^5 - 16x^2y^2 + 4x^4y^3}{-2x^2y} = \dfrac{8x^3y^5}{-2x^2y} + \dfrac{-16x^2y^2}{-2x^2y} + \dfrac{4x^4y^3}{-2x^2y}$

$$= -4xy^4 + 8y - 2x^2y^2$$

b. $\dfrac{10a^4b^2 + 8ab^3 - 12a^3b + 6ab}{4a^2b^2}$

$$= \frac{10a^4b^2}{4a^2b^2} + \frac{8ab^3}{4a^2b^2} - \frac{12a^3b}{4a^2b^2} + \frac{6ab}{4a^2b^2}$$

$$= \frac{5a^2}{2} + \frac{2b}{a} - \frac{3a}{b} + \frac{3}{2ab} \qquad ▲$$

Practice Problems

1. Divide: $\dfrac{12x^4 - 18x^3 + 24x^2}{6x}$.

2. Divide.

a. $\dfrac{27x^4y^7 - 81x^5y^3}{-9x^3y^2}$

b. $\dfrac{12a^5 + 8a^4 + 16a^3 + 4a^2}{8a^4}$

Answers
1. $2x^3 - 3x^2 + 4x$
2a. $-3xy^5 + 9x^2y$
b. $\dfrac{3a}{2} + 1 + \dfrac{2}{a} + \dfrac{1}{2a^2}$

Notice in part b of Example 2 that the result is not a polynomial because of the last three terms. If we were to write each as a product, some of the variables would have negative exponents. For example, the second term would be

$$\frac{2b}{a} = 2a^{-1}b$$

Dividing a Polynomial by a Polynomial

Since division of a polynomial by a polynomial is very similar to long division with whole numbers, we begin with a detailed example of whole-number division.

▼ **Example 3**   Divide: $25\overline{)4628}$

Solution

$$\begin{array}{r} 1 \\ 25\overline{)4628} \\ \underline{25} \\ 21 \end{array}$$ ⟵ Estimate: 25 into 46
⟵ Multiply: $1 \times 25 = 25$
⟵ Subtract: $46 - 25 = 21$

$$\begin{array}{r} 1 \\ 25\overline{)4628} \\ \underline{25\downarrow} \\ 212 \end{array}$$ ⟵ Bring down the 2

These are the four basic steps in long division: estimate, multiply, subtract, and bring down the next term. To complete the problem we simply perform the same four steps again.

$$\begin{array}{r} 18 \\ 25\overline{)4628} \\ \underline{25} \\ 212 \\ \underline{200\downarrow} \\ 128 \end{array}$$ ⟵ 8 is the estimate

⟵ Multiply to get 200
⟵ Subtract to get 12, then bring down the 8

One more time:

$$\begin{array}{r} 185 \\ 25\overline{)4628} \\ \underline{25} \\ 212 \\ \underline{200\downarrow} \\ 128 \\ \underline{125} \\ 3 \end{array}$$ ⟵ 5 is the estimate

⟵ Multiply to get 125
⟵ Subtract to get 3

Since 3 is less than 25, we have our answer:

$$\frac{4628}{25} = 185 + \frac{3}{25}$$

To check our answer, we multiply 185 by 25, then add 3 to the result:

$$25(185) + 3 = 4625 + 3 = 4628$$

3.   Divide: $35\overline{)7546}$.

Note: You may realize when looking over this example that you don't have a very good idea why you proceed as you do with the steps in long division. What you do know is the process always works. We are going to approach the explanation for division of two polynomials with this in mind. That is, we won't always be sure why the steps we use are important, only that they always produce the correct result.

The method used to divide a polynomial by a polynomial is very similar to the method used to divide the numbers in Example 3. Both use the same four basic steps: estimate, multiply, subtract, and bring down the next term.

▼ **Example 4** Divide: $\dfrac{2x^2 - 7x + 9}{x - 2}$.

4. Divide: $\dfrac{3x^2 - 8x - 1}{x - 3}$.

Solution

$$
\begin{array}{r}
2x \phantom{{}-7x+9} \\
x - 2 \overline{)\ 2x^2 - 7x + 9} \\
\end{array}
$$
$\longleftarrow$ Estimate: $2x^2 \div x = 2x$

$$
\begin{array}{r}
 -\quad + \\
+2x^2 - 4x \\
\end{array}
$$
$\longleftarrow$ Multiply: $2x(x - 2) = 2x^2 - 4x$
$$- 3x $$
$\longleftarrow$ Subtract: $(2x^2 - 7x) - (2x^2 - 4x) = -3x$

$$
\begin{array}{r}
2x \phantom{{}-7x+9}\\
x - 2 \overline{)\ 2x^2 - 7x + 9}\\
-\quad + \downarrow\\
+2x^2 - 4x \downarrow\\
\hline
- 3x + 9
\end{array}
$$
$\longleftarrow$ Bring down the 9

Notice we change the signs on $2x^2 - 4x$ and add in the subtraction step. Subtracting a polynomial is equivalent to adding its opposite.
We repeat the four steps again:

$$
\begin{array}{r}
2x \ - \ 3 \\
x - 2 \overline{)\ 2x^2 - 7x + 9}\\
-\quad + \\
+2x^2 - 4x \\
\hline
- 3x + 9\\
\end{array}
$$
$\longleftarrow$ -3 is the estimate: $-3x \div x = -3$

$$
\begin{array}{r}
+ \quad - \\
- 3x + 6\\
\hline
3
\end{array}
$$
$\longleftarrow$ Multiply: $-3(x - 2) = -3x + 6$
$\longleftarrow$ Subtract: $(-3x + 9) - (-3x + 6) = 3$

Since we have no other term to bring down, we have our answer:

$$\frac{2x^2 - 7x + 9}{x - 2} = 2x - 3 + \frac{3}{x - 2}$$

To check we multiply $(2x - 3)(x - 2)$ to get $2x^2 - 7x + 6$; then, adding the remainder 3 to this result, we have $2x^2 - 7x + 9$. ▲

In setting up a division problem involving two polynomials, we must remember two things: (1) both polynomials should be in decreasing powers of the variable, and (2) neither should skip any powers from the highest power down to the constant term. If there are any missing terms, they can be filled in using a coefficient of 0.

Answer

4. $3x + 1 + \dfrac{2}{x - 3}$

5. Divide: $x - 2\overline{)3x^3 + 3x + 1}$.

▼ **Example 5** Divide: $2x - 4\overline{)4x^3 - 6x - 11}$.

Solution Since the first trinomial is missing a term in x^2, we can fill it in with $0x^2$:

$$4x^3 - 6x - 11 = 4x^3 + 0x^2 - 6x - 11$$

Adding $0x^2$ does not change our original problem.

$$
\begin{array}{r}
2x^2 + 4x + 5 \\
2x - 4\overline{)\,4x^3 + 0x^2 - 6x - 11\,} \\
\end{array}
$$

Notice: Adding the $0x^2$ term gives us a column in which to write $+8x^2$.

$$
\begin{array}{r}
{\scriptstyle -} \quad\quad {\scriptstyle +} \\
+4x^3 - 8x^2 \\
\hline
+8x^2 - 6x \\
{\scriptstyle -} \quad\quad {\scriptstyle +} \\
+8x^2 - 16x \\
\hline
+10x - 11 \\
{\scriptstyle -} \quad\quad {\scriptstyle +} \\
+10x - 20 \\
\hline
+9
\end{array}
$$

$$\frac{4x^3 - 6x - 11}{2x - 4} = 2x^2 + 4x + 5 + \frac{9}{2x - 4}$$

To check this result we multiply $2x - 4$ and $2x^2 + 4x + 5$

$$
\begin{array}{r}
2x^2 + 4x + 5 \\
2x - 4 \\
\hline
- 8x^2 - 16x - 20 \\
4x^3 + 8x^2 + 10x \\
\hline
4x^3 \quad\quad - 6x - 20
\end{array}
$$

Adding 9 (the remainder) to this result gives us the polynomial $4x^3 - 6x - 11$. Our answer checks. ▲

6. Divide: $\dfrac{2x^2 - 5xy + 3y^2}{x - y}$.

▼ **Example 6** Divide: $\dfrac{x^2 - 6xy - 7y^2}{x + y}$.

Solution

$$
\begin{array}{r}
x - 7y \\
x + y\overline{)\,x^2 - 6xy - 7y^2\,} \\
{\scriptstyle -} \quad\quad {\scriptstyle -} \\
+x^2 + xy \\
\hline
- 7xy - 7y^2 \\
{\scriptstyle +} \quad\quad {\scriptstyle +} \\
- 7xy - 7y^2 \\
\hline
0
\end{array}
$$

In this case the remainder is 0 and we have

$$\frac{x^2 - 6xy - 7y^2}{x + y} = x - 7y$$

which is easy to check since

$$(x + y)(x - 7y) = x^2 - 6xy - 7y^2$$ ▲

Answers

5. $3x^2 + 6x + 15 + \dfrac{31}{x - 2}$

6. $2x - 3y$

Problem Set 3.6

Find the following quotients.

1. $\dfrac{4x^3 - 8x^2 + 6x}{2x}$

2. $\dfrac{6x^3 + 12x^2 - 9x}{3x}$

3. $\dfrac{10x^4 + 15x^3 - 20x^2}{-5x^2}$

4. $\dfrac{12x^5 - 18x^4 - 6x^3}{6x^3}$

5. $\dfrac{8y^5 + 10y^3 - 6y}{4y^3}$

6. $\dfrac{6y^4 - 3y^3 + 18y^2}{9y^2}$

7. $\dfrac{5x^3 - 8x^2 - 6x}{-2x^2}$

8. $\dfrac{-9x^5 + 10x^3 - 12x}{-6x^4}$

9. $\dfrac{28a^3b^5 + 42a^4b^3}{7a^2b^2}$

10. $\dfrac{a^2b + ab^2}{ab}$

Name _____

Class _____

Date _____

Answers

1. _____

2. _____

3. _____

4. _____

5. _____

6. _____

7. _____

8. _____

9. _____

10. _____

Answers

11. _____

12. _____

13. _____

14. _____

15. _____

16. _____

17. _____

18. _____

11. $\dfrac{10x^3y^2 - 20x^2y^3 - 30x^3y^3}{-10x^2y}$

12. $\dfrac{9x^4y^4 + 18x^3y^4 - 27x^2y^4}{-9xy^3}$

13. $\dfrac{8x^3 - 6x^2y + 10xy^2 + 4y^3}{2xy}$

14. $\dfrac{6x^3 + 12x^2y - 9xy^2 - 15y^3}{3xy}$

15. $\dfrac{a^{9N} - a^{6N}}{a^{3N}}$

16. $\dfrac{a^{5r} + a^{4r} + a^{3r}}{a^{2r}}$

17. $\dfrac{24x^{6M} - 18x^{3M} + 12x^M}{6x^M}$

18. $\dfrac{10x^{2M} - 25x^{3M} - 30x^{5M}}{5x^{2M}}$

Do each division problem using the long division method.

19. $\dfrac{x^2 - 5x - 7}{x + 2}$

20. $\dfrac{x^2 + 4x - 8}{x - 3}$

21. $\dfrac{6x^2 + 7x - 18}{3x - 4}$

22. $\dfrac{8x^2 - 26x - 9}{2x - 7}$

23. $\dfrac{2x^3 - 3x^2 - 4x + 5}{x + 1}$

24. $\dfrac{3x^3 - 5x^2 + 2x - 1}{x - 2}$

25. $\dfrac{8x^2 - 6xy + 9y^2}{2x - 3y}$

26. $\dfrac{6x^2 - 13xy - 8y^2}{3x + y}$

Name _____

Class _____

Date _____

Answers

19. _____

20. _____

21. _____

22. _____

23. _____

24. _____

25. _____

26. _____

Answers

27. _____

28. _____

29. _____

30. _____

31. _____

32. _____

33. _____

34. _____

35. _____

36. _____

27. $\dfrac{x^4 - 2x + 5}{x - 2}$

28. $\dfrac{x^4 + x^3 - 1}{x + 2}$

29. $\dfrac{y^4 - 16}{y - 2}$

30. $\dfrac{y^4 - 81}{y - 3}$

31. $\dfrac{x^3 - y^3}{x - y}$

32. $\dfrac{x^3 + y^3}{x + y}$

Review Problems   The following problems review material we covered in Section 3.4.

Multiply.

33. $5x^3(5x^2 + 4x - 6)$

34. $8a^2b^3(2a^3b - 3b^2 - a)$

35. $(x + y)(x + 5)$

36. $(x + a)(x + b)$

Section 3.7   The Greatest Common Factor and Factoring by Grouping

In general, factoring is the reverse of multiplication. The following diagram illustrates the relationship between factoring and multiplication:

Multiplication

$$\text{Factors} \quad \rightarrow \quad 3 \cdot 7 = 21 \quad \leftarrow \quad \text{Product}$$

Factoring

Reading from left to right we say the product of 3 and 7 is 21. Reading in the other direction, from right to left, we say 21 factors into 3 times 7. Or, 3 and 7 are factors of 21.

DEFINITION   The *greatest common factor* for a polynomial is the largest monomial that divides (is a factor of) each term of the polynomial.

The greatest common factor for the polynomial $25x^5 + 20x^4 - 30x^3$ is $5x^3$ since it is the largest monomial that is a factor of each term. We can apply the distributive property and write

$$25x^5 + 20x^4 - 30x^3 = 5x^3(5x^2) + 5x^3(4x) + 5x^3(-6)$$
$$= 5x^3(5x^2 + 4x - 6)$$

The last line is written in factored form.

Once we recognize the greatest common factor for a polynomial, we apply the distributive property and factor it from each term. We rewrite the original polynomial as the product of its greatest common factor and the polynomial that remains after the greatest common factor has been factored from each term.

▼ **Example 1**   Factor the greatest common factor from

$$16a^5b^4 - 24a^2b^5 - 8a^3b^3$$

Solution   The largest monomial that divides each term is $8a^2b^3$. We write each term of the original polynomial in terms of $8a^2b^3$ and apply the distributive property to write the polynomial in factored form:

$$16a^5b^4 - 24a^2b^5 - 8a^3b^3$$
$$= 8a^2b^3(2a^3b) + 8a^2b^3(-3b^2) + 8a^2b^3(-a)$$
$$= 8a^2b^3(2a^3b - 3b^2 - a) \qquad \blacktriangle$$

Here are some further examples of factoring out the greatest common factor.

▼ **Example 2**   Factor out the greatest common factor.

a. $16x^3y^4z^5 + 10x^4y^3z^2 - 12x^2y^3z^4$
$$= 2x^2y^3z^2(8xyz^3) + 2x^2y^3z^2(5x^2) - 2x^2y^3z^2(6z^2)$$
$$= 2x^2y^3z^2(8xyz^3 + 5x^2 - 6z^2)$$

b. $5(a + b)^3 - 10(a + b)^2 + 5(a + b)$
$$= 5(a + b)(a + b)^2 - 5(a + b)2(a + b) + 5(a + b)(1)$$
$$= 5(a + b)[(a + b)^2 - 2(a + b) + 1] \qquad \blacktriangle$$

Practice Problems

1.   Factor the greatest common factor from $15a^7 - 25a^5 + 30a^3$.

Note: The term *largest monomial* as used here refers to the monomial with the largest integer exponents whose coefficient has the greatest absolute value. We could have factored the polynomial in Example 1 correctly by taking out $-8a^2b^3$. We usually keep the coefficient of the greatest common factor positive. However, it is not incorrect (and is sometimes useful) to have the coefficient negative.

2.   Factor.

a. $12x^4y^5 - 9x^3y^4 - 15x^5y^3$

b. $4(a + b)^4 - 6(a + b)^3 + 16(a + b)^2$

Answers
1. $5a^3(3a^4 - 5a^2 + 6)$
2a. $3x^3y^3(4xy^2 - 3y - 5x^2)$
b. $2(a + b)^2[2(a + b)^2 - 3(a + b) + 8]$

The second step in the two parts of the preceding example is not necessary. It is shown here simply to emphasize use of the distributive property.

Factoring by Grouping

Many polynomials have no greatest common factor other than the number 1. Some of these can be factored using the distributive property if those terms with a common factor are grouped together.

For example, the polynomial $5x + 5y + x^2 + xy$ can be factored by noticing that the first two terms have a 5 in common, whereas the last two have an x in common.

Applying the distributive property we have

$$5x + 5y + x^2 + xy = 5(x + y) + x(x + y)$$

This last expression can be thought of as having two terms, $5(x + y)$ and $x(x + y)$, each of which has a common factor $(x + y)$. We apply the distributive property again to factor $(x + y)$ from each term:

$$5(x + y) + x(x + y)$$
$$= (5 + x)(x + y)$$

3. Factor $ab^3 + b^3 + 6a + 6$.

▼ **Example 3** Factor $a^2b^2 + b^2 + 8a^2 + 8$.

Solution The first two terms have b^2 in common; the last two have 8 in common.

$$a^2b^2 + b^2 + 8a^2 + 8 = b^2(a^2 + 1) + 8(a^2 + 1)$$
$$= (b^2 + 8)(a^2 + 1) \qquad ▲$$

4. Factor $12 - 3y^2 - 4x^2 + x^2y^2$.

▼ **Example 4** Factor $15 - 5y^4 - 3x^3 + x^3y^4$.

Solution Let's try factoring a 5 from the first two terms and an x^3 from the last two terms:

$$15 - 5y^4 - 3x^3 + x^3y^4 = 5(3 - y^4) + x^3(-3 + y^4)$$

Now, $3 - y^4$ and $-3 + y^4$ are not equal and we cannot factor further. Notice, however, that we can factor $-x^3$ instead of x^3 from the last two terms and obtain the desired result:

$$15 - 5y^4 - 3x^3 + x^3y^4 = 5(3 - y^4) - x^3(3 - y^4)$$
$$= (5 - x^3)(3 - y^4) \qquad ▲$$

Answers
3. $(a + 1)(b^3 + 6)$
4. $(3 - x^2)(4 - y^2)$

Problem Set 3.7

Factor the greatest common factor from each of the following. (The answers in the back of the book all show greatest common factors whose coefficients are positive.)

1. $10x^3 - 15x^2$

2. $12x^5 + 18x^7$

3. $9y^6 + 18y^3$

4. $24y^4 - 8y^2$

5. $9a^2b - 6ab^2$

6. $30a^3b^4 + 20a^4b^3$

7. $21xy^4 + 7x^2y^2$

8. $14x^6y^3 - 6x^2y^4$

9. $3a^2 - 21a + 30$

10. $3a^2 - 3a - 6$

11. $4x^3 - 16x^2 - 20x$

12. $2x^3 - 14x^2 + 20x$

13. $10x^4y^2 + 20x^3y^3 - 30x^2y^4$

14. $6x^4y^2 + 18x^3y^3 - 24x^2y^4$

15. $-x^2y + xy^2 - x^2y^2$

16. $-x^3y^2 - x^2y^3 - x^2y^2$

17. $4x^3y^2z - 8x^2y^2z^2 + 6xy^2z^3$

18. $7x^4y^3z^2 - 21x^2y^2z^2 - 14x^2y^3z^4$

19. $20a^2b^2c^2 - 30ab^2c + 25a^2bc^2$

20. $8a^3bc^5 - 48a^2b^4c + 16ab^3c^5$

21. $5x(a - 2b) - 3y(a - 2b)$

22. $3a(x - y) - 7b(x - y)$

23. $3x^2(x + y)^2 - 6y^2(x + y)^2$

24. $10x^3(2x - 3y) - 15x^2(2x - 3y)$

25. $2x^2(x + 5) + 7x(x + 5) + 6(x + 5)$

26. $2x^2(x + 2) + 13x(x + 2) + 15(x + 2)$

Name _____

Class _____

Date _____

Answers

1. _____   2. _____

3. _____   4. _____

5. _____   6. _____

7. _____   8. _____

9. _____   10. _____

11. _____

12. _____

13. _____

14. _____

15. _____

16. _____

17. _____

18. _____

19. _____

20. _____

21. _____

22. _____

23. _____

24. _____

25. _____

26. _____

Answers

27. _____

28. _____

29. _____

30. _____

31. _____

32. _____

33. _____

34. _____

35. _____

36. _____

37. _____

38. _____

39. _____

40. _____

41. _____

42. _____

43. _____

44. _____

45. _____

46. _____

47. _____

48. _____

49. _____

50. _____

51. _____

52. _____

Factor each of the following by grouping.

27. $3xy + 3y + 2ax + 2a$
28. $5xy^2 + 5y^2 + 3ax + 3a$

29. $x^2y + x + 3xy + 3$
30. $x^3y^3 + 2x^3 + 5x^2y^3 + 10x^2$

31. $a + b + 5ax + 5bx$
32. $a + b + 7ax + 7bx$

33. $3x - 2y + 6x - 4y$
34. $4x - 5y + 12x - 15y$

35. $3xy^2 - 6y^2 + 4x - 8$
36. $8x^2y - 4x^2 + 6y - 3$

37. $2xy^3 - 8y^3 + x - 4$
38. $8x^2y^4 - 4y^4 + 14x^2 - 7$

39. $x^2 - ax - bx + ab$
40. $ax - x^2 - bx + ab$

41. $ab + 5a - b - 5$
42. $x^2 - xy - ax + ay$

43. $a^4b^2 + a^4 - 5b^2 - 5$
44. $2a^2 - bc^2 - a^2b + 2c^2$

45. The greatest common factor of the binomial $3x - 9$ is 3. The greatest common factor of the binomial $6x - 2$ is 2. What is the greatest common factor of their product, $(3x - 9)(6x - 2)$, when it has been multiplied out?

46. The greatest common factors of the binomials $5x - 10$ and $2x + 4$ are 5 and 2 respectively. What is the greatest common factor of their product, $(5x - 10)(2x + 4)$, when it has been multiplied out?

Review Problems   The following problems review material we covered in Section 3.4. Reviewing these problems will help you with the next section.

Multiply using the FOIL method.

47. $(x + 2)(x + 3)$
48. $(x - 2)(x - 3)$

49. $(x + 2)(x - 3)$
50. $(x - 2)(x + 3)$

51. $(x - 6)(x - 1)$
52. $(x + 6)(x + 1)$

Section 3.8 Factoring Trinomials

Factoring trinomials is probably the most common type of factoring found in algebra. We begin this section by considering trinomials that have a leading coefficient of 1. The remainder of the section is concerned with trinomials with leading coefficients other than 1. The more familiar we are with multiplication of binomials, the easier factoring trinomials will be.

In Section 3.4 we multiplied binomials:

$$(x - 2)(x + 3) = x^2 + x - 6$$
$$(x + 5)(x + 2) = x^2 + 7x + 10$$

In each case the product of two binomials is a trinomial. The first term in the resulting trinomial is obtained by multiplying the first term in each binomial. The middle term comes from adding the product of the two inside terms and the two outside terms. The last term is the product of the last term in each binomial.

In general,

$$(x + a)(x + b) = x^2 + ax + bx + ab$$
$$= x^2 + (a + b)x + ab$$

Writing this as a factoring problem we have

$$x^2 + (a + b)x + ab = (x + a)(x + b)$$

To factor a trinomial with a leading coefficient of 1, we simply find the two numbers a and b whose sum is the coefficient of the middle term and whose product is the constant term.

▼ **Example 1** Factor $x^2 + 5x + 6$.

Solution The leading coefficient is 1. We need two numbers whose sum is 5 and whose product is 6. The numbers are 2 and 3. (6 and 1 do not work because their sum is not 5.)

$$x^2 + 5x + 6 = (x + 2)(x + 3)$$

To check our work we simply multiply:

$$(x + 2)(x + 3) = x^2 + 3x + 2x + 6$$
$$= x^2 + 5x + 6 \qquad ▲$$

▼ **Example 2** Factor $x^2 + 2x - 15$.

Solution Again the leading coefficient is 1. We need two integers whose product is -15 and whose sum is $+2$. The integers are $+5$ and -3.

$$x^2 + 2x - 15 = (x + 5)(x - 3) \qquad ▲$$

If a trinomial is factorable, then its factors are unique. For instance, in the preceding example we found factors of $x + 5$ and $x - 3$. These are the only

Practice Problems

1. Factor $x^2 + 6x + 8$.

2. Factor $x^2 - x - 12$.

3. Factor $x^2 + 2xy - 15y^2$.

4. Factor $x^2 + x + 1$.

5. Factor $5x^2 + 25x + 30$.

Note: As a general rule, it is best to factor out the greatest common factor first.

two factors for $x^2 + 2x - 15$. There is no other pair of binomials whose product is $x^2 + 2x - 15$.

▼ **Example 3**   Factor $x^2 - xy - 12y^2$.

Solution   We need two numbers whose product is $-12y^2$ and whose sum is $-y$. The numbers are $-4y$ and $3y$:

$$x^2 - xy - 12y^2 = (x - 4y)(x + 3y)$$

Checking this result gives

$$(x - 4y)(x + 3y) = x^2 + 3xy - 4xy - 12y^2$$
$$= x^2 - xy - 12y^2$$

▼ **Example 4**   Factor $x^2 - 8x + 6$.

Solution   Since there is no pair of integers whose product is 6 and whose sum is 8, the trinomial $x^2 - 8x + 6$ is not factorable. We say it is a *prime polynomial*.

▼ **Example 5**   Factor $3x^4 - 15x^3y - 18x^2y^2$.

Solution   The leading coefficient is not 1. However, each term is divisible by $3x^2$. Factoring this out to begin with we have

$$3x^4 - 15x^3y - 18x^2y^2 = 3x^2(x^2 - 5xy - 6y^2)$$

Factoring the resulting trinomial as in the examples above gives

$$3x^2(x^2 - 5xy - 6y^2) = 3x^2(x - 6y)(x + y)$$

We want to turn our attention now to trinomials with leading coefficients other than 1 and with no greatest common factor other than 1.

Suppose we want to factor $3x^2 - x - 2$. The factors will be a pair of binomials. The product of the first terms will be $3x^2$ and the product of the last terms will be -2. We can list all the possible factors along with their products as follows.

Possible factors	First term	Middle term	Last term
$(x + 2)(3x - 1)$	$3x^2$	$+5x$	-2
$(x - 2)(3x + 1)$	$3x^2$	$-5x$	-2
$(x + 1)(3x - 2)$	$3x^2$	$+x$	-2
$(x - 1)(3x + 2)$	$3x^2$	$-x$	-2

From the last line we see that the factors of $3x^2 - x - 2$ are $(x - 1)(3x + 2)$. That is,

$$3x^2 - x - 2 = (x - 1)(3x + 2)$$

To factor trinomials with leading coefficients other than 1, when the greatest common factor is 1, we must use trial and error or list all the possible factors. In either case the idea is this: look only at pairs of binomials whose

Answers
3. $(x + 5y)(x - 3y)$ **4.** Does not factor **5.** $5(x + 3)(x + 2)$

products give the correct first and last terms, then look for combinations that will give the correct middle term.

▼ **Example 6** Factor $2x^2 + 13xy + 15y^2$.

Solution Listing all possible factors the product of whose first terms is $2x^2$ and the product of whose last terms is $+15y^2$ yields

Possible factors	Middle term of product
$(2x - 5y)(x - 3y)$	$-11xy$
$(2x - 3y)(x - 5y)$	$-13xy$
$(2x + 5y)(x + 3y)$	$+11xy$
$(2x + 3y)(x + 5y)$	$+13xy$

The last line has the correct middle term:

$$2x^2 + 13xy + 15y^2 = (2x + 3y)(x + 5y)$$

Actually, we did not need to check the first two pairs of possible factors in the preceding list. All the signs in the trinomial $2x^2 + 13xy + 15y^2$ are positive. The binomial factors must then be of the form $(ax + b)(cx + d)$, where a, b, c, and d are all positive. ▲

There are other ways to reduce the number of possible factors to consider. For example, if we were to factor the trinomial $2x^2 - 11x + 12$, we would not have to consider the pair of possible factors $(2x - 4)(x - 3)$. If the original trinomial has no greatest common factor other than 1, then neither of its binomial factors will either. The trinomial $2x^2 - 11x + 12$ has a greatest common factor of 1, but the possible factor $2x - 4$ has a greatest common factor of 2: $2x - 4 = 2(x - 2)$. Therefore, we do not need to consider $2x - 4$ as a possible factor.

▼ **Example 7** Factor $18x^3y + 3x^2y^2 - 36xy^3$.

Solution First factor out the greatest common factor $3xy$. Then factor the remaining trinomial:

$$18x^3y + 3x^2y^2 - 36xy^3 = 3xy(6x^2 + xy - 12y^2)$$
$$= 3xy(3x - 4y)(2x + 3y) \quad ▲$$

▼ **Example 8** Factor $12x^4 + 17x^2 + 6$.

Solution This is a trinomial in x^2:

$$12x^4 + 17x^2 + 6 = (4x^2 + 3)(3x^2 + 2)$$

We could have made the substitution $y = x^2$ to begin with, in order to simplify the trinomial, and then factor as

$$12y^2 + 17y + 6 = (4y + 3)(3y + 2)$$

Again using $y = x^2$, we have:

$$(4y + 3)(3y + 2) = (4x^2 + 3)(3x^2 + 2) \quad ▲$$

6. Factor $3x^2 - x - 2$.

7. Factor $15x^3y + 25x^2y^2 - 10xy^3$.

8. Factor $15x^4 + x^2 - 2$.

Answers
6. $(3x + 2)(x - 1)$
7. $5xy(3x - y)(x + 2y)$
8. $(5x^2 + 2)(3x^2 - 1)$

9. Factor

$$3x^2(x - 2) - 7x(x - 2) + 2(x - 2)$$

▼ **Example 9** Factor $2x^2(x - 3) - 5x(x - 3) - 3(x - 3)$.

Solution We begin by factoring out the greatest common factor $(x - 3)$. Then we factor the trinomial that remains.

$$2x^2(x - 3) - 5x(x - 3) - 3(x - 3)$$
$$= (x - 3)(2x^2 - 5x - 3)$$
$$= (x - 3)(2x + 1)(x - 3)$$
$$= (x - 3)^2(2x + 1)$$ ▲

Answer
9. $(x - 2)^2(3x - 1)$

Problem Set 3.8

Name _____

Class _____

Date _____

Factor each of the following trinomials:

1. $x^2 + 7x + 12$

2. $x^2 - 7x + 12$

3. $x^2 - x - 12$

4. $x^2 + x - 12$

5. $y^2 + y - 6$

6. $y^2 - y - 6$

7. $x^2 - 6x - 16$

8. $x^2 + 2x - 3$

9. $x^2 + 8x + 12$

10. $x^2 - 2x - 15$

Factor completely by first factoring out the greatest common factor and then factoring the trinomial that remains.

11. $3a^2 - 21a + 30$

12. $3a^2 - 3a - 6$

13. $4x^3 - 16x^2 - 20x$

14. $2x^3 - 14x^2 + 20x$

Factor.

15. $x^2 + 3xy + 2y^2$

16. $x^2 - 5xy - 24y^2$

17. $a^2 + 3ab - 18b^2$

18. $a^2 - 8ab - 9b^2$

19. $x^2 - 2xa - 48a^2$

20. $x^2 + 14xa + 48a^2$

21. $x^2 - 12xb + 36b^2$

22. $x^2 + 10xb + 25b^2$

Answers

1. _____

2. _____

3. _____

4. _____

5. _____

6. _____

7. _____

8. _____

9. _____

10. _____

11. _____

12. _____

13. _____

14. _____

15. _____

16. _____

17. _____

18. _____

19. _____

20. _____

21. _____

22. _____

Answers

23. _____

24. _____

25. _____

26. _____

27. _____

28. _____

29. _____

30. _____

31. _____

32. _____

33. _____

34. _____

35. _____

36. _____

37. _____

38. _____

39. _____

40. _____

41. _____

42. _____

43. _____

44. _____

Factor completely. Be sure to factor out the greatest common factor first if it is other than 1.

23. $3x^2 - 6xy - 9y^2$

24. $5x^2 + 25xy + 20y^2$

25. $2a^5 + 4a^4b + 4a^3b^2$

26. $3a^4 - 18a^3b + 27a^2b^2$

27. $10x^4y^2 + 20x^3y^3 - 30x^2y^4$

28. $6x^4y^2 + 18x^3y^3 - 24x^2y^4$

29. $2x^2 + 7x - 15$

30. $2x^2 - 7x - 15$

31. $2x^2 + x - 15$

32. $2x^2 - x - 15$

33. $2x^2 - 13x + 15$

34. $2x^2 + 13x + 15$

35. $2x^2 - 11x + 15$

36. $2x^2 + 11x + 15$

37. $2x^2 + 7x + 15$

38. $2x^2 + x - 15$

39. $6a^2 + 7a + 2$

40. $6a^2 - 7a + 2$

41. $4y^2 - y - 3$

42. $6y^2 + 5y - 6$

43. $6x^2 - x - 2$

44. $3x^2 + 2x - 5$

Factor completely.

45. $4r^2 - 12r + 9$

46. $4r^2 + 20r + 25$

47. $4x^2 - 11xy - 3y^2$

48. $3x^2 + 19xy - 14y^2$

49. $10x^2 - 3xa - 18a^2$

50. $9x^2 + 9xa - 10a^2$

51. $18a^2 + 3ab - 28b^2$

52. $6a^2 - 7ab - 5b^2$

53. $8x^2 + 8x - 6$

54. $35x^2 - 60x - 20$

55. $9y^4 + 9y^3 - 10y^2$

56. $4y^5 + 7y^4 - 2y^3$

57. $12a^4 - 2a^3 - 24a^2$

58. $20a^4 + 65a^3 - 60a^2$

59. $8x^4y^2 - 2x^3y^3 - 6x^2y^4$

60. $8x^4y^2 - 47x^3y^3 - 6x^2y^4$

61. $3x^4 + 10x^2 + 3$

62. $6x^4 - x^2 - 7$

63. $20a^4 + 37a^2 + 15$

64. $20a^4 + 13a^2 - 15$

65. $12r^4 + 3r^2 - 9$

66. $30r^4 - 4r^2 - 2$

Name _____

Class _____

Date _____

Answers

45. _____

46. _____

47. _____

48. _____

49. _____

50. _____

51. _____

52. _____

53. _____

54. _____

55. _____

56. _____

57. _____

58. _____

59. _____

60. _____

61. _____

62. _____

63. _____

64. _____

65. _____

66. _____

Answers

67. _____

68. _____

69. _____

70. _____

71. _____

72. _____

73. _____

74. _____

75. _____

76. _____

77. _____

78. _____

79. _____

80. _____

Factor each of the following by first factoring out the greatest common factor, and then factoring the trinomial that remains.

67. $2x^2(x + 5) + 7x(x + 5) + 6(x + 5)$

68. $2x^2(x + 2) + 13x(x + 2) + 15(x + 2)$

69. $x^2(2x + 3) + 7x(2x + 3) + 10(2x + 3)$

70. $2x^2(x + 1) + 7x(x + 1) + 6(x + 1)$

71. What polynomial, when factored, gives $(3x + 5y)(3x - 5y)$?

72. What polynomial, when factored, gives $(7x + 2y)(7x - 2y)$?

73. One factor of the trinomial $a^2 + 260a + 2500$ is $a + 10$. What is the other factor?

74. One factor of the trinomial $a^2 - 75a - 2500$ is $a + 25$. What is the other factor?

Review Problems   The following problems review some of the material we covered in Section 3.4. Reviewing these problems will help you with the next section.

Multiply.

75. $(x + 3)^2$

76. $(x - 3)^2$

77. $(2x - 5)^2$

78. $(2x + 5)^2$

79. $(x + 2)(x^2 - 2x + 4)$

80. $(x - 2)(x^2 + 2x + 4)$

Section 3.9   Special Factoring

In this section we will consider some special formulas. Some of the formulas are familiar, others are not. In any case, the formulas will work best if they are memorized.

Perfect Square Trinomials

We previously listed some special products found in multiplying polynomials. Two of the formulas looked like this:

$$(a + b)^2 = a^2 + 2ab + b^2$$
$$(a - b)^2 = a^2 - 2ab + b^2$$

If we exchange the left and right sides of each formula we have two special formulas for factoring:

$$a^2 + 2ab + b^2 = (a + b)^2$$
$$a^2 - 2ab + b^2 = (a - b)^2$$

The left side of each formula is called a *perfect square trinomial*. The right sides are binomial squares. Perfect square trinomials can always be factored using the usual methods for factoring trinomials. However, if we notice that the first and last terms of a trinomial are perfect squares, it is wise to see if the trinomial factors as a binomial square before attempting to factor by the usual method.

▼ **Example 1**   Factor $x^2 - 6x + 9$.

Solution   Since the first and last terms are perfect squares, we attempt to factor according to the preceding formulas:

$$x^2 - 6x + 9 = (x - 3)^2$$

If we expand $(x - 3)^2$, we have $x^2 - 6x + 9$, indicating we have factored correctly.   ▲

▼ **Example 2**   Factor $8x^2 - 24xy + 18y^2$.

Solution   We begin by factoring the greatest common factor 2 from each term. We then proceed as in Example 1:

$$8x^2 - 24xy + 18y^2 = 2(4x^2 - 12xy + 9y^2)$$
$$= 2(2x - 3y)^2 \qquad ▲$$

The Difference of Two Squares

Recall the formula that results in the difference of two squares: $(a - b)(a + b) = a^2 - b^2$. Writing this as a factoring formula we have

$$a^2 - b^2 = (a - b)(a + b)$$

Practice Problems

1. Factor $x^2 - 10x + 25$.

2. Factor $27x^2 - 36x + 12$.

Answers
1. $(x - 5)^2$ **2.** $3(3x - 2)^2$

3. Factor $25x^2 - 36y^2$.

Note: The sum of two squares never factors into the product of two binomials. That is, if we were to attempt to factor $(4x^2 + 9y^2)$ in the last example, we would be unable to find two binomials (or any other polynomials) whose product is $4x^2 + 9y^2$. The factors do not exist as polynomials.

4. Factor $(x - 4)^2 - 9$.

5. Factor $x^2 - 6x + 9 - y^2$.

▼ **Example 3** Factor $16x^4 - 81y^4$.

Solution The first and last terms are perfect squares. We factor according to the preceding formula:

$$16x^4 - 81y^4 = (4x^2)^2 - (9y^2)^2$$
$$= (4x^2 - 9y^2)(4x^2 + 9y^2)$$

Notice that the first factor is also the difference of two squares. Factoring completely we have

$$16x^4 - 81y^4 = (2x - 3y)(2x + 3y)(4x^2 + 9y^2) \quad ▲$$

Here is another example of the difference of two squares.

▼ **Example 4** Factor $(x - 3)^2 - 25$.

Solution This example has the form $a^2 - b^2$ where a is $x - 3$ and b is 5. We factor it according to the formula for the difference of two squares.

$$
\begin{array}{ll}
(x - 3)^2 - 25 = (x - 3)^2 - 5^2 & \text{Write 25 as } 5^2 \\
\quad = [(x - 3) - 5][(x - 3) + 5] & \text{Factor} \\
\quad = (x - 8)(x + 2) & \text{Simplify}
\end{array}
$$

Notice in this example we could have expanded $(x - 3)^2$, subtracted 25, and then factored to obtain the same result. Like this

$$
\begin{array}{ll}
(x - 3)^2 - 25 = x^2 - 6x + 9 - 25 & \text{Expand } (x - 3)^2 \\
\quad = x^2 - 6x - 16 & \text{Simplify} \\
\quad = (x - 8)(x + 2) & \text{Factor} \quad ▲
\end{array}
$$

▼ **Example 5** Factor $x^2 - 10x + 25 - y^2$.

Solution Notice the first three terms form a perfect square trinomial. That is, $x^2 - 10x + 25 = (x - 5)^2$. If we replace the first three terms by $(x - 5)^2$ the expression that results has the form $a^2 - b^2$. We can then factor as we did in Example 4.

$$
\begin{array}{ll}
x^2 - 10x + 25 - y^2 & \\
= (x^2 - 10x + 25) - y^2 & \text{Group first 3 terms together} \\
= (x - 5)^2 - y^2 & \text{This has the form } a^2 - b^2 \\
= [(x - 5) - y][(x - 5) + y] & \text{Factor according to the formula} \\
& \qquad a^2 - b^2 = (a - b)(a + b) \\
= (x - 5 - y)(x - 5 + y) & \text{Simplify}
\end{array}
$$

We could check this result by multiplying the two factors together. (You may want to do that to convince yourself that we have the correct result.) ▲

The Sum and Difference of Two Cubes

Here are the formulas for factoring the sum and difference of two cubes:

$$a^3 + b^3 = (a + b)(a^2 - ab + b^2)$$
$$a^3 - b^3 = (a - b)(a^2 + ab + b^2)$$

Since these formulas are unfamiliar, it is important that we verify them.

Answers
3. $(5x + 6y)(5x - 6y)$
4. $(x + 1)(x - 7)$
5. $(x - 3 + y)(x - 3 - y)$

▼ **Example 6**   Verify the two formulas.

Solution   We verify the formulas by multiplying the right sides and comparing the results with the left sides:

$$
\begin{array}{r}
a^2 \;-\; ab \;+\; b^2 \\
a \;+\; b \\
\hline
a^2b \;-\; ab^2 \;+\; b^3 \\
a^3 \;-\; a^2b \;+\; ab^2 \\
\hline
a^3 \qquad\qquad\qquad\quad +\; b^3
\end{array}
$$

The first formula is correct.

$$
\begin{array}{r}
a^2 \;+\; ab \;+\; b^2 \\
a \;-\; b \\
\hline
-\;a^2b \;-\; ab^2 \;-\; b^3 \\
a^3 \;+\; a^2b \;+\; ab^2 \\
\hline
a^3 \qquad\qquad\qquad\quad -\; b^3
\end{array}
$$

The second formula is correct.   ▲

Here are some examples using the formulas for factoring the sum and difference of two cubes.

▼ **Example 7**   Factor $x^3 - 8$.

Solution   Since the two terms are perfect cubes, we write them as such and apply the formula

$$
\begin{aligned}
x^3 - 8 &= x^3 - 2^3 \\
&= (x - 2)(x^2 + 2x + 4) \quad ▲
\end{aligned}
$$

▼ **Example 8**   Factor $27x^3 + 125y^3$.

Solution   Writing both terms as perfect cubes, we have

$$
\begin{aligned}
27x^3 + 125y^3 &= (3x)^3 + (5y)^3 \\
&= (3x + 5y)(9x^2 - 15xy + 25y^2) \quad ▲
\end{aligned}
$$

▼ **Example 9**   Factor $x^6 - y^6$.

Solution   We have a choice of how we want to write the two terms to begin with. We can write the expression as the difference of two squares, $(x^3)^2 - (y^3)^2$, or as the difference of two cubes, $(x^2)^3 - (y^2)^3$. It is better to use the difference of two squares if we have a choice:

$$
\begin{aligned}
x^6 - y^6 &= (x^3)^2 - (y^3)^2 \\
&= (x^3 - y^3)(x^3 + y^3) \\
&= (x - y)(x^2 + xy + y^2)(x + y)(x^2 - xy + y^2)
\end{aligned}
$$

Try this example again writing the first line as the difference of two cubes instead of the difference of two squares. It will become apparent why it is better to use the difference of two squares.   ▲

6.   Multiply: $(x - 3)(x^2 + 3x + 9)$.

7.   Factor $x^3 - 27$.

Note: The second factor does not factor further. If you have the idea that it does factor, you should try it to convince yourself that it does not.

8.   Factor $8x^3 + y^3$.

9.   Factor $x^6 - 1$.

Answers
6. $x^3 - 27$ **7.** $(x - 3)(x^2 + 3x + 9)$
8. $(2x + y)(4x^2 - 2xy + y^2)$
9. $(x + 1)(x^2 - x + 1)(x - 1)(x^2 + x + 1)$

Problem Set 3.9

Factor each perfect square trinomial.

1. $x^2 - 6x + 9$

2. $x^2 + 10x + 25$

3. $a^2 - 12a + 36$

4. $36 - 12a + a^2$

5. $9x^2 + 24x + 16$

6. $4x^2 - 12xy + 9y^2$

7. $16a^2 + 40ab + 25b^2$

8. $25a^2 - 40ab + 16b^2$

9. $16x^2 - 48x + 36$

10. $36x^2 + 48x + 16$

11. $75a^3 + 30a^2 + 3a$

12. $45a^4 - 30a^3 + 5a^2$

Factor each as the difference of two squares. Be sure to factor completely.

13. $x^2 - 9$

14. $x^2 - 16$

15. $4a^2 - 1$

16. $25a^2 - 1$

17. $9x^2 - 16y^2$

18. $25x^2 - 49y^2$

19. $x^4 - 81$

20. $x^4 - 16$

21. $16a^4 - 81$

22. $81a^4 - 16b^4$

23. $x^6 - y^6$

24. $x^6 - 1$

25. $a^6 - 64$

26. $64a^6 - 1$

Name _____

Class _____

Date _____

Answers

1. _____

2. _____

3. _____

4. _____

5. _____

6. _____

7. _____

8. _____

9. _____

10. _____

11. _____

12. _____

13. _____

14. _____

15. _____

16. _____

17. _____

18. _____

19. _____

20. _____

21. _____

22. _____

23. _____

24. _____

25. _____

26. _____

Answers

27. _____

28. _____

29. _____

30. _____

31. _____

32. _____

33. _____

34. _____

35. _____

36. _____

37. _____

38. _____

39. _____

40. _____

41. _____

42. _____

43. _____

44. _____

45. _____

46. _____

47. _____

48. _____

49. _____

50. _____

51. _____

52. _____

53. _____ 54. _____

55. _____ 56. _____

57. _____ 58. _____

Factor completely. Be sure to look for the greatest common factor first.

27. $5x^2 - 125$

28. $16x^2 - 36$

29. $3a^4 - 48$

30. $7a^4 - 7$

31. $(x - 2)^2 - 9$

32. $(x + 2)^2 - 9$

33. $(y + 4)^2 - 16$

34. $(y - 4)^2 - 16$

35. $25 - (a + 3)^2$

36. $49 - (a - 1)^2$

37. $x^2 - 10x + 25 - y^2$

38. $x^2 - 6x + 9 - y^2$

39. $a^2 + 8a + 16 - b^2$

40. $a^2 + 12a + 36 - b^2$

41. $x^2 + 2xy + y^2 - a^2$

42. $a^2 + 2ab + b^2 - y^2$

Factor each of the following as the sum or difference of two cubes.

43. $x^3 - y^3$

44. $x^3 + y^3$

45. $a^3 + 8$

46. $a^3 - 8$

47. $y^3 - 1$

48. $y^3 + 1$

49. $r^3 - 125$

50. $r^3 + 125$

51. $8x^3 - 27y^3$

52. $27x^3 - 8y^3$

Review Problems   The following problems review the material we covered in Section 2.3.

Solve each inequality.

53. $-5x \le 35$

54. $-3x > -12$

55. $9 - 2a > -3$

56. $7 - 4a \le -9$

57. $3x + 5 < 7x - 3$

58. $2x + 7 \ge 6x - 9$

Section 3.10   Factoring: A General Review

In this section we will review the different methods of factoring that we have presented in the previous sections of this chapter. This section is important because it will give you an opportunity to factor a variety of polynomials. We begin this section by listing the steps that can be used to factor polynomials of any type.

To Factor a Polynomial

Step 1:   If the polynomial has a greatest common factor other than 1, then factor out the greatest common factor.

Step 2:   If the polynomial has two terms (it is a binomial) then see if it is the difference of two squares, or the sum or difference of two cubes, and then factor accordingly. Remember, if it is the sum of two squares it will not factor.

Step 3:   If the polynomial has three terms (a trinomial), then it is either a perfect square trinomial which will factor into the square of a binomial, or it is not a perfect square trinomial, in which case you use the trial and error method developed in Section 3.8.

Step 4:   If the polynomial has more than three terms, then try to factor it by grouping.

Step 5:   As a final check, look and see if any of the factors you have written can be factored further. If you have overlooked a common factor, you can catch it here.

Here are some examples illustrating how we use the steps in our list. There are no new factoring problems in this section. The problems here are all similar to the problems you have seen before. What is different is that they are not all of the same type.

▼ **Example 1**   Factor $2x^5 - 8x^3$.

Solution   First we check to see if the greatest common factor is other than 1. Since the greatest common factor is $2x^3$, we begin by factoring it. Once we have done so, we notice that the binomial that remains is the difference of two squares, which we factor according to the formula

$$a^2 - b^2 = (a + b)(a - b)$$

$2x^5 - 8x^3 = 2x^3(x^2 - 4)$ Factor out the greatest
                                                        common factor $2x^3$

$\qquad\quad = 2x^3(x + 2)(x - 2)$ Factor the difference
                                                        of two squares   ▲

▼ **Example 2**   Factor $3x^4 - 18x^3 + 27x^2$.

Solution   Step 1 is to factor out the greatest common factor $3x^2$. After we have done so, we notice that the trinomial that remains is a perfect square trinomial, which will factor as the square of a binomial.

$3x^4 - 18x^3 + 27x^2 = 3x^2(x^2 - 6x + 9)$ Factor out $3x^2$
$\qquad\qquad\qquad\quad = 3x^2(x - 3)^2$ $x^2 - 6x + 9$ is the
                                                                    square of $x - 3$ ▲

Note: Prior to this section, the polynomials you have worked with have been grouped together according to the method used to factor them. That is, in Section 3.8 all the polynomials you factored were trinomials. What usually happens in a situation like this is that you will become proficient at factoring the kind of polynomial you are working with at the time, but will have trouble when given a variety of polynomials to factor.

Practice Problems

1.   Factor $3x^8 - 27x^6$.

Note: Note that the greatest common factor $2x^3$ that we factored from each term in the first step of Example 1 remains as part of the answer to the problem.

2.   Factor $4x^4 + 40x^3 + 100x^2$.

Note: When one of our factors is a monomial like $3x^2$, we do not factor it further. That is, it is not appropriate to write $3x^2$ as $3x \cdot x$.

Answers
1. $3x^6(x + 3)(x - 3)$ **2.** $4x^2(x + 5)^2$

3. Factor $y^4 + 36y^2$.

▼ **Example 3** Factor $y^3 + 25y$.

Solution We begin by factoring out the y that is common to both terms. The binomial that remains after we have done so is the sum of two squares which does not factor, so after the first step, we are finished.

$$y^3 + 25y = y(y^2 + 25)$$ ▲

4. Factor $6x^2 - x - 15$.

▼ **Example 4** Factor $6a^2 - 11a + 4$.

Solution Here we have a trinomial that does not have a greatest common factor other than 1. Since it is not a perfect square trinomial, we factor it by trial and error. Without showing all the different possibilities, here is the answer.

$$6a^2 - 11a + 4 = (3a - 4)(2a - 1)$$ ▲

5. Factor $3x^5 - 81x^2$.

▼ **Example 5** Factor $2x^4 + 16x$.

Solution This binomial has a greatest common factor of $2x$. The binomial that remains after the $2x$ has been factored from each term is the sum of two cubes, which we factor according to the formula $a^3 + b^3 = (a + b)(a^2 - ab + b^2)$.

$$\begin{aligned} 2x^4 + 16x &= 2x(x^3 + 8) &&\text{Factor } 2x \text{ from each term} \\ &= 2x(x + 2)(x^2 - 2x + 4) &&\text{The sum of two cubes} \end{aligned}$$ ▲

6. Factor $3a^2b^3 + 6a^2b^2 - 3a^2b$.

▼ **Example 6** Factor $2ab^5 + 8ab^4 + 2ab^3$.

Solution The greatest common factor is $2ab^3$. We begin by factoring it from each term. After that we find that the trinomial that remains cannot be factored further.

$$2ab^5 + 8ab^4 + 2ab^3 = 2ab^3(b^2 + 4b + 1)$$ ▲

7. Factor $x^2 - 10x + 25 - b^2$. (Hint: Group the first 3 terms together.)

▼ **Example 7** Factor $4x^2 - 6x + 2ax - 3a$.

Solution Our polynomial has four terms so we factor by grouping.

$$\begin{aligned} 4x^2 - 6x + 2ax - 3a &= 2x(2x - 3) + a(2x - 3) \\ &= (2x - 3)(2x + a) \end{aligned}$$ ▲

Answers
3. $y^2(y^2 + 36)$ **4.** $(3x - 5)(2x + 3)$
5. $3x^2(x - 3)(x^2 + 3x + 9)$
6. $3a^2b(b^2 + 2b - 1)$
7. $(x - 5 + b)(x - 5 - b)$

Problem Set 3.10

Name _____

Class _____

Date _____

Factor each of the following polynomials completely. That is, once you are finished factoring, none of the factors you obtain should be factorable. Also, note that the even-numbered problems are not necessarily similar to the odd-numbered problems that precede them in this problem set.

Answers

1. $x^2 - 81$

2. $x^2 - 18x + 81$

3. $x^2 + 2x - 15$

4. $15x^2 + 13x - 6$

5. $x^2(x + 2) + 6x(x + 2) + 9(x + 2)$

6. $12x^2 - 11x + 2$

7. $x^2y^2 + 2y^2 + x^2 + 2$

8. $21y^2 - 25y - 4$

9. $2a^3b + 6a^2b + 2ab$

10. $6a^2 - ab - 15b^2$

11. $x^2 + x + 1$

12. $x^2y + 3y + 2x^2 + 6$

13. $12a^2 - 75$

14. $18a^2 - 50$

15. $9x^2 - 12xy + 4y^2$

16. $x^3 - x^2$

17. $4x^3 + 16xy^2$

18. $16x^2 + 49y^2$

19. $2y^3 + 20y^2 + 50y$

20. $x^2 + 5bx - 2ax - 10ab$

21. $a^7 + 8a^4b^3$

22. $5a^2 - 45b^2$

23. $x^4 - 16$

24. $x^4 - 81$

25. $5a^2 + 10ab + 5b^2$

26. $3a^3b^2 + 15a^2b^2 + 3ab^2$

27. $x^2 + 49$

28. $16 - x^4$

1. _____   2. _____

3. _____   4. _____

5. _____   6. _____

7. _____   8. _____

9. _____   10. _____

11. _____   12. _____

13. _____   14. _____

15. _____   16. _____

17. _____   18. _____

19. _____   20. _____

21. _____   22. _____

23. _____   24. _____

25. _____   26. _____

27. _____   28. _____

Answers

29. _____   30. _____

31. _____   32. _____

33. _____   34. _____

35. _____   36. _____

37. _____   38. _____

39. _____   40. _____

41. _____   42. _____

43. _____   44. _____

45. _____   46. _____

47. _____   48. _____

49. _____   50. _____

51. _____   52. _____

53. _____

54. _____

55. _____

56. _____

29. $3x^2 + 15xy + 18y^2$

30. $3x^2 + 27xy + 54y^2$

31. $x^2(x - 3) - 14x(x - 3) + 49(x - 3)$

32. $x^2 + 3ax - 2bx - 6ab$

33. $x^2 - 64$

34. $9x^2 - 4$

35. $49a^7 - 9a^5$

36. $a^6 - b^6$

37. $49x^2 + 9y^2$

38. $12x^4 - 62x^3 + 70x^2$

39. $25a^3 + 20a^2 + 3a$

40. $16a^5 - 54a^2$

41. $24a^5b - 3a^2b$

42. $18a^4b^2 - 24a^3b^3 + 8a^2b^4$

43. $20x^4 - 45x^2$

44. $16x^3 + 16x^2 + 3x$

45. $16x^5 - 44x^4 + 30x^3$

46. $16x^2 + 16x - 1$

47. $y^6 - 1$

48. $25y^7 - 16y^5$

49. $12x^4y^2 + 36x^3y^3 + 27x^2y^4$

50. $16x^3y^2 - 4xy^2$

51. $x^2 - 4x + 4 - y^2$

52. $x^2 - 12x + 36 - b^2$

Review Problems   The following problems review material we covered in Section 2.5.

Graph the solution to each inequality.

53. $|x + 2| < 3$

54. $|x + 2| > 3$

55. $|2x - 1| + 2 \geq 5$

56. $|2x - 1| + 2 \leq 5$

Chapter 3   Summary and Review

Examples

PROPERTIES OF EXPONENTS [3.1, 3.2]

If a and b represent real numbers and r and s represent integers, then

1. $a^r \cdot a^s = a^{r+s}$

2. $(a^r)^s = a^{r \cdot s}$

3. $(ab)^r = a^r \cdot b^r$

4. $a^{-r} = \dfrac{1}{a^r}$ $(a \neq 0)$

5. $\left(\dfrac{a}{b}\right)^r = \dfrac{a^r}{b^r}$ $(b \neq 0)$

6. $\dfrac{a^r}{a^s} = a^{r-s}$ $(a \neq 0)$

7. $a^1 = a$
$a^0 = 1$ $(a \neq 0)$

1.   These expressions illustrate the properties of exponents.

a. $x^2 \cdot x^3 = x^{2+3} = x^5$

b. $(x^2)^3 = x^{2 \cdot 3} = x^6$

c. $(3x)^2 = 3^2 \cdot x^2 = 9x^2$

d. $2^{-3} = \dfrac{1}{2^3} = \dfrac{1}{8}$

e. $\left(\dfrac{x}{5}\right)^2 = \dfrac{x^2}{5^2} = \dfrac{x^2}{25}$

f. $\dfrac{x^7}{x^5} = x^{7-5} = x^2$

g. $3^1 = 3$
$3^0 = 1$

SCIENTIFIC NOTATION [3.1]

A number is written in scientific notation when it is written as the product of a number between 1 and 10 with an integer power of 10. That is, when it has the form

$$n \times 10^r$$

where $1 \leq n < 10$ and $r =$ an integer.

2. $49{,}800{,}000 = 4.98 \times 10^7$
$0.00462 = 4.62 \times 10^{-3}$

ADDITION OF POLYNOMIALS [3.3]

To add two polynomials simply combine the coefficients of similar terms.

3. $(3x^2 + 2x - 5) + (4x^2 - 7x + 2)$
$= 7x^2 - 5x - 3$

NEGATIVE SIGN PRECEDING PARENTHESES [3.3]

If there is a negative sign directly preceding the parentheses surrounding a polynomial, we may remove the parentheses and preceding negative sign by changing the sign of each term within the parentheses. (This procedure is actually just another application of the distributive property.)

4. $-(2x^2 - 8x - 9)$
$= -2x^2 + 8x + 9$

MULTIPLICATION OF POLYNOMIALS [3.4]

To multiply two polynomials, multiply each term in the first by each term in the second.

5. $(3x - 5)(x + 2)$
$= 3x^2 + 6x - 5x - 10$
$= 3x^2 + x - 10$

SPECIAL PRODUCTS [3.4]

$$(a + b)^2 = a^2 + 2ab + b^2$$
$$(a - b)^2 = a^2 - 2ab + b^2$$
$$(a + b)(a - b) = a^2 - b^2$$

6.   The following are examples of the three special products:

$$(x + 3)^2 = x^2 + 6x + 9$$
$$(x - 5)^2 = x^2 - 10x + 25$$
$$(x + 7)(x - 7) = x^2 - 49$$

DIVIDING A POLYNOMIAL BY A MONOMIAL [3.5]

To divide a polynomial by a monomial, divide each term of the polynomial by the monomial.

7. $\dfrac{15x^3 - 20x^2 + 10x}{5x}$

$= 3x^2 - 4x + 2$

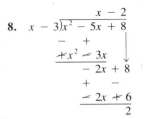

8.

$$x - 3 \overline{\smash{)}x^2 - 5x + 8}$$

with quotient $x - 2$, and remainder 2.

9. The greatest common factor of $10x^5 - 15x^4 + 30x^3$ is $5x^3$. Factoring it out of each term we have

$$5x^3(2x^2 - 3x + 6)$$

10.
$$x^2 + 5x + 6 = (x + 2)(x + 3)$$
$$x^2 - 5x + 6 = (x - 2)(x - 3)$$
$$x^2 + x - 6 = (x - 2)(x + 3)$$
$$x^2 - x - 6 = (x + 2)(x - 3)$$

11. Here are some binomials that have been factored this way.

$$x^2 + 6x + 9 = (x + 3)^2$$
$$x^2 - 6x + 9 = (x - 3)^2$$
$$x^2 - 9 = (x - 3)(x + 3)$$
$$x^3 - 27 = (x - 3)(x^2 + 3x + 9)$$
$$x^3 + 27 = (x + 3)(x^2 - 3x + 9)$$

12. Factor completely.

a. $3x^3 - 6x^2 = 3x^2(x - 2)$

b. $x^2 - 9 = (x + 3)(x - 3)$
$x^3 - 8 = (x - 2)(x^2 + 2x + 4)$
$x^3 + 27 = (x + 3)(x^2 - 3x + 9)$

c. $x^2 - 6x + 9 = (x - 3)^2$
$6x^2 - 7x - 5 = (2x + 1)(3x - 5)$

d. $x^2 + ax + bx + ab$
$= x(x + a) + b(x + a)$
$= (x + a)(x + b)$

LONG DIVISION WITH POLYNOMIALS [3.6]

To divide a polynomial by another polynomial with more than one term we use a process similar to long division with whole numbers. The steps in the process are: estimate, multiply, subtract, and bring down the next term.

GREATEST COMMON FACTOR [3.7]

The greatest common factor of a polynomial is the largest monomial (the monomial with the largest coefficient and highest exponent) that divides each term of the polynomial. The first step in factoring a polynomial is to factor the greatest common factor (if it is other than 1) out of each term.

FACTORING TRINOMIALS [3.8]

We factor a trinomial by writing it as the product of two binomials. (This refers to trinomials whose greatest common factor is 1.) Each factorable trinomial has a unique set of factors. Finding the factors is sometimes a matter of trial and error.

SPECIAL FACTORING [3.9]

$$a^2 + 2ab + b^2 = (a + b)^2$$
$$a^2 - 2ab + b^2 = (a - b)^2$$
$$a^2 - b^2 = (a - b)(a + b) \qquad \text{Difference of two squares}$$
$$a^3 - b^3 = (a - b)(a^2 + ab + b^2) \qquad \text{Difference of two cubes}$$
$$a^3 + b^3 = (a + b)(a^2 - ab + b^2) \qquad \text{Sum of two cubes}$$

TO FACTOR POLYNOMIALS IN GENERAL [3.10]

Step 1: If the polynomial has a greatest common factor other than 1, then factor out the greatest common factor.

Step 2: If the polynomial has two terms (it is a binomial) then see if it is the difference of two squares, or the sum or difference of two cubes, and then factor accordingly. Remember, if it is the sum of two squares it will not factor.

Step 3: If the polynomial has three terms (a trinomial), then it is either a perfect square trinomial which will factor into the square of a binomial, or it is not a perfect square trinomial, in which case you use the trial and error method developed in Section 3.8.

Step 4: If the polynomial has more than three terms, then try to factor it by grouping.

Step 5: As a final check, look and see if any of the factors you have written can be factored further. If you have overlooked a common factor, you can catch it here.

COMMON MISTAKES

1. Confusing the expressions $(-5)^2$ and -5^2. The base in the expression $(-5)^2$ is -5. The base in the expression -5^2 is just 5.

$$(-5)^2 = (-5)(-5) = 25$$
$$-5^2 = -5 \cdot 5 = -25$$

2. When we subtract one polynomial from another, it is common to forget to add the opposite of each term in the second polynomial. For example:

$$(6x - 5) - (3x + 4) = 6x - 5 - 3x + 4 \qquad \text{Mistake}$$
$$= 3x - 1$$

This mistake occurs if the negative sign outside the second set of parentheses is not distributed over all terms inside the parentheses. To avoid this mistake, remember: The opposite of a sum is the sum of the opposite, or,

$$-(3x + 4) = -3x + (-4)$$

3. Interpreting the square of a sum to be the sum of the squares. That is,

$$(x + y)^2 = x^2 + y^2 \qquad \text{Mistake}$$

This can easily be shown as false by trying a couple of numbers for x and y. If $x = 4$ and $y = 3$, we have

$$(4 + 3)^2 = 4^2 + 3^2$$
$$7^2 = 16 + 9$$
$$49 = 25$$

There has obviously been a mistake. The correct formula for $(a + b)^2$ is

$$(a + b)^2 = a^2 + 2ab + b^2$$

Chapter 3 Test

Name _____

Class _____

Date _____

Simplify. (Assume all variables are non-negative.) [3.1, 3.2]

1. $x^4 \cdot x^7 \cdot x^{-3}$

2. 2^{-5}

3. $(\frac{3}{4})^{-2}$

4. $(2x^2y)^3(2x^3y^4)^2$

5. $\dfrac{a^{-5}}{a^{-7}}$

6. $\dfrac{x^{n+1}}{x^{n-5}}$

7. $\dfrac{(2ab^3)^{-2}(a^4b^{-3})}{(a^{-4}b^3)^4(2a^{-2}b^2)^{-3}}$

Write each number in scientific notation. [3.1]

8. 6,530,000

9. 0.00087

Perform the indicated operations and write your answers in scientific notation. [3.2]

10. $(2.9 \times 10^{12})(3 \times 10^{-5})$

11. $\dfrac{(6 \times 10^{-4})(4 \times 10^9)}{8 \times 10^{-3}}$

Simplify. [3.3]

12. $(3x^3 - 4x^2 - 6) - (x^2 + 8x - 2)$

13. $3 - 4[2x - 3(x + 6)]$

Multiply. [3.4, 3.5]

14. $(3y - 7)(2y + 5)$

15. $(2x - 5)(x^2 + 4x - 3)$

16. $(4a - 3b)^2$

17. $(6y - 1)(6y + 1)$

18. $2x(x - 3)(2x + 5)$

Answers

1. _____

2. _____

3. _____

4. _____

5. _____

6. _____

7. _____

8. _____

9. _____

10. _____

11. _____

12. _____

13. _____

14. _____

15. _____

16. _____

17. _____

18. _____

Answers

19. _____

20. _____

21. _____

22. _____

23. _____

24. _____

25. _____

26. _____

27. _____

28. _____

29. _____

30. _____

19. Divide $30x^5y^3 - 15x^2y^2 + 20x^3y^5$ by $10xy^3$. [3.6]

20. Divide using long division. [3.6]

$$\frac{2x^3 - 9x^2 + 10}{2x - 1}$$

Factor completely. [3.7, 3.8, 3.9, 3.10]

21. $x^2 + x - 12$

22. $12x^2 + 26x - 10$

23. $16a^4 - 81y^4$

24. $7ax^2 - 14ay - b^2x^2 + 2b^2y$

25. $x^3 + 27$

26. $4a^5b - 24a^4b^2 - 64a^3b^3$

27. $x^2 - 10x + 25 - b^2$

28. $x^4 - 81$

29. $x^2(x + 2) - 4x(x + 2) + 4(x + 2)$

30. $4a^5 - 32a^2$

4 Rational Expressions

To the student:

This chapter is mostly concerned with simplifying a certain kind of algebraic expression. The expressions are called rational expressions because they are to algebra what rational numbers are to arithmetic. Most of the work we will do with rational expressions parallels the work you have done in previous math classes with fractions.

Once we have learned to add, subtract, multiply, and divide rational expressions, we will turn our attention to equations involving rational expressions. Equations of this type are used to describe a number of concepts in science, medicine, and other fields. For example, in electronics, it is a well-known fact that if R is the equivalent resistance of two resistors, R_1 and R_2, connected in parallel, then

$$\frac{1}{R} = \frac{1}{R_1} + \frac{1}{R_2}$$

This formula involves three fractions or rational expressions. If two of the resistances are known, we can solve for the third using the methods we will develop in this chapter.

The single most important tool needed for success in this chapter is factoring. Almost every problem encountered in this chapter involves factoring at one point or another. You may be able to understand all the theory and steps involved in solving the problems, but unless you can factor the polynomials in the problems, you will be unable to work any of them. Essentially, this chapter is a review of the properties of fractions and an exercise in factoring.

Section 4.1 Basic Properties and Reducing to Lowest Terms

We will begin this section with the definition of a rational expression. We will then develop the two basic properties associated with rational expressions, and end the section by applying one of the properties to reduce rational expressions to lowest terms.

Recall from Chapter 1 that a *rational number* is any number that can be expressed as the ratio of two integers:

$$\text{Rational numbers} = \left\{ \frac{a}{b} \middle| a \text{ and } b \text{ are integers, } b \neq 0 \right\}$$

A rational expression is defined similarly as any expression that can be written as the ratio of two polynomials:

$$\text{Rational expressions} = \left\{ \frac{P}{Q} \middle| P \text{ and } Q \text{ are polynomials, } Q \neq 0 \right\}$$

Some examples of rational expressions are

$$\frac{2x - 3}{x + 5} \qquad \frac{x^2 - 5x - 6}{x^2 - 1} \qquad \frac{a - b}{b - a}$$

Basic Properties

The basic properties associated with rational expressions are equivalent to the properties of fractions. It is important when working with fractions that we are able to change the form of a fraction (as when reducing to lowest terms or writing with a common denominator) without changing the value of the fraction.

For rational expressions, multiplying the numerator and denominator by the same nonzero expression may change the form of the rational expression, but it will always produce an expression equivalent to the original one. The same is true when dividing the numerator and denominator by the same nonzero quantity.

Note: These two statements are equivalent since division is defined as multiplication by the reciprocal. We choose to state them separately for clarity.

Properties of Rational Expressions

If P, Q, and K are polynomials with $Q \neq 0$ and $K \neq 0$, then

$$\frac{P}{Q} = \frac{PK}{QK} \quad \text{and} \quad \frac{P}{Q} = \frac{P/K}{Q/K}$$

Reducing to Lowest Terms

The fraction $\frac{6}{8}$ can be written in lowest terms as $\frac{3}{4}$. The process is shown here:

$$\frac{6}{8} = \frac{3 \cdot \overset{1}{\cancel{2}}}{4 \cdot \underset{1}{\cancel{2}}} = \frac{3}{4}$$

Reducing $\frac{6}{8}$ to $\frac{3}{4}$ involves dividing the numerator and denominator by 2, the factor they have in common. Before dividing out the common factor 2, we must notice that the common factor *is* 2! (This may not be obvious since we are very familiar with the numbers 6 and 8 and therefore do not have to put much thought into finding what number divides both of them.)

We reduce rational expressions to lowest terms by first factoring the numerator and denominator and then dividing both numerator and denominator by any factors they have in common.

▼ **Example 1** Reduce $\dfrac{x^2 - 9}{x - 3}$ to lowest terms.

Solution Factoring, we have

$$\frac{x^2 - 9}{x - 3} = \frac{(x + 3)(x - 3)}{x - 3}$$

The numerator and denominator have the factor $x - 3$ in common. Dividing the numerator and denominator by $x - 3$, we have

$$\frac{(x + 3)\overset{1}{\cancel{(x - 3)}}}{\underset{1}{\cancel{x - 3}}} = \frac{x + 3}{1} = x + 3$$

Here are some other examples of reducing rational expressions to lowest terms.

▼ **Example 2** Reduce to lowest terms.

a. $\dfrac{y^2 - 5y - 6}{y^2 - 1} = \dfrac{(y - 6)\cancel{(y + 1)}}{(y - 1)\cancel{(y + 1)}}$ Factor numerator and denominator

$$= \frac{y - 6}{y - 1}$$ Divide out common factor $(y + 1)$

b. $\dfrac{2a^3 - 16}{4a^2 - 12a + 8} = \dfrac{2(a^3 - 8)}{4(a^2 - 3a + 2)}$

$$= \frac{2\cancel{(a - 2)}(a^2 + 2a + 4)}{4\cancel{(a - 2)}(a - 1)}$$ Factor numerator and denominator

$$= \frac{a^2 + 2a + 4}{2(a - 1)}$$ Divide out common factor $2(a - 2)$

c. $\dfrac{x^2 - 3x + ax - 3a}{x^2 - ax - 3x + 3a} = \dfrac{x(x - 3) + a(x - 3)}{x(x - a) - 3(x - a)}$ Factor numerator and denominator

$$= \frac{\cancel{(x - 3)}(x + a)}{\cancel{(x - 3)}(x - a)}$$

$$= \frac{x + a}{x - a}$$ Divide out common factor $(x - 3)$ ▲

The answer to part c in Example 2 is $(x + a)/(x - a)$. The problem cannot be reduced further. It is a fairly common mistake to attempt to divide out an x or an a in this last expression. Remember, we can divide out only the factors common to the numerator and denominator of a rational expression. For the last expression in Example 2, part c, neither the numerator nor the denominator can be factored further; x is not a factor of the numerator or the denominator and neither is a. The expression is in lowest terms.

Practice Problems

1. Reduce to lowest terms.

$$\frac{x^2 - 9}{x + 3}$$

Note: The lines drawn through the $(x - 3)$ in the numerator and denominator indicate that we have divided through by $(x - 3)$. As the problems become more involved these lines will help keep track of which factors have been divided out and which have not.

2. Reduce to lowest terms.

a. $\dfrac{y^2 - y - 6}{y^2 - 4}$

b. $\dfrac{3a^3 + 3}{6a^2 - 6a + 6}$

c. $\dfrac{x^2 + 4x + ax + 4a}{x^2 + ax + 4x + 4a}$

Note: In Example 2 we are no longer showing the 1's that result when we divide out our common factors. If you need to show the 1's to remind you that you are *dividing*, then be sure to do so.

The next example involves what we may call a trick. The trick is to reverse the order of the terms in a difference by factoring -1 from each term. The next examples illustrate how this is done.

3. Replace a with 7 and b with 4 and then simplify.

$$\frac{a - b}{b - a}$$

▼ **Example 3**   Reduce to lowest terms $\dfrac{a - b}{b - a}$.

Solution   The relationship between $a - b$ and $b - a$ is that they are opposites. We can show this fact by factoring -1 from each term in the numerator:

$$\frac{a - b}{b - a} = \frac{-1(-a + b)}{b - a} \qquad \text{Factor } -1 \text{ from each term in the numerator}$$

$$= \frac{-1(b - a)}{b - a} \qquad \text{Reverse the order of the terms in the numerator}$$

$$= -1 \qquad \text{Divide out common factor } b - a \quad ▲$$

4. Reduce to lowest terms.

$$\frac{7 - x}{x^2 - 49}$$

▼ **Example 4**   Reduce to lowest terms $\dfrac{x^2 - 25}{5 - x}$.

Solution   We begin by factoring the numerator:

$$\frac{x^2 - 25}{5 - x} = \frac{(x - 5)(x + 5)}{5 - x}$$

The factors $(x - 5)$ and $(5 - x)$ are similar but are not exactly the same. We can reverse the order of either by factoring -1 from them. That is:
$5 - x = -1(-5 + x) = -1(x - 5)$.

$$\frac{(x - 5)(x + 5)}{5 - x} = \frac{(x - 5)(x + 5)}{-1(x - 5)}$$

$$= \frac{x + 5}{-1}$$

$$= -(x + 5) \qquad ▲$$

Sometimes we can apply the trick before we actually factor the polynomials in our rational expression.

5. Reduce to lowest terms.

$$\frac{x^2 - 10x + 25}{25 - x^2}$$

▼ **Example 5**   Reduce to lowest terms $\dfrac{x^2 - 6xy + 9y^2}{9y^2 - x^2}$.

Solution   We begin by factoring -1 from the denominator to reverse the order of the terms in $9y^2 - x^2$:

$$\frac{x^2 - 6xy + 9y^2}{9y^2 - x^2} = \frac{x^2 - 6xy + 9y^2}{-1(x^2 - 9y^2)}$$

$$= \frac{(x - 3y)(x - 3y)}{-1(x - 3y)(x + 3y)}$$

$$= -\frac{x - 3y}{x + 3y} \qquad ▲$$

Answers

3. -1 **4.** $\dfrac{-1}{x + 7}$

5. $-\dfrac{x - 5}{x + 5}$ or $\dfrac{5 - x}{5 + x}$

Problem Set 4.1

Reduce each rational expression to lowest terms.

1. $\dfrac{x^2 - 16}{6x + 24}$

2. $\dfrac{5x + 25}{x^2 - 25}$

3. $\dfrac{12x - 9y}{3x^2 + 3xy}$

4. $\dfrac{x^3 - xy^2}{4x + 4y}$

5. $\dfrac{a^4 - 81}{a - 3}$

6. $\dfrac{a + 4}{a^2 - 16}$

7. $\dfrac{y^2 - y - 12}{y - 4}$

8. $\dfrac{y^2 + 7y + 10}{y + 5}$

9. $\dfrac{a^2 - 4a - 12}{a^2 + 8a + 12}$

10. $\dfrac{a^2 - 7a + 12}{a^2 - 9a + 20}$

Name _____

Class _____

Date _____

Answers

1. _____

2. _____

3. _____

4. _____

5. _____

6. _____

7. _____

8. _____

9. _____

10. _____

Answers

11. _____

12. _____

13. _____

14. _____

15. _____

16. _____

17. _____

18. _____

19. _____

20. _____

11. $\dfrac{4y^2 - 9}{2y^2 - y - 3}$

12. $\dfrac{9y^2 - 1}{3y^2 - 10y + 3}$

13. $\dfrac{x^2 + x - 6}{x^2 + 2x - 3}$

14. $\dfrac{x^2 + 10x + 25}{x^2 - 25}$

15. $\dfrac{(x - 3)^2(x + 2)}{(x + 2)^2(x - 3)}$

16. $\dfrac{(x - 4)^3(x + 3)}{(x + 3)^2(x - 4)}$

17. $\dfrac{a^3 + b^3}{a^2 - b^2}$

18. $\dfrac{a^2 - b^2}{a^3 - b^3}$

19. $\dfrac{6x^2 + 7xy - 3y^2}{6x^2 + xy - y^2}$

20. $\dfrac{4x^2 - y^2}{4x^2 - 8xy - 5y^2}$

21. $\dfrac{ax + 2x + 3a + 6}{ay + 2y - 4a - 8}$

22. $\dfrac{ax - x - 5a + 5}{ax + x - 5a - 5}$

23. $\dfrac{x^2 + bx - 3x - 3b}{x^2 - 2bx - 3x + 6b}$

24. $\dfrac{x^2 - 3ax - 2x + 6a}{x^2 - 3ax + 2x - 6a}$

Refer to Examples 3, 4, and 5 in this section and reduce the following to lowest terms.

25. $\dfrac{x - 4}{4 - x}$

26. $\dfrac{6 - x}{x - 6}$

27. $\dfrac{y^2 - 36}{6 - y}$

28. $\dfrac{1 - y}{y^2 - 1}$

29. $\dfrac{1 - 9a^2}{9a^2 - 6a + 1}$

30. $\dfrac{1 - a^2}{a^2 - 2a + 1}$

31. $\dfrac{6 - 5x - x^2}{x^2 + 5x - 6}$

32. $\dfrac{x^2 - 5x + 6}{6 - x - x^2}$

Name _____

Class _____

Date _____

Answers

21. _____

22. _____

23. _____

24. _____

25. _____

26. _____

27. _____

28. _____

29. _____

30. _____

31. _____

32. _____

Answers

33. _____

34. _____

35. _____

36. _____

37. _____ 38. _____

39. _____ 40. _____

41. _____ 42. _____

43. _____ 44. _____

45. _____ 46. _____

Explain the mistake made in each of the following problems.

33. $\dfrac{x^2 - 9}{x - 3} = x - 3$

34. $\dfrac{x^2 - 6x + 9}{x^2 + x - 6} = \dfrac{3}{2}$

35. $\dfrac{x + y}{x} = y$

36. $\dfrac{x - 3}{3} = x$

37. Replace x with 3 in the expression $\dfrac{x^3 - 1}{x - 1}$, and then simplify. The result should be the same as what you would get if you replaced x with 3 in the expression $x^2 + x + 1$.

38. Replace x with 7 in the expression $\dfrac{x - 4}{4 - x}$ and simplify. Now, replace x with 10 and simplify. The result in both cases should be the same. Can you think of a number to replace x with, that will not give the same result?

Review Problems The following problems review material we covered in Section 1.6. Reviewing these problems will help you get started in the next section.

Divide.

39. $\dfrac{3}{5} \div \dfrac{2}{7}$

40. $\dfrac{2}{7} \div \dfrac{3}{5}$

41. $\dfrac{3}{4} \div \dfrac{6}{11}$

42. $\dfrac{6}{8} \div \dfrac{3}{5}$

43. $\dfrac{4}{9} \div 8$

44. $\dfrac{3}{7} \div 6$

45. $8 \div \dfrac{1}{4}$

46. $12 \div \dfrac{2}{3}$

Section 4.2 Multiplication and Division of Rational Expressions

In Section 4.1 we found the process of reducing rational expressions to lowest terms to be the same process used in reducing fractions to lowest terms. The similarity also holds for the process of multiplication or division of rational expressions.

Multiplication with fractions is the simplest of the four basic operations. To multiply two fractions we simply multiply numerators and multiply denominators. That is, if a, b, c, and d are real numbers, with $b \neq 0$ and $d \neq 0$, then

$$\frac{a}{b} \cdot \frac{c}{d} = \frac{ac}{bd}$$

▼ Example 1 Multiply: $\frac{6}{7} \cdot \frac{14}{18}$.

Solution

$$\frac{6}{7} \cdot \frac{14}{18} = \frac{6(14)}{7(18)} \qquad \text{Multiply numerators}$$
$$\text{and denominators}$$

$$= \frac{2 \cdot 3(2 \cdot 7)}{7(2 \cdot 3 \cdot 3)} \qquad \text{Factor}$$

$$= \frac{2}{3} \qquad \text{Divide out common}$$
$$\text{factors} \qquad \blacktriangle$$

Our next example is similar to some of the problems we worked in Chapter 3. We multiply fractions whose numerators and denominators are monomials by multiplying numerators and multiplying denominators and then reducing to lowest terms. Here is how it looks.

▼ Example 2 Multiply: $\frac{8x^3}{27y^8} \cdot \frac{9y^3}{12x^2}$.

Solution We multiply numerators without actually carrying out the multiplication:

$$\frac{8x^3}{27y^8} \cdot \frac{9y^3}{12x^2} = \frac{8 \cdot 9x^3y^3}{27 \cdot 12x^2y^8} \qquad \text{Multiply numerators}$$
$$\text{Multiply denominators}$$

$$= \frac{4 \cdot 2 \cdot 9x^3y^3}{9 \cdot 3 \cdot 4 \cdot 3x^2y^8} \qquad \text{Factor coefficients}$$

$$= \frac{2x}{9y^5} \qquad \text{Divide out}$$
$$\text{common factors} \qquad \blacktriangle$$

The product of two rational expressions is the product of their numerators over the product of their denominators.

Once again we should mention that the little slashes we have drawn through the factors are simply used to denote the factors we have divided out of the numerator and denominator.

Practice Problems

1. Multiply $\frac{3}{4} \cdot \frac{12}{27}$.

2. Multiply $\frac{6x^4}{4y^9} \cdot \frac{12y^5}{3x^2}$.

Note: Notice how we factor the coefficients just enough so that we can see the factors they have in common. If you want to show this step without showing the factoring, it would look like this:

$$\frac{\overset{2}{8} \cdot \overset{1}{9}x^3y^3}{\underset{3}{27} \cdot \underset{3}{12}x^2y^8}$$

Answers

1. $\frac{1}{3}$ 2. $\frac{6x^2}{y^4}$

3. Multiply $\dfrac{x+5}{x^2-25} \cdot \dfrac{x-5}{x^2-10x+25}$.

▼ **Example 3** Multiply: $\dfrac{x-3}{x^2-4} \cdot \dfrac{x+2}{x^2-6x+9}$.

Solution We begin by multiplying numerators and denominators. We then factor all polynomials and divide out factors common to the numerator and denominator:

$$\frac{x-3}{x^2-4} \cdot \frac{x+2}{x^2-6x+9}$$

$$= \frac{(x-3)(x+2)}{(x^2-4)(x^2-6x+9)} \qquad \text{Multiply}$$

$$= \frac{\cancel{(x-3)}\cancel{(x+2)}}{\cancel{(x+2)}(x-2)\cancel{(x-3)}(x-3)} \qquad \text{Factor}$$

$$= \frac{1}{(x-2)(x-3)} \qquad \begin{array}{l}\text{Divide out}\\\text{common factors}\end{array} \ \ \blacktriangle$$

The first two steps can be combined to save time. We can perform the multiplication and factoring steps together.

4. Multiply.

$$\frac{3y^2-3y}{3y-12} \cdot \frac{y^2-2y-8}{y^2+3y+2}$$

▼ **Example 4** Multiply: $\dfrac{2y^2-4y}{2y^2-2} \cdot \dfrac{y^2-2y-3}{y^2-5y+6}$.

Solution

$$\frac{2y^2-4y}{2y^2-2} \cdot \frac{y^2-2y-3}{y^2-5y+6} = \frac{2y\cancel{(y-2)}\cancel{(y-3)}\cancel{(y+1)}}{2\cancel{(y+1)}(y-1)\cancel{(y-3)}\cancel{(y-2)}}$$

$$= \frac{y}{y-1} \qquad\qquad\qquad \blacktriangle$$

Notice in both of the preceding examples that we did not actually multiply the polynomials as we did in Chapter 3. It would be senseless to do that since we would then have to factor each of the resulting products to reduce them to lowest terms.

The quotient of two rational expressions is the product of the first and the reciprocal of the second. That is, we find the quotient of two rational expressions the same way we find the quotient of two fractions. Here is an example that reviews division with fractions.

5. Divide $\frac{5}{9} \div \frac{10}{27}$.

▼ **Example 5** Divide: $\frac{6}{8} \div \frac{3}{5}$.

Solution

$$\frac{6}{8} \div \frac{3}{5} = \frac{6}{8} \cdot \frac{5}{3} \qquad \begin{array}{l}\text{Write division in terms}\\\text{of multiplication}\end{array}$$

$$= \frac{6(5)}{8(3)} \qquad \begin{array}{l}\text{Multiply numerators and}\\\text{denominators}\end{array}$$

$$= \frac{\cancel{2}\cdot\cancel{3}(5)}{\cancel{2}\cdot 2\cdot 2(\cancel{3})} \qquad \text{Factor}$$

$$= \frac{5}{4} \qquad\qquad \text{Divide out common factors} \ \ \blacktriangle$$

Answers

3. $\dfrac{1}{(x-5)^2}$ **4.** $\dfrac{y(y-1)}{y+1}$ **5.** $\frac{3}{2}$

To divide one rational expression by another, we use the definition of division to multiply by the reciprocal of the expression that follows the division symbol.

▼ **Example 6**   Divide: $\dfrac{8x^3}{5y^2} \div \dfrac{4x^2}{10y^6}$.

Solution   First we rewrite the problem in terms of multiplication. Then we multiply.

$$\frac{8x^3}{5y^2} \div \frac{4x^2}{10y^6} = \frac{8x^3}{5y^2} \cdot \frac{10y^6}{4x^2}$$

$$= \frac{\overset{2}{\cancel{8}} \cdot \overset{2}{\cancel{10}}x^3 y^6}{\cancel{4} \cdot \cancel{5}x^2 y^2}$$

$$= 4xy^4 \qquad ▲$$

▼ **Example 7**   Divide: $\dfrac{x^2 - y^2}{x^2 - 2xy + y^2} \div \dfrac{x^3 + y^3}{x^3 - x^2 y}$.

Solution   We begin by writing the problem as the product of the first and the reciprocal of the second and then proceed as in the previous two examples:

$$\frac{x^2 - y^2}{x^2 - 2xy + y^2} \div \frac{x^3 + y^3}{x^3 - x^2 y}$$

$$= \frac{x^2 - y^2}{x^2 - 2xy + y^2} \cdot \frac{x^3 - x^2 y}{x^3 + y^3} \qquad \begin{array}{l}\text{Multiply by the} \\ \text{reciprocal of the} \\ \text{divisor}\end{array}$$

$$= \frac{\cancel{(x-y)}\cancel{(x+y)}(x^2)\cancel{(x-y)}}{\cancel{(x-y)}\cancel{(x-y)}\cancel{(x+y)}(x^2 - xy + y^2)} \qquad \begin{array}{l}\text{Factor and} \\ \text{multiply}\end{array}$$

$$= \frac{x^2}{x^2 - xy + y^2} \qquad \begin{array}{l}\text{Divide out common} \\ \text{factors} \qquad ▲\end{array}$$

Here are some more examples of multiplication and division with rational expressions.

▼ **Example 8**   Perform the indicated operations.

$$\frac{a^2 - 8a + 15}{a + 4} \cdot \frac{a + 2}{a^2 - 5a + 6} \div \frac{a^2 - 3a - 10}{a^2 + 2a - 8}$$

Solution   First we rewrite the division as multiplication by the reciprocal. Then we proceed as usual.

$$\frac{a^2 - 8a + 15}{a + 4} \cdot \frac{a + 2}{a^2 - 5a + 6} \div \frac{a^2 - 3a - 10}{a^2 + 2a - 8}$$

$$= \frac{(a^2 - 8a + 15)(a + 2)(a^2 + 2a - 8)}{(a + 4)(a^2 - 5a + 6)(a^2 - 3a - 10)} \qquad \begin{array}{l}\text{Change division to} \\ \text{multiplication by} \\ \text{using the reciprocal}\end{array}$$

$$= \frac{\cancel{(a-5)}\cancel{(a-3)}\cancel{(a+2)}\cancel{(a+4)}\cancel{(a-2)}}{\cancel{(a+4)}\cancel{(a-3)}\cancel{(a-2)}\cancel{(a-5)}\cancel{(a+2)}} \qquad \text{Factor}$$

$$= 1 \qquad \begin{array}{l}\text{Divide out common} \\ \text{factors} \qquad ▲\end{array}$$

6.   Divide $\dfrac{9x^4}{4y^3} \div \dfrac{3x^2}{8y^5}$.

7.   Divide.

$$\frac{xy^2 - y^3}{x^2 - y^2} \div \frac{x^3 + y^3}{x^2 + 2xy + y^2}$$

8.   Perform the indicated operations.

$$\frac{a^2 + 3a - 4}{a - 4} \cdot \frac{a + 3}{a^2 - 4a + 3} \div \frac{a + 1}{a^2 - 2a - 3}$$

Answers

6. $6x^2 y^2$ 7. $\dfrac{y^2}{x^2 - xy + y^2}$

8. $\dfrac{(a + 4)(a + 3)}{a - 4}$

Our next example involves factoring by grouping. As you may have noticed, working the problems in this chapter gives you a very detailed review of factoring.

9. Multiply.

$$\frac{xa + xb - ya - yb}{xa + 2x + ya + 2y} \cdot \frac{xa + 2x + ya + 2y}{xa + xb + ya + yb}$$

▼ **Example 9** Multiply: $\dfrac{xa + xb + ya + yb}{xa - xb - ya + yb} \cdot \dfrac{xa + xb - ya - yb}{xa - xb + ya - yb}$.

Solution We will factor each polynomial by grouping, which takes two steps.

$$\frac{xa + xb + ya + yb}{xa - xb - ya + yb} \cdot \frac{xa + xb - ya - yb}{xa - xb + ya - yb}$$

$$= \frac{x(a + b) + y(a + b)}{x(a - b) - y(a - b)} \cdot \frac{x(a + b) - y(a + b)}{x(a - b) + y(a - b)} \quad \left.\begin{array}{c} \\ \\ \end{array}\right\} \begin{array}{c} \text{Factor by} \\ \text{grouping} \end{array}$$

$$= \frac{(x + y)(a + b)(x - y)(a + b)}{(x - y)(a - b)(x + y)(a - b)}$$

$$= \frac{(a + b)^2}{(a - b)^2} \qquad\qquad ▲$$

10. Multiply.

$$(5x^2 - 45) \cdot \frac{3}{5x - 15}$$

▼ **Example 10** Multiply: $(4x^2 - 36) \cdot \dfrac{12}{4x + 12}$

Solution We can think of $4x^2 - 36$ as having a denominator of 1. Thinking of it in this way allows us to proceed as we did in the previous examples.

$$(4x^2 - 36) \cdot \frac{12}{4x + 12}$$

$$= \frac{4x^2 - 36}{1} \cdot \frac{12}{4x + 12} \qquad \text{Write } 4x^2 - 36 \text{ with denominator 1}$$

$$= \frac{4(x - 3)(x + 3)12}{4(x + 3)} \qquad \text{Factor}$$

$$= 12(x - 3) \qquad\qquad \text{Divide out common factors} \qquad ▲$$

11. Multiply.

$$4(x + 3)(x - 3) \cdot \frac{x}{x^2 - 9}$$

▼ **Example 11** Multiply: $3(x - 2)(x - 1) \cdot \dfrac{5}{x^2 - 3x + 2}$.

Solution This problem is very similar to the problem in Example 10. Writing the first rational expression with a denominator of 1 we have

$$\frac{3(x - 2)(x - 1)}{1} \cdot \frac{5}{x^2 - 3x + 2} = \frac{3(x - 2)(x - 1)5}{(x - 2)(x - 1)}$$

$$= 3 \cdot 5$$

$$= 15 \qquad ▲$$

Answers

9. $\dfrac{x - y}{x + y}$ **10.** $3(x + 3)$ **11.** $4x$

Problem Set 4.2

Name _____

Class _____

Date _____

Perform the indicated operations involving fractions.

1. $\dfrac{2}{9} \cdot \dfrac{3}{4}$

2. $\dfrac{5}{6} \cdot \dfrac{7}{8}$

3. $\dfrac{3}{4} \div \dfrac{1}{3}$

4. $\dfrac{3}{8} \div \dfrac{5}{4}$

5. $\dfrac{3}{7} \cdot \dfrac{14}{24} \div \dfrac{1}{2}$

6. $\dfrac{6}{5} \cdot \dfrac{10}{36} \div \dfrac{3}{4}$

7. $\dfrac{10x^2}{5y^2} \cdot \dfrac{15y^3}{2x^4}$

8. $\dfrac{8x^3}{7y^4} \cdot \dfrac{14y^6}{16x^2}$

9. $\dfrac{11a^2b}{5ab^2} \div \dfrac{22a^3b^2}{10ab^4}$

10. $\dfrac{8ab^3}{9a^2b} \div \dfrac{16a^2b^2}{18ab^3}$

11. $\dfrac{6x^2}{5y^3} \cdot \dfrac{11z^2}{2x^2} \div \dfrac{33z^5}{10y^8}$

12. $\dfrac{4x^3}{7y^2} \cdot \dfrac{6z^5}{5x^6} \div \dfrac{24z^2}{35x^6}$

Perform the indicated operations. Be sure to write all answers in lowest terms.

13. $\dfrac{x^2 - 9}{x^2 - 4} \cdot \dfrac{x - 2}{x - 3}$

14. $\dfrac{x^2 - 16}{x^2 - 25} \cdot \dfrac{x - 5}{x - 4}$

15. $\dfrac{y^2 - 1}{y + 2} \cdot \dfrac{y^2 + 5y + 6}{y^2 + 2y - 3}$

16. $\dfrac{y - 1}{y^2 - y - 6} \cdot \dfrac{y^2 + 5y + 6}{y^2 - 1}$

17. $\dfrac{3x - 12}{x^2 - 4} \cdot \dfrac{x^2 + 6x + 8}{x - 4}$

18. $\dfrac{x^2 + 5x + 1}{4x - 4} \cdot \dfrac{x - 1}{x^2 + 5x + 1}$

Answers

1. _____ 2. _____

3. _____ 4. _____

5. _____ 6. _____

7. _____ 8. _____

9. _____ 10. _____

11. _____ 12. _____

13. _____

14. _____

15. _____

16. _____

17. _____

18. _____

Answers

19. _____

20. _____

21. _____

22. _____

23. _____

24. _____

25. _____

26. _____

27. _____

28. _____

19. $\dfrac{a^2 - 5a + 6}{a^2 - 2a - 3} \div \dfrac{a - 5}{a^2 + 3a + 2}$

20. $\dfrac{a^2 + 7a + 12}{a - 5} \div \dfrac{a^2 + 9a + 18}{a^2 - 7a + 10}$

21. $\dfrac{2x^2 - 5x - 12}{4x^2 + 8x + 3} \div \dfrac{x^2 - 16}{2x^2 + 7x + 3}$

22. $\dfrac{x^2 - 2x + 1}{3x^2 + 7x - 20} \div \dfrac{x^2 + 3x - 4}{3x^2 - 2x - 5}$

23. $\dfrac{x^2 + 5x + 6}{x + 1} \cdot \dfrac{x^2 - 1}{x^2 + 7x + 10} \div \dfrac{x^2 + 2x - 3}{x + 5}$

24. $\dfrac{2x^2 - x - 1}{x^2 - 2x - 15} \cdot \dfrac{x - 5}{4x^2 - 1} \div \dfrac{x - 1}{x^2 - 9}$

25. $\dfrac{x^3 - 1}{x^4 - 1} \cdot \dfrac{x^2 - 1}{x^2 + x + 1}$

26. $\dfrac{x^3 - 8}{x^4 - 16} \cdot \dfrac{x^2 + 4}{x^2 + 2x + 4}$

27. $\dfrac{a^2 - 16}{a^2 - 8a + 16} \cdot \dfrac{a^2 - 9a + 20}{a^2 - 7a + 12} \div \dfrac{a^2 - 25}{a^2 - 6a + 9}$

28. $\dfrac{a^2 - 6a + 9}{a^2 - 4} \cdot \dfrac{a^2 - 5a + 6}{(a - 3)^2} \div \dfrac{a^2 - 9}{a^2 - a - 6}$

29. $\dfrac{xy - 2x + 3y - 6}{xy + 2x - 4y - 8} \cdot \dfrac{xy + x - 4y - 4}{xy - x + 3y - 3}$

30. $\dfrac{ax + bx + 2a + 2b}{ax - 3a + bx - 3b} \cdot \dfrac{ax - bx - 3a + 3b}{ax - bx - 2a + 2b}$

31. $\dfrac{xy - y + 4x - 4}{xy - 3y + 4x - 12} \div \dfrac{xy + 2x + y + 2}{xy - 3y + 2x - 6}$

32. $\dfrac{xb - 2b + 3x - 6}{xb + 3b + 3x + 9} \cdot \dfrac{xb - 2b - 2x + 4}{xb + 3b - 2x - 6}$

Use the method shown in Examples 10 and 11 to find the following products.

33. $(3x - 6) \cdot \dfrac{x}{x - 2}$

34. $(4x + 8) \cdot \dfrac{x}{x + 2}$

35. $(x^2 - 25) \cdot \dfrac{2}{x - 5}$

36. $(x^2 - 49) \cdot \dfrac{5}{x + 7}$

37. $(x^2 - 3x + 2) \cdot \dfrac{3}{3x - 3}$

38. $(x^2 - 3x + 2) \cdot \dfrac{-1}{x - 2}$

Name _____

Class _____

Date _____

Answers

29. _____

30. _____

31. _____

32. _____

33. _____

34. _____

35. _____

36. _____

37. _____

38. _____

Answers

39. _____

40. _____

41. _____

42. _____

43. ←——————————→

44. ←——————————→

45. ←——————————→

46. ←——————————→

47. ←——————————→

48. ←——————————→

39. $(y - 3)(y - 4)(y + 3) \cdot \dfrac{-1}{y^2 - 9}$

40. $(y + 1)(y + 4)(y - 1) \cdot \dfrac{3}{y^2 - 1}$

41. $a(a + 5)(a - 5) \cdot \dfrac{a + 1}{a^2 + 5a}$

42. $a(a + 3)(a - 3) \cdot \dfrac{a - 1}{a^2 - 3a}$

Review Problems The following problems review material we covered in Section 2.5.

Solve each inequality, and graph the solution.

43. $|x - 3| > 5$

44. $|x - 5| > 2$

45. $|2x - 5| < 3$

46. $|3x - 6| < 12$

47. $|2x + 1| \le 3$

48. $|4x - 3| \le 9$

Section 4.3 Addition and Subtraction of Rational Expressions

This section is concerned with addition and subtraction of rational expressions. In the first part of this section we will look at addition of expressions that have the same denominator. In the second part of this section we will look at addition of expressions that have different denominators.

Addition and Subtraction with the Same Denominator

To add two expressions that have the same denominator, we simply add numerators and put the sum over the common denominator. Since the process we use to add and subtract rational expressions is the same process used to add and subtract fractions, we will begin with an example involving fractions.

▼ **Example 1** Add: $\frac{4}{9} + \frac{2}{9}$.

Solution We add fractions with the same denominator by adding numerators and putting the result over the common denominator because of the distributive property. Here is a detailed look at the steps involved.

$$
\begin{aligned}
\frac{4}{9} + \frac{2}{9} &= 4\left(\frac{1}{9}\right) + 2\left(\frac{1}{9}\right) \\
&= (4 + 2)\left(\frac{1}{9}\right) \qquad \text{Distributive property} \\
&= 6\left(\frac{1}{9}\right) \\
&= \frac{6}{9} \\
&= \frac{2}{3} \qquad \text{Divide numerator and denominator} \\
&\qquad\qquad \text{by common factor 3}
\end{aligned}
$$

Note that the important thing about the fractions in this example is that they each have a denominator of 9. If they did not have the same denominator, we could not have written them as two terms with a factor of $\frac{1}{9}$ in common. Without the $\frac{1}{9}$ common to each term, we couldn't apply the distributive property. And without the distributive property, we would not have been able to add the two fractions. ▲

In the examples that follow, we will not show all the steps we have shown in Example 1. The steps are shown in Example 1 so that you will see why both fractions must have the same denominator before we can add them. In actual practice we simply add numerators and place the result over the common denominator.

Practice Problems

1. Add $\frac{3}{8} + \frac{1}{8}$.

Note: You probably already know how to add two fractions with the same denominator. But, are you sure you know *why* you add them the way you do? If not, then you should pay close attention to the details in Example 1, because that's the point of Example 1: to show you the *why* behind the work you do when you add fractions.

Answer
1. $\frac{1}{2}$

We add and subtract rational expressions with the same denominator by combining numerators and writing the result over the common denominator. Then we reduce the result to lowest terms if possible. Here is an example.

2. Add $\dfrac{x}{x^2 - 9} + \dfrac{3}{x^2 - 9}$.

▼ **Example 2**   Add: $\dfrac{x}{x^2 - 1} + \dfrac{1}{x^2 - 1}$.

Solution   Since the denominators are the same, we simply add numerators:

$$\frac{x}{x^2 - 1} + \frac{1}{x^2 - 1} = \frac{x + 1}{x^2 - 1} \qquad \text{Add numerators}$$

$$= \frac{\cancel{x + 1}}{(x - 1)\cancel{(x + 1)}} \qquad \text{Factor denominator}$$

$$= \frac{1}{x - 1} \qquad \begin{array}{l}\text{Divide out common} \\ \text{factor } x + 1 \end{array} \quad ▲$$

Our next example involves subtraction of rational expressions. Pay careful attention to what happens to the signs of the terms in the numerator of the second expression when we subtract it from the first expression.

3. Subtract $\dfrac{2x - 7}{x - 2} - \dfrac{x - 5}{x - 2}$.

▼ **Example 3**   Subtract: $\dfrac{2x - 5}{x - 2} - \dfrac{x - 3}{x - 2}$.

Solution   Since each expression has the same denominator, we simply subtract the numerator in the second expression from the numerator in the first expression and write the difference over the common denominator $x - 2$. We must be careful, however, that we subtract both terms in the second numerator. To ensure that we do, we will enclose that numerator in parentheses.

$$\frac{2x - 5}{x - 2} - \frac{x - 3}{x - 2} = \frac{2x - 5 - (x - 3)}{x - 2} \qquad \text{Subtract numerators}$$

$$= \frac{2x - 5 - x + 3}{x - 2} \qquad \text{Remove parentheses}$$

$$= \frac{x - 2}{x - 2} \qquad \begin{array}{l}\text{Combine similar terms} \\ \text{in the numerator}\end{array}$$

$$= 1 \qquad \text{Reduce (or divide)}$$

Note: If you got an answer of

$$\frac{x - 12}{x - 2}$$

for Practice Problem 3, then you made the mistake talked about in Example 3. Look at the first two lines in the solution to Example 3 again and see if you can find your mistake.

Note the $+3$ in the numerator of the second step. It is a very common mistake to write this as -3, by forgetting to subtract both terms in the numerator of the second expression. Whenever the expression we are subtracting has two or more terms in its numerator, we have to watch for this mistake. ▲

Next we consider addition and subtraction of fractions and rational expressions that have different denominators.

Answers

2. $\dfrac{1}{x - 3}$ **3.** 1

Addition and Subtraction with Different Denominators

Before we look at an example of addition of fractions with different denominators, we need to define the least common denominator.

DEFINITION   The *least common denominator,* abbreviated LCD, for a set of denominators is the smallest expression that is divisible by each of the denominators.

The first step in combining two fractions is to find the LCD. Once we have the common denominator, we rewrite each fraction as an equivalent fraction with the common denominator. After that, we simply add or subtract as we did in our first three examples.

Example 4 shows the step-by-step procedure used to add two fractions with different denominators.

▼   **Example 4**   Add: $\frac{3}{14} + \frac{7}{30}$.

Solution

Step 1:   Find the LCD.
To do this we first factor both denominators into prime factors.

$$\text{Factor 14:} \quad 14 = 2 \cdot 7$$
$$\text{Factor 30:} \quad 30 = 2 \cdot 3 \cdot 5$$

Since the LCD must be divisible by 14, it must have factors of $2 \cdot 7$. It must also be divisible by 30 and therefore have factors of $2 \cdot 3 \cdot 5$. We do not need to repeat the 2 that appears in both the factors of 14 and those of 30. Therefore,

$$\text{LCD} = 2 \cdot 3 \cdot 5 \cdot 7 = 210$$

Step 2:   Change to equivalent fractions.
Since we want each fraction to have a denominator of 210 and at the same time keep its original value, we multiply each by 1 in the appropriate form.
Change $\frac{3}{14}$ to a fraction with denominator 210:

$$\frac{3}{14} \cdot \frac{15}{15} = \frac{45}{210}$$

Change $\frac{7}{30}$ to a fraction with denominator 210:

$$\frac{7}{30} \cdot \frac{7}{7} = \frac{49}{210}$$

Step 3:   Add numerators of equivalent fractions found in step 2:

$$\frac{45}{210} + \frac{49}{210} = \frac{94}{210}$$

Step 4:   Reduce to lowest terms if necessary:

$$\frac{94}{210} = \frac{47}{105} \qquad ▲$$

The main idea in adding fractions is to write each fraction again with the LCD for a denominator. In doing so, we must be sure not to change the value of either of the original fractions.

4.   Add $\frac{3}{10} + \frac{11}{42}$.

Note: When we multiply $\frac{3}{14}$ by $\frac{15}{15}$ we obtain a fraction with the same value as $\frac{3}{14}$ (because we multiplied by 1) but with the common denominator 210.

Answer
4. $\dfrac{59}{105}$

5. Add $\dfrac{-3}{x^2 - 2x - 8} + \dfrac{4}{x^2 - 16}$.

▼ **Example 5** Add: $\dfrac{-2}{x^2 - 2x - 3} + \dfrac{3}{x^2 - 9}$.

Solution

Step 1: Factor each denominator and build the LCD from the factors:

$$\left.\begin{array}{l} x^2 - 2x - 3 = (x - 3)(x + 1) \\ x^2 - 9 \quad = (x - 3)(x + 3) \end{array}\right\} \ \text{LCD} = (x - 3)(x + 3)(x + 1)$$

Step 2: Change each rational expression to an equivalent expression that has the LCD for a denominator:

$$\frac{-2}{x^2 - 2x - 3} = \frac{-2}{(x - 3)(x + 1)} \cdot \frac{(x + 3)}{(x + 3)} = \frac{-2x - 6}{(x - 3)(x + 3)(x + 1)}$$

$$\frac{3}{x^2 - 9} = \frac{3}{(x - 3)(x + 3)} \cdot \frac{(x + 1)}{(x + 1)} = \frac{3x + 3}{(x - 3)(x + 3)(x + 1)}$$

Step 3: Add numerators of the rational expressions found in step 2:

$$\frac{-2x - 6}{(x - 3)(x + 3)(x + 1)} + \frac{3x + 3}{(x - 3)(x + 3)(x + 1)}$$

$$= \frac{x - 3}{(x - 3)(x + 3)(x + 1)}$$

Step 4: Reduce to lowest terms by dividing out the common factor $x - 3$.

$$= \frac{1}{(x + 3)(x + 1)}$$ ▲

6. Subtract.

$$\frac{x}{x^2 + 5x - 6} - \frac{2}{7x - 7}$$

▼ **Example 6** Subtract: $\dfrac{2x}{x^2 + 7x + 10} - \dfrac{3}{5x + 10}$.

Solution Factoring the denominators, we have

$$\frac{2x}{x^2 + 7x + 10} - \frac{3}{5x + 10} = \frac{2x}{(x + 2)(x + 5)} - \frac{3}{5(x + 2)}$$

The LCD is $5(x + 2)(x + 5)$. Completing the problem, we have

$$= \frac{5}{5} \cdot \frac{2x}{(x + 2)(x + 5)} - \frac{3}{5(x + 2)} \cdot \frac{(x + 5)}{(x + 5)}$$

$$= \frac{10x}{5(x + 2)(x + 5)} - \frac{3x + 15}{5(x + 2)(x + 5)}$$

$$= \frac{10x - (3x + 15)}{5(x + 2)(x + 5)}$$

$$= \frac{7x - 15}{5(x + 2)(x + 5)}$$

This last expression is in lowest terms because the numerator and denominator do not have any factors in common. ▲

Our last two examples are a little different from the ones we have done so far. The first one involves a trick similar to the one we used in Section 4.1 to rewrite $7 - x$ as $-1(x - 7)$.

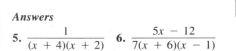

Answers

5. $\dfrac{1}{(x + 4)(x + 2)}$ **6.** $\dfrac{5x - 12}{7(x + 6)(x - 1)}$

▼ **Example 7** Add: $\dfrac{x^2}{x-7} + \dfrac{6x+7}{7-x}$.

Solution In Section 4.1 we were able to reverse the terms in a factor such as $7 - x$ by factoring -1 from each term. In a problem like this, the same result can be obtained by multiplying the numerator and denominator by -1:

$$\frac{x^2}{x-7} + \frac{6x+7}{7-x} \cdot \frac{-1}{-1} = \frac{x^2}{x-7} + \frac{-6x-7}{x-7}$$

$$= \frac{x^2 - 6x - 7}{x-7} \qquad \text{Add numerators}$$

$$= \frac{(x-7)(x+1)}{(x-7)} \qquad \text{Factor numerator}$$

$$= x + 1 \qquad \text{Divide out } (x - 7)$$

▲

For our last example we will look at a problem in which we combine a whole number and a rational expression.

▼ **Example 8** Subtract: $2 - \dfrac{9}{3x+1}$.

Solution To subtract these two expressions, we think of 2 as a rational expression with a denominator of 1.

$$2 - \frac{9}{3x+1} = \frac{2}{1} - \frac{9}{3x+1}$$

The LCD is $3x + 1$. Multiplying the numerator and denominator of the first expression by $3x + 1$ gives us a rational expression equivalent to 2, but with a denominator of $3x + 1$.

$$\frac{2}{1} \cdot \frac{3x+1}{3x+1} - \frac{9}{3x+1} = \frac{6x+2-9}{3x+1}$$

$$= \frac{6x-7}{3x+1}$$

The numerator and denominator of this last expression do not have any factors in common other than 1, so the expression is in lowest terms.

▲

7. Add $\dfrac{x^2}{x-4} + \dfrac{x+12}{4-x}$.

8. Add $2 + \dfrac{25}{5x-1}$.

Problem Set 4.3

Combine the following fractions.

1. $\dfrac{3}{4} + \dfrac{1}{2}$

2. $\dfrac{5}{6} + \dfrac{1}{3}$

3. $\dfrac{2}{5} - \dfrac{1}{15}$

4. $\dfrac{5}{8} - \dfrac{1}{4}$

5. $\dfrac{5}{6} + \dfrac{7}{8}$

6. $\dfrac{3}{4} + \dfrac{2}{3}$

7. $\dfrac{9}{48} - \dfrac{3}{54}$

8. $\dfrac{6}{28} - \dfrac{5}{42}$

9. $\dfrac{3}{4} - \dfrac{1}{8} + \dfrac{2}{3}$

10. $\dfrac{1}{3} - \dfrac{5}{6} + \dfrac{5}{12}$

Combine the following rational expressions. Reduce all answers to lowest terms.

11. $\dfrac{x}{x + 3} + \dfrac{3}{x + 3}$

12. $\dfrac{5x}{5x + 2} + \dfrac{2}{5x + 2}$

13. $\dfrac{4}{y - 4} - \dfrac{y}{y - 4}$

14. $\dfrac{8}{y + 8} + \dfrac{y}{y + 8}$

15. $\dfrac{x}{x^2 - y^2} - \dfrac{y}{x^2 - y^2}$

16. $\dfrac{x}{x^2 - y^2} + \dfrac{y}{x^2 - y^2}$

Name _____

Class _____

Date _____

Answers

1. _____   2. _____

3. _____   4. _____

5. _____   6. _____

7. _____   8. _____

9. _____   10. _____

11. _____   12. _____

13. _____   14. _____

15. _____   16. _____

Answers

17. _____

18. _____

19. _____

20. _____

21. _____

22. _____

23. _____

24. _____

25. _____

26. _____

27. _____

28. _____

17. $\dfrac{2x-3}{x-2} - \dfrac{x-1}{x-2}$

18. $\dfrac{2x-4}{x+2} - \dfrac{x-6}{x+2}$

19. $\dfrac{7x-2}{2x+1} - \dfrac{5x-3}{2x+1}$

20. $\dfrac{7x-1}{3x+2} - \dfrac{4x-3}{3x+2}$

21. $\dfrac{x^2}{x-3} - \dfrac{x+6}{x-3}$

22. $\dfrac{x^2}{x-2} - \dfrac{x+2}{x-2}$

23. $\dfrac{5}{x-1} + \dfrac{x}{x^2-1}$

24. $\dfrac{1}{x+3} + \dfrac{x}{x^2-9}$

25. $\dfrac{x}{x^2-5x+6} - \dfrac{3}{3-x}$

26. $\dfrac{x}{x^2+4x+4} - \dfrac{2}{2+x}$

27. $\dfrac{1}{a^2-5a+6} + \dfrac{3}{a^2-a-2}$

28. $\dfrac{-3}{a^2+a-2} + \dfrac{5}{a^2-a-6}$

29. $\dfrac{8}{y^2 - 16} - \dfrac{7}{y^2 - y - 12}$ **30.** $\dfrac{6}{y^2 - 9} - \dfrac{5}{y^2 - y - 6}$

31. $\dfrac{4a}{a^2 + 6a + 5} - \dfrac{3a}{a^2 + 5a + 4}$ **32.** $\dfrac{3a}{a^2 + 7a + 10} - \dfrac{2a}{a^2 + 6a + 8}$

33. $\dfrac{2x - 1}{x^2 + x - 6} - \dfrac{x + 2}{x^2 + 5x + 6}$ **34.** $\dfrac{4x + 1}{x^2 + 5x + 4} - \dfrac{x + 3}{x^2 + 4x + 3}$

35. $\dfrac{2}{x^2 + 5x + 6} - \dfrac{4}{x^2 + 4x + 3} + \dfrac{3}{x^2 + 3x + 2}$

36. $\dfrac{-5}{x^2 + 3x - 4} + \dfrac{5}{x^2 + 2x - 3} + \dfrac{1}{x^2 + 7x + 12}$

37. $2 + \dfrac{3}{2x + 1}$ **38.** $3 - \dfrac{2}{2x + 3}$

Name _____

Class _____

Date _____

Answers

29. _____

30. _____

31. _____

32. _____

33. _____

34. _____

35. _____

36. _____

37. _____

38. _____

Answers

39. _____

40. _____

41. _____

42. _____

43. _____

44. _____

45. _____

46. _____

47. _____

48. _____

49. _____

50. _____

39. $\dfrac{x}{x + 2} + \dfrac{1}{2x + 4} - \dfrac{3}{x^2 + 2x}$

40. $\dfrac{x}{x + 3} + \dfrac{7}{3x + 9} - \dfrac{2}{x^2 + 3x}$

41. $\dfrac{1}{x} + \dfrac{x}{2x + 4} - \dfrac{2}{x^2 + 2x}$

42. $\dfrac{1}{x} + \dfrac{x}{3x + 9} - \dfrac{3}{x^2 + 3x}$

43. The formula $P = \dfrac{1}{a} + \dfrac{1}{b}$ is used by optometrists to help determine how strong to make the lenses for a pair of eyeglasses. If a is 10 and b is 0.2, find the corresponding value of P.

44. Show that the formula in Problem 43 can be written $P = \dfrac{a + b}{ab}$, and then let $a = 10$ and $b = 0.2$ in this new form of the formula to find P.

Review Problems   The following problems review material we covered in Section 4.2.

Multiply or divide as indicated.

45. $xy \cdot \dfrac{1}{x}$

46. $xy \cdot \dfrac{1}{y}$

47. $\dfrac{2x - 1}{x^2 - x} \div \dfrac{1}{x^2 - x}$

48. $\dfrac{x + y}{2x^2} \div \dfrac{x + y}{4x}$

49. $\dfrac{x + 1}{x^2 - 4} \div \dfrac{x^2 - 1}{x + 2}$

50. $\dfrac{x - 2}{x^2 - 9} \div \dfrac{x^2 - 4}{x + 3}$

Section 4.4 Complex Fractions

The quotient of two fractions or two rational expressions is called a *complex fraction*. This section is concerned with the simplification of complex fractions.

Practice Problems

▼ **Example 1** Simplify $\dfrac{\frac{3}{4}}{\frac{5}{8}}$.

1. Simplify $\dfrac{\frac{2}{3}}{\frac{5}{6}}$. (Try both methods.)

Solution There are generally two methods that can be used to simplify complex fractions.

METHOD 1   We can multiply the numerator and denominator of the complex fraction by the LCD for both of the fractions, which in this case is 8.

$$\frac{\frac{3}{4}}{\frac{5}{8}} = \frac{\frac{3}{4}\cdot 8}{\frac{5}{8}\cdot 8} = \frac{6}{5}$$

Note: You should become proficient at both methods. Each method can be useful in simplifying complex fractions.

METHOD 2   Instead of dividing by $\frac{5}{8}$ we can multiply by $\frac{8}{5}$.

$$\frac{\frac{3}{4}}{\frac{5}{8}} = \frac{3}{4} \times \frac{8}{5} = \frac{24}{20} = \frac{6}{5}$$

▲

Here are some examples of complex fractions involving rational expressions. Most can be solved using either of the two methods shown in Example 1.

▼ **Example 2** Simplify $\dfrac{\frac{1}{x} + \frac{1}{y}}{\frac{1}{x} - \frac{1}{y}}$.

2. Simplify $\dfrac{\frac{1}{x} - \frac{1}{3}}{\frac{1}{x} + \frac{1}{3}}$.

Solution This problem is most easily solved using method 1. We begin by multiplying both the numerator and denominator by the quantity xy, which is the LCD for all the fractions:

$$\frac{\frac{1}{x} + \frac{1}{y}}{\frac{1}{x} - \frac{1}{y}} = \frac{\left(\frac{1}{x} + \frac{1}{y}\right)\cdot xy}{\left(\frac{1}{x} - \frac{1}{y}\right)\cdot xy}$$

$$= \frac{\frac{1}{x}(xy) + \frac{1}{y}(xy)}{\frac{1}{x}(xy) - \frac{1}{y}(xy)}$$

Apply the distributive property to distribute xy over both terms in the numerator and denominator

$$= \frac{y + x}{y - x}$$

▲

Answers

1. $\frac{4}{5}$ **2.** $\dfrac{3 - x}{3 + x}$

3. Simplify $\dfrac{\frac{x + 5}{x^2 - 16}}{\frac{x^2 - 25}{x - 4}}$.

Note: We could have used method 1 just as easily: we would have multiplied the numerator and denominator of the complex fraction by $(x + 3)(x - 3)$.

4. Simplify $\dfrac{1 - \frac{9}{x^2}}{1 - \frac{1}{x} - \frac{6}{x^2}}$.

5. Simplify $2 + \dfrac{5}{x - \frac{1}{5}}$.

Note: As you can see, to simplify the expression in Example 5, we use some of what we have learned in this section and some of what we learned in Section 4.3.

Answers

3. $\dfrac{1}{(x + 4)(x - 5)}$ 4. $\dfrac{x + 3}{x + 2}$

5. $\dfrac{10x + 23}{5x - 1}$

▼ **Example 3** Simplify $\dfrac{\frac{x - 2}{x^2 - 9}}{\frac{x^2 - 4}{x + 3}}$.

Solution Applying method 2, we have

$$\dfrac{\frac{x - 2}{x^2 - 9}}{\frac{x^2 - 4}{x + 3}} = \frac{x - 2}{x^2 - 9} \cdot \frac{x + 3}{x^2 - 4}$$

$$= \frac{(x - 2)(x + 3)}{(x + 3)(x - 3)(x + 2)(x - 2)}$$

$$= \frac{1}{(x - 3)(x + 2)}$$ ▲

▼ **Example 4** Simplify $\dfrac{1 - \frac{4}{x^2}}{1 - \frac{1}{x} - \frac{6}{x^2}}$.

Solution The simplest way to simplify this complex fraction is to multiply the numerator and denominator by the LCD, x^2:

$$\frac{1 - \frac{4}{x^2}}{1 - \frac{1}{x} - \frac{6}{x^2}} = \frac{x^2\left(1 - \frac{4}{x^2}\right)}{x^2\left(1 - \frac{1}{x} - \frac{6}{x^2}\right)} \qquad \text{Multiply numerator and denominator by } x^2$$

$$= \frac{x^2 \cdot 1 - x^2 \cdot \frac{4}{x^2}}{x^2 \cdot 1 - x^2 \cdot \frac{1}{x} - x^2 \cdot \frac{6}{x^2}} \qquad \text{Distributive property}$$

$$= \frac{x^2 - 4}{x^2 - x - 6} \qquad \text{Simplify}$$

$$= \frac{(x - 2)(x + 2)}{(x - 3)(x + 2)} \qquad \text{Factor}$$

$$= \frac{x - 2}{x - 3} \qquad \text{Reduce}$$ ▲

▼ **Example 5** Simplify $2 - \dfrac{3}{x + \frac{1}{3}}$.

Solution First we simplify the expression that follows the subtraction sign.

$$2 - \frac{3}{x + \frac{1}{3}} = 2 - \frac{3 \cdot 3}{3(x + \frac{1}{3})} = 2 - \frac{9}{3x + 1}$$

Now we subtract by rewriting the first term, 2, with the LCD, $3x + 1$.

$$2 - \frac{9}{3x + 1} = \frac{2}{1} \cdot \frac{3x + 1}{3x + 1} - \frac{9}{3x + 1} = \frac{6x + 2 - 9}{3x + 1} = \frac{6x - 7}{3x + 1}$$ ▲

Problem Set 4.4

Simplify each of the following as much as possible.

1. $\dfrac{\frac{3}{4}}{\frac{2}{3}}$

2. $\dfrac{\frac{5}{9}}{\frac{7}{12}}$

3. $\dfrac{\frac{1}{3}-\frac{1}{4}}{\frac{1}{2}+\frac{1}{8}}$

4. $\dfrac{\frac{1}{6}-\frac{1}{3}}{\frac{1}{4}-\frac{1}{8}}$

5. $\dfrac{3+\frac{2}{5}}{1-\frac{3}{7}}$

6. $\dfrac{2+\frac{5}{6}}{1-\frac{7}{8}}$

7. $\dfrac{\frac{1}{x}}{1+\frac{1}{x}}$

8. $\dfrac{1-\frac{1}{x}}{\frac{1}{x}}$

9. $\dfrac{1+\frac{1}{a}}{1-\frac{1}{a}}$

10. $\dfrac{1-\frac{2}{a}}{1-\frac{3}{a}}$

Answers

11. _____ 12. _____

13. _____ 14. _____

15. _____ 16. _____

17. _____ 18. _____

19. _____ 20. _____

11. $\dfrac{\dfrac{1}{x} - \dfrac{1}{y}}{\dfrac{1}{x} + \dfrac{1}{y}}$

12. $\dfrac{\dfrac{1}{x} + \dfrac{2}{y}}{\dfrac{2}{x} + \dfrac{1}{y}}$

13. $\dfrac{\dfrac{x-5}{x^2-4}}{\dfrac{x^2-25}{x+2}}$

14. $\dfrac{\dfrac{3x+1}{x^2-49}}{\dfrac{9x^2-1}{x-7}}$

15. $\dfrac{\dfrac{4a}{2a^3+2}}{\dfrac{8a}{4a+4}}$

16. $\dfrac{\dfrac{2a}{3a^3-3}}{\dfrac{4a}{6a-6}}$

17. $\dfrac{1 - \dfrac{9}{x^2}}{1 - \dfrac{1}{x} - \dfrac{6}{x^2}}$

18. $\dfrac{4 - \dfrac{1}{x^2}}{4 + \dfrac{4}{x} + \dfrac{1}{x^2}}$

19. $\dfrac{2 + \dfrac{5}{a} - \dfrac{3}{a^2}}{2 - \dfrac{5}{a} + \dfrac{2}{a^2}}$

20. $\dfrac{3 + \dfrac{5}{a} - \dfrac{2}{a^2}}{3 - \dfrac{10}{a} + \dfrac{3}{a^2}}$

21. $\dfrac{1 - \dfrac{1}{a+1}}{1 + \dfrac{1}{a-1}}$

22. $\dfrac{\dfrac{1}{a-1} + 1}{\dfrac{1}{a+1} - 1}$

23. $\dfrac{\dfrac{y+1}{y-1} + \dfrac{y-1}{y+1}}{\dfrac{y+1}{y-1} + \dfrac{y-1}{y+1}}$

24. $\dfrac{\dfrac{y-1}{y+1} - \dfrac{y+1}{y-1}}{\dfrac{y-1}{y+1} + \dfrac{y+1}{y-1}}$

25. $1 - \dfrac{x}{1 - \dfrac{1}{x}}$

26. $x - \dfrac{1}{x - \dfrac{1}{2}}$

27. $1 + \dfrac{1}{1 + \dfrac{1}{1 + 1}}$

28. $1 - \dfrac{1}{1 - \dfrac{1}{1 - \frac{1}{2}}}$

29. $\dfrac{1 - \dfrac{1}{x + \frac{1}{2}}}{1 + \dfrac{1}{x + \frac{1}{2}}}$

30. $\dfrac{2 + \dfrac{1}{x - \frac{1}{3}}}{2 - \dfrac{1}{x - \frac{1}{3}}}$

Answers

31. _____   32. _____

33. _____   34. _____

35. _____   36. _____

37. _____   38. _____

39. _____   40. _____

41. _____   42. _____

31. The formula $f = \dfrac{ab}{a + b}$ is used in optics to find the focal length of a lens. Show that the formula $f = (a^{-1} + b^{-1})^{-1}$ is equivalent to the preceding formula by rewriting it without the negative exponents, and then simplifying the results.

32. Show that the expression $(a^{-1} - b^{-1})^{-1}$ can be simplified to $\dfrac{ab}{b - a}$ by first writing it without the negative exponents, and then simplifying the result.

33. Show that the expression $\dfrac{1 - x^{-1}}{1 + x^{-1}}$ can be written as $\dfrac{x - 1}{x + 1}$.

34. Show that the formula $(1 + x^{-1})^{-1}$ can be written as $\dfrac{x}{x + 1}$.

Review Problems   The following problems review material we covered in Sections 2.1 and 2.2. Reviewing these problems will help you with the next section.

Solve each equation.

35. $3x + 60 = 15$ 36. $3x - 18 = 4$

37. $3(a - 4) = 48$ 38. $2(a + 5) = 28$

39. $3(y - 3) = 2(y - 2)$ 40. $5(y + 2) = 4(y + 1)$

41. $10 - 2(x + 3) = x + 1$ 42. $15 - 3(x - 1) = x - 2$

Section 4.5   Equations Involving Rational Expressions

The first step in solving an equation that contains one or more rational expressions is to find the LCD for all denominators in the equation. We then multiply both sides of the equation by the LCD to clear the equation of all fractions. That is, after we have multiplied through by the LCD, each term in the resulting equation will have a denominator of 1.

Practice Problems

▼ **Example 1**   Solve $\frac{x}{2} - 3 = \frac{2}{3}$.

1. Solve $\frac{x}{3} + 1 = \frac{1}{2}$.

Solution   The LCD for 2 and 3 is 6. Multiplying both sides by 6, we have

$$6\left(\frac{x}{2} - 3\right) = 6\left(\frac{2}{3}\right)$$

$$6\left(\frac{x}{2}\right) - 6(3) = 6\left(\frac{2}{3}\right)$$

$$3x - 18 = 4$$

$$3x = 22$$

$$x = \frac{22}{3}$$ ▲

Multiplying both sides of an equation by the LCD clears the equation of fractions because the LCD has the property that all the denominators divide it evenly.

▼ **Example 2**   Solve $\frac{6}{a - 4} = \frac{3}{8}$.

2. Solve $\frac{2}{a + 5} = \frac{1}{3}$.

Solution   The LCD for $a - 4$ and 8 is $8(a - 4)$. Multiplying both sides by this quantity yields

$$8(a - 4) \cdot \frac{6}{a - 4} = 8(a - 4) \cdot \frac{3}{8}$$

$$48 = (a - 4) \cdot 3$$

$$48 = 3a - 12$$

$$60 = 3a$$

$$20 = a$$

The solution set is {20}, which checks in the original equation.   ▲

When we multiply both sides of an equation by an expression containing the variable, we must be sure to check our solutions. The multiplication property of equality does not allow multiplication by 0. If the expression we multiply by contains the variable, then it has the possibility of being 0. In the last example we multiplied both sides by $8(a - 4)$. This gives a restriction $a \neq 4$ for any solution we come up with.

3. Solve $\dfrac{x}{x+1} - \dfrac{1}{2} = \dfrac{-1}{x+1}$.

▼ **Example 3**   Solve $\dfrac{x}{x-2} + \dfrac{2}{3} = \dfrac{2}{x-2}$.

Solution   The LCD is $3(x-2)$. We are assuming $x \neq 2$ when we multiply both sides of the equation by $3(x-2)$:

$$3(x-2) \cdot \left[\frac{x}{x-2} + \frac{2}{3} \right] = 3(x-2) \cdot \frac{2}{x-2}$$
$$3x + (x-2) \cdot 2 = 3 \cdot 2$$
$$3x + 2x - 4 = 6$$
$$5x - 4 = 6$$
$$5x = 10$$
$$x = 2$$

The only possible solution is $x = 2$. Checking this value back in the original equation gives

$$\frac{2}{2-2} + \frac{2}{3} = \frac{2}{2-2}$$
$$\frac{2}{0} + \frac{2}{3} = \frac{2}{0}$$

The first and last terms are undefined. The proposed solution, $x = 2$, does not check in the original equation. The solution set is the empty set. There is no solution to the original equation.   ▲

When the proposed solution to an equation is not actually a solution, it is called an *extraneous* solution. In the last example, $x = 2$ is an extraneous solution.

Note: In the process of solving the equation, we multiplied both sides by $3(x-2)$, solved for x, and got $x = 2$ for our solution. But when x is 2, the quantity $3(x-2) = 3(2-2) = 3(0) = 0$, which means we multiplied both sides of our equation by 0, which is not allowed under the multiplication property of equality.

4. Solve.

$$\frac{x}{x^2-9} - \frac{1}{x+3} = \frac{1}{4x-12}$$

▼ **Example 4**   Solve $\dfrac{5}{x^2-3x+2} - \dfrac{1}{x-2} = \dfrac{1}{3x-3}$.

Solution   Writing the equation again with the denominators in factored form, we have

$$\frac{5}{(x-2)(x-1)} - \frac{1}{x-2} = \frac{1}{3(x-1)}$$

The LCD is $3(x-2)(x-1)$. Multiplying through by the LCD, we have

$$3(x-2)(x-1)\frac{5}{(x-2)(x-1)} - 3(x-2)(x-1) \cdot \frac{1}{(x-2)}$$
$$= 3(x-2)(x-1) \cdot \frac{1}{3(x-1)}$$
$$3 \cdot 5 - 3(x-1) \cdot 1 = (x-2) \cdot 1$$
$$15 - 3x + 3 = x - 2$$
$$-3x + 18 = x - 2$$
$$-4x + 18 = -2$$
$$-4x = -20$$
$$x = 5$$

Note: We can check the proposed solution in any of the equations obtained before multiplying through by the LCD. We cannot check the proposed solution in an equation obtained *after* multiplying through by the LCD since, if we have multiplied by 0, the resulting equations will not be equivalent to the original one.

Checking the proposed solution $x = 5$ in the original equation yields a true statement. Try it and see.   ▲

Problem Set 4.5

Solve each of the following equations.

1. $\dfrac{x}{5} + 4 = \dfrac{5}{3}$

2. $\dfrac{x}{5} = \dfrac{x}{2} - 9$

3. $\dfrac{a}{3} + 2 = \dfrac{4}{5}$

4. $\dfrac{a}{4} + \dfrac{1}{2} = \dfrac{2}{3}$

5. $\dfrac{y}{2} + \dfrac{y}{4} + \dfrac{y}{6} = 3$

6. $\dfrac{y}{3} - \dfrac{y}{6} + \dfrac{y}{2} = 1$

7. $\dfrac{5}{2x} = \dfrac{1}{x} + \dfrac{3}{4}$

8. $\dfrac{1}{2a} = \dfrac{2}{a} - \dfrac{3}{8}$

9. $\dfrac{1}{x} = \dfrac{1}{3} - \dfrac{2}{3x}$

10. $\dfrac{5}{2x} = \dfrac{2}{x} - \dfrac{1}{12}$

11. $\dfrac{2x}{x-3} + 2 = \dfrac{2}{x-3}$

12. $\dfrac{2}{x+5} = \dfrac{2}{5} - \dfrac{x}{x+5}$

Answers

13. _____ 14. _____

15. _____ 16. _____

17. _____ 18. _____

19. _____ 20. _____

21. _____ 22. _____

13. $\dfrac{x+2}{x+1} = \dfrac{1}{x+1} + 2$

14. $\dfrac{x+6}{x+3} = \dfrac{3}{x+3} + 2$

15. $\dfrac{3}{a-2} = \dfrac{2}{a-3}$

16. $\dfrac{5}{a+1} = \dfrac{4}{a+2}$

17. $\dfrac{1}{x-1} - \dfrac{1}{x+1} = \dfrac{3x}{x^2-1}$

18. $\dfrac{5}{x-1} + \dfrac{2}{x-1} = \dfrac{4}{x+1}$

19. $\dfrac{2}{x-3} + \dfrac{x}{x^2-9} = \dfrac{4}{x+3}$

20. $\dfrac{2}{x+5} + \dfrac{3}{x+4} = \dfrac{2x}{x^2+9x+20}$

21. $\dfrac{3}{2} - \dfrac{1}{x-4} = \dfrac{-2}{2x-8}$

22. $\dfrac{2}{x} - \dfrac{1}{x+1} = \dfrac{-2}{5x+5}$

23. $\dfrac{3}{y - 4} - \dfrac{2}{y + 1} = \dfrac{5}{y^2 - 3y - 4}$ **24.** $\dfrac{1}{y + 2} - \dfrac{2}{y - 3} = \dfrac{-2y}{y^2 - y - 6}$

25. $\dfrac{2}{1 + a} = \dfrac{3}{1 - a} + \dfrac{5}{a}$ **26.** $\dfrac{1}{a + 3} - \dfrac{a}{a^2 - 9} = \dfrac{2}{3 - a}$

27. $\dfrac{3}{2x - 6} - \dfrac{x + 1}{4x - 12} = 4$ **28.** $\dfrac{2x - 3}{5x + 10} + \dfrac{3x - 2}{4x + 8} = 1$

29. $\dfrac{4}{2x - 6} - \dfrac{12}{4x + 12} = \dfrac{12}{x^2 - 9}$ **30.** $\dfrac{1}{x + 2} + \dfrac{1}{x - 2} = \dfrac{4}{x^2 - 4}$

31. $\dfrac{2}{y^2 - 7y + 12} - \dfrac{1}{y^2 - 9} = \dfrac{4}{y^2 - y - 12}$

32. $\dfrac{1}{y^2 + 5y + 4} + \dfrac{3}{y^2 - 1} = \dfrac{-1}{y^2 + 3y - 4}$

Name _____

Class _____

Date _____

Answers

23. _____   24. _____

25. _____   26. _____

27. _____   28. _____

29. _____   30. _____

31. _____   32. _____

Answers

33. _____   34. _____

35. _____   36. _____

37. _____   38. _____

39. _____   40. _____

33. The following diagram shows a section of an electronic circuit with a 3-ohm resistor and a 5-ohm resistor connected in parallel.

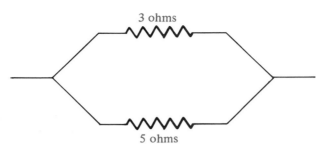

3 ohms

5 ohms

If R is the resistance equivalent to the two resistors connected in parallel, then the relationship between them is given by

$$\frac{1}{R} = \frac{1}{3} + \frac{1}{5}$$

Solve for R.

34. If a convex lens has a focal length of 15 cm, the image of an object 20 cm from the lens will appear d centimeters from the lens, where d is given by the equation

$$\frac{1}{d} = \frac{1}{15} - \frac{1}{20}$$

Solve this equation for d.

35. Solve the equation $6x^{-1} + 4 = 7$ by multiplying both sides by x. (Remember, $x^{-1} \cdot x = x^{-1} \cdot x^1 = x^0 = 1$.)

36. Solve the equation $3x^{-1} - 5 = 2x^{-1} - 3$ by multiplying both sides by x.

Review Problems   The following problems review material we covered in Section 2.7. Reviewing these problems will get you ready for the next section. In each case, be sure to show the equation used.

37. Twice the sum of a number and 3 is 16. Find the number.

38. The sum of two consecutive odd integers is 48. Find the two integers.

39. The length of a rectangle is 3 less than twice the width. The perimeter is 42 meters. Find the length and width.

40. Kelley is 3 years older than his sister Lisa. In 4 years the sum of their ages will be 35. How old are they now?

Section 4.6   Word Problems

The procedure used to solve the word problems in this section is the same procedure used in the past to solve word problems. Here, however, translating the problems from words into symbols will result in equations that involve rational expressions.

▼   **Example 1**   One number is twice another. The sum of their reciprocals is 2. Find the numbers.

Solution   Let x = the smaller number. The larger number is $2x$. Their reciprocals are $1/x$ and $1/2x$. The equation that describes the situation is

$$\frac{1}{x} + \frac{1}{2x} = 2$$

Multiplying both sides by the LCD $2x$, we have

$$2x \cdot \frac{1}{x} + 2x \cdot \frac{1}{2x} = 2x(2)$$

$$2 + 1 = 4x$$
$$3 = 4x$$
$$x = \tfrac{3}{4}$$

The smaller number is $\tfrac{3}{4}$. The larger is $2(\tfrac{3}{4}) = \tfrac{6}{4} = \tfrac{3}{2}$. Adding their reciprocals, we have

$$\tfrac{4}{3} + \tfrac{2}{3} = \tfrac{6}{3} = 2$$

The sum of the reciprocals of $\tfrac{3}{4}$ and $\tfrac{3}{2}$ is 2.   ▲

▼   **Example 2**   The speed of a boat in still water is 20 mi/hr. It takes the same amount of time for the boat to travel 3 miles downstream (with the current) as it does to travel 2 miles upstream (against the current). Find the speed of the current.

Solution   The following table will be helpful in finding the equation necessary to solve this problem.

	d (distance)	r (rate)	t (time)
Upstream			
Downstream			

If we let x = the speed of the current, the speed (rate) of the boat upstream is $(20 - x)$ since it is traveling against the current. The rate downstream is $(20 + x)$ since the boat is then traveling with the current. The distance traveled upstream is 2 miles, while the distance traveled downstream is 3 miles. Putting the information given here into the table, we have

	d	r	t
Upstream	2	$20 - x$	
Downstream	3	$20 + x$	

To fill in the last two spaces in the table we must use the relationship $d = r \cdot t$. Since we know the spaces to be filled in are in the time column, we solve the equation $d = r \cdot t$ for t and get

$$t = \frac{d}{r}$$

Practice Problems

1.   One number is three times another. The sum of their reciprocals is $\tfrac{4}{3}$. Find the numbers.

2.   A boat can travel at 15 mi/hr in still water. If it takes the same amount of time for the boat to travel 2 miles downstream as it does to travel 1 mile upstream, find the speed of the current.

Answers
1. 1, 3   **2.**   5 mph

The completed table then is

	d	r	t
Upstream	2	$20 - x$	$\dfrac{2}{20 - x}$
Downstream	3	$20 + x$	$\dfrac{3}{20 + x}$

Reading the problem again, we find that the time moving upstream is equal to the time moving downstream, or

$$\frac{2}{20 - x} = \frac{3}{20 + x}$$

Multiplying both sides by the LCD $(20 - x)(20 + x)$ gives

$$(20 + x) \cdot 2 = 3(20 - x)$$
$$40 + 2x = 60 - 3x$$
$$5x = 20$$
$$x = 4$$

The speed of the current is 4 mi/hr. ▲

3. Tim can do a certain job in 8 hours, while it takes John only 6 hours to do the same job. If they work together, how long will it take to get the job done?

▼ **Example 3** John can do a certain job in 3 hours, while it takes Bob 5 hours to do the same job. How long will it take them, working together, to get the job done?

Solution In order to solve a problem like this we must assume that each person works at a constant rate. That is, they do the same amount of work in the first hour as they do in the last hour.

Solving a problem like this seems to be easier if we think in terms of how much work is done by each person in 1 hour.

If it takes John 3 hours to do the whole job, then in 1 hour he must do 1/3 of the job.

If we let $x =$ the amount of time it takes to complete the job working together, then in 1 hour they must do $1/x$ of the job. Here is the equation that describes the situation:

In 1 hour

$$\begin{bmatrix} \text{Amount of work} \\ \text{done by John} \end{bmatrix} + \begin{bmatrix} \text{Amount of work} \\ \text{done by Bob} \end{bmatrix} = \begin{bmatrix} \text{Total amount} \\ \text{of work done} \end{bmatrix}$$
$$\frac{1}{3} \qquad + \qquad \frac{1}{5} \qquad = \qquad \frac{1}{x}$$

Multiplying through by the LCD $15x$, we have

$$15x \cdot \frac{1}{3} + 15x \cdot \frac{1}{5} = 15x \cdot \frac{1}{x}$$
$$5x + 3x = 15$$
$$8x = 15$$
$$x = \frac{15}{8}$$

It takes them $\frac{15}{8}$ hours to do the job when they work together. ▲

▼ **Example 4**   An inlet pipe can fill a pool in 10 hours, while an outlet pipe can empty it in 12 hours. If the pool is empty and both pipes are open, how long will it take to fill the pool?

Solution   This problem is very similar to the problem in Example 3. It is helpful to think in terms of how much work is done by each pipe in 1 hour.

Let x = the time it takes to fill the pool with both pipes open.

If the inlet pipe can fill the pool in 10 hours, then in 1 hour it is 1/10 full.

If the outlet pipe empties the pool in 12 hours, then in 1 hour it is 1/12 empty.

If the pool can be filled in x hours with both pipes open, then in 1 hour it is $1/x$ full when both pipes are open.

Here is the equation:

In 1 hour

$$\begin{bmatrix} \text{Amount full by} \\ \text{inlet pipe} \end{bmatrix} - \begin{bmatrix} \text{Amount empty by} \\ \text{outlet pipe} \end{bmatrix} = \begin{bmatrix} \text{Fraction of pool} \\ \text{filled by both} \end{bmatrix}$$

$$\frac{1}{10} - \frac{1}{12} = \frac{1}{x}$$

Multiplying through by $60x$, we have

$$60x \cdot \frac{1}{10} - 60x \cdot \frac{1}{12} = 60x \cdot \frac{1}{x}$$
$$6x - 5x = 60$$
$$x = 60$$

It takes 60 hours to fill the pool if both the inlet pipe and the outlet pipe are open.   ▲

4.   The hot-water faucet can fill a sink in 3 minutes. The drain will empty the sink in 4 minutes. If the hot-water faucet is on and the drain is open, how long will it take to fill the sink?

Problem Set 4.6

Solve each of the following word problems. Be sure to show the equation in each case.

Number Problems

1. One number is 3 times another. The sum of their reciprocals is $\frac{20}{3}$. Find the numbers.

2. One number is 3 times another. The sum of their reciprocals is $\frac{4}{9}$. Find the numbers.

3. If a certain number is added to the numerator and denominator of $\frac{7}{9}$, the result is $\frac{5}{6}$. Find the number.

4. Find the number you would add to both the numerator and denominator of $\frac{8}{11}$ so the result would be $\frac{6}{7}$.

Name _____

Class _____

Date _____

Answers

1. _____   2. _____

3. _____   4. _____

Answers

5. _____   6. _____

7. _____   8. _____

Rate Problems

5. The speed of a boat in still water is 5 mi/hr. If the boat travels 3 miles downstream in the same amount of time it takes to travel 1.5 miles upstream, what is the speed of the current?

6. A boat, which moves at 18 mi/hr in still water, travels 14 miles downstream in the same amount of time it takes to travel 10 miles upstream. Find the speed of the current.

7. Train *A* has a speed 15 mi/hr greater than that of train *B*. If train *A* travels 150 miles in the same time train *B* travels 120 miles, what are the speeds of the two trains?

8. A train travels 30 mi/hr faster than a car. If the train covers 120 miles in the same time the car covers 80 miles, what is the speed of each of them?

Work Problems

Name _____

Class _____

Date _____

Answers

9. _____   10. _____

11. _____   12. _____

13. _____   14. _____

9. If Sam can do a certain job in 3 days, while it takes Fred 6 days to do the same job, how long will it take them, working together, to complete the job?

10. Tim can finish a certain job in 10 hours. It takes his wife JoAnn only 8 hours to do the same job. If they work together, how long will it take them to complete the job?

11. Two people working together can complete a job in 6 hours. If one of them works twice as fast as the other, how long would it take the faster person, working alone, to do the job?

12. If two people working together can do a job in 3 hours, how long will it take the slower person to do the same job if one of them is 3 times as fast as the other?

13. A water tank can be filled by an inlet pipe in 8 hours. It takes twice that long for the outlet pipe to empty the tank. How long will it take to fill the tank if both pipes are open?

14. A sink can be filled from the faucet in 5 minutes. It takes only 3 minutes to empty the sink when the drain is open. If the sink is full and both the faucet and the drain are open, how long will it take to empty the sink?

Answers

15. _____ 16. _____

17. _____ 18. _____

19. _____ 20. _____

21. _____ 22. _____

15. It takes 10 hours to fill a pool with the inlet pipe. It can be emptied in 15 hours with the outlet pipe. If the pool is half-full to begin with, how long will it take to fill it from there if both pipes are open?

16. A sink is $\frac{1}{4}$ full when both the faucet and the drain are opened. The faucet alone can fill the sink in 6 minutes, while it takes 8 minutes to empty it with the drain. How long will it take to fill the remaining $\frac{3}{4}$ of the sink?

Review Problems   The following problems review material we covered in Section 2.6.

17. Solve $A = 2l + 2w$ for l.

18. Solve $A = P + Prt$ for t.

19. Solve $y = mx + b$ for m.

20. Solve $y = 3x - 4$ for x.

21. Solve $A = a + (n - 1)d$ for n.

22. Solve $A = \frac{1}{2}(b + B)h$ for b.

Chapter 4   Summary and Review

RATIONAL NUMBERS AND EXPRESSIONS [4.1]

A *rational number* is any number that can be expressed as the ratio of two integers:

$$\text{Rational numbers} = \left\{ \frac{a}{b} \,\middle|\, a \text{ and } b \text{ are integers}, b \neq 0 \right\}$$

A *rational expression* is any quantity that can be expressed as the ratio of two polynomials:

$$\text{Rational expressions} = \left\{ \frac{P}{Q} \,\middle|\, P \text{ and } Q \text{ are polynomials}, Q \neq 0 \right\}$$

1. $\frac{3}{4}$ is a rational number.

$\frac{x-3}{x^2-9}$ is a rational expression.

PROPERTIES OF RATIONAL EXPRESSIONS [4.1]

If P, Q, and K are polynomials with $Q \neq 0$ and $K \neq 0$, then

$$\frac{P}{Q} = \frac{PK}{QK} \quad \text{and} \quad \frac{P}{Q} = \frac{P/K}{Q/K}$$

which is to say that multiplying or dividing the numerator and denominator of a rational expression by the same nonzero quantity always produces an equivalent rational expression.

REDUCING TO LOWEST TERMS [4.1]

To reduce a rational expression to lowest terms we first factor the numerator and denominator and then divide the numerator and denominator by any factors they have in common.

2.
$$\frac{x-3}{x^2-9} = \frac{x-3}{(x-3)(x+3)}$$
$$= \frac{1}{x+3}$$

MULTIPLICATION [4.2]

To multiply two rational numbers or rational expressions, multiply numerators and multiply denominators. In symbols,

$$\frac{P}{Q} \cdot \frac{R}{S} = \frac{PR}{QS} \qquad (Q \neq 0 \text{ and } S \neq 0)$$

In actual practice, we don't really multiply, but rather, we factor and then divide out common factors.

3.
$$\frac{x+1}{x^2-4} \cdot \frac{x+2}{3x+3}$$
$$= \frac{(x+1)(x+2)}{(x-2)(x+2)(3)(x+1)}$$
$$= \frac{1}{3(x-2)}$$

DIVISION [4.2]

To divide one rational expression by another, we use the definition of division to rewrite our division problem as an equivalent multiplication problem. Instead of dividing by a rational expression we multiply by its reciprocal. In symbols,

$$\frac{P}{Q} \div \frac{R}{S} = \frac{P}{Q} \cdot \frac{S}{R} = \frac{PS}{QR} \qquad (Q \neq 0, S \neq 0, R \neq 0)$$

4.
$$\frac{x^2-y^2}{x^3+y^3} \div \frac{x-y}{x^2-xy+y^2}$$
$$= \frac{x^2-y^2}{x^3+y^3} \cdot \frac{x^2-xy+y^2}{x-y}$$
$$= \frac{(x+y)(x-y)(x^2-xy+y^2)}{(x+y)(x^2-xy+y^2)(x-y)}$$
$$= 1$$

LEAST COMMON DENOMINATOR [4.3]

The *least common denominator*, LCD, for a set of denominators is the smallest quantity divisible by each of the denominators.

5. The LCD for $\frac{2}{x-3}$ and $\frac{3}{5}$ is $5(x-3)$.

6. $\dfrac{2}{x-3} + \dfrac{3}{5}$

$= \dfrac{2}{x-3} \cdot \dfrac{5}{5} + \dfrac{3}{5} \cdot \dfrac{x-3}{x-3}$

$= \dfrac{3x+1}{5(x-3)}$

7. $\dfrac{\dfrac{1}{x} + \dfrac{1}{y}}{\dfrac{1}{x} - \dfrac{1}{y}} = \dfrac{xy\left(\dfrac{1}{x} + \dfrac{1}{y}\right)}{xy\left(\dfrac{1}{x} - \dfrac{1}{y}\right)}$

$= \dfrac{y+x}{y-x}$

8. Solve $\dfrac{x}{2} + 3 = \dfrac{1}{3}$.

$6\left(\dfrac{x}{2}\right) + 6 \cdot 3 = 6 \cdot \dfrac{1}{3}$

$3x + 18 = 2$

$x = -\dfrac{16}{3}$

ADDITION AND SUBTRACTION [4.3]

If P, Q, and R represent polynomials, $R \neq 0$, then

$$\frac{P}{R} + \frac{Q}{R} = \frac{P+Q}{R} \quad \text{and} \quad \frac{P}{R} - \frac{Q}{R} = \frac{P-Q}{R}$$

When adding or subtracting rational expressions with different denominators, we must find the LCD for all denominators and change each rational expression to an equivalent expression that has the LCD.

COMPLEX FRACTIONS [4.4]

A rational expression that contains, in its numerator or denominator, other rational expressions is called a complex fraction. One method of simplifying a complex fraction is to multiply the numerator and denominator by the LCD for all denominators.

EQUATIONS INVOLVING RATIONAL EXPRESSIONS [4.5]

To solve an equation involving rational expressions we first find the LCD for all denominators appearing on either side of the equation. We then multiply both sides by the LCD to clear the equation of all fractions and solve as usual.

COMMON MISTAKES

1. Attempting to divide the numerator and denominator of a rational expression by a quantity that is not a factor of both. Like this:

$$\dfrac{\overset{3}{\cancel{x^2 - 9x - 20}}}{\underset{1}{\cancel{x^2 - 3x - 10}}} \quad \text{Mistake}$$

This makes no sense at all. The numerator and denominator must be factored completely before any factors they have in common can be recognized:

$$\frac{x^2 - 9x + 20}{x^2 - 3x - 10} = \frac{\cancel{(x-5)}(x-4)}{\cancel{(x-5)}(x+2)}$$

$$= \frac{x-4}{x+2}$$

2. Forgetting to check solutions to equations involving rational expressions. When we multiply both sides of an equation by a quantity containing the variable, we must be sure to check for extraneous solutions (see Section 4.5).

Chapter 4 Test

Name _____

Class _____

Date _____

Reduce to lowest terms. [4.1]

1. $\dfrac{x^2 - y^2}{x - y}$

2. $\dfrac{2x^2 - 5x + 3}{2x^2 - x - 3}$

Answers

1. _____   2. _____

3. _____   4. _____

5. _____   6. _____

7. _____   8. _____

9. _____   10. _____

Multiply and divide as indicated. [4.2]

3. $\dfrac{a^2 - 16}{5a - 15} \cdot \dfrac{10(a - 3)^2}{a^2 - 7a + 12}$

4. $\dfrac{a^4 - 81}{a^2 + 9} \div \dfrac{a^2 - 8a + 15}{4a - 20}$

5. $\dfrac{x^3 - 8}{2x^2 - 9x + 10} \div \dfrac{x^2 + 2x + 4}{2x^2 + x - 15}$

Add and subtract as indicated. [4.3]

6. $\frac{4}{21} + \frac{6}{35}$

7. $\frac{3}{4} - \frac{1}{2} + \frac{5}{8}$

8. $\dfrac{a}{a^2 - 9} + \dfrac{3}{a^2 - 9}$

9. $\dfrac{1}{x} + \dfrac{2}{x - 3}$

10. $\dfrac{4x}{x^2 + 6x + 5} - \dfrac{3x}{x^2 + 5x + 4}$

Answers

11. _____ 12. _____

13. _____ 14. _____

15. _____ 16. _____

17. _____ 18. _____

Simplify each complex fraction. [4.4]

11. $\dfrac{\dfrac{3}{8}}{\dfrac{6}{40}}$

12. $\dfrac{3 - \dfrac{1}{a + 3}}{3 + \dfrac{1}{a + 3}}$

13. $\dfrac{1 - \dfrac{9}{x^2}}{1 + \dfrac{1}{x} - \dfrac{6}{x^2}}$

Solve each of the following equations. [4.5]

14. $\dfrac{1}{x} + 3 = \dfrac{4}{3}$

15. $\dfrac{x}{x - 3} + 3 = \dfrac{3}{x - 3}$

16. $\dfrac{y + 3}{2y} + \dfrac{5}{y - 1} = \dfrac{1}{2}$

Solve the following word problems. Be sure to show the equation in each case. [4.6]

17. What number must be subtracted from the denominator of $\frac{10}{23}$ to make the result $\frac{1}{3}$?

18. An inlet pipe can fill a pool in 10 hours while an outlet pipe can empty it in 15 hours. If the pool is half-full and both pipes are left open, how long will it take to fill the pool the rest of the way?

5 Rational Exponents and Roots

To the student:

This chapter is concerned with fractional exponents, roots, and complex numbers. As we will see, expressions involving fractional exponents are actually just radical expressions. That is, fractional exponents are used to denote square roots, cube roots, and so forth. We use fractional exponents as an alternative to radical notation (radical notation involves the use of the symbol $\sqrt{}$).

Many of the formulas that describe the characteristics of objects in the universe involve roots. The formula for the length of the diagonal of a square involves a square root. The length of time it takes a pendulum (as on a grandfather clock) to swing through one complete cycle depends on the square root of the length of the pendulum. The formulas that describe the changes in length, mass, and time for objects traveling at velocities close to the speed of light also contain roots.

We begin the chapter with some simple roots and the correlation between fractional exponents and roots. We will then list the properties associated with radicals and use these properties to write some radical expressions in simplified form. Combinations of radical expressions and equations involving radicals are considered next. The chapter concludes with the definition for complex numbers and some applications of this definition. The work we have done previously with exponents and polynomials will be very useful in understanding the concepts developed here. Radical expressions and complex numbers behave like polynomials. As was the case in the preceding chapter, the distributive property is used extensively as justification for many of the properties developed in this chapter.

Section 5.1 Rational Exponents

In Chapter 3 we developed notation (exponents) to give us the square, cube, or any power of a number. For instance, if we wanted the square of 3, we wrote $3^2 = 9$. If we wanted the cube of 3, we wrote $3^3 = 27$. In this section we will develop notation that will take us in the reverse direction, that is, from the square of a number, say 25, back to the original number, 5.

DEFINITION If x is a positive real number, then the expression $\sqrt{x}$ is called the *positive square root* of x and is such that

$$(\sqrt{x})^2 = x$$

In words: $\sqrt{x}$ is the positive number we square to get x.

The negative square root of x, $-\sqrt{x}$, is defined in a similar manner.

Practice Problems

1. Give the two square roots of 36.

Note: It is a common mistake to assume that an expression like $\sqrt{25}$ indicates both square roots, $+5$ and -5. The expression $\sqrt{25}$ indicates only the positive square root of 25, which is 5. If we want the negative square root, we must use a negative sign: $-\sqrt{25} = -5$.

▼ **Example 1** The positive square root of 64 is 8 because 8 is the positive number with the property $8^2 = 64$. The negative square root of 64 is -8 since -8 is the negative number whose square is 64. We can summarize both of these facts by saying

$$\sqrt{64} = 8 \quad \text{and} \quad -\sqrt{64} = -8 \qquad ▲$$

The higher roots, cube roots, fourth roots, and so on, are defined by definitions similar to that of square roots.

DEFINITION If x is a real number, and n is a positive integer, then

Positive square root of x, $\sqrt{x}$, is such that $(\sqrt{x})^2 = x$ *(x positive)*
Cube root of x, $\sqrt[3]{x}$, is such that $(\sqrt[3]{x})^3 = x$
Positive Fourth root of x, $\sqrt[4]{x}$, is such that $(\sqrt[4]{x})^4 = x$ *(x positive)*
Fifth root of x, $\sqrt[5]{x}$, is such that $(\sqrt[5]{x})^5 = x$
$$\vdots \qquad \vdots \quad \vdots$$

The nth root of x, $\sqrt[n]{x}$, such that $(\sqrt[n]{x})^n = x$ *(x positive if n is even)*

Note: We have restricted the even roots in this definition to positive numbers. Even roots of negative numbers exist, but are not represented by real numbers. That is, $\sqrt{-4}$ is not a real number since there is no real number whose square is -4. We will have to wait until the last two sections of this chapter to see how to deal with even roots of negative numbers.

Here is a table of the most common roots used in this book. Any of the roots that are unfamiliar should be memorized.

Square roots		Cube roots	Fourth roots
$\sqrt{0} = 0$	$\sqrt{49} = 7$	$\sqrt[3]{0} = 0$	$\sqrt[4]{0} = 0$
$\sqrt{1} = 1$	$\sqrt{64} = 8$	$\sqrt[3]{1} = 1$	$\sqrt[4]{1} = 1$
$\sqrt{4} = 2$	$\sqrt{81} = 9$	$\sqrt[3]{8} = 2$	$\sqrt[4]{16} = 2$
$\sqrt{9} = 3$	$\sqrt{100} = 10$	$\sqrt[3]{27} = 3$	$\sqrt[4]{81} = 3$
$\sqrt{16} = 4$	$\sqrt{121} = 11$	$\sqrt[3]{64} = 4$	
$\sqrt{25} = 5$	$\sqrt{144} = 12$	$\sqrt[3]{125} = 5$	
$\sqrt{36} = 6$	$\sqrt{169} = 13$		

Answer
1. -6 and 6

We will now develop a second kind of notation involving exponents that will allow us to designate square roots, cube roots, and so on in another way.

Consider the equation $x = 8^{1/3}$. Although we have not encountered fractional exponents before, let's assume that all the properties of exponents hold in this case. Cubing both sides of the equation, we have

$$x^3 = (8^{1/3})^3$$
$$x^3 = 8^{(1/3)(3)}$$
$$x^3 = 8^1$$
$$x^3 = 8$$

The last line tells us that x is the number whose cube is 8. It must be true, then, that x is the cube root of 8, $x = \sqrt[3]{8}$. Since we started with $x = 8^{1/3}$, it follows that

$$8^{1/3} = \sqrt[3]{8}$$

It seems reasonable, then, to define fractional exponents as indicating roots. Here is the formal definition.

DEFINITION   If x is a real number and n is a positive integer, then

$$x^{1/n} = \sqrt[n]{x} \qquad (x \geq 0 \text{ when } n \text{ is even})$$

In words: the quantity $x^{1/n}$ is the nth root of x.

With this definition we have a way of representing roots with exponents. Here are some examples.

▼ **Example 2**

a. $8^{1/3} = \sqrt[3]{8} = 2$

b. $36^{1/2} = \sqrt{36} = 6$

c. $-25^{1/2} = -\sqrt{25} = -5$

d. $(-25)^{1/2} = \sqrt{-25}$, which is not a real number

e. $\left(\frac{4}{9}\right)^{1/2} = \sqrt{\frac{4}{9}} = \frac{2}{3}$

f. $16^{1/2} \cdot 27^{1/3} = \sqrt{16}\sqrt[3]{27} = 4 \cdot 3 = 12$

g. $125^{1/3} + 81^{1/4} = \sqrt[3]{125} + \sqrt[4]{81} = 5 + 3 = 8$ ▲

The properties of exponents developed in Chapter 3 apply to integer exponents only. We will now extend these properties to include rational exponents also. We do so without proof.

Properties of Exponents   If a and b are real numbers and r and s are rational numbers, and a and b are positive whenever r and s indicate even roots, then

1. $a^r \cdot a^s = a^{r+s}$

2. $(a^r)^s = a^{rs}$

3. $(ab)^r = a^r b^r$

4. $\left(\dfrac{a}{b}\right)^r = \dfrac{a^r}{b^r} \qquad (b \neq 0)$

5. $a^{-r} = \dfrac{1}{a^r} \qquad (a \neq 0)$

6. $\dfrac{a^r}{a^s} = a^{r-s} \qquad (a \neq 0)$

---

2.   Simplify each expression.

a. $9^{1/2}$

b. $27^{1/3}$

c. $-49^{1/2}$

d. $(-49)^{1/2}$

e. $\left(\dfrac{16}{25}\right)^{1/2}$

f. $8^{1/3} \cdot 9^{1/2}$

g. $16^{1/4} + 4^{1/2}$

Note: If we were using a scientific calculator to work part a of Example 2, this is how the sequence of key strokes would look:

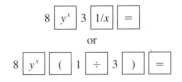

We can extend our properties of exponents with the following theorem:

Note: We can prove Theorem 5.1 using the properties of exponents. Since $\frac{m}{n} = m(\frac{1}{n})$ we have

$$a^{m/n} = a^{m(1/n)} \qquad a^{m/n} = a^{(1/n)(m)}$$
$$= (a^m)^{1/n} \qquad\qquad = (a^{1/n})^m$$

Theorem 5.1 If a is a positive real number, m is an integer, and n is a positive integer, then

$$a^{m/n} = (a^{1/n})^m = (a^m)^{1/n}$$

Here is an example that illustrates how we use this theorem.

3. Simplify each expression as much as possible.

a. $9^{3/2}$

b. $16^{3/4}$

c. $8^{-2/3}$

Note: On a scientific calculator, part a of Example 3 would look like this:

8 y^x (2 ÷ 3) =

▼ **Example 3** Simplify as much as possible.

a. $8^{2/3} = (8^{1/3})^2$ Theorem 5.1
$= 2^2$ Definition of fractional exponents
$= 4$ The square of 2 is 4

b. $25^{3/2} = (25^{1/2})^3$ Theorem 5.1
$= 5^3$ Definition of fractional exponents
$= 125$ The cube of 5 is 125

c. $9^{-3/2} = (9^{1/2})^{-3}$ Theorem 5.1
$= 3^{-3}$ Definition of fractional exponents
$= \frac{1}{3^3}$ Property 5 for exponents
$= \frac{1}{27}$ The cube of 3 is 27 ▲

The following examples show the application of the properties of exponents to rational exponents.

4. Assume all variables represent positive quantities and simplify.

a. $x^{1/2} \cdot x^{1/4}$

b. $(y^{2/5})^{5/3}$

c. $(x^{1/4} \cdot y^{1/2})^8$

d. $\frac{x^{2/3}}{x^{1/4}}$

▼ **Example 4** Assume x, y, and z all represent positive quantities and simplify as much as possible.

a. $x^{1/3} \cdot x^{5/6} = x^{1/3+5/6}$
$= x^{2/6+5/6}$
$= x^{7/6}$

b. $(y^{2/3})^{3/4} = y^{(2/3)(3/4)}$
$= y^{1/2}$

c. $(x^{1/3}y^{2/5}z^{3/7})^4 = x^{4/3}y^{8/5}z^{12/7}$

d. $\frac{x^{1/3}}{x^{1/4}} = x^{1/3-1/4}$
$= x^{4/12-3/12}$
$= x^{1/12}$ ▲

As you can see from Example 4, the properties of exponents can be applied to fractional exponents in the same way we applied them to integer exponents.

Answers
3a. 27   **b.** 8   **c.** $\frac{1}{4}$ **4a.** $x^{3/4}$ **b.** $y^{2/3}$
c. x^2y^4 **d.** $x^{5/12}$

Problem Set 5.1

Name _____

Class _____

Date _____

Use the definition of fractional exponents to write each of the following with the appropriate root; then simplify.

1. $36^{1/2}$

2. $49^{1/2}$

3. $-9^{1/2}$

4. $-16^{1/2}$

5. $8^{1/3}$

6. $-8^{1/3}$

7. $(-8)^{1/3}$

8. $-27^{1/3}$

9. $32^{1/5}$

10. $81^{1/4}$

11. $\left(\dfrac{81}{25}\right)^{1/2}$

12. $\left(\dfrac{9}{16}\right)^{1/2}$

13. $\left(\dfrac{64}{125}\right)^{1/3}$

14. $\left(\dfrac{8}{27}\right)^{1/3}$

Use Theorem 5.1 to simplify each of the following as much as possible.

15. $27^{2/3}$

16. $8^{4/3}$

17. $25^{3/2}$

18. $9^{3/2}$

19. $16^{3/4}$

20. $81^{3/4}$

Answers

1. _____   2. _____

3. _____   4. _____

5. _____   6. _____

7. _____   8. _____

9. _____   10. _____

11. _____   12. _____

13. _____   14. _____

15. _____   16. _____

17. _____   18. _____

19. _____   20. _____

Answers

21. _____	22. _____
23. _____	24. _____
25. _____	26. _____
27. _____	28. _____
29. _____	30. _____
31. _____	32. _____
33. _____	34. _____
35. _____	36. _____

Simplify each expression. Remember, negative exponents give reciprocals.

21. $27^{-1/3}$

22. $9^{-1/2}$

23. $81^{-3/4}$

24. $4^{-3/2}$

25. $\left(\frac{25}{36}\right)^{-1/2}$

26. $\left(\frac{16}{49}\right)^{-1/2}$

27. $\left(\frac{81}{16}\right)^{-3/4}$

28. $\left(\frac{27}{8}\right)^{-2/3}$

29. $16^{1/2} + 27^{1/3}$

30. $25^{1/2} + 100^{1/2}$

31. $8^{-2/3} + 4^{-1/2}$

32. $49^{-1/2} + 25^{-1/2}$

Use the properties of exponents to simplify each of the following as much as possible. Assume all bases are positive.

33. $x^{3/5} \cdot x^{1/5}$

34. $x^{3/4} \cdot x^{5/4}$

35. $(a^{3/4})^{4/3}$

36. $(a^{2/3})^{3/4}$

37. $\dfrac{x^{1/5}}{x^{3/5}}$

38. $\dfrac{x^{2/7}}{x^{5/7}}$

39. $(a^{3/4} \cdot b^{1/3})^2$

40. $(a^{5/6} \cdot b^{2/5})^3$

41. $x^{2/3} \cdot x^{2/5}$

42. $x^{1/3} \cdot x^{3/4}$

43. $\dfrac{x^{5/6}}{x^{2/3}}$

44. $\dfrac{x^{7/8}}{x^{8/7}}$

45. $(x^{3/5}y^{5/6}z^{1/3})^{3/5}$

46. $(x^{3/4}y^{1/8}z^{5/6})^{4/5}$

47. $\dfrac{x^{3/4}y^{2/3}}{x^{1/4}y^{1/3}}$

48. $\dfrac{x^{5/6}y^{3/5}}{x^{1/6}y^{2/5}}$

49. $\dfrac{a^{3/4}b^{2}}{a^{7/8}b^{1/4}}$

50. $\dfrac{a^{1/3}b^{4}}{a^{3/5}b^{1/3}}$

51. $\dfrac{(y^{2/3})^{3/4}}{(y^{1/3})^{3/5}}$

52. $\dfrac{(y^{5/4})^{2/5}}{(y^{1/4})^{4/3}}$

Name _____

Class _____

Date _____

Answers

37. _____   38. _____

39. _____   40. _____

41. _____   42. _____

43. _____   44. _____

45. _____   46. _____

47. _____   48. _____

49. _____   50. _____

51. _____   52. _____

Answers

53. _____ 54. _____

55. _____ 56. _____

57. _____ 58. _____

59. _____ 60. _____

61. _____ 62. _____

63. _____ 64. _____

65. _____ 66. _____

53. Show that the expression $(a^{1/2} + b^{1/2})^2$ is not equal to $a + b$ by replacing a with 9 and b with 4 in both expressions and then simplifying each.

54. Show that the statement $(a^2 + b^2)^{1/2} = a + b$ is not, in general, true by replacing a with 3 and b with 4 and then simplifying both sides.

55. You may have noticed, if you have been using a calculator to find roots, that you can find the fourth root of a number by pressing the square root button twice. Written in symbols, this fact looks like this:

$$\sqrt{\sqrt{a}} = \sqrt[4]{a} \qquad (a \geq 0)$$

Show that this statement is true by rewriting each side with exponents instead of radical notation, and then simplifying the left side.

56. Show that the statement below is true by rewriting each side with exponents instead of radical notation, and then simplifying the left side.

$$\sqrt[3]{\sqrt{a}} = \sqrt[6]{a} \qquad (a \geq 0)$$

57. The maximum speed (v) that an automobile can travel around a curve of radius r without skidding is given by the equation

$$v = \left(\frac{5r}{2}\right)^{1/2}$$

where v is in mi/hr and r is measured in feet. What is the maximum speed a car can travel around a curve with a radius of 250 feet without skidding?

58. The equation $L = \left(1 - \dfrac{v^2}{c^2}\right)^{1/2}$ gives the relativistic length of a 1-foot ruler traveling with velocity v. Find L if $\dfrac{v}{c} = \dfrac{3}{5}$.

Review Problems The following problems review material we covered in Section 3.1.

Simplify each expression. Write your answer with positive exponents only.

59. $x^5 \cdot x^4 \cdot x^{-7}$

60. $x^{10} \cdot x^{-3} \cdot x^{-4}$

61. $(27a^6c^3)(2b^2c)$

62. $(8a^3b^3)(5a^2b)$

63. $(6x^2)(-3x^4)(2x^5)$

64. $(5x^3)(-7x^4)(-2x^6)$

65. $(5y^4)^{-3}(2y^{-2})^3$

66. $(3y^5)^{-2}(2y^{-4})^3$

Section 5.2 Simplified Form for Radicals

Any expression containing a radical is called a *radical expression*. In the expression $\sqrt[3]{8}$, the 3 is called the *index*, the $\sqrt{}$ is the *radical sign*, and 8 is called the *radicand*. The index of a radical must be a positive integer greater than 1. If no index is written, it is assumed to be 2.

There are two properties of radicals. For these two properties we will assume a and b are nonnegative real numbers whenever n is an even number.

Property 1 for Radicals

$$\sqrt[n]{ab} = \sqrt[n]{a}\sqrt[n]{b}$$

In words: the nth root of a product is the product of the nth roots.

PROOF OF PROPERTY 1

$$\sqrt[n]{ab} = (ab)^{1/n} \qquad \text{Definition of fractional exponents}$$

$$= a^{1/n}b^{1/n} \qquad \text{Exponents distribute over products}$$

$$= \sqrt[n]{a}\sqrt[n]{b} \qquad \text{Definition of fractional exponents}$$

Note: There is no property for radicals that says the nth root of a sum is the sum of the nth roots. That is,

$$\sqrt[n]{a+b} \neq \sqrt[n]{a} + \sqrt[n]{b}$$

Property 2 for Radicals

$$\sqrt[n]{\frac{a}{b}} = \frac{\sqrt[n]{a}}{\sqrt[n]{b}} \qquad (b \neq 0)$$

In words: the nth root of a quotient is the quotient of the nth roots.

The proof of Property 2 is similar to the proof of Property 1.

These two properties of radicals allow us to change the form and simplify radical expressions without changing their value.

Simplified Form for Radical Expressions

A radical expression is in *simplified form* if:

1. none of the factors of the radicand (the quantity under the radical sign) can be written as powers greater than or equal to the index— that is, no perfect squares can be factors of the quantity under a square root sign, no perfect cubes can be factors of what is under a cube root sign, and so forth;
2. there are no fractions under the radical sign; and
3. there are no radicals in the denominator.

Note: Writing a radical expression in simplified form does not always result in a simpler-looking expression. Simplified form for radicals is a way of writing radicals so they are easiest to work with.

Satisfying the first condition for simplified form actually amounts to taking as much out from under the radical sign as possible. The following examples illustrate the first condition for simplified form.

Practice Problems

1. Write $\sqrt{18}$ in simplified form.

▼ **Example 1**   Write $\sqrt{50}$ in simplified form.

Solution   The largest perfect square that divides 50 is 25. We write 50 as $25 \cdot 2$ and apply Property 1 for radicals:

$$
\begin{aligned}
\sqrt{50} &= \sqrt{25 \cdot 2} & 50 &= 25 \cdot 2 \\
&= \sqrt{25}\sqrt{2} & \text{Property 1} & \\
&= 5\sqrt{2} & \sqrt{25} &= 5
\end{aligned}
$$

We have taken as much as possible out from under the radical sign—in this case, factoring 25 from 50 and then writing $\sqrt{25}$ as 5.   ▲

2. Write $\sqrt{50x^2y^3}$ in simplified form. Assume $x,\ y \geq 0$.

▼ **Example 2**   Write in simplified form: $\sqrt{48x^4y^3}$, where $x,\ y \geq 0$.

Solution   The largest perfect square that is a factor of the radicand is $16x^4y^2$. Applying Property 1 again, we have

$$
\begin{aligned}
\sqrt{48x^4y^3} &= \sqrt{16x^4y^2 \cdot 3y} \\
&= \sqrt{16x^4y^2}\sqrt{3y} \\
&= 4x^2y\sqrt{3y}
\end{aligned}
$$
   ▲

3. Write $\sqrt[3]{27a^4b^3}$ in simplified form.

▼ **Example 3**   Write $\sqrt[3]{40a^5b^4}$ in simplified form.

Solution   We now want to factor the largest perfect cube from the radicand. We write $40a^5b^4$ as $8a^3b^3 \cdot 5a^2b$ and proceed as we did in Examples 1 and 2.

$$
\begin{aligned}
\sqrt[3]{40a^5b^4} &= \sqrt[3]{8a^3b^3 \cdot 5a^2b} \\
&= \sqrt[3]{8a^3b^3}\sqrt[3]{5a^2b} \\
&= 2ab\sqrt[3]{5a^2b}
\end{aligned}
$$
   ▲

Here are some further examples concerning the first condition for simplified form.

4. Write each expression in simplified form.

a. $\sqrt{75x^5y^8}$

b. $\sqrt[4]{48a^8b^5c^4}$

▼ **Example 4**   Write each expression in simplified form.

a.
$$
\begin{aligned}
\sqrt{12x^7y^6} &= \sqrt{4x^6y^6 \cdot 3x} \\
&= \sqrt{4x^6y^6}\sqrt{3x} \\
&= 2x^3y^3\sqrt{3x}
\end{aligned}
$$

b.
$$
\begin{aligned}
\sqrt[3]{54a^6b^2c^4} &= \sqrt[3]{27a^6c^3 \cdot 2b^2c} \\
&= \sqrt[3]{27a^6c^3}\sqrt[3]{2b^2c} \\
&= 3a^2c\sqrt[3]{2b^2c}
\end{aligned}
$$
   ▲

The second property of radicals is used to simplify a radical that contains a fraction.

5. Simplify $\sqrt{\dfrac{5}{9}}$.

▼ **Example 5**   Simplify $\sqrt{\dfrac{3}{4}}$.

Solution   Applying Property 2 for radicals, we have

$$
\begin{aligned}
\sqrt{\frac{3}{4}} &= \frac{\sqrt{3}}{\sqrt{4}} & \text{Property 2} \\
&= \frac{\sqrt{3}}{2} & \sqrt{4} &= 2
\end{aligned}
$$

The last expression is in simplified form because it satisfies all three conditions for simplified form.   ▲

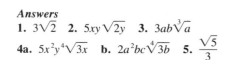

Answers
1. $3\sqrt{2}$ **2.** $5xy\sqrt{2y}$ **3.** $3ab\sqrt[3]{a}$
4a. $5x^2y^4\sqrt{3x}$ **b.** $2a^2bc\sqrt[4]{3b}$ **5.** $\dfrac{\sqrt{5}}{3}$

▼ **Example 6** Write $\sqrt{\dfrac{5}{6}}$ in simplified form.

Solution Proceeding as in Example 5, we have

$$\sqrt{\frac{5}{6}} = \frac{\sqrt{5}}{\sqrt{6}}$$

The resulting expression satisfies the second condition for simplified form since neither radical contains a fraction. It does, however, violate condition 3 since it has a radical in the denominator. Getting rid of the radical in the denominator is called *rationalizing the denominator* and is accomplished, in this case, by multiplying the numerator and denominator by $\sqrt{6}$:

$$\frac{\sqrt{5}}{\sqrt{6}} = \frac{\sqrt{5}}{\sqrt{6}} \cdot \frac{\sqrt{6}}{\sqrt{6}}$$

$$= \frac{\sqrt{30}}{\sqrt{6^2}}$$

$$= \frac{\sqrt{30}}{6} \qquad \blacktriangle$$

▼ **Example 7** Rationalize the denominator.

a.
$$\frac{4}{\sqrt{3}} = \frac{4}{\sqrt{3}} \cdot \frac{\sqrt{3}}{\sqrt{3}}$$

$$= \frac{4\sqrt{3}}{\sqrt{3^2}}$$

$$= \frac{4\sqrt{3}}{3}$$

b.
$$\frac{2\sqrt{3x}}{\sqrt{5y}} = \frac{2\sqrt{3x}}{\sqrt{5y}} \cdot \frac{\sqrt{5y}}{\sqrt{5y}}$$

$$= \frac{2\sqrt{15xy}}{\sqrt{(5y)^2}}$$

$$= \frac{2\sqrt{15xy}}{5y} \qquad \blacktriangle$$

When the denominator involves a cube root, we must multiply by a radical that will produce a perfect cube under the cube root sign in the denominator, as our next example illustrates.

▼ **Example 8** Rationalize the denominator in $\dfrac{7}{\sqrt[3]{4}}$.

Solution Since $4 = 2^2$, we can multiply both numerator and denominator by $\sqrt[3]{2}$ and obtain $\sqrt[3]{2^3}$ in the denominator:

$$\frac{7}{\sqrt[3]{4}} = \frac{7}{\sqrt[3]{2^2}}$$

$$= \frac{7}{\sqrt[3]{2^2}} \cdot \frac{\sqrt[3]{2}}{\sqrt[3]{2}}$$

$$= \frac{7\sqrt[3]{2}}{\sqrt[3]{2^3}}$$

$$= \frac{7\sqrt[3]{2}}{2} \qquad \blacktriangle$$

6. Write $\sqrt{\dfrac{2}{3}}$ in simplified form.

Note: The idea behind rationalizing the denominator is to produce a perfect square under the square root sign in the denominator. This is accomplished by multiplying both the numerator and denominator by the appropriate radical.

7. Rationalize the denominator.

a. $\dfrac{5}{\sqrt{2}}$

b. $\dfrac{3\sqrt{5x}}{\sqrt{2y}}$

8. Rationalize the denominator:

$$\frac{5}{\sqrt[3]{9}}$$

Answers
6. $\dfrac{\sqrt{6}}{3}$ **7a.** $\dfrac{5\sqrt{2}}{2}$ **b.** $\dfrac{3\sqrt{10xy}}{2y}$

8. $\dfrac{5\sqrt[3]{3}}{3}$

9. Simplify $\sqrt{\dfrac{48x^3y^4}{7z}}$.

As a last example we consider a radical expression that requires the use of both properties to meet the three conditions for simplified form.

▼ **Example 9** Simplify $\sqrt{\dfrac{12x^5y^3}{5z}}$

Solution We use Property 2 to write the numerator and denominator as two separate radicals:

$$\sqrt{\frac{12x^5y^3}{5z}} = \frac{\sqrt{12x^5y^3}}{\sqrt{5z}}$$

Simplifying the numerator, we have

$$\frac{\sqrt{12x^5y^3}}{\sqrt{5z}} = \frac{\sqrt{4x^4y^2}\sqrt{3xy}}{\sqrt{5z}}$$

$$= \frac{2x^2y\sqrt{3xy}}{\sqrt{5z}}$$

To rationalize the denominator we multiply the numerator and denominator by $\sqrt{5z}$:

$$\frac{2x^2y\sqrt{3xy}}{\sqrt{5z}} \cdot \frac{\sqrt{5z}}{\sqrt{5z}} = \frac{2x^2y\sqrt{15xyz}}{\sqrt{(5z)^2}}$$

$$= \frac{2x^2y\sqrt{15xyz}}{5z}$$ ▲

Answer

9. $\dfrac{4xy^2\sqrt{21xz}}{7z}$

Problem Set 5.2

Use Property 1 for radicals to write each of the following expressions in simplified form. (Assume all variables are positive throughout the problem set.)

1. $\sqrt{8}$

2. $\sqrt{32}$

3. $\sqrt{18}$

4. $\sqrt{98}$

5. $\sqrt{75}$

6. $\sqrt{12}$

7. $\sqrt{288}$

8. $\sqrt{128}$

9. $\sqrt{48}$

10. $\sqrt{27}$

11. $\sqrt{45}$

12. $\sqrt{20}$

13. $\sqrt[3]{54}$

14. $\sqrt[3]{24}$

15. $\sqrt[3]{128}$

16. $\sqrt[3]{162}$

17. $\sqrt[5]{64}$

18. $\sqrt[4]{48}$

Name _____

Class _____

Date _____

Answers

1. _____   2. _____

3. _____   4. _____

5. _____   6. _____

7. _____   8. _____

9. _____   10. _____

11. _____   12. _____

13. _____   14. _____

15. _____   16. _____

17. _____   18. _____

Answers

19. _____   20. _____

21. _____   22. _____

23. _____   24. _____

25. _____   26. _____

27. _____   28. _____

29. _____   30. _____

31. _____   32. _____

33. _____   34. _____

35. _____   36. _____

19. $\sqrt{54}$

20. $\sqrt{63}$

21. $\sqrt[3]{40}$

22. $\sqrt[3]{48}$

23. $\sqrt{99}$

24. $\sqrt{44}$

25. $\sqrt{18x^3}$

26. $\sqrt{27x^5}$

27. $\sqrt{32y^7}$

28. $\sqrt{20y^3}$

29. $\sqrt[3]{40x^4y^7}$

30. $\sqrt[3]{128x^6y^2}$

31. $\sqrt{48a^2b^3c^4}$

32. $\sqrt{72a^4b^3c^2}$

33. $\sqrt[3]{48a^2b^3c^4}$

34. $\sqrt[3]{72a^4b^3c^2}$

35. $\sqrt[5]{64x^8y^{12}}$

36. $\sqrt[4]{32x^9y^{10}}$

Rationalize the denominator in each of the following expressions.

37. $\dfrac{2}{\sqrt{3}}$

38. $\dfrac{3}{\sqrt{2}}$

39. $\dfrac{5}{\sqrt{6}}$

40. $\dfrac{7}{\sqrt{5}}$

41. $\sqrt{\dfrac{1}{2}}$

42. $\sqrt{\dfrac{1}{3}}$

43. $\sqrt{\dfrac{1}{5}}$

44. $\sqrt{\dfrac{1}{6}}$

45. $\dfrac{4}{\sqrt[3]{2}}$

46. $\dfrac{5}{\sqrt[3]{3}}$

47. $\dfrac{2}{\sqrt[3]{9}}$

48. $\dfrac{3}{\sqrt[3]{4}}$

49. $\sqrt{\dfrac{3}{2x}}$

50. $\sqrt{\dfrac{5}{3x}}$

51. $\sqrt[3]{\dfrac{4x}{3y}}$

52. $\sqrt[3]{\dfrac{7x}{6y}}$

Name _____

Class _____

Date _____

Answers

37. _____   38. _____

39. _____   40. _____

41. _____   42. _____

43. _____   44. _____

45. _____   46. _____

47. _____   48. _____

49. _____   50. _____

51. _____   52. _____

Answers

53. _____

54. _____

55. _____

56. _____

57. _____

58. _____

59. _____

60. _____

61. _____

62. _____

63. _____

64. _____

65. _____

66. _____

67. _____

68. _____

Write each of the following in simplified form.

53. $\sqrt{\dfrac{27x^3}{5y}}$
54. $\sqrt{\dfrac{12x^5}{7y}}$
55. $\sqrt{\dfrac{75x^3y^2}{2z}}$

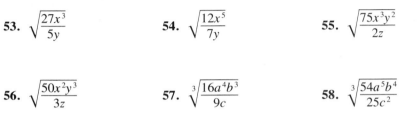

56. $\sqrt{\dfrac{50x^2y^3}{3z}}$
57. $\sqrt[3]{\dfrac{16a^4b^3}{9c}}$
58. $\sqrt[3]{\dfrac{54a^5b^4}{25c^2}}$

59. Suppose $x + 3$ is nonnegative and simplify $\sqrt{x^2 + 6x + 9}$ by first writing $x^2 + 6x + 9$ as $(x + 3)^2$.

60. Assume $x - 5$ is nonnegative and simplify $\sqrt{x^2 - 10x + 25}$.

61. The distance (d) between opposite corners of a rectangular room with length l and width w is given by

$$d = \sqrt{l^2 + w^2}$$

How far is it between opposite corners of a living room that measures 10 by 15 feet?

62. The radius r of a sphere with volume V can be found by using the formula

$$r = \sqrt[3]{\dfrac{3V}{4\pi}}$$

Find the radius of a sphere with volume 9 cubic feet. Write your answer in simplified form. (Use 22/7 for π.)

Review Problems The following problems review material we covered in Section 3.3. Reviewing these problems will help you with the next section.

Combine similar terms.

63. $3x^2 + 4x^2$
64. $7x^2 + 5x^2$

65. $5a^3 - 4a^3 + 6a^3$
66. $7a^4 - 2a^4 + 3a^4$

67. $(2x^2 - 5x + 3) - (x^2 - 3x + 7)$

68. $(6x^2 - 3x - 4) - (2x^2 - 3x + 5)$

Section 5.3 Addition and Subtraction of Radical Expressions

In Chapter 3 we found that we could add only similar terms when combining polynomials. The same idea applies to addition and subtraction of radical expressions.

DEFINITION Two radicals are said to be *similar radicals* if they have the same index and the same radicand.

The expressions $5\sqrt[3]{7}$ and $-8\sqrt[3]{7}$ are similar since the index is ^{3} in both cases and the radicands are 7. The expressions $3\sqrt[4]{5}$ and $7\sqrt[3]{5}$ are not similar since they have different indices, while the expressions $2\sqrt[5]{8}$ and $3\sqrt[5]{9}$ are not similar because the radicands are not the same.

We add and subtract radical expressions in the same way we add and subtract polynomials—by combining similar terms under the distributive property.

▼ **Example 1** Combine: $5\sqrt{3} - 4\sqrt{3} + 6\sqrt{3}$.

Solution All three radicals are similar. We apply the distributive property to get

$$5\sqrt{3} - 4\sqrt{3} + 6\sqrt{3} = (5 - 4 + 6)\sqrt{3}$$
$$= 7\sqrt{3}$$
▲

▼ **Example 2** Combine: $3\sqrt{8} + 5\sqrt{18}$.

Solution The two radicals do not seem to be similar. We must write each in simplified form before applying the distributive property.

$$3\sqrt{8} + 5\sqrt{18} = 3\sqrt{4 \cdot 2} + 5\sqrt{9 \cdot 2}$$
$$= 3\sqrt{4}\sqrt{2} + 5\sqrt{9}\sqrt{2}$$
$$= 3 \cdot 2\sqrt{2} + 5 \cdot 3\sqrt{2}$$
$$= 6\sqrt{2} + 15\sqrt{2}$$
$$= (6 + 15)\sqrt{2}$$
$$= 21\sqrt{2}$$
▲

The result of Example 2 can be generalized to the following rule for sums and differences of radical expressions.

Rule To add or subtract two radical expressions, put each in simplified form and apply the distributive property if possible. We can add only similar radicals. We must write each expression in simplified form for radicals before we can tell if the radicals are similar.

▼ **Example 3** Combine: $7\sqrt{75xy^3} - 4y\sqrt{12xy}$, where $x, y \geq 0$.

Solution We write each expression in simplified form and combine similar radicals:

$$7\sqrt{75xy^3} - 4y\sqrt{12xy} = 7\sqrt{25y^2}\sqrt{3xy} - 4y\sqrt{4}\sqrt{3xy}$$
$$= 35y\sqrt{3xy} - 8y\sqrt{3xy}$$
$$= (35y - 8y)\sqrt{3xy}$$
$$= 27y\sqrt{3xy}$$
▲

Practice Problems

1. Combine: $3\sqrt{5} - 2\sqrt{5} + 4\sqrt{5}$.

2. Combine: $4\sqrt{50} + 3\sqrt{8}$.

3. Assume $x, y \geq 0$ and combine:
$$4\sqrt{18x^2y} - 3x\sqrt{50y}$$

Answers
1. $5\sqrt{5}$ 2. $26\sqrt{2}$ 3. $-3x\sqrt{2y}$

4. Combine:

$$2\sqrt[3]{27a^2b^4} + 3b\sqrt[3]{125a^2b}$$

▼ **Example 4** Combine: $10\sqrt[3]{8a^4b^2} + 11a\sqrt[3]{27ab^2}$.

Solution Writing each radical in simplified form and combining similar terms, we have

$$10\sqrt[3]{8a^4b^2} + 11a\sqrt[3]{27ab^2} = 10\sqrt[3]{8a^3}\sqrt[3]{ab^2} + 11a\sqrt[3]{27}\sqrt[3]{ab^2}$$
$$= 20a\sqrt[3]{ab^2} + 33a\sqrt[3]{ab^2}$$
$$= 53a\sqrt[3]{ab^2} \qquad ▲$$

Our next example involves rationalizing a denominator and addition of fractions, as well as combining similar radicals.

5. Combine: $\dfrac{\sqrt{5}}{3} + \dfrac{1}{\sqrt{5}}$.

▼ **Example 5** Combine: $\dfrac{\sqrt{3}}{2} + \dfrac{1}{\sqrt{3}}$.

Solution We begin by writing the second term in simplified form.

$$\frac{\sqrt{3}}{2} + \frac{1}{\sqrt{3}} = \frac{\sqrt{3}}{2} + \frac{1}{\sqrt{3}} \cdot \frac{\sqrt{3}}{\sqrt{3}}$$
$$= \frac{\sqrt{3}}{2} + \frac{\sqrt{3}}{3}$$
$$= \frac{1}{2}\sqrt{3} + \frac{1}{3}\sqrt{3}$$
$$= \left(\frac{1}{2} + \frac{1}{3}\right)\sqrt{3}$$

The common denominator is 6. Multiplying $\frac{1}{2}$ by $\frac{3}{3}$ and $\frac{1}{3}$ by $\frac{2}{2}$ we have

$$= \left(\frac{3}{6} + \frac{2}{6}\right)\sqrt{3}$$
$$= \frac{5}{6}\sqrt{3}$$
$$= \frac{5\sqrt{3}}{6} \qquad ▲$$

Answers

4. $21b\sqrt[3]{a^2b}$ **5.** $\dfrac{8\sqrt{5}}{15}$

Problem Set 5.3

Combine the following expressions. (Assume any variables under an even root are positive.)

1. $3\sqrt{5} + 4\sqrt{5}$

2. $6\sqrt{3} - 5\sqrt{3}$

3. $7\sqrt{6} + 9\sqrt{6}$

4. $4\sqrt{2} - 10\sqrt{2}$

5. $3x\sqrt{7} - 4x\sqrt{7}$

6. $6y\sqrt{a} + 7y\sqrt{a}$

7. $5\sqrt[3]{10} - 4\sqrt[3]{10}$

8. $6\sqrt[4]{2} + 9\sqrt[4]{2}$

9. $8\sqrt{6} - 2\sqrt{6} + 3\sqrt{6}$

10. $7\sqrt{7} - \sqrt{7} + 4\sqrt{7}$

11. $3x\sqrt{2} - 4x\sqrt{2} + x\sqrt{2}$

12. $5x\sqrt{6} - 3x\sqrt{6} - 2x\sqrt{6}$

13. $\sqrt{18} + \sqrt{2}$

14. $\sqrt{12} + \sqrt{3}$

15. $\sqrt{20} - \sqrt{80} + \sqrt{45}$

16. $\sqrt{8} - \sqrt{32} - \sqrt{18}$

Name _____

Class _____

Date _____

Answers

1. _____ 2. _____

3. _____ 4. _____

5. _____ 6. _____

7. _____ 8. _____

9. _____ 10. _____

11. _____ 12. _____

13. _____ 14. _____

15. _____ 16. _____

Answers

17. _____ 18. _____

19. _____ 20. _____

21. _____ 22. _____

23. _____ 24. _____

25. _____ 26. _____

27. _____ 28. _____

17. $4\sqrt{8} - 2\sqrt{50} - 5\sqrt{72}$ **18.** $\sqrt{48} - 3\sqrt{27} + 2\sqrt{75}$

19. $5x\sqrt{8} + 3\sqrt{32x^2} - 5\sqrt{50x^2}$ **20.** $2\sqrt{50x^2} - 8x\sqrt{18} - 3\sqrt{72x^2}$

21. $5\sqrt[3]{16} - 4\sqrt[3]{54}$ **22.** $\sqrt[3]{81} + 3\sqrt[3]{24}$

23. $\sqrt[3]{x^4y^2} + 7x\sqrt[3]{xy^2}$ **24.** $2\sqrt[3]{x^8y^6} - 3y^2\sqrt[3]{8x^8}$

25. $5a^2\sqrt{27ab^3} - 6b\sqrt{12a^5b}$ **26.** $9a\sqrt{20a^3b^2} + 7b\sqrt{45a^5}$

27. $b\sqrt[3]{24a^5b} + 3a\sqrt[3]{81a^2b^4}$ **28.** $7\sqrt[3]{a^4b^3c^2} - 6ab\sqrt[3]{ac^2}$

29. $\dfrac{\sqrt{2}}{2} + \dfrac{1}{\sqrt{2}}$

30. $\dfrac{\sqrt{3}}{3} + \dfrac{1}{\sqrt{3}}$

31. $\dfrac{\sqrt{5}}{3} + \dfrac{1}{\sqrt{5}}$

32. $\dfrac{\sqrt{6}}{2} + \dfrac{1}{\sqrt{6}}$

33. $\sqrt{3} - \dfrac{1}{\sqrt{3}}$

34. $\sqrt{5} - \dfrac{1}{\sqrt{5}}$

35. $\dfrac{\sqrt{18}}{6} + \sqrt{\dfrac{1}{2}} + \dfrac{\sqrt{2}}{2}$

36. $\dfrac{\sqrt{12}}{6} + \sqrt{\dfrac{1}{3}} + \dfrac{\sqrt{3}}{3}$

37. $\sqrt{6} - \sqrt{\dfrac{2}{3}}$

38. $\sqrt{15} - \sqrt{\dfrac{3}{5}}$

Name _____

Class _____

Date _____

Answers

29. _____ **30.** _____

31. _____ **32.** _____

33. _____ **34.** _____

35. _____ **36.** _____

37. _____ **38.** _____

Answers

39. _____

40. _____

41. _____

42. _____

43. _____

44. _____

45. _____

46. _____

47. _____

48. _____

49. _____

50. _____

51. _____

52. _____

53. _____

54. _____

39. Use the table of powers, roots, and prime factors in the back of the book to find a decimal approximation for $\sqrt{12}$ and for $2\sqrt{3}$.

40. Use the table in the back of the book to find decimal approximations for $\sqrt{50}$ and $5\sqrt{2}$.

41. Use the table in the back of the book to find a decimal approximation for $\sqrt{8} + \sqrt{18}$. Is it equal to the decimal approximations for $\sqrt{26}$ or $\sqrt{50}$?

42. Use the table in the back of the book to find a decimal approximation for $\sqrt{3} + \sqrt{12}$. Is it equal to the decimal approximation for $\sqrt{15}$ or $\sqrt{27}$?

Each statement below is false. Correct the right side of each one.

43. $3\sqrt{2x} + 5\sqrt{2x} = 8\sqrt{4x}$ **44.** $5\sqrt{3} - 7\sqrt{3} = -2\sqrt{9}$

45. $\sqrt{9 + 16} = 3 + 4$ **46.** $\sqrt{36 + 64} = 6 + 8$

Review Problems   The following problems review material we covered in Section 3.4. Reviewing these problems will help you understand the next section.

Multiply.

47. $2x(3x - 5)$ **48.** $5x(4x - 3)$

49. $(a + 5)(2a - 5)$ **50.** $(3a + 4)(a + 2)$

51. $(3x - 2y)^2$ **52.** $(2x + 3y)^2$

53. $(x + 2)(x - 2)$ **54.** $(5x - 7y)(5x + 7y)$

Section 5.4 Multiplication and Division of Radical Expressions

We use the same process to multiply radical expressions as we have in the past to multiply polynomials.

▼ **Example 1** Multiply: $\sqrt{3}(2\sqrt{6} - 5\sqrt{12})$.

Solution Applying the distributive property, we have

$$\sqrt{3}(2\sqrt{6} - 5\sqrt{12}) = \sqrt{3} \cdot 2\sqrt{6} - \sqrt{3} \cdot 5\sqrt{12}$$
$$= 2\sqrt{18} - 5\sqrt{36}$$

Writing each radical in simplified form gives

$$2\sqrt{18} - 5\sqrt{36} = 2\sqrt{9}\sqrt{2} - 5\sqrt{36}$$
$$= 6\sqrt{2} - 30 \qquad ▲$$

▼ **Example 2** Multiply: $(\sqrt{3} + \sqrt{5})(4\sqrt{3} - \sqrt{5})$.

Solution The same principle that applies to multiply two binomials applies to this product. We must multiply each term in the first expression by each term in the second one. Any convenient method can be used. Let's use the FOIL method.

$$(\sqrt{3} + \sqrt{5})(4\sqrt{3} - \sqrt{5})$$
$$\overset{F}{} \qquad \overset{O}{} \qquad \overset{I}{} \qquad \overset{L}{}$$
$$= \sqrt{3} \cdot 4\sqrt{3} - \sqrt{3}\sqrt{5} + \sqrt{5} \cdot 4\sqrt{3} - \sqrt{5}\sqrt{5}$$
$$= 4 \cdot 3 - \sqrt{15} + 4\sqrt{15} - 5$$
$$= 12 + 3\sqrt{15} - 5$$
$$= 7 + 3\sqrt{15} \qquad ▲$$

▼ **Example 3** Expand and simplify $(\sqrt{x} + 3)^2$.

Solution 1 We can write this problem as a multiplication problem and proceed as we did in Example 2:

$$(\sqrt{x} + 3)^2 = (\sqrt{x} + 3)(\sqrt{x} + 3)$$
$$\overset{F}{} \qquad \overset{O}{} \qquad \overset{I}{} \qquad \overset{L}{}$$
$$= \sqrt{x} \cdot \sqrt{x} + 3\sqrt{x} + 3\sqrt{x} + 3 \cdot 3$$
$$= x + 3\sqrt{x} + 3\sqrt{x} + 9$$
$$= x + 6\sqrt{x} + 9$$

Solution 2 We can obtain the same result by applying the formula for the square of a sum: $(a + b)^2 = a^2 + 2ab + b^2$.

$$(\sqrt{x} + 3)^2 = (\sqrt{x})^2 + 2(\sqrt{x})(3) + 3^2$$
$$= x + 6\sqrt{x} + 9 \qquad ▲$$

▼ **Example 4** Expand $(3\sqrt{x} - 2\sqrt{y})^2$ and simplify the result.

Solution Let's apply the formula for the difference of a sum, $(a - b)^2 = a^2 - 2ab + b^2$:

$$(3\sqrt{x} - 2\sqrt{y})^2 = (3\sqrt{x})^2 - 2(3\sqrt{x})(2\sqrt{y}) + (-2\sqrt{y})^2$$
$$= 9x - 12\sqrt{xy} + 4y \qquad ▲$$

Practice Problems

1. Multiply: $\sqrt{2}(3\sqrt{5} - 4\sqrt{2})$.

2. Multiply:
$$(\sqrt{2} + \sqrt{7})(\sqrt{2} - 3\sqrt{7})$$

3. Expand and simplify
$$(\sqrt{x} + 5)^2$$

4. Expand $(5\sqrt{a} - 3\sqrt{b})^2$ and simplify the result.

Answers
1. $3\sqrt{10} - 8$ 2. $-19 - 2\sqrt{14}$
3. $x + 10\sqrt{x} + 25$
4. $25a - 30\sqrt{ab} + 9b$

5. Multiply:

$$(\sqrt{5} + \sqrt{3})(\sqrt{5} - \sqrt{3})$$

Note: We can prove that conjugates always multiply to yield a rational number as follows: If a and b are positive rational numbers, then

$$(\sqrt{a} + \sqrt{b})(\sqrt{a} - \sqrt{b})$$
$$= \sqrt{a}\sqrt{a} - \sqrt{a}\sqrt{b}$$
$$\quad + \sqrt{a}\sqrt{b} + \sqrt{b}\sqrt{b}$$
$$= a - \sqrt{ab} + \sqrt{ab} + b$$
$$= a + b$$

which is rational if a and b are rational.

6. Divide: $\dfrac{3}{\sqrt{7} - \sqrt{3}}$.

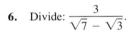

▼ **Example 5** Multiply: $(\sqrt{6} + \sqrt{2})(\sqrt{6} - \sqrt{2})$.

Solution We notice the product is of the form $(a + b)(a - b)$, which always gives the difference of two squares, $a^2 - b^2$:

$$(\sqrt{6} + \sqrt{2})(\sqrt{6} - \sqrt{2}) = (\sqrt{6})^2 - (\sqrt{2})^2$$
$$= 6 - 2$$
$$= 4 \qquad \blacktriangle$$

In Example 5 the two expressions $(\sqrt{6} + \sqrt{2})$ and $(\sqrt{6} - \sqrt{2})$ are called *conjugates*. In general, the conjugate of $\sqrt{a} + \sqrt{b}$ is $\sqrt{a} - \sqrt{b}$. Multiplying conjugates of this form always produces a rational number.

Division with radical expressions is the same as rationalizing the denominator. In Section 5.2 we were able to divide $\sqrt{3}$ by $\sqrt{2}$ by rationalizing the denominator:

$$\frac{\sqrt{3}}{\sqrt{2}} = \frac{\sqrt{3}}{\sqrt{2}} \cdot \frac{\sqrt{2}}{\sqrt{2}}$$

We can accomplish the same result with expressions such as

$$\frac{6}{\sqrt{5} - \sqrt{3}}$$

by multiplying the numerator and denominator by the conjugate of the denominator.

▼ **Example 6** Divide: $\dfrac{6}{\sqrt{5} - \sqrt{3}}$. (Rationalize the denominator.)

Solution Since the product of two conjugates is a rational number, we multiply the numerator and denominator by the conjugate of the denominator:

$$\frac{6}{\sqrt{5} - \sqrt{3}} = \frac{6}{\sqrt{5} - \sqrt{3}} \cdot \frac{(\sqrt{5} + \sqrt{3})}{(\sqrt{5} + \sqrt{3})}$$
$$= \frac{6\sqrt{5} + 6\sqrt{3}}{(\sqrt{5})^2 - (\sqrt{3})^2}$$
$$= \frac{6\sqrt{5} + 6\sqrt{3}}{5 - 3}$$
$$= \frac{6\sqrt{5} + 6\sqrt{3}}{2}$$
$$= \frac{2(3\sqrt{5} + 3\sqrt{3})}{2}$$
$$= 3\sqrt{5} + 3\sqrt{3} \qquad \blacktriangle$$

Answers

5. 2 **6.** $\dfrac{3\sqrt{7} + 3\sqrt{3}}{4}$

Problem Set 5.4

Name _____

Class _____

Date _____

Find the following products. (Assume all variables are positive.)

1. $\sqrt{3}(\sqrt{2} - 3\sqrt{3})$

2. $\sqrt{2}(5\sqrt{3} + 4\sqrt{2})$

3. $6\sqrt{6}(2\sqrt{2} + 1)$

4. $7\sqrt{5}(3\sqrt{15} - 2)$

5. $(\sqrt{3} + \sqrt{2})(3\sqrt{3} - \sqrt{2})$

6. $(\sqrt{5} - \sqrt{2})(3\sqrt{5} + 2\sqrt{2})$

7. $(\sqrt{x} + 5)(\sqrt{x} - 3)$

8. $(\sqrt{x} + 4)(\sqrt{x} + 2)$

9. $(3\sqrt{6} + 4\sqrt{2})(\sqrt{6} + 2\sqrt{2})$

10. $(\sqrt{7} - 3\sqrt{3})(2\sqrt{7} - 4\sqrt{3})$

11. $(\sqrt{3} + 4)^2$

12. $(\sqrt{5} - 2)^2$

13. $(\sqrt{x} - 3)^2$

14. $(\sqrt{x} + 4)^2$

15. $(2\sqrt{a} - 3\sqrt{b})^2$

16. $(5\sqrt{a} - 2\sqrt{b})^2$

17. $(\sqrt{3} - \sqrt{2})(\sqrt{3} + \sqrt{2})$

18. $(\sqrt{5} - \sqrt{2})(\sqrt{5} + \sqrt{2})$

19. $(2\sqrt{6} - 3)(2\sqrt{6} + 3)$

20. $(3\sqrt{5} - 1)(3\sqrt{5} + 1)$

21. $(\sqrt{a} + 7)(\sqrt{a} - 7)$

22. $(\sqrt{a} + 5)(\sqrt{a} - 5)$

Answers

1. _____
2. _____
3. _____
4. _____
5. _____
6. _____
7. _____
8. _____
9. _____
10. _____
11. _____
12. _____
13. _____
14. _____
15. _____
16. _____
17. _____
18. _____
19. _____
20. _____
21. _____
22. _____

Answers

23. _____

24. _____

25. _____

26. _____

27. _____

28. _____

29. _____

30. _____

31. _____

32. _____

Rationalize the denominator in each of the following. (Assume all variables are positive.)

23. $\dfrac{2}{\sqrt{3} + \sqrt{2}}$

24. $\dfrac{3}{\sqrt{5} - \sqrt{2}}$

25. $\dfrac{\sqrt{2}}{\sqrt{6} - \sqrt{2}}$

26. $\dfrac{\sqrt{5}}{\sqrt{5} + \sqrt{3}}$

27. $\dfrac{\sqrt{x}}{\sqrt{x} - 3}$

28. $\dfrac{\sqrt{x}}{\sqrt{x} + 2}$

29. $\dfrac{\sqrt{5}}{2\sqrt{5} - 3}$

30. $\dfrac{\sqrt{7}}{3\sqrt{7} - 2}$

31. $\dfrac{3}{\sqrt{x} - \sqrt{y}}$

32. $\dfrac{2}{\sqrt{x} + \sqrt{y}}$

33. $\dfrac{\sqrt{2} + \sqrt{6}}{\sqrt{2} - \sqrt{6}}$

34. $\dfrac{\sqrt{3} - \sqrt{5}}{\sqrt{3} + \sqrt{5}}$

35. $\dfrac{\sqrt{a} + \sqrt{b}}{\sqrt{a} - \sqrt{b}}$

36. $\dfrac{\sqrt{a} - \sqrt{b}}{\sqrt{a} + \sqrt{b}}$

37. $\dfrac{2\sqrt{3} - \sqrt{7}}{3\sqrt{3} + \sqrt{7}}$

38. $\dfrac{5\sqrt{6} + 2\sqrt{2}}{\sqrt{6} - \sqrt{2}}$

39. $\dfrac{3\sqrt{x} + 2}{1 + \sqrt{x}}$

40. $\dfrac{5\sqrt{x} - 1}{2 + \sqrt{x}}$

Name _____

Class _____

Date _____

Answers

33. _____

34. _____

35. _____

36. _____

37. _____

38. _____

39. _____

40. _____

Answers

41. _____ 42. _____

43. _____ 44. _____

45. _____ 46. _____

47. _____ 48. _____

49. _____ 50. _____

51. _____ 52. _____

53. _____ 54. _____

55. _____ 56. _____

41. Show that the product $(\sqrt[3]{2} + \sqrt[3]{3})(\sqrt[3]{4} - \sqrt[3]{6} + \sqrt[3]{9})$ is 5. (You may want to look back to Section 3.4 to see how we multiplied a binomial by a trinomial.)

42. Show that the product $(\sqrt[3]{x} + 2)(\sqrt[3]{x^2} - 2\sqrt[3]{x} + 4)$ is $x + 8$.

Each statement below is false. Correct the right side of each one.

43. $5(2\sqrt{3}) = 10\sqrt{15}$

44. $3(2\sqrt{x}) = 6\sqrt{3x}$

45. $(\sqrt{x} + 3)^2 = x + 9$

46. $(\sqrt{x} - 7)^2 = x - 49$

47. $(5\sqrt{3})^2 = 15$

48. $(3\sqrt{5})^2 = 15$

49. If an object is dropped from the top of a 100-ft building, the amount of time t, in seconds, that it takes for the object to be h feet from the ground is given by the formula

$$t = \frac{\sqrt{100 - h}}{4}$$

How long does it take before the object is 50 feet from the ground? How long does it takes to reach the ground? (When it is on the ground, h is 0.)

50. Use the formula given in Problem 49 to determine the height from which the ball should be dropped if it is to take exactly 1.25 seconds to hit the ground.

Review Problems   The following problems review material we covered in Sections 2.1 and 2.2.

Solve each equation.

51. $3x + 4 = 25$

52. $4x - 7 = 9$

53. $3y - 4 = y + 6$

54. $4y + 7 = y + 2$

55. $4(2a + 1) - (3a - 5) = 24$

56. $5(6a - 3) - (2a - 4) = 45$

Section 5.5 Equations with Radicals

This section is concerned with solving equations that involve one or more radicals. The first step in solving an equation that contains a radical is to eliminate the radical from the equation. To do so we need an additional property.

Squaring Property of Equality   If both sides of an equation are squared, the solutions to the original equation are solutions to the resulting equation.

We will never lose solutions to our equations by squaring both sides. We may, however, introduce *extraneous solutions*. Extraneous solutions satisfy the equation obtained by squaring both sides of the original equation, but do not satisfy the original equation.

We know that if two real numbers a and b are equal, then so are their squares:

$$\text{If} \quad a = b$$
$$\text{then} \quad a^2 = b^2$$

On the other hand, extraneous solutions are introduced when we square opposites. That is, even though opposites are not equal, their squares are. For example,

$$5 = -5 \qquad \text{A false statement}$$
$$(5)^2 = (-5)^2 \qquad \text{Square both sides}$$
$$25 = 25 \qquad \text{A true statement}$$

We are free to square both sides of an equation any time it is convenient. We must be aware, however, that doing so may introduce extraneous solutions. We must, therefore, check all our solutions in the original equation if at any time we square both sides of the original equation.

Practice Problems

▼ **Example 1**   Solve for x: $\sqrt{3x + 4} = 5$.

Solution   We square both sides and proceed as usual:

$$\sqrt{3x + 4} = 5$$
$$(\sqrt{3x + 4})^2 = 5^2$$
$$3x + 4 = 25$$
$$3x = 21$$
$$x = 7$$

Checking $x = 7$ in the original equation, we have

$$\sqrt{3(7) + 4} = 5$$
$$\sqrt{21 + 4} = 5$$
$$\sqrt{25} = 5$$
$$5 = 5$$

The solution $x = 7$ satisfies the original equation. ▲

1. Solve for x: $\sqrt{2x + 4} = 4$.

Answer

2. Solve $\sqrt{7x - 3} = -5$.

▼ **Example 2** Solve $\sqrt{4x - 7} = -3$.

Solution Squaring both sides, we have

$$\sqrt{4x - 7} = -3$$
$$(\sqrt{4x - 7})^2 = (-3)^2$$
$$4x - 7 = 9$$
$$4x = 16$$
$$x = 4$$

Checking $x = 4$ in the original equation gives

$$\sqrt{4(4) - 7} = -3$$
$$\sqrt{16 - 7} = -3$$
$$\sqrt{9} = -3$$
$$3 = -3$$ ▲

Note: The fact that there is no solution to the equation in Example 2 was obvious to begin with. Notice that the left side of the equation is the *positive* square root of $4x - 7$, which must be a positive number or 0. The right side of the equation is -3. Since we cannot have a number that is either positive or zero equal to a negative number, there is no solution to the equation.

The solution $x = 4$ produces a false statement when checked in the original equation. Since $x = 4$ was the only possible solution, there is no solution to the original equation. The possible solution $x = 4$ is an extraneous solution. It satisfies the equation obtained by squaring both sides of the original equation, but does not satisfy the original equation.

3. Solve $\sqrt{4x + 5} + 2 = 7$.

▼ **Example 3** Solve $\sqrt{5x - 1} + 3 = 7$.

Solution We must isolate the radical on the left side of the equation. If we attempt to square both sides without doing so, the resulting equation will also contain a radical. Adding -3 to both sides, we have

$$\sqrt{5x - 1} + 3 = 7$$
$$\sqrt{5x - 1} = 4$$

We can now square both sides and proceed as usual:

$$(\sqrt{5x - 1})^2 = (4)^2$$
$$5x - 1 = 16$$
$$5x = 17$$
$$x = \tfrac{17}{5}$$

Checking $x = \tfrac{17}{5}$, we have

$$\sqrt{5(\tfrac{17}{5}) - 1} + 3 = 7$$
$$\sqrt{17 - 1} + 3 = 7$$
$$4 + 3 = 7$$
$$7 = 7$$ ▲

4. Solve $\sqrt{2x + 1} - \sqrt{4x - 5} = 0$.

▼ **Example 4** Solve $\sqrt{3y - 4} - \sqrt{y + 6} = 0$.

Solution We add $\sqrt{y + 6}$ to both sides, square both sides, and solve as usual:

$$\sqrt{3y - 4} - \sqrt{y + 6} = 0$$
$$\sqrt{3y - 4} = \sqrt{y + 6}$$
$$(\sqrt{3y - 4})^2 = (\sqrt{y + 6})^2$$
$$3y - 4 = y + 6$$
$$2y = 10$$
$$y = 5$$

Answers
2. No solution **3.** 5 **4.** 3

Substituting $y = 5$ into the original equation, we have

$$\sqrt{3(5) - 4} - \sqrt{5 + 6} = 0$$
$$\sqrt{15 - 4} - \sqrt{11} = 0$$
$$\sqrt{11} - \sqrt{11} = 0$$
$$0 = 0 \qquad \blacktriangle$$

For our next example we consider an equation in which the radicals cannot all be eliminated by squaring each side of the equation. That is, after we square each side of the equation, the resulting equation still contains a radical. To eliminate the radical that remains, we square both sides again.

▼ **Example 5** Solve $\sqrt{x - 3} = \sqrt{x} - 3$.

5. Solve $\sqrt{x - 9} = \sqrt{x} - 3$.

Solution We begin by squaring both sides. Note carefully what happens when we square the right side of the equation, and compare the square of the right side with the square of the left side. You must convince yourself that these results are correct. (The note in the margin will help if you are having trouble convincing yourself that what is written below is true.)

$$(\sqrt{x - 3})^2 = (\sqrt{x} - 3)^2$$
$$x - 3 = x - 6\sqrt{x} + 9$$

Now we still have a radical in our equation, so we will have to square both sides again. Before we do, though, let's isolate the remaining radical.

$$
\begin{array}{ll}
x - 3 = x - 6\sqrt{x} + 9 & \\
-3 = -6\sqrt{x} + 9 & \text{Add } -x \text{ to each side} \\
-12 = -6\sqrt{x} & \text{Add } -9 \text{ to each side} \\
2 = \sqrt{x} & \text{Divide each side by } -6 \\
4 = x & \text{Square each side}
\end{array}
$$

Note: It is very important that you realize that the square of $(\sqrt{x} - 3)$ is not $x + 9$. Remember, when we square a difference with two terms, we use the formula

$$(a - b)^2 = a^2 - 2ab + b^2$$

Applying this formula to $(\sqrt{x} - 3)^2$, we have

$$(\sqrt{x} - 3)^2 = (\sqrt{x})^2 - 2(\sqrt{x})(3) + 3^2$$
$$= x - 6\sqrt{x} + 9$$

If you are more comfortable using the FOIL method, then the product would look like this:

$$(\sqrt{x} - 3)^2$$
$$= (\sqrt{x} - 3)(\sqrt{x} - 3)$$
$$= \sqrt{x}\sqrt{x} - 3\sqrt{x} - 3\sqrt{x} + 9$$
$$= x - 6\sqrt{x} + 9$$

Our only possible solution is $x = 4$, which we check in our original equation as follows:

$$\sqrt{4 - 3} = \sqrt{4} - 3$$
$$\sqrt{1} = 2 - 3$$
$$1 = -1 \qquad \text{A false statement}$$

Substituting 4 for x in the original equation yields a false statement. Since 4 was our only possible solution, there is no solution to our equation. ▲

Here is another example of an equation for which we must apply our squaring property twice before all radicals are eliminated.

Answer
5. 9

6. Solve $\sqrt{x + 2} = \sqrt{x + 3} - 1$.

7. Solve $\sqrt[3]{3x - 7} = 2$.

Answers
6. -2 7. 5

▼ **Example 6** Solve $\sqrt{x + 1} = \sqrt{x + 2} - 1$.

Solution Squaring both sides we have

$$(\sqrt{x + 1})^2 = (\sqrt{x + 2} - 1)^2$$
$$x + 1 = x + 2 - 2\sqrt{x + 2} + 1$$

Once again we are left with a radical in our equation. Before we square each side again, we must isolate the radical on the right side of the equation.

$$x + 1 = x + 3 - 2\sqrt{x + 2} \qquad \text{Simplify the right side}$$
$$1 = 3 - 2\sqrt{x + 2} \qquad \text{Add } -x \text{ to each side}$$
$$-2 = -2\sqrt{x + 2} \qquad \text{Add } -3 \text{ to each side}$$
$$1 = \sqrt{x + 2} \qquad \text{Divide each side by } -2$$
$$1 = x + 2 \qquad \text{Square both sides}$$
$$-1 = x \qquad \text{Add } -2 \text{ to each side}$$

Checking our only possible solution $x = -1$ in our original equation we have

$$\sqrt{-1 + 1} = \sqrt{-1 + 2} - 1$$
$$\sqrt{0} = \sqrt{1} - 1$$
$$0 = 1 - 1$$
$$0 = 0 \qquad \text{A true statement}$$

Our solution checks. ▲

It is also possible to raise both sides of an equation to powers greater than 2. We only need to check for extraneous solutions when we raise both sides of an equation to an even power. Raising both sides of an equation to an odd power will not produce extraneous solutions.

▼ **Example 7** Solve $\sqrt[3]{4x + 5} = 3$.

Solution Cubing both sides we have

$$(\sqrt[3]{4x + 5})^3 = 3^3$$
$$4x + 5 = 27$$
$$4x = 22$$
$$x = \frac{22}{4}$$
$$x = \frac{11}{2}$$

We do not need to check $x = \frac{11}{2}$ since we raised both sides to an odd power. ▲

Problem Set 5.5

Solve each of the following equations.

Name _____

Class _____

Date _____

Answers

1. $\sqrt{2x + 1} = 3$

2. $\sqrt{3x + 1} = 4$

1. _____   2. _____

3. _____   4. _____

5. _____   6. _____

7. _____   8. _____

9. _____   10. _____

11. _____   12. _____

3. $\sqrt{4x + 1} = -5$

4. $\sqrt{6x + 1} = -5$

5. $\sqrt{2y - 1} = 3$

6. $\sqrt{3y - 1} = 2$

7. $\sqrt{5x - 7} = -1$

8. $\sqrt{8x + 3} = -6$

9. $\sqrt{2x - 3} - 2 = 4$

10. $\sqrt{3x + 1} - 4 = 1$

11. $\sqrt{4a + 1} + 3 = 2$

12. $\sqrt{5a - 3} + 6 = 2$

Answers

13. _____ 14. _____

15. _____ 16. _____

17. _____ 18. _____

19. _____ 20. _____

21. _____ 22. _____

23. _____ 24. _____

13. $\sqrt[4]{3x + 1} = 2$

14. $\sqrt[4]{4x + 1} = 3$

15. $\sqrt[3]{2x - 5} = 1$

16. $\sqrt[3]{5x + 7} = 2$

17. $\sqrt[3]{3a + 5} = -3$

18. $\sqrt[3]{2a + 7} = -2$

19. $\sqrt{2x + 4} = \sqrt{1 - x}$

20. $\sqrt{3x + 4} = -\sqrt{2x + 3}$

21. $\sqrt{4a + 7} = -\sqrt{a + 2}$

22. $\sqrt{7a - 1} = \sqrt{2a + 4}$

23. $\sqrt[4]{5x - 8} = \sqrt[4]{4x - 1}$

24. $\sqrt[4]{6x + 7} = \sqrt[4]{x + 5}$

25. $\sqrt{y - 8} = \sqrt{8 - y}$ **26.** $\sqrt{2y - 5} = \sqrt{5y - 2}$

27. $\sqrt[3]{3x + 5} = \sqrt[3]{5 - 2x}$ **28.** $\sqrt[3]{4x + 9} = \sqrt[3]{3 - 2x}$

The following equations will require that you square both sides twice before all the radicals are eliminated. Solve each equation using the methods shown in Examples 5 and 6.

29. $\sqrt{x - 8} = \sqrt{x} - 2$ **30.** $\sqrt{x + 3} = \sqrt{x} - 3$

31. $\sqrt{x + 1} = \sqrt{x} + 1$ **32.** $\sqrt{x - 1} = \sqrt{x} - 1$

Name _____

Class _____

Date _____

Answers

25. _____   26. _____

27. _____   28. _____

29. _____   30. _____

31. _____   32. _____

Answers

33. _____   34. _____

35. _____   36. _____

37. _____   38. _____

39. _____   40. _____

41. _____   42. _____

43. _____   44. _____

33. $\sqrt{x + 8} = \sqrt{x - 4} + 2$

34. $\sqrt{x + 5} = \sqrt{x - 3} + 2$

35. $\sqrt{x - 5} - 3 = \sqrt{x - 8}$

36. $\sqrt{x - 3} - 4 = \sqrt{x - 3}$

37. Solve the following formula for h.
$$t = \frac{\sqrt{100 - h}}{4}$$

38. Solve the following formula for h.
$$t = \sqrt{\frac{2h - 40t}{g}}$$

Review Problems   The following problems review material we covered in Section 3.1.

Simplify each expression.

39. $x^3 \cdot x^2$

40. $x^2 \cdot x$

41. $(x^4)^{10}$

42. $(x^3)^4$

43. $(x^4)^7 \cdot x^2$

44. $(x^4)^5 \cdot x$

Section 5.6 Addition and Subtraction of Complex Numbers

The equation $x^2 = -9$ has no real solutions since the square of a real number is always positive. We have been unable to work with square roots of negative numbers like $\sqrt{-25}$ and $\sqrt{-16}$ for the same reason. Complex numbers allow us to expand our work with radicals to include square roots of negative numbers and to solve equations like $x^2 = -9$ and $x^2 = -64$. Our work with complex numbers is based on the following definition.

DEFINITION The number i is such that $i = \sqrt{-1}$ (which is the same as saying $i^2 = -1$).

The number i is not a real number. The number i can be used to eliminate the negative sign under a square root.

▼ **Example 1** Write (a) $\sqrt{-25}$, (b) $-\sqrt{-49}$, (c) $\sqrt{-12}$, and (d) $-\sqrt{-17}$ in terms of i.

a. $\sqrt{-25} = \sqrt{25(-1)} = \sqrt{25}\sqrt{-1} = 5i$

b. $-\sqrt{-49} = -\sqrt{49(-1)} = -\sqrt{49}\sqrt{-1} = -7i$

c. $\sqrt{-12} = \sqrt{12(-1)} = \sqrt{12}\sqrt{-1} = 2\sqrt{3}i = 2i\sqrt{3}$

d. $-\sqrt{-17} = -\sqrt{17(-1)} = -\sqrt{17}\sqrt{-1} = -\sqrt{17}i = -i\sqrt{17}$ ▲

If we assume all the properties of exponents hold when the base is i, we can write any power of i as either i, -1, $-i$, or 1. Using the fact that $i^2 = -1$, we have

$$i^1 = i$$
$$i^2 = -1$$
$$i^3 = i^2 \cdot i = -1(i) = -i$$
$$i^4 = i^2 \cdot i^2 = -1(-1) = 1$$

Since $i^4 = 1$, i^5 will simplify to i, and we will begin repeating the sequence i, -1, $-i$, 1 as we simplify higher powers of i:

$$i^5 = i^4 \cdot i = 1(i) = i$$
$$i^6 = i^4 \cdot i^2 = 1(-1) = -1$$
$$i^7 = i^4 \cdot i^3 = 1(-i) = -i$$
$$i^8 = i^4 \cdot i^4 = 1(1) = 1$$

Any power of i simplifies to i, -1, $-i$, or 1. The easiest way to simplify higher powers of i is to write them in terms of i^2. For instance, to simplify i^{21} we would write it as

$$(i^2)^{10} \cdot i \qquad \text{because } 2 \cdot 10 + 1 = 21$$

then, since $i^2 = -1$, we have

$$(-1)^{10}i = 1 \cdot i = i$$

▼ **Example 2** Simplify as much as possible:

a. $i^{30} = (i^2)^{15} = (-1)^{15} = -1$

b. $i^{11} = (i^2)^5 \cdot i = (-1)^5 \cdot i = (-1)i = -i$

c. $i^{40} = (i^2)^{20} = (-1)^{20} = 1$ ▲

Practice Problems

1. Write in terms of i.

a. $\sqrt{-36}$

b. $-\sqrt{-64}$

c. $\sqrt{-18}$

d. $-\sqrt{-19}$

Note: In parts c and d of Example 1 we wrote i before the radical simply to avoid confusion. If we were to write the answer to part c as $2\sqrt{3}i$, some people would think the i was under the radical sign when it is not.

2. Simplify.

a. i^{20}

b. i^{23}

c. i^{50}

Answers
1a. $6i$ **b.** $-8i$ **c.** $3i\sqrt{2}$
d. $-i\sqrt{19}$ **2a.** 1 **b.** $-i$ **c.** -1

DEFINITION   A *complex number* is any number that can be put in the form

$$a + bi$$

where a and b are real numbers and $i = \sqrt{-1}$. The form $a + bi$ is called *standard form* for complex numbers. The number a is called the *real part* of the complex number. The number b is called the *imaginary part* of the complex number.

Every real number is also a complex number. The real number 8, for example, can be written as $8 + 0i$; therefore, 8 is also considered a complex number.

Equality for Complex Numbers

Two complex numbers are equal if and only if their real parts are equal and their imaginary parts are equal. That is, for real numbers a, b, c, and d,

$$a + bi = c + di \quad \text{if and only if} \quad a = c \quad \text{and} \quad b = d$$

3. Find x and y if $4x + 7i = 8 - 14yi$.

▼ **Example 3**   Find x and y if $3x + 4i = 12 - 8yi$.

Solution   Since the two complex numbers are equal, their real parts are equal and their imaginary parts are equal:

$$3x = 12 \quad \text{and} \quad 4 = -8y$$
$$x = 4 \qquad\qquad y = -\tfrac{1}{2}$$ ▲

4. Find x and y if

$(2x - 1) + 9i = 5 + (4y + 1)i$

▼ **Example 4**   Find x and y if $(4x - 3) + 7i = 5 + (2y - 1)i$.

Solution   The real parts are $4x - 3$ and 5. The imaginary parts are 7 and $2y - 1$.

$$4x - 3 = 5 \quad \text{and} \quad 7 = 2y - 1$$
$$4x = 8 \qquad\qquad 8 = 2y$$
$$x = 2 \qquad\qquad y = 4$$ ▲

Addition and Subtraction of Complex Numbers

To add two complex numbers, add their real parts and add their imaginary parts. That is, if a, b, c, and d are real numbers, then

$$(a + bi) + (c + di) = (a + c) + (b + d)i$$

If we assume that the commutative, associative, and distributive properties hold for the number i, then the definition of addition is simply an extension of these properties.

We define subtraction in a similar manner. If a, b, c, and d are real numbers, then

$$(a + bi) - (c + di) = (a - c) + (b - d)i$$

5. Add or subtract as indicated.

a. $(2 + 6i) + (3 - 4i)$

b. $(6 + 5i) - (4 + 3i)$

c. $(7 - i) - (8 - 2i)$

▼ **Example 5**   Add or subtract as indicated.

a. $(3 + 4i) + (7 - 6i) = (3 + 7) + (4 - 6)i$
$$= 10 - 2i$$

b. $(7 + 3i) - (5 + 6i) = (7 - 5) + (3 - 6)i$
$$= 2 - 3i$$

c. $(5 - 2i) - (9 - 4i) = (5 - 9) + (-2 + 4)i$
$$= -4 + 2i$$ ▲

Answers
3. $x = 2$, $y = -\tfrac{1}{2}$ **4.** $x = 3$, $y = 2$
5a. $5 + 2i$ **b.** $2 + 2i$ **c.** $-1 + i$

Problem Set 5.6

Name _____

Class _____

Date _____

Write the following in terms of i and simplify as much as possible.

1. $\sqrt{-36}$ **2.** $\sqrt{-49}$

3. $-\sqrt{-25}$ **4.** $-\sqrt{-81}$

5. $\sqrt{-72}$ **6.** $\sqrt{-48}$

7. $-\sqrt{-12}$ **8.** $-\sqrt{-75}$

Write each of the following as i, -1, $-i$, or 1.

9. i^{28} **10.** i^{31}

11. i^{26} **12.** i^{37}

13. i^{75} **14.** i^{42}

Find x and y so each of the following equations is true:

15. $2x + 3yi = 6 - 3i$ **16.** $4x - 2yi = 4 + 8i$

17. $2 - 5i = -x + 10yi$ **18.** $4 + 7i = 6x - 14yi$

19. $2x + 10i = -16 - 2yi$ **20.** $4x - 5i = -2 + 3yi$

21. $(2x - 4) - 3i = 10 - 6yi$ **22.** $(4x - 3) - 2i = 8 + yi$

23. $(7x - 1) + 4i = 2 + (5y + 2)i$ **24.** $(5x + 2) - 7i = 4 + (2y + 1)i$

Answers

1. _____   2. _____

3. _____   4. _____

5. _____   6. _____

7. _____   8. _____

9. _____   10. _____

11. _____   12. _____

13. _____   14. _____

15. _____   16. _____

17. _____   18. _____

19. _____   20. _____

21. _____   22. _____

23. _____   24. _____

Answers

25. _____   26. _____

27. _____   28. _____

29. _____   30. _____

31. _____   32. _____

33. _____   34. _____

35. _____   36. _____

37. _____   38. _____

39. _____   40. _____

41. _____   42. _____

43. _____   44. _____

45. _____   46. _____

Combine the following complex numbers:

25. $(2 + 3i) + (3 + 6i)$ **26.** $(4 + i) + (3 + 2i)$

27. $(3 - 5i) + (2 + 4i)$ **28.** $(7 + 2i) + (3 - 4i)$

29. $(5 + 2i) - (3 + 6i)$ **30.** $(6 + 7i) - (4 + i)$

31. $(3 - 5i) - (2 + i)$ **32.** $(7 - 3i) - (4 + 10i)$

33. $[(3 + 2i) - (6 + i)] + (5 + i)$ **34.** $[(4 - 5i) - (2 + i)] + (2 + 5i)$

35. $[(7 - i) - (2 + 4i)] - (6 + 2i)$ **36.** $[(3 - i) - (4 + 7i)] - (3 - 4i)$

37. $(3 + 2i) - [(3 - 4i) - (6 + 2i)]$

38. $(7 - 4i) - [(-2 + i) - (3 + 7i)]$

39. $(4 - 9i) + [(2 - 7i) - (4 + 8i)]$

40. $(10 - 2i) - [(2 + i) - (3 - i)]$

Review Problems   The following problems review material we covered in Section 5.4. Reviewing these problems will help you with the next section.

Multiply.

41. $\sqrt{2}(\sqrt{3} - \sqrt{2})$ **42.** $(\sqrt{x} - 4)(\sqrt{x} + 5)$

43. $(\sqrt{x} + 5)^2$ **44.** $(\sqrt{5} + \sqrt{3})(\sqrt{5} - \sqrt{3})$

Rationalize the denominator.

45. $\dfrac{\sqrt{x}}{\sqrt{x} + 3}$ **46.** $\dfrac{\sqrt{5} - \sqrt{3}}{\sqrt{5} + \sqrt{3}}$

Section 5.7   Multiplication and Division of Complex Numbers

Since complex numbers have the same form as binomials, we find the product of two complex numbers the same way we find the product of two binomials.

▼ **Example 1**   Multiply: $(3 - 4i)(2 + 5i)$.

Solution   Multiplying each term in the second complex number by each term in the first, we have

$$
\overset{F}{}\quad\overset{O}{}\quad\overset{I}{}\quad\overset{L}{}
$$
$$(3 - 4i)(2 + 5i) = 3 \cdot 2 + 3 \cdot 5i - 2 \cdot 4i - 5i(4i)$$
$$= 6 + 15i - 8i - 20i^2$$

Combining similar terms and using the fact that $i^2 = -1$, we can simplify as follows:

$$6 + 15i - 8i - 20i^2 = 6 + 7i - 20(-1)$$
$$= 6 + 7i + 20$$
$$= 26 + 7i$$

The product of the complex numbers $3 - 4i$ and $2 + 5i$ is the complex number $26 + 7i$.   ▲

▼ **Example 2**   Multiply: $2i(4 - 6i)$.

Solution   Applying the distributive property gives us

$$2i(4 - 6i) = 2i \cdot 4 - 2i(6i)$$
$$= 8i - 12i^2$$
$$= 12 + 8i$$ ▲

▼ **Example 3**   Expand $(3 + 5i)^2$.

Solution   We treat this like the square of a binomial. Remember: $(a + b)^2 = a^2 + 2ab + b^2$.

$$(3 + 5i)^2 = 3^2 + 2(3)(5i) + (5i)^2$$
$$= 9 + 30i + 25i^2$$
$$= 9 + 30i - 25$$
$$= -16 + 30i$$ ▲

▼ **Example 4**   Multiply: $(2 - 3i)(2 + 3i)$.

Solution   This product has the form $(a - b)(a + b)$, which we know results in the difference of two squares, $a^2 - b^2$:

$$(2 - 3i)(2 + 3i) = 2^2 - (3i)^2$$
$$= 4 - 9i^2$$
$$= 4 + 9$$
$$= 13$$ ▲

The product of the two complex numbers $2 - 3i$ and $2 + 3i$ is the real number 13. The two complex numbers $2 - 3i$ and $2 + 3i$ are called complex conjugates. The fact that their product is a real number is very useful.

---

1. Multiply: $(2 + 3i)(1 - 4i)$.

2. Multiply: $-3i(2 + 3i)$.

3. Expand $(2 + 4i)^2$.

Note: We can obtain the same result by writing $(3 + 5i)^2$ as $(3 + 5i)(3 + 5i)$ and applying the FOIL method as we did with the problem in Example 1.

4. Multiply: $(3 - 5i)(3 + 5i)$.

Note: Again, the FOIL method would have worked just as well here. If you don't like using the formulas, then use the FOIL method.

Answers
1. $14 - 5i$ **2.** $9 - 6i$
3. $-12 + 16i$ **4.** 34

DEFINITION   The complex numbers $a + bi$ and $a - bi$ are called *complex conjugates*. One important property they have is that their product is the real number $a^2 + b^2$. Here's why:

$$\begin{aligned}(a + bi)(a - bi) &= a^2 - (bi)^2 \\ &= a^2 - b^2i^2 \\ &= a^2 - b^2(-1) \\ &= a^2 + b^2\end{aligned}$$

The fact that the product of two complex conjugates is a real number is the key to division with complex numbers.

5. Divide: $\dfrac{3 + 2i}{2 - 5i}$.

▼ **Example 5**   Divide: $\dfrac{2 + i}{3 - 2i}$.

Solution   We want a complex number in standard form that is equivalent to the quotient $(2 + i)/(3 - 2i)$. We need to eliminate i from the denominator. Multiplying the numerator and denominator by $3 + 2i$ will give us what we want:

$$\begin{aligned}\frac{2 + i}{3 - 2i} &= \frac{2 + i}{3 - 2i} \cdot \frac{(3 + 2i)}{(3 + 2i)} \\ &= \frac{6 + 4i + 3i + 2i^2}{9 - 4i^2} \\ &= \frac{6 + 7i - 2}{9 + 4} \\ &= \frac{4 + 7i}{13} \\ &= \tfrac{4}{13} + \tfrac{7}{13}i\end{aligned}$$

Dividing the complex number $2 + i$ by $3 - 2i$ gives the complex number $\tfrac{4}{13} + \tfrac{7}{13}i$. The second step in Example 5 is shown for clarity. It takes a while to get used to the idea that $i^2 = -1$.   ▲

6. Divide: $\dfrac{3 + 2i}{i}$.

▼ **Example 6**   Divide: $\dfrac{7 - 4i}{i}$.

Solution   The conjugate of the denominator is $-i$. Multiplying numerator and denominator by this number, we have

$$\begin{aligned}\frac{7 - 4i}{i} &= \frac{7 - 4i}{i} \cdot \frac{-i}{-i} \\ &= \frac{-7i + 4i^2}{-i^2} \\ &= \frac{-7i + 4(-1)}{-(-1)} \\ &= -4 - 7i\end{aligned}$$

   ▲

Answers
5. $-\tfrac{4}{29} + \tfrac{19}{29}i$
6. $2 - 3i$

Problem Set 5.7

Find the following products:

1. $3i(4 + 5i)$

2. $2i(3 + 4i)$

3. $-7i(1 + i)$

4. $-6i(3 - 8i)$

5. $6i(4 - 3i)$

6. $11i(2 - i)$

7. $(3 + 2i)(4 + i)$

8. $(2 - 4i)(3 + i)$

9. $(4 + 9i)(3 - i)$

10. $(5 - 2i)(1 + i)$

11. $(-3 - 4i)(2 - 5i)$

12. $(-6 - 2i)(3 - 4i)$

13. $(2 + 5i)^2$

14. $(3 + 2i)^2$

Name _____

Class _____

Date _____

Answers

1. _____   2. _____

3. _____   4. _____

5. _____   6. _____

7. _____   8. _____

9. _____   10. _____

11. _____   12. _____

13. _____   14. _____

Answers

15. _____   16. _____

17. _____   18. _____

19. _____   20. _____

21. _____   22. _____

23. _____   24. _____

25. _____   26. _____

15. $(1 - i)^2$

16. $(1 + i)^2$

17. $(3 - 4i)^2$

18. $(6 - 5i)^2$

19. $(2 + i)(2 - i)$

20. $(3 + i)(3 - i)$

21. $(6 - 2i)(6 + 2i)$

22. $(5 + 4i)(5 - 4i)$

23. $(2 + 3i)(2 - 3i)$

24. $(2 - 7i)(2 + 7i)$

25. $(10 + 8i)(10 - 8i)$

26. $(11 - 7i)(11 + 7i)$

Find the following quotients. Write all answers in standard form for complex numbers.

27. $\dfrac{2 - 3i}{i}$

28. $\dfrac{3 + 4i}{i}$

29. $\dfrac{5 + 2i}{-i}$

30. $\dfrac{4 - 3i}{-i}$

31. $\dfrac{4}{2 - 3i}$

32. $\dfrac{3}{4 - 5i}$

33. $\dfrac{6}{-3 + 2i}$

34. $\dfrac{-1}{-2 - 5i}$

35. $\dfrac{2 + 3i}{2 - 3i}$

36. $\dfrac{4 - 7i}{4 + 7i}$

Name _____

Class _____

Date _____

Answers

27. _____   28. _____

29. _____   30. _____

31. _____   32. _____

33. _____   34. _____

35. _____   36. _____

Answers

37. _____ 38. _____

39. _____ 40. _____

41. _____ 42. _____

43. _____ 44. _____

45. _____ 46. _____

37. $\dfrac{5 + 4i}{3 + 6i}$

38. $\dfrac{2 + i}{5 - 6i}$

39. $\dfrac{3 - 7i}{9 - 5i}$

40. $\dfrac{4 + 10i}{3 + 6i}$

Review Problems The following problems review material we covered in Section 4.1.

Reduce each rational expression to lowest terms.

41. $\dfrac{x^2 - 9}{x - 3}$

42. $\dfrac{x^2 - 5x - 6}{x^2 - 1}$

43. $\dfrac{x^2 - 4x - 12}{x^2 + 8x + 12}$

44. $\dfrac{6x^2 + 7x - 3}{6x^2 + x - 1}$

45. $\dfrac{x^3 + y^3}{x^2 - y^2}$

46. $\dfrac{x^3 - 8}{x^2 - 4}$

Chapter 5 Summary and Review

SQUARE ROOTS [5.1]

Every positive real number x has two square roots. The *positive square root* of x is written $\sqrt{x}$, while the *negative square root* of x is written $-\sqrt{x}$. Both the positive and the negative square roots of x are numbers we square to get x. That is,

$$\text{and} \quad \left.\begin{array}{r} (\sqrt{x})^2 = x \\ (-\sqrt{x})^2 = x \end{array}\right\} \quad \text{for } x \geq 0$$

1. The number 49 has two square roots, 7 and -7. They are written like this:
$$\sqrt{49} = 7 \qquad -\sqrt{49} = -7$$

HIGHER ROOTS [5.1]

In the expression $\sqrt[n]{a}$, n is the *index*, a is the *radicand*, and $\sqrt{}$ is the *radical sign*. The expression $\sqrt[n]{a}$ is such that

$$(\sqrt[n]{a})^n = a \qquad a \geq 0 \text{ when } n \text{ is even}$$

2. $\quad \sqrt[3]{8} = 2$
$$\sqrt[3]{-27} = -3$$

FRACTIONAL EXPONENTS [5.1]

Fractional exponents are used to indicate roots. The relationship between fractional exponents and roots is as follows:

$$a^{1/n} = \sqrt[n]{a} \quad \text{and} \quad a^{m/n} = (a^{1/n})^m = (a^m)^{1/n} \quad a \geq 0 \text{ when } n \text{ is even}$$

3. $\quad 25^{1/2} = \sqrt{25} = 5$
$$8^{2/3} = (\sqrt[3]{8})^2 = 2^2 = 4$$
$$9^{3/2} = (\sqrt{9})^3 = 3^3 = 27$$

PROPERTIES OF RADICALS [5.2]

If a and b are nonnegative real numbers whenever n is even, then

1. $\sqrt[n]{ab} = \sqrt[n]{a}\sqrt[n]{b}$

2. $\sqrt[n]{\dfrac{a}{b}} = \dfrac{\sqrt[n]{a}}{\sqrt[n]{b}} \qquad (b \neq 0)$

4. $\quad \sqrt{4 \cdot 5} = \sqrt{4}\sqrt{5} = 2\sqrt{5}$
$$\sqrt{\frac{7}{9}} = \frac{\sqrt{7}}{\sqrt{9}} = \frac{\sqrt{7}}{3}$$

SIMPLIFIED FORM FOR RADICALS [5.2]

A radical expression is said to be in *simplified form*

1. if there is no factor of the radicand that can be written as a power greater than or equal to the index;
2. if there are no fractions under the *radical sign*; and
3. if there are no radicals in the denominator.

5. $\quad \sqrt{\dfrac{4}{5}} = \dfrac{\sqrt{4}}{\sqrt{5}}$
$$= \frac{2}{\sqrt{5}} \cdot \frac{\sqrt{5}}{\sqrt{5}}$$
$$= \frac{2\sqrt{5}}{5}$$

ADDITION AND SUBTRACTION OF RADICAL EXPRESSIONS [5.3]

We add and subtract radical expressions by using the distributive property to combine similar radicals. Similar radicals are radicals with the same index and the same radicand.

6. $\quad 5\sqrt{3} - 7\sqrt{3} = (5 - 7)\sqrt{3}$
$$= -2\sqrt{3}$$
$$\sqrt{20} + \sqrt{45} = 2\sqrt{5} + 3\sqrt{5}$$
$$= (2 + 3)\sqrt{5}$$
$$= 5\sqrt{5}$$

MULTIPLICATION OF RADICAL EXPRESSIONS [5.4]

We multiply radical expressions in the same way that we multiply polynomials. We can use the distributive property and the FOIL method.

7. $\quad (\sqrt{x} + 2)(\sqrt{x} + 3)$
$$= \sqrt{x}\sqrt{x} + 3\sqrt{x} + 2\sqrt{x} + 2 \cdot 3$$
$$= x + 5\sqrt{x} + 6$$

8.
$$\frac{3}{\sqrt{2}} = \frac{3}{\sqrt{2}} \cdot \frac{\sqrt{2}}{\sqrt{2}} = \frac{3\sqrt{2}}{2}$$

$$\frac{3}{\sqrt{5} - \sqrt{3}} = \frac{3}{\sqrt{5} - \sqrt{3}} \cdot \frac{\sqrt{5} + \sqrt{3}}{\sqrt{5} + \sqrt{3}}$$

$$= \frac{3\sqrt{5} + 3\sqrt{3}}{5 - 3}$$

$$= \frac{3\sqrt{5} - 3\sqrt{3}}{2}$$

9.
$$\sqrt{2x + 1} = 3$$
$$(\sqrt{2x + 1})^2 = 3^2$$
$$2x + 1 = 9$$
$$x = 4$$

10. $3 + 4i$ is a complex number.

Addition

$$(3 + 4i) + (2 - 5i) = 5 - i$$

Multiplication

$$(3 + 4i)(2 - 5i)$$
$$= 6 - 15i + 8i - 20i^2$$
$$= 6 - 7i + 20$$
$$= 26 - 7i$$

Division

$$\frac{2}{3 + 4i} = \frac{2}{3 + 4i} \cdot \frac{3 - 4i}{3 - 4i}$$

$$= \frac{6 - 8i}{9 + 16}$$

$$= \frac{6}{25} - \frac{8}{25}i$$

RATIONALIZING THE DENOMINATOR [5.2, 5.4]

When a fraction contains a radical in the denominator, we rationalize the denominator by multiplying numerator and denominator by

1. the radical itself if there is only one term in the denominator, or
2. by the conjugate of the denominator if there are two terms in the denominator.

Rationalizing the denominator can also be called division of radical expressions.

SQUARING PROPERTY OF EQUALITY [5.5]

We may square both sides of an equation any time it is convenient to do so, as long as we check all resulting solutions in the original equation.

COMPLEX NUMBERS [5.6, 5.7]

A *complex number* is any number that can be put in the form

$$a + bi$$

where a and b are real numbers and $i = \sqrt{-1}$. The *real part* of the complex number is a, and b is the *imaginary part*.

If a, b, c, and d are real numbers, then we have the following definitions associated with complex numbers:

1. Equality

   $$a + bi = c + di \quad \text{if and only if} \quad a = c \text{ and } b = d$$

2. Addition and subtraction

   $$(a + bi) + (c + di) = (a + c) + (b + d)i$$
   $$(a + bi) - (c + di) = (a - c) + (b - d)i$$

3. Multiplication

   $$(a + bi)(c + di) = (ac - bd) + (ad + bc)i$$

4. Division is similar to rationalizing the denominator.

COMMON MISTAKES

1. The most common mistake when working with radicals is to assume that the square root of a sum is the sum of the square roots—or:

$$\sqrt{x + y} = \sqrt{x} + \sqrt{y} \qquad \text{Mistake}$$

The problem with this is it just isn't true. If we try it with 16 and 9, the mistake becomes obvious:

$$\sqrt{16 + 9} \stackrel{?}{=} \sqrt{16} + \sqrt{9}$$
$$\sqrt{25} \stackrel{?}{=} 4 + 3$$
$$5 \neq 7$$

2. A common mistake when working with complex numbers is to mistake i for -1. The letter i is not -1; it is the square root of -1. That is, $i = \sqrt{-1}$.

Chapter 5 Test

Simplify each of the following. [5.1]

1. $27^{-2/3}$

2. $\left(\dfrac{25}{49}\right)^{-1/2}$

3. $a^{3/4} \cdot a^{-1/3}$

4. $\dfrac{(x^{2/3}y^{-3})^{1/2}}{(x^{3/4}y^{1/2})^{-1}}$

Write in simplified form. [5.2]

5. $\sqrt{125x^3y^5}$

6. $\sqrt[3]{40x^7y^8}$

7. $\sqrt{\tfrac{2}{3}}$

8. $\sqrt{\dfrac{12a^4b^3}{5c}}$

Combine. [5.3]

9. $3\sqrt{12} - 4\sqrt{27}$

10. $2\sqrt[3]{24a^3b^3} - 5a\sqrt[3]{3b^3}$

Multiply. [5.4]

11. $(\sqrt{x} + 7)(\sqrt{x} - 4)$

12. $(3\sqrt{2} - \sqrt{3})^2$

Rationalize the denominator. [5.4]

13. $\dfrac{5}{\sqrt{3} - 1}$

14. $\dfrac{\sqrt{x} - \sqrt{2}}{\sqrt{x} + \sqrt{2}}$

Name _____

Class _____

Date _____

Answers

1. _____

2. _____

3. _____

4. _____

5. _____

6. _____

7. _____

8. _____

9. _____

10. _____

11. _____

12. _____

13. _____

14. _____

Answers

15. _____   16. _____

17. _____   18. _____

19. _____   20. _____

21. _____   22. _____

23. _____   24. _____

25. _____   26. _____

27. _____   28. _____

Solve for x. [5.5]

15. $\sqrt{5x - 1} = 7$

16. $\sqrt{3x + 2} + 4 = 0$

17. $\sqrt[3]{2x + 7} = -1$

18. $\sqrt{x + 3} = \sqrt{x + 4} - 1$

Solve for x and y so that each of the following equations is true. [5.6]

19. $3x - 4i = 2 - 8yi$

20. $(2x + 5) - 4i = 6 - (y - 3)i$

Perform the indicated operations. [5.6, 5.7]

21. $(3 - 7i) - (4 + 2i)$

22. $(3 + 2i) - [(7 - i) - (4 + 3i)]$

23. $(2 - 3i)(4 + 3i)$

24. $(5 - 4i)^2$

25. $\dfrac{3 + 2i}{i}$

26. $\dfrac{5}{2 - 3i}$

27. $\dfrac{2 - 3i}{2 + 3i}$

28. Show that i^{38} can be written as -1. [5.6]

•6 Quadratic Equations

To the student:

If an object is thrown straight up into the air with an initial velocity of 32 feet/second, and we neglect the friction of the air on the object, then its height *h* above the ground, *t* seconds later, can be found by using the equation

$$h = 32t - 16t^2$$

Notice that the height depends only on *t*. The height of the object does not depend on the size or weight of the object. If we neglect the resistance of air on the object, then any object, whether it is a golf ball or a bowling ball, that is thrown into the air with an initial velocity of 32 feet/second, will reach the same height. If we want to find how long it takes the object to hit the ground, we let $h = 0$ (it is 0 feet above the ground when it hits the ground) and solve for *t* in

$$0 = 32t - 16t^2$$

This last equation is called a quadratic equation because it contains a polynomial of degree 2. Until now we have solved only first-degree equations. This chapter is about solving second-degree equations in one variable: quadratic equations. To be successful in this chapter you should have a working knowledge of factoring, binomial squares, square roots, and complex numbers.

Section 6.1 Solving Quadratic Equations by Factoring

We are going to combine our ability to solve first-degree equations with our knowledge of factoring to solve quadratic equations.

283

DEFINITION Any equation that can be written in the form

$$ax^2 + bx + c = 0$$

where a, b, and c are constants and a is not 0 ($a \neq 0$), is called a *quadratic equation*. The form $ax^2 + bx + c = 0$ is called *standard form* for quadratic equations.

Each of the following is a quadratic equation:

$$2x^2 = 5x + 3 \qquad 5x^2 = 75 \qquad 4x^2 - 3x + 2 = 0$$

Notation: For a quadratic equation written in standard form, the first term, ax^2, is called the *quadratic term;* the second term, bx, is the *linear term;* and the last term, c, is called the *constant term.*

In the past we have noticed that the number 0 is a special number. That is, 0 has some unique properties. In some situations it does not behave like other numbers. For example, division by 0 does not make sense, whereas division by all other real numbers does. Note also that 0 is the only number without a reciprocal. There is another property of 0 that is the key to solving quadratic equations. It is called the *zero-factor property*.

Zero-Factor Property For all real numbers r and s,

$$r \cdot s = 0 \quad \text{if and only if} \quad r = 0 \quad \text{or} \quad s = 0 \quad \text{(or both)}$$

Note: The third equation is clearly a quadratic equation since it is in standard form. (Notice that a is 4, b is -3, and c is 2.) The first two equations are also quadratic because they could be put in the form $ax^2 + bx + c = 0$ by using the addition property of equality.

Practice Problems

1. Solve $x^2 - x - 6 = 0$.

Note: What the zero-factor property says in words is that we can't multiply and get 0 without multiplying by 0. That is, if we multiply two numbers and get 0, then one or both of the original two numbers we multiplied must have been 0.

Note: We are placing a question mark over the equal sign because we don't know yet if the expression on the left will be equal to the expression on the right.

▼ **Example 1** Solve $x^2 - 2x - 24 = 0$.

Solution We begin by factoring the left side as $(x - 6)(x + 4)$ and get

$$(x - 6)(x + 4) = 0$$

Now both $(x - 6)$ and $(x + 4)$ represent real numbers. We notice that their product is 0. By the zero-factor property, one or both of them must be 0:

$$x - 6 = 0 \text{ or } x + 4 = 0$$

We have used factoring and the zero-factor property to rewrite our original second-degree equation as two first-degree equations connected by the word *or*. Completing the solution, we solve the two first-degree equations:

$$x - 6 = 0 \text{ or } x + 4 = 0$$
$$x = 6 \text{ or } \qquad x = -4$$

We check our solutions in the original equation as follows:

Check $x = 6$	Check $x = -4$
$6^2 - 2(6) - 24 \stackrel{?}{=} 0$	$(-4)^2 - 2(-4) - 24 \stackrel{?}{=} 0$
$36 - 12 - 24 = 0$	$16 + 8 - 24 = 0$
$0 = 0$	$0 = 0$

In both cases the result is a true statement, which means that both 6 and -4 are solutions to the original equation. ▲

Answer
1. $-2, 3$

▼ **Example 2**   Solve $2x^2 = 5x + 3$.

Solution   We begin by adding $-5x$ and -3 to both sides in order to rewrite the equation in standard form:

$$2x^2 - 5x - 3 = 0$$

We then factor the left side and use the zero-factor property to set each factor to zero:

$$(2x + 1)(x - 3) = 0 \qquad \text{Factor}$$
$$2x + 1 = 0 \quad \text{or} \quad x - 3 = 0 \qquad \text{Zero-factor property}$$

Solving each of the resulting first-degree equations, we have

$$x = -\tfrac{1}{2} \quad \text{or} \qquad x = 3$$

The solution set is $\{-\tfrac{1}{2}, 3\}$.   ▲

To generalize the preceding example, here are the steps used in solving a quadratic equation by factoring.

To Solve a Quadratic Equation by Factoring

Step 1:   Write the equation in standard form.
Step 2:   Factor the left side.
Step 3:   Use the zero-factor property to set each factor equal to 0.
Step 4:   Solve the resulting first-degree equations.

▼ **Example 3**   Solve $x^2 = 3x$.

Solution   We begin by writing the equation in standard form and factoring:

$$x^2 = 3x$$
$$x^2 - 3x = 0 \qquad \text{Standard form}$$
$$x(x - 3) = 0 \qquad \text{Factor}$$

Using the zero-factor property to set each factor to 0, we have

$$x = 0 \quad \text{or} \quad x - 3 = 0$$
$$x = 3$$

The two solutions are 0 and 3.   ▲

▼ **Example 4**   Solve $(x - 2)(x + 1) = 4$.

Solution   We begin by multiplying the two factors on the left side. (Notice that it would be incorrect to set each of the factors on the left side equal to 4. The fact that the product is 4 does not imply that either of the factors must be 4.)

$$(x - 2)(x + 1) = 4$$
$$x^2 - x - 2 = 4 \qquad \text{Multiply the left side}$$
$$x^2 - x - 6 = 0 \qquad \text{Standard form}$$
$$(x - 3)(x + 2) = 0 \qquad \text{Factor}$$
$$x - 3 = 0 \quad \text{or} \quad x + 2 = 0 \qquad \text{Zero-factor property}$$
$$x = 3 \quad \text{or} \qquad x = -2 \qquad ▲$$

2. Solve $3x^2 = 5x + 2$.

3. Solve $x^2 = 5x$.

4. Solve $(x + 1)(x + 2) = 12$.

Answers
2. $-\tfrac{1}{3}, 2$ **3.** $0, 5$ **4.** $-5, 2$

5. Solve $1 - \dfrac{2}{x} = \dfrac{8}{x^2}$.

▼ **Example 5** Solve $3 + \dfrac{1}{x} = \dfrac{10}{x^2}$.

Solution To clear the equation of denominators we multiply both sides by x^2:

$$x^2\left(3 + \frac{1}{x}\right) = \frac{10}{x^2}(x^2)$$

$$3(x^2) + \left(\frac{1}{x}\right)(x^2) = \left(\frac{10}{x^2}\right)(x^2)$$

$$3x^2 + x = 10$$

Rewrite in standard form and solve:

$$3x^2 + x - 10 = 0$$
$$(3x - 5)(x + 2) = 0$$
$$3x - 5 = 0 \quad \text{or} \quad x + 2 = 0$$
$$x = \frac{5}{3} \quad \text{or} \qquad x = -2$$

The solution set is $\{-2, \frac{5}{3}\}$. Both solutions check in the original equation. Remember: We have to check *all solutions* any time we multiply both sides of the equation by an expression that contains the variable, just to be sure we haven't multiplied by 0. ▲

6. Solve $\sqrt{2x^2 - 3x} = 3$.

▼ **Example 6** Solve $\sqrt{6x^2 + 5x} = 5$.

Solution To eliminate the radical we begin by squaring both sides of the equation. We then write the resulting equation in standard form and solve as before:

$$(\sqrt{6x^2 + 5x})^2 = 5^2 \qquad \text{Square both sides}$$
$$6x^2 + 5x = 25 \qquad \text{Simplify}$$
$$6x^2 + 5x - 25 = 0 \qquad \text{Standard form}$$
$$(3x - 5)(2x + 5) = 0 \qquad \text{Factor}$$
$$3x - 5 = 0 \quad \text{or} \quad 2x + 5 = 0 \qquad \text{Zero-factor property}$$
$$x = \frac{5}{3} \quad \text{or} \qquad x = -\frac{5}{2}$$

Since we raised both sides of the original equation to an even power, we have the possibility that one or both of the solutions are extraneous. We must check each solution in the original equation.

Check $x = \dfrac{5}{3}$ Check $x = -\dfrac{5}{2}$

$$\sqrt{6\left(\frac{25}{9}\right) + 5\left(\frac{5}{3}\right)} \overset{?}{=} 5 \qquad \sqrt{6\left(\frac{25}{4}\right) + 5\left(-\frac{5}{2}\right)} \overset{?}{=} 5$$

$$\sqrt{\frac{50}{3} + \frac{25}{3}} = 5 \qquad \sqrt{\frac{75}{2} - \frac{25}{2}} = 5$$

$$\sqrt{\frac{75}{3}} = 5 \qquad \sqrt{\frac{50}{2}} = 5$$

$$\sqrt{25} = 5 \qquad \sqrt{25} = 5$$

$$5 = 5 \qquad 5 = 5$$

Since both checks result in a true statement, neither of the two possible solutions is extraneous. ▲

Answers
5. $4, -2$ **6.** $-\frac{3}{2}, 3$

Problem Set 6.1

The following quadratic equations are in standard form. Factor the left side and solve.

1. $x^2 - 5x - 6 = 0$

2. $x^2 + 5x - 6 = 0$

3. $3y^2 + 11y - 4 = 0$

4. $3y^2 - y - 4 = 0$

5. $6x^2 - 13x + 6 = 0$

6. $9x^2 + 6x - 8 = 0$

7. $t^2 - 25 = 0$

8. $4t^2 - 49 = 0$

Write each of the following in standard form and solve for the indicated variable.

9. $x^2 = 4x + 21$

10. $x^2 = -4x + 21$

11. $2y^2 - 20 = -3y$

12. $3y^2 + 10 = 17y$

13. $2r + 1 = 15r^2$

14. $2r - 1 = -8r^2$

15. $9a^2 = 16$

16. $16a^2 = 25$

17. $-10x = x^2$

18. $8x = x^2$

Name _____

Class _____

Date _____

Answers

1. _____   2. _____

3. _____   4. _____

5. _____   6. _____

7. _____   8. _____

9. _____   10. _____

11. _____   12. _____

13. _____   14. _____

15. _____   16. _____

17. _____   18. _____

Answers

19. _____   20. _____

21. _____   22. _____

23. _____   24. _____

25. _____   26. _____

27. _____   28. _____

29. _____   30. _____

Multiply out the left side of each equation and then solve as usual.

19. $(x + 6)(x - 2) = -7$ 20. $(x - 7)(x + 5) = -20$

21. $(y - 4)(y + 1) = -6$ 22. $(y - 6)(y + 1) = -12$

23. $(x + 1)^2 = 3x + 7$ 24. $(x + 2)^2 = 9x$

25. $(2r + 3)(2r - 1) = -(3r + 1)$ 26. $(3r + 2)(r - 1) = -(7r - 7)$

Multiply each of the following by its least common denominator and solve for the indicated variable.

27. $1 - \dfrac{1}{x} = \dfrac{12}{x^2}$ 28. $2 + \dfrac{5}{x} = \dfrac{3}{x^2}$

29. $x - \dfrac{4}{3x} = -\dfrac{1}{3}$ 30. $\dfrac{x}{2} - \dfrac{4}{x} = -\dfrac{7}{2}$

31. $1 = \dfrac{9}{y^2}$

32. $1 = \dfrac{4}{x^2}$

33. $6 - \dfrac{5}{x^2} = \dfrac{7}{x}$

34. $10 - \dfrac{3}{x^2} = -\dfrac{1}{x}$

Name _____

Class _____

Date _____

Answers

31. _____	**32.** _____
33. _____	**34.** _____
35. _____	**36.** _____
37. _____	**38.** _____
39. _____	**40.** _____
41. _____	**42.** _____

Square both sides of the following equations and solve for the indicated variable. (When you get to problems 41 and 42 you will have to isolate the radical on the left side before you square both sides.)

35. $\sqrt{6x^2 + 5x} = 2$

36. $\sqrt{2x^2 - 5x} = 5$

37. $\sqrt{y + 2} = y - 4$

38. $\sqrt{11 - 5x} = x - 3$

39. $\sqrt{5y + 1} = 11 - 5y$

40. $4\sqrt{x + 2} = x + 5$

41. $\sqrt{3x^2 + 4x} - 2 = 0$

42. $\sqrt{2x^2 + 3x} - 3 = 0$

Answers

43. _____

44. _____

45. _____

46. _____

47. _____

48. _____

49. _____

50. _____

51. _____

52. _____

43. In the introduction to this chapter we said the height h of an object thrown straight up into the air with an initial velocity of 32 feet/second could be found by using the equation $h = 32t - 16t^2$. When does the object hit the ground?

44. An object is tossed straight up with an initial velocity of 64 feet/second. The equation that gives the height at time t is

$$h = 64t - 16t^2$$

When is the object on the ground?

Review Problems   The following problems review material we covered in Sections 3.4 and 3.7. Reviewing these problems will help you understand the next section.

Multiply.

45. $(x + 3)^2$

46. $(x - 5)^2$

47. $(x - 4)^2$

48. $(x + 6)^2$

Factor.

49. $x^2 - 6x + 9$

50. $x^2 + 10x + 25$

51. $x^2 + 4x + 4$

52. $x^2 - 16x + 64$

Section 6.2   Completing the Square

In this section we will look at another method of solving quadratic equations. The method is called *completing the square*. Completing the square on a quadratic equation allows us to obtain solutions, regardless of whether or not the equation can be factored. Before we solve equations by completing the square we need to learn how to solve equations by taking square roots of both sides.

Consider the equation

$$x^2 = 16$$

We could solve it by writing it in standard form, factoring the left side, and proceeding as we did in the last section. However, we can shorten our work considerably if we simply notice that x must be either the positive square root of 16 or the negative square root of 16. That is,

$$\text{If } x^2 = 16$$
$$\text{then} \quad x = \sqrt{16} \quad \text{or} \quad x = -\sqrt{16}$$
$$x = 4 \quad \text{or} \quad x = -4$$

We can generalize this result into a theorem as follows.

Theorem 6.2   If $a^2 = b$ where b is a real number, then $a = \sqrt{b}$ or $a = -\sqrt{b}$.

Notation: The expression $a = \sqrt{b}$ or $a = -\sqrt{b}$ can be written in shorthand form as $a = \pm\sqrt{b}$. The symbol $\pm$ is read "plus or minus."

We can apply Theorem 6.2 to some fairly complicated quadratic equations.

▼   **Example 1**   Solve $(2x - 3)^2 = 25$.

Solution
$$(2x - 3)^2 = 25$$
$$2x - 3 = \pm\sqrt{25} \qquad \text{Theorem 6.2}$$
$$2x - 3 = \pm 5 \qquad \sqrt{25} = 5$$
$$2x = 3 \pm 5 \qquad \text{Add 3 to both sides}$$
$$x = \frac{3 \pm 5}{2} \qquad \text{Divide both sides by 2}$$

The last equation can be written as two separate statements:

$$x = \frac{3 + 5}{2} \quad \text{or} \quad x = \frac{3 - 5}{2}$$
$$= \frac{8}{2} \qquad\qquad = -\frac{2}{2}$$
$$= 4 \quad \text{or} \quad = -1$$

The solution set is $\{4, -1\}$.   ▲

Practice Problems

1. Solve $(3x + 2)^2 = 16$.

2. Solve $(4x - 3)^2 = -50$.

▼ **Example 2**   Solve for x: $(3x - 1)^2 = -12$.

Solution

$$(3x - 1)^2 = -12$$

$$3x - 1 = \pm\sqrt{-12} \qquad \text{Theorem 6.2}$$

$$3x - 1 = \pm 2i\sqrt{3} \qquad \sqrt{-12} = \sqrt{12}i = \sqrt{4}\sqrt{3}i = 2i\sqrt{3}$$

$$3x = 1 \pm 2i\sqrt{3} \qquad \text{Add 1 to both sides}$$

$$x = \frac{1 \pm 2i\sqrt{3}}{3} \qquad \text{Divide both sides by 3}$$

The solution set is

$$\left\{ \frac{1 + 2i\sqrt{3}}{3}, \ \frac{1 - 2i\sqrt{3}}{3} \right\}$$

Both solutions are complex. Although the arithmetic is somewhat more complicated, we check each solution in the usual manner. Here is a check of the first solution:

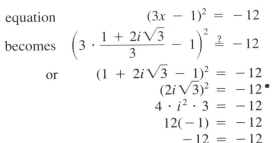

When $\qquad\qquad\qquad\qquad x = \dfrac{1 + 2i\sqrt{3}}{3}$

the equation $\qquad\qquad (3x - 1)^2 = -12$

becomes $\qquad \left(3 \cdot \dfrac{1 + 2i\sqrt{3}}{3} - 1\right)^2 \stackrel{?}{=} -12$

$$\text{or} \qquad (1 + 2i\sqrt{3} - 1)^2 = -12$$

$$(2i\sqrt{3})^2 = -12$$

$$4 \cdot i^2 \cdot 3 = -12$$

$$12(-1) = -12$$

$$-12 = -12 \qquad ▲$$

Note: We are showing the check here so you can see that the complex numbers really are solutions. Some people don't believe it at first.

The method of completing the square is simply a way of transforming any quadratic equation into an equation of the form found in the preceding two examples.

The key to understanding the method of completing the square lies in recognizing the relationship between the last two terms of any perfect square trinomial whose leading coefficient is 1.

Consider the following list of perfect square trinomials and their corresponding binomial squares:

$$x^2 - 6x + 9 = (x - 3)^2$$
$$x^2 + 8x + 16 = (x + 4)^2$$
$$x^2 - 10x + 25 = (x - 5)^2$$
$$x^2 + 12x + 36 = (x + 6)^2$$

In each case the leading coefficient is 1. A more important observation comes from noticing the relationship between the linear and constant terms (middle and last terms) in each trinomial. Observe that the constant term in each case is the square of half the coefficient of x in the middle term. For example, in the last expression, the constant term, 36, is the square of half of 12, where 12 is the coefficient of x in the middle term. (Notice also that the second terms in all the binomials on the right side are half the coefficients of the middle terms of the trinomials on the left side.) We can use these

Answer

2. $\dfrac{3 \pm 5i\sqrt{2}}{4}$

observations to build our own perfect square trinomials, and in doing so, solve some quadratic equations. Consider the following equation:

$$x^2 + 6x = 3$$

We can think of the left side as having the first two terms of a perfect square trinomial. We need only add the correct constant term. If we take half the coefficient of x, we get 3. If we then square this quantity, we have 9. Adding the 9 to both sides, the equation becomes

$$x^2 + 6x + \mathbf{9} = 3 + \mathbf{9}$$

The left side is the perfect square $(x + 3)^2$; the right side is 12:

$$(x + 3)^2 = 12$$

The equation is now in the correct form. We can apply Theorem 6.2 and finish the solution:

$$
\begin{aligned}
(x + 3)^2 &= 12 \\
x + 3 &= \pm\sqrt{12} \qquad \text{Theorem 6.2} \\
x + 3 &= \pm 2\sqrt{3} \\
x &= -3 \pm 2\sqrt{3}
\end{aligned}
$$

The solution set is $\{-3 + 2\sqrt{3}, -3 - 2\sqrt{3}\}$. The method just used is called *completing the square,* since we complete the square on the left side of the original equation by adding the appropriate constant term.

Note: This is the step in which we actually complete the square.

▼ **Example 3** Solve by completing the square: $x^2 + 5x - 2 = 0$.

Solution We must begin by adding 2 to both sides. (The left side of the equation, as it is, is not a perfect square because it does not have the correct constant term. We will simply "move" that term to the other side and use our own constant term.)

$$x^2 + 5x = 2$$

We complete the square by adding the square of half the coefficient of the linear term to both sides:

$$x^2 + 5x + \frac{\mathbf{25}}{\mathbf{4}} = 2 + \frac{\mathbf{25}}{\mathbf{4}} \qquad \text{Half of 5 is } \tfrac{5}{2}\text{, the square of which is } \tfrac{25}{4}$$

$$\left(x + \frac{5}{2}\right)^2 = \frac{33}{4} \qquad 2 + \frac{25}{4} = \frac{8}{4} + \frac{25}{4} = \frac{33}{4}$$

$$x + \frac{5}{2} = \pm\sqrt{\frac{33}{4}} \qquad \text{Theorem 6.2}$$

$$x + \frac{5}{2} = \pm\frac{\sqrt{33}}{2} \qquad \text{Simplify the radical}$$

$$x = -\frac{5}{2} \pm \frac{\sqrt{33}}{2} \qquad \text{Add } -\tfrac{5}{2} \text{ to both sides}$$

$$x = \frac{-5 \pm \sqrt{33}}{2}$$

The solution set is $\left\{\dfrac{-5 + \sqrt{33}}{2}, \dfrac{-5 - \sqrt{33}}{2}\right\}$.   ▲

3. Solve $x^2 + 3x - 4 = 0$ by completing the square.

Note: We can use a calculator to get decimal approximations to these solutions. If $\sqrt{33} = 5.75$ then

$$\frac{-5 + 5.75}{2} = .375$$

$$\frac{-5 - 5.75}{2} = -5.375$$

Answer
3. 1, -4

4. Solve $5x^2 - 3x + 2 = 0$.

▼ **Example 4** Solve for x: $3x^2 - 8x + 7 = 0$.

Solution

$$3x^2 - 8x + 7 = 0$$
$$3x^2 - 8x = -7 \qquad \text{Add } -7 \text{ to both sides}$$

We cannot complete the square on the left side because the leading coefficient is not 1. We take an extra step and divide both sides by 3:

$$\frac{3x^2}{3} - \frac{8x}{3} = -\frac{7}{3}$$

$$x^2 - \frac{8}{3}x = -\frac{7}{3}$$

Half of $\frac{8}{3}$ is $\frac{4}{3}$, the square of which is $\frac{16}{9}$.

$$x^2 - \frac{8}{3}x + \frac{16}{9} = -\frac{7}{3} + \frac{16}{9} \qquad \text{Add } \frac{16}{9} \text{ to both sides}$$

$$\left(x - \frac{4}{3}\right)^2 = -\frac{5}{9} \qquad \text{Simplify right side}$$

$$x - \frac{4}{3} = \pm\sqrt{-\frac{5}{9}} \qquad \text{Theorem 6.2}$$

$$x - \frac{4}{3} = \pm\frac{i\sqrt{5}}{3} \qquad \sqrt{-\frac{5}{9}} = \frac{\sqrt{-5}}{3} = \frac{i\sqrt{5}}{3}$$

$$x = \frac{4}{3} \pm \frac{i\sqrt{5}}{3} \qquad \text{Add } \frac{4}{3} \text{ to both sides}$$

$$x = \frac{4 \pm i\sqrt{5}}{3}$$

The solution set is $\left\{\dfrac{4 + i\sqrt{5}}{3}, \dfrac{4 - i\sqrt{5}}{3}\right\}$. ▲

To Solve a Quadratic Equation by Completing the Square

To summarize the method used in the preceding two examples, we list the following steps:

Step 1: Write the equation in the form $ax^2 + bx = c$.

Step 2: If the leading coefficient is not 1, divide both sides by the coefficient so that the resulting equation has a leading coefficient of 1. That is, if $a \neq 1$, then divide both sides by a.

Step 3: Add the square of half the coefficient of the linear term to both sides of the equation.

Step 4: Write the left side of the equation as the square of a binomial and simplify the right side if possible.

Step 5: Apply Theorem 6.2 and solve as usual.

Answer

4. $\dfrac{3 \pm i\sqrt{31}}{10}$

Problem Set 6.2

Solve the following by applying Theorem 6.2.

1. $x^2 = 25$

2. $x^2 = 16$

3. $a^2 = -9$

4. $a^2 = -49$

5. $(x - 5)^2 = 9$

6. $(x + 2)^2 = 16$

7. $(2y - 1)^2 = 25$

8. $(3y + 7)^2 = 1$

9. $(2a + 3)^2 = -9$

10. $(3a - 5)^2 = -49$

Name _____

Date _____

Class _____

Answers

1. _____   2. _____

3. _____   4. _____

5. _____   6. _____

7. _____   8. _____

9. _____   10. _____

Answers

11. _____

12. _____

13. _____

14. _____

15. _____

16. _____

17. _____

18. _____

19. _____   **20.** _____

21. _____   **22.** _____

23. _____   **24.** _____

Fill in the blanks so that the left side of each is a perfect square trinomial. That is, complete the square.

11. $x^2 + 12x +$ ___ $= (x +$ ___$)^2$ **12.** $x^2 + 6x +$ ___ $= (x +$ ___$)^2$

13. $x^2 - 4x +$ ___ $= (x -$ ___$)^2$ **14.** $x^2 - 2x +$ ___ $= (x -$ ___$)^2$

15. $a^2 - 10a +$ ___ $= (a -$ ___$)^2$ **16.** $a^2 - 8a +$ ___ $= (a -$ ___$)^2$

17. $x^2 + 5x +$ ___ $= (x +$ ___$)^2$ **18.** $x^2 + 3x +$ ___ $= (x +$ ___$)^2$

Solve each of the following quadratic equations by completing the square.

19. $x^2 + 4x = 12$ **20.** $x^2 - 2x = 8$

21. $x^2 + 12x = -27$ **22.** $x^2 - 6x = 16$

23. $a^2 - 2a + 5 = 0$ **24.** $a^2 + 10a + 22 = 0$

25. $y^2 - 8y + 1 = 0$ **26.** $y^2 + 6y - 1 = 0$

Name _____

Class _____

Date _____

Answers

25. _____   26. _____

27. _____   28. _____

29. _____   30. _____

31. _____   32. _____

27. $x^2 - 5x - 3 = 0$ **28.** $x^2 - 5x - 2 = 0$

Divide both sides of each equation by the leading coefficient and then complete the square. (See Example 4.)

29. $2x^2 - 4x - 8 = 0$ **30.** $3x^2 - 9x - 12 = 0$

31. $3t^2 - 8t + 1 = 0$ **32.** $5t^2 + 12t - 1 = 0$

Answers

33. _____   34. _____

35. _____   36. _____

37. _____   38. _____

39. _____   40. _____

41. _____   42. _____

43. _____   44. _____

33. Check the solution $x = -2 + 3\sqrt{2}$ in the equation $(x + 2)^2 = 18$.

34. Check the solution $x = 2 - 5\sqrt{2}$ in the equation $(x - 2)^2 = 50$.

35. Check the solution $x = 3 - 2\sqrt{3}$ in the equation $x^2 - 6x - 3 = 0$.

36. Check the solution $x = -2 + 3\sqrt{2}$ in the equation $x^2 + 4x - 14 = 0$.

37. The table at the back of the book gives the decimal approximation for $\sqrt{5}$ as 2.236. Use this number to find a decimal approximation for $\dfrac{2 + \sqrt{5}}{2}$ and $\dfrac{2 - \sqrt{5}}{2}$.

38. A decimal approximation for $\sqrt{13}$ is 3.606. Use this number to find decimal approximations for $\dfrac{-3 + \sqrt{13}}{2}$ and $\dfrac{-3 - \sqrt{13}}{2}$.

Review Problems   The following problems review material we have covered previously in a number of sections.

Let $a = 2$, $b = -3$, and $c = -1$ in each of the following expressions and then simplify.

39. b^2 **40.** $4ac$

41. $b^2 - 4ac$ **42.** $\sqrt{b^2 - 4ac}$

43. $-b + \sqrt{b^2 - 4ac}$ **44.** $\dfrac{-b + \sqrt{b^2 - 4ac}}{2a}$

Section 6.3   The Quadratic Formula

In this section we will use the method of completing the square from the preceding section to derive the quadratic formula. The quadratic formula is a very useful tool in mathematics. It allows us to solve all types of quadratic equations.

Theorem 6.3 (The Quadratic Theorem)   For any quadratic equation in the form $ax^2 + bx + c = 0$, where $a \neq 0$, the two solutions are

$$x = \frac{-b + \sqrt{b^2 - 4ac}}{2a} \quad \text{and} \quad x = \frac{-b - \sqrt{b^2 - 4ac}}{2a}$$

PROOF   We will prove the quadratic theorem by completing the square on $ax^2 + bx + c = 0$.

$$ax^2 + bx + c = 0$$
$$ax^2 + bx = -c \qquad \text{Add } -c \text{ to both sides}$$
$$x^2 + \frac{b}{a}x = -\frac{c}{a} \qquad \text{Divide both sides by } a$$

To complete the square on the left side we add the square of 1/2 of b/a to both sides. (1/2 of b/a is $b/2a$.)

$$x^2 + \frac{b}{a}x + \left(\frac{b}{2a}\right)^2 = -\frac{c}{a} + \left(\frac{b}{2a}\right)^2$$

We now simplify the right side as a separate step. We square the second term and combine the two terms by writing each with the least common denominator $4a^2$:

$$-\frac{c}{a} + \left(\frac{b}{2a}\right)^2 = -\frac{c}{a} + \frac{b^2}{4a^2} = \frac{4a}{4a}\left(\frac{-c}{a}\right) + \frac{b^2}{4a^2} = \frac{-4ac + b^2}{4a^2}$$

It is convenient to write this last expression as

$$\frac{b^2 - 4ac}{4a^2}$$

Continuing with the proof, we have

$$x^2 + \frac{b}{a}x + \left(\frac{b}{2a}\right)^2 = \frac{b^2 - 4ac}{4a^2}$$

$$\left(x + \frac{b}{2a}\right)^2 = \frac{b^2 - 4ac}{4a^2} \qquad \text{Write left side as a binomial square}$$

$$x + \frac{b}{2a} = \pm\frac{\sqrt{b^2 - 4ac}}{2a} \qquad \text{Theorem 6.2}$$

$$x = -\frac{b}{2a} \pm \frac{\sqrt{b^2 - 4ac}}{2a} \qquad \text{Add } -\frac{b}{2a} \text{ to both sides}$$

$$x = \frac{-b \pm \sqrt{b^2 - 4ac}}{2a}$$

Note: The proof of the quadratic theorem is to show how we arrive at the quadratic formula. Some people have trouble understanding why the formula looks the way it looks. The reason is in the proof.

Practice Problems

1. Solve $6x^2 + 7x + 2 = 0$ using the quadratic formula.

Note: We could have solved the equation in Example 1 by factoring.

$$6x^2 + 7x - 5 = 0$$
$$(3x + 5)(2x - 1) = 0$$
$$3x + 5 = 0 \quad \text{or} \quad 2x - 1 = 0$$
$$x = -\frac{5}{3} \quad \text{or} \qquad x = \frac{1}{2}$$

When an equation is factorable, then factoring is usually the faster method of solution. It is best to try to factor first, and then if you have trouble factoring, to go to the quadratic formula. The quadratic formula always works. That is, you can use it to solve any quadratic equation.

2. Solve $\dfrac{x^2}{2} + x = \dfrac{1}{3}$.

Our proof is now complete. What we have is this: If our equation is in the form $ax^2 + bx + c = 0$ (standard form), where $a \neq 0$, the two solutions are always given by the formula

$$x = \frac{-b \pm \sqrt{b^2 - 4ac}}{2a}$$

This formula is known as the *quadratic formula*. If we substitute the coefficients a, b, and c of any quadratic equation in standard form into the formula, we need only perform some basic arithmetic to arrive at the solution set.

▼ **Example 1** Use the quadratic formula to solve $6x^2 + 7x - 5 = 0$.

Solution Using the coefficients $a = 6$, $b = 7$, and $c = -5$ in the formula

$$x = \frac{-b \pm \sqrt{b^2 - 4ac}}{2a}$$

we have
$$x = \frac{-7 \pm \sqrt{49 - 4(6)(-5)}}{2(6)}$$

or
$$x = \frac{-7 \pm \sqrt{49 + 120}}{12}$$

$$= \frac{-7 \pm \sqrt{169}}{12}$$

$$= \frac{-7 \pm 13}{12}$$

We separate the last equation into the two statements

$$x = \frac{-7 + 13}{12} \quad \text{or} \quad x = \frac{-7 - 13}{12}$$

$$x = \frac{1}{2} \qquad \text{or} \quad x = -\frac{5}{3}$$

The solution set is $\{\frac{1}{2}, -\frac{5}{3}\}$.   ▲

▼ **Example 2** Solve $\dfrac{x^2}{3} - x = -\dfrac{1}{2}$.

Solution Multiplying through by 6 and writing the result in standard form, we have

$$2x^2 - 6x + 3 = 0$$

In this case $a = 2$, $b = -6$, and $c = 3$. The two solutions are given by

$$x = \frac{-(-6) \pm \sqrt{36 - 4(2)(3)}}{2(2)}$$

$$= \frac{6 \pm \sqrt{12}}{4}$$

$$= \frac{6 \pm 2\sqrt{3}}{4} \qquad \sqrt{12} = \sqrt{4 \cdot 3} = \sqrt{4}\sqrt{3} = 2\sqrt{3}$$

Answers

1. $-\frac{1}{2}, -\frac{2}{3}$ **2.** $\dfrac{-3 \pm \sqrt{15}}{3}$

We can reduce this last expression to lowest terms by dividing the numerator and denominator by 2:

$$x = \frac{\cancel{2}(3 \pm \sqrt{3})}{\cancel{2} \cdot 2}$$

$$= \frac{3 \pm \sqrt{3}}{2}$$

The solution set is

$$\left\{ \frac{3 + \sqrt{3}}{2}, \frac{3 - \sqrt{3}}{2} \right\}$$

▲

▼ **Example 3**   Solve $\dfrac{1}{x + 2} - \dfrac{1}{x} = \dfrac{1}{3}$.

Solution   In order to solve this equation we must first put it in standard form. To do so we must clear the equation of fractions by multiplying each side by the LCD for all the denominators, which is $3x(x + 2)$. Multiplying both sides by the LCD we have

$$3x(x + 2)\left(\frac{1}{x + 2} - \frac{1}{x}\right) = \frac{1}{3} \cdot 3x(x + 2) \qquad \text{Multiply each by the LCD}$$

$$3x\cancel{(x + 2)} \cdot \frac{1}{\cancel{x + 2}} - 3\cancel{x}(x + 2) \cdot \frac{1}{\cancel{x}} = \frac{1}{\cancel{3}} \cdot \cancel{3}x(x + 2)$$

$$3x - 3(x + 2) = x(x + 2)$$
$$3x - 3x - 6 = x^2 + 2x \qquad \text{Multiplication}$$
$$-6 = x^2 + 2x \qquad \text{Simplify left side}$$
$$0 = x^2 + 2x + 6 \qquad \text{Add 6 to each side}$$

Since the right side of our last equation is not factorable, we must use the quadratic formula. From our last equation we have $a = 1$, $b = 2$, and $c = 6$. Using these numbers for a, b, and c in the quadratic formula gives us

$$x = \frac{-2 \pm \sqrt{4 - 4(1)(6)}}{2(1)}$$

$$= \frac{-2 \pm \sqrt{4 - 24}}{2} \qquad \text{Simplify inside the radical}$$

$$= \frac{-2 \pm \sqrt{-20}}{2} \qquad 4 - 24 = -20$$

$$= \frac{-2 \pm 2i\sqrt{5}}{2} \qquad \sqrt{-20} = i\sqrt{20} = i\sqrt{4}\sqrt{5} = 2i\sqrt{5}$$

$$= \frac{\cancel{2}(-1 \pm i\sqrt{5})}{\cancel{2}}$$

$$= -1 \pm i\sqrt{5} \qquad \text{Divide numerator and denominator by 2}$$

Since neither of the two solutions, $-1 + i\sqrt{5}$ nor $-1 - i\sqrt{5}$, will make any of the denominators in our original equation 0, they are both solutions.   ▲

Note: If you were to show the work involved in reducing this expression to lowest terms, you would first factor a 2 from the numerator and denominator

$$\frac{6 \pm 2\sqrt{3}}{4} = \frac{\cancel{2}(3 \pm \sqrt{3})}{\cancel{2} \cdot 2} = \frac{3 \pm \sqrt{3}}{2}$$

3.   Solve $\dfrac{1}{x + 4} - \dfrac{1}{x} = \dfrac{1}{2}$.

Answer
3. $-2 \pm 2i$

Problem Set 6.3

Name _____

Class _____

Date _____

Solve each equation. Use factoring or the quadratic formula, whichever is appropriate. (Try factoring first. If you have any difficulty factoring, then go right to the quadratic formula.)

1. $x^2 + 5x + 6 = 0$

2. $x^2 + 5x - 6 = 0$

Answers

1. _____ 2. _____

3. _____ 4. _____

5. _____ 6. _____

7. _____ 8. _____

9. _____ 10. _____

3. $a^2 - 4a + 1 = 0$

4. $a^2 + 4a + 1 = 0$

5. $x^2 - 3x + 2 = 0$

6. $x^2 + x - 2 = 0$

7. $\dfrac{x^2}{2} + 1 = \dfrac{2x}{3}$

8. $\dfrac{x^2}{2} + \dfrac{2}{3} = -\dfrac{2x}{3}$

9. $\dfrac{2t^2}{3} - t = -\dfrac{1}{6}$

10. $\dfrac{t^2}{3} - \dfrac{t}{2} = -\dfrac{3}{2}$

Answers

11. _____   12. _____

13. _____   14. _____

15. _____   16. _____

17. _____   18. _____

19. _____   20. _____

11. $x^2 + 6x - 8 = 0$

12. $2x^2 - 3x + 5 = 0$

13. $2x + 3 = -2x^2$

14. $2x - 3 = 3x^2$

15. $x^2 - 2x + 1 = 0$

16. $x^2 - 6x + 9 = 0$

17. $3r^2 = r - 4$

18. $5r^2 = 8r + 2$

19. $\dfrac{x^2}{3} - \dfrac{5x}{6} = \dfrac{1}{2}$

20. $\dfrac{x^2}{6} + \dfrac{5}{6} = -\dfrac{x}{3}$

Multiply both sides of each equation by its LCD. Then solve the resulting equation.

21. $\dfrac{1}{x+1} - \dfrac{1}{x} = \dfrac{1}{2}$

22. $\dfrac{1}{x+1} + \dfrac{1}{x} = \dfrac{1}{3}$

23. $\dfrac{1}{y-1} + \dfrac{1}{y+1} = 1$

24. $\dfrac{2}{y+2} + \dfrac{3}{y-2} = 1$

25. $\dfrac{1}{x+2} + \dfrac{1}{x+3} = 1$

26. $\dfrac{1}{x+3} + \dfrac{1}{x+4} = 1$

27. $\dfrac{6}{r^2-1} - \dfrac{1}{2} = \dfrac{1}{r+1}$

28. $2 + \dfrac{5}{r-1} = \dfrac{12}{(r-1)^2}$

Name _____

Class _____

Date _____

Answers

21. _____   22. _____

23. _____   24. _____

25. _____   26. _____

27. _____   28. _____

Answers

29. _____

30. _____

31. _____

32. _____

33. _____

34. _____

35. _____   36. _____

37. _____   38. _____

39. _____   40. _____

29. Solve $2x^3 + 2x^2 + 3x = 0$ by first factoring out the common factor x, and then using the quadratic formula. There are three solutions.

30. Solve $6x^3 - 4x^2 + 6x = 0$ by first factoring out the greatest common factor, and then applying the quadratic formula. There are three solutions.

31. One solution to a quadratic equation is $\dfrac{-3 + 2i}{5}$. What do you think the other solution is?

32. One solution to a quadratic equation is $\dfrac{-2 + 3i\sqrt{2}}{5}$. What is the other solution?

33. A manufacturer can produce x items at a total cost of $C = -x^2 + 40x$. He sells each item for $11.00, so his total revenue for selling x items is $R = 11x$. The manufacturer will break even when his total revenue is equal to his total cost— that is, when $R = C$. How many items must he sell to break even?

34. If the cost to produce x items is $C = -x^2 + 100x$, while the revenue for x items is $R = 15x$, how many items must be sold in order to break even?

Review Problems   The following problems review material we covered in Section 5.1.

Simplify each expression.

35. $25^{1/2}$

36. $8^{1/3}$

37. $9^{3/2}$

38. $16^{3/4}$

39. $8^{-2/3}$

40. $4^{-3/2}$

Section 6.4 The Discriminant

 The quadratic formula

$$x = \frac{-b \pm \sqrt{b^2 - 4ac}}{2a}$$

gives the solutions to any quadratic equation in standard form. There are times, when working with quadratic equations, when it is only important to know what kind of solutions the equation has.

DEFINITION   The expression under the radical in the quadratic formula is called the *discriminant:*

$$\text{Discriminant} = D = b^2 - 4ac$$

The discriminant gives the number and type of solutions to a quadratic equation, when the original equation has integer coefficients. For example, when the discriminant is negative, the quadratic formula will contain the square root of a negative number. Hence, the equation will have complex solutions. If the discriminant were 0, the formula would be

$$x = \frac{-b \pm 0}{2a} = \frac{-b}{2a}$$

and the equation would have one rational solution: the number $-b/2a$.

The following table gives the relationship between the discriminant and the type of solutions to the equation.

For the equation $ax^2 + bx + c = 0$ where a, b, and c are integers and $a \neq 0$:

If the discriminant $b^2 - 4ac$ is	Then the equation will have
Negative	Two complex solutions
Zero	One rational solution
A positive number that is also a perfect square	Two rational solutions
A positive number that is not a perfect square	Two irrational solutions

In the second and third cases, when the discriminant is 0 or a positive perfect square, the solutions are rational numbers. The quadratic equations in these two cases are the ones that can be factored.

▼   **Example 1**   For each equation give the number and kind of solutions.

a. $x^2 - 3x - 40 = 0$

Solution   Using $a = 1$, $b = -3$, and $c = -40$ in $b^2 - 4ac$, we have $(-3)^2 - 4(1)(-40) = 9 + 160 = 169$.

The discriminant is a perfect square. Therefore, the equation has two rational solutions.

Practice Problems

1. Give the number and kind of solution to each equation.

a. $x^2 - 3x - 28 = 0$

Answer
1a. Two rational

b. $x^2 - 6x + 9 = 0$

c. $3x^2 - 2x + 4 = 0$

d. $x^2 + 1 = 4x$

2. Find k so that the equation $9x^2 + kx = -4$ has exactly one rational solution.

---

b. $2x^2 - 3x + 4 = 0$

Solution Using $a = 2$, $b = -3$, and $c = 4$, we have

$$b^2 - 4ac = (-3)^2 - 4(2)(4) = 9 - 32 = -23$$

The discriminant is negative, implying the equation has two complex solutions.

c. $4x^2 - 12x + 9 = 0$

Solution Using $a = 4$, $b = -12$, and $c = 9$, the discriminant is

$$b^2 - 4ac = (-12)^2 - 4(4)(9) = 144 - 144 = 0$$

Since the discriminant is 0, the equation will have one rational solution.

d. $x^2 + 6x = 8$

Solution We must first put the equation in standard form by adding -8 to each side. If we do so, the resulting equation is

$$x^2 + 6x - 8 = 0$$

Now we identify a, b, and c as 1, 6, and -8 respectively.

$$b^2 - 4ac = 6^2 - 4(1)(-8) = 36 + 32 = 68$$

The discriminant is a positive number, but not a perfect square. Therefore, the equation will have two irrational solutions. ▲

▼ **Example 2** Find an appropriate k so that the equation $4x^2 - kx = -9$ has exactly one rational solution.

Solution We begin by writing the equation in standard form:

$$4x^2 - kx + 9 = 0$$

Using $a = 4$, $b = -k$, and $c = 9$, we have

$$b^2 - 4ac = (-k)^2 - 4(4)(9)$$
$$= k^2 - 144$$

An equation has exactly one rational solution when the discriminant is 0. We set the discriminant equal to 0 and solve:

$$k^2 - 144 = 0$$
$$k^2 = 144$$
$$k = \pm 12$$

Choosing k to be 12 or -12 will result in an equation with one rational solution. ▲

Answers
1b. One rational   **c.** Two complex
d. Two irrational   **2.** ± 12

Problem Set 6.4

Use the discriminant to find the number and kind of solution for each of the following equations. (See Example 1.)

1. $x^2 - 6x + 5 = 0$ **2.** $x^2 - x - 12 = 0$ **3.** $4x^2 - 4x = -1$

4. $9x^2 + 12x = -4$ **5.** $x^2 + x - 1 = 0$ **6.** $x^2 - 2x + 3 = 0$

7. $2y^2 = 3y + 1$ **8.** $3y^2 = 4y - 2$ **9.** $x^2 - 9 = 0$

10. $4x^2 - 81 = 0$ **11.** $5a^2 - 4a = 5$ **12.** $3a = 4a^2 - 5$

Name _____

Class _____

Date _____

Answers

1. _____

2. _____

3. _____

4. _____

5. _____

6. _____

7. _____

8. _____

9. _____

10. _____

11. _____

12. _____

Answers

13. _____ 14. _____

15. _____ 16. _____

17. _____ 18. _____

19. _____ 20. _____

21. _____ 22. _____

23. _____ 24. _____

25. _____ 26. _____

27. _____ 28. _____

Determine k so that each of the following has exactly one real solution. (See Example 2.)

13. $x^2 - kx + 25 = 0$ **14.** $x^2 + kx + 25 = 0$

15. $x^2 = kx - 36$ **16.** $x^2 = kx - 49$

17. $4x^2 - 12x + k = 0$ **18.** $9x^2 + 30x + k = 0$

19. $kx^2 - 40x = 25$ **20.** $kx^2 - 2x = -1$

21. $3x^2 - kx + 2 = 0$ **22.** $5x^2 + kx + 1 = 0$

Review Problems   The following problems review material we covered in Section 3.2.

Simplify each expression and write your answers with positive exponents only.

23. $\dfrac{3^{-2}}{3^{-4}}$ **24.** $\dfrac{5^{-6}}{5^{-8}}$

25. $\dfrac{2x^{-3}}{x^4}$ **26.** $\dfrac{3x^2}{x^{-3}}$

27. $\left(\dfrac{x^3}{x^{-2}}\right)^{-4}$ **28.** $\left(\dfrac{x^{-2}}{x^3}\right)^{4}$

Section 6.5   Other Equations Reducible to Quadratic Equations

We are now in a position to put our knowledge of quadratic equations to work to solve a variety of equations.

▼ **Example 1**   Solve $(x + 3)^2 - 2(x + 3) - 8 = 0$.

Solution   We can see that this equation is quadratic in form by replacing $x + 3$ with another variable, say y. Replacing $x + 3$ with y we have

$$y^2 - 2y - 8 = 0$$

We can solve this equation by factoring the left side and then setting each factor to 0.

$$
\begin{array}{ll}
y^2 - 2y - 8 = 0 & \\
(y - 4)(y + 2) = 0 & \text{Factor} \\
y - 4 = 0 \text{ or } y + 2 = 0 & \text{Set factors to 0} \\
y = 4 \text{ or } \quad y = -2 &
\end{array}
$$

Since our original equation was written in terms of the variable x, we would like our solutions in terms of x also. Replacing y with $x + 3$, and then solving for x we have

$$
\begin{array}{ll}
x + 3 = 4 & \text{or} \quad x + 3 = -2 \\
x = 1 & \text{or} \qquad x = -5
\end{array}
$$

The solutions to our original equation are 1 and -5.

The method we have just shown lends itself well to other types of equations that are quadratic in form, as we will see. In this example, however, there is another method that works just as well. Let's solve our original equation again, but this time, let's begin by expanding $(x + 3)^2$ and $2(x + 3)$.

$$
\begin{array}{ll}
(x + 3)^2 - 2(x + 3) - 8 = 0 & \\
x^2 + 6x + 9 - 2x - 6 - 8 = 0 & \text{Multiply} \\
x^2 + 4x - 5 = 0 & \text{Combine similar terms} \\
(x - 1)(x + 5) = 0 & \text{Factor} \\
x - 1 = 0 \quad \text{or} \quad x + 5 = 0 & \text{Set factors to 0} \\
x = 1 \quad \text{or} \qquad x = -5 &
\end{array}
$$

As you can see, either method produces the same result.   ▲

▼ **Example 2**   Solve $4x^4 + 7x^2 = 2$.

Solution   This equation is quadratic in x^2. We can make it easier to look at by using the substitution $y = x^2$. (The choice of the letter y is arbitrary. We could just as easily use the substitution $m = x^2$.) Making the substitutions $y = x^2$ and then solving the resulting equation we have

1.   Solve $(x - 2)^2 - 3(x - 2) - 10 = 0$.

2.   Solve $6x^4 - 13x^2 = 5$.

1. 7, 0   **2.** $\pm\dfrac{i\sqrt{3}}{3}$, $\pm\dfrac{\sqrt{10}}{2}$

$$4y^2 + 7y = 2$$
$$4y^2 + 7y - 2 = 0 \qquad \text{Standard form}$$
$$(4y - 1)(y + 2) = 0 \qquad \text{Factor}$$
$$4y - 1 = 0 \quad \text{or} \quad y + 2 = 0 \qquad \text{Set factors to } 0$$
$$y = \tfrac{1}{4} \quad \text{or} \qquad y = -2$$

Now we replace y with x^2 in order to solve for x

$$x^2 = \tfrac{1}{4} \qquad \text{or} \quad x^2 = -2$$
$$x = \pm\sqrt{\tfrac{1}{4}} \quad \text{or} \quad x = \pm\sqrt{-2} \qquad \text{Theorem 6.2}$$
$$x = \pm\tfrac{1}{2} \quad \text{or} \quad x = \pm i\sqrt{2}$$

The solution set is $\{\tfrac{1}{2}, -\tfrac{1}{2}, i\sqrt{2}, -i\sqrt{2}\}$. ▲

3. Solve for x: $x - \sqrt{x} - 12 = 0$.

▼ **Example 3** Solve for x: $x + \sqrt{x} - 6 = 0$.

Solution To see that this equation is quadratic in form, we have to notice that $(\sqrt{x})^2 = x$. That is, the equation can be rewritten as

$$(\sqrt{x})^2 + \sqrt{x} - 6 = 0$$

Replacing $\sqrt{x}$ with y and solving as usual we have

$$y^2 + y - 6 = 0$$
$$(y + 3)(y - 2) = 0$$
$$y + 3 = 0 \qquad \text{or} \quad y - 2 = 0$$
$$y = -3 \quad \text{or} \qquad y = 2$$

Again, to find x we replace y with $\sqrt{x}$ and solve:

$$\sqrt{x} = -3 \quad \text{or} \quad \sqrt{x} = 2$$
$$x = 9 \qquad\qquad x = 4 \qquad \begin{array}{l}\text{Square both sides}\\\text{of each equation}\end{array}$$

Since we squared both sides of each equation, we have the possibility of obtaining extraneous solutions. We have to check both solutions in our original equation.

$$\begin{array}{ll}\text{When} & x = 9 \\ \text{the equation} & x + \sqrt{x} - 6 = 0 \\ \text{becomes} & 9 + \sqrt{9} - 6 \overset{?}{=} 0 \\ & 9 + 3 - 6 = 0 \\ & \qquad\qquad 6 = 0 \qquad \text{A false statement}\end{array}$$

This implies 9 is extraneous.

$$\begin{array}{ll}\text{When} & x = 4 \\ \text{the equation} & x + \sqrt{x} - 6 = 0 \\ \text{becomes} & 4 + \sqrt{4} - 6 \overset{?}{=} 0 \\ & 4 + 2 - 6 = 0 \\ & \qquad\qquad 0 = 0 \qquad \text{A true statement}\end{array}$$

This means 4 is a solution.

The only solution to the equation $x + \sqrt{x} - 6 = 0$ is $x = 4$. ▲

Answer
3. 16

We should note here that the two possible solutions, 9 and 4, to the equation in Example 3 can be obtained by another method. Instead of substituting for $\sqrt{x}$, we can isolate it on one side of the equation and then square both sides to clear the equation of radicals.

$$x + \sqrt{x} - 6 = 0$$

$$
\begin{array}{lll}
\sqrt{x} = -x + 6 & & \text{Isolate } \sqrt{x} \\
x = x^2 - 12x + 36 & & \text{Square both sides} \\
0 = x^2 - 13x + 36 & & \text{Add } -x \text{ to both sides} \\
0 = (x - 4)(x - 9) & & \text{Factor}
\end{array}
$$

$$
\begin{array}{ccc}
x - 4 = 0 & \text{or} & x - 9 = 0 \\
x = 4 & & x = 9
\end{array}
$$

We obtain the same two possible solutions. Since we squared both sides of the equation to find them, we would have to check each one in the original equation. As was the case in Example 3, only $x = 4$ is a solution; $x = 9$ is extraneous.

▼ **Example 4** Solve $\sqrt{x + 1} + \sqrt{2x} = 1$.

Solution This equation has two separate terms involving radical signs. In this situation it is usually best to separate the radical terms on opposite sides of the equal sign. [*Note:* If we were to square both sides of the equation in its present form, we would not get $(x + 1) + (2x)$ for the left side. The square of the left side is $(\sqrt{x + 1} + \sqrt{2x})^2 = (x + 1) + 2\sqrt{x + 1}\sqrt{2x} + 2x.$]

Adding $-\sqrt{2x}$ to both sides, we have

$$\sqrt{x + 1} = 1 - \sqrt{2x}$$

Squaring both sides gives

$$
\begin{array}{ll}
x + 1 = 1 - 2\sqrt{2x} + 2x & \text{Recall: } (a + b)^2 = a^2 + 2ab + b^2 \\
-x = -2\sqrt{2x} & \text{Add } -2x \text{ and } -1 \text{ to both sides} \\
x^2 = 4(2x) & \text{Square both sides} \\
x^2 - 8x = 0 & \text{Standard form} \\
x(x - 8) = 0 & \text{Factor} \\
x = 0 \quad \text{or} \quad x - 8 = 0 & \text{Set factors to 0} \\
x = 0 \quad \text{or} \quad\quad\; x = 8 &
\end{array}
$$

Since we squared both sides, we have the possibility that one or both of the solutions are extraneous. We must check each one in the original equation:

When $x = 8$
we have $\sqrt{8 + 1} + \sqrt{2 \cdot 8} \overset{?}{=} 1$
$\sqrt{9} + \sqrt{16} = 1$
$3 + 4 = 1$
$7 = 1$
which implies $x = 8$
is extraneous

When $x = 0$
we have $\sqrt{0 + 1} + \sqrt{2(0)} \overset{?}{=} 1$
$\sqrt{1} + \sqrt{0} = 1$
$1 + 0 = 1$
$1 = 1$
which implies $x = 0$
is a solution ▲

4. Solve $\sqrt{x + 4} + \sqrt{3x} = 2$.

Problem Set 6.5

Solve each equation.

1. $(x - 3)^2 + 3(x - 3) + 2 = 0$

2. $(x + 4)^2 - (x + 4) - 6 = 0$

3. $2(x + 4)^2 + 5(x + 4) - 12 = 0$

4. $3(x - 5)^2 + 14(x - 5) - 5 = 0$

5. $x^4 - 6x^2 - 27 = 0$

6. $x^4 + 2x^2 - 8 = 0$

7. $2(4a + 2)^2 = 3(4a + 2) + 20$

8. $6(2a + 4)^2 = (2a + 4) + 2$

9. $6t^4 = -t^2 + 5$

10. $3t^4 = -2t^2 + 8$

Name _____

Class _____

Date _____

Answers

1. _____
2. _____
3. _____
4. _____
5. _____
6. _____
7. _____
8. _____
9. _____
10. _____

Answers

11. _____   12. _____

13. _____   14. _____

15. _____   16. _____

17. _____

18. _____

Solve each of the following equations. Remember if you square both sides of an equation in the process of solving it, you have to check all solutions in the original equation.

11. $x - 7\sqrt{x} + 10 = 0$

12. $x - 6\sqrt{x} + 8 = 0$

13. $t - 2\sqrt{t} - 15 = 0$

14. $t - 3\sqrt{t} - 10 = 0$

15. $6x + 11\sqrt{x} = 35$

16. $2x + \sqrt{x} = 15$

17. $(a - 2) - 11\sqrt{a - 2} + 30 = 0$

18. $(a - 3) - 9\sqrt{a - 3} + 20 = 0$

Solve the following equations by first clearing each of the radicals.

19. $\sqrt{x + 5} = \sqrt{x} + 1$

20. $\sqrt{x - 2} = 2 - \sqrt{x}$

21. $\sqrt{x + 4} = 2 - \sqrt{2x}$

22. $\sqrt{5y + 1} = 1 + \sqrt{3y}$

23. $\sqrt{y + 21} + \sqrt{y} = 7$

24. $\sqrt{y - 3} - \sqrt{y} = -1$

25. $\sqrt{y + 9} - \sqrt{y - 6} = 3$

26. $\sqrt{y + 7} - \sqrt{y + 2} = 1$

Name _____

Class _____

Date _____

Answers

19. _____ **20.** _____

21. _____ **22.** _____

23. _____ **24.** _____

25. _____ **26.** _____

Answers

27. _____

28. _____

29. _____

30. _____

31. _____

32. _____

27. Solve $x^3 - 8 = 0$ by factoring $x^3 - 8$ and then setting each factor to 0. (You will have to use the quadratic formula on the second factor.) There are three solutions.

28. Solve $x^3 - 27 = 0$ by factoring $x^3 - 27$ and setting each factor to 0.

Review Problems   The following problems review material we covered in Section 2.7. They are taken from the book *A First Course in Algebra,* written by Wallace C. Boyden and published by Silver, Burdett and Company in 1894.

29. A man bought 12 pairs of boots and 6 suits of clothes for $168. If a suit of clothes cost $2 less than four times as much as a pair of boots, what was the price of each?

30. A farmer pays just as much for 4 horses as he does for 6 cows. If a cow costs 15 dollars less than a horse, what is the cost of each?

31. Two men whose wages differ by 8 dollars receive both together $44 per month. How much does each receive?

32. Mr. Ames builds three houses. The first cost $2000 more than the second, and the third twice as much as the first. If they all together cost $18,000, what was the cost of each house?

Section 6.6   Word Problems

We will use the same four steps in solving word problems in this section that we have used in the past. The most important part of solving word problems is finding an equation that describes the situation.

▼   **Example 1**   The sum of the squares of two consecutive integers is 25. Find the two integers.

>   **Solution**   Let x = the first integer; then $x + 1$ = the next consecutive integer. The sum of the squares of x and $x + 1$ is 25.

$$x^2 + (x + 1)^2 = 25$$
$$x^2 + x^2 + 2x + 1 = 25$$
$$2x^2 + 2x - 24 = 0$$
$$x^2 + x - 12 = 0 \qquad \text{Divide both sides by 2}$$
$$(x + 4)(x - 3) = 0$$
$$x = -4 \quad \text{or} \quad x = 3$$

>   These are the possible values for the first integer:

$$\begin{array}{ll} \text{If} \quad x = -4 & \text{If} \quad x = 3 \\ \text{then} \quad x + 1 = -3 & \text{then} \quad x + 1 = 4 \end{array}$$

>   There are two pairs of consecutive integers, the sum of whose squares is 25. They are $\{-4, -3\}$ and $\{3, 4\}$.   ▲

Many word problems dealing with area can best be described by quadratic equations.

▼   **Example 2**   A vegetable garden, 20 feet by 30 feet, has a walkway of uniform width around it. If the area of the garden and walkway together is 704 square feet, what is the width of the walkway?

>   **Solution**   Let x = the width of the walkway. Figure 1 shows a picture of the garden and walkway.

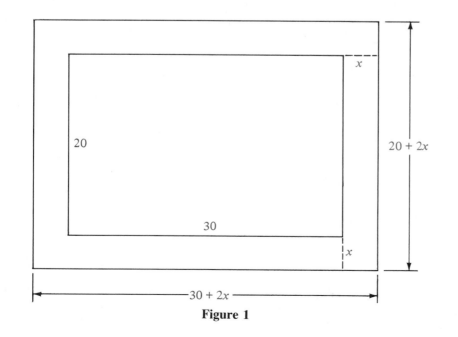

Figure 1

From the diagram the dimensions on the outside of the walkway are $(20 + 2x)$ and $(30 + 2x)$. The enclosed area is given as 704 square feet. Since the area is length times width, we have

$$(30 + 2x)(20 + 2x) = 704$$
$$600 + 100x + 4x^2 = 704$$
$$4x^2 + 100x - 104 = 0$$
$$x^2 + 25x - 26 = 0 \qquad \text{Divide both sides by 4}$$
$$(x + 26)(x - 1) = 0$$
$$x = -26 \quad \text{or} \quad x = 1$$

Our two possible solutions are 1 foot and -26 feet. Since -26 feet is impossible, the width of the walkway must be 1 foot. ▲

Another application of quadratic equations involves the Pythagorean Theorem, an important theorem from geometry. The theorem gives the relationship between the sides of any right triangle (a triangle with a 90° angle). We state it here without proof.

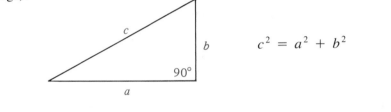

Pythagorean Theorem In any right triangle, the square of the longest side (hypotenuse) is equal to the sum of the squares of the other two sides (legs).

$$c^2 = a^2 + b^2$$

3. The longest side of a right triangle is 4 more than the shortest side. The third side is 2 more than the shortest side. Find the length of each side.

▼ **Example 3** The lengths of the three sides of a right triangle are given by three consecutive integers. Find the lengths of the three sides.

Solution Let x = first integer (shortest side).

Then $x + 1$ = next consecutive integer
     $x + 2$ = last consecutive integer (longest side)

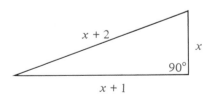

By the Pythagorean Theorem, we have

$$(x + 2)^2 = (x + 1)^2 + x^2$$
$$x^2 + 4x + 4 = x^2 + 2x + 1 + x^2$$
$$x^2 - 2x - 3 = 0$$
$$(x - 3)(x + 1) = 0$$
$$x = 3 \quad \text{or} \quad x = -1$$

The shortest side is 3. The other two sides are 4 and 5. ▲

▼ **Example 4**   If an object is thrown downward with an initial velocity of 20 feet/second, the distance s it travels in an amount of time t is given by the equation $s = 20t + 16t^2$. (This is because of the acceleration of the object due to gravity. The equation does not take into account the force of friction on the object due to its falling through air.) How long does it take the object to fall 40 feet?

Solution   In this example, the equation that describes the situation is given. We simply let $s = 40$ and solve for t:

$$
\begin{array}{ll}
\text{When} & s = 40 \\
\text{the equation} & s = 20t + 16t^2 \\
\text{becomes} & 40 = 20t + 16t^2 \\
\text{or} \quad 16t^2 + 20t - 40 = 0 \\
\quad 4t^2 + 5t - 10 = 0 & \text{Divide by 4}
\end{array}
$$

Using the quadratic formula, we have

$$t = \frac{-5 \pm \sqrt{25 - 4(4)(-10)}}{2(4)}$$

$$= \frac{-5 \pm \sqrt{185}}{8}$$

$$t = \frac{-5 + \sqrt{185}}{8} \quad \text{or} \quad t = \frac{-5 - \sqrt{185}}{8}$$

The second solution is impossible since it is a negative number and t must be positive.

It takes

$$t = \frac{-5 + \sqrt{185}}{8}$$

or approximately

$$\frac{-5 + 13.60}{8} = 1.08 \text{ seconds}$$

for the object to fall 40 feet.   ▲

▼ **Example 5**   The current of a river is 3 miles/hour. It takes a motorboat a total of 3 hours to travel 12 miles upstream and return 12 miles downstream. What is the speed of the boat in still water?

Solution   Let $x =$ the speed of the boat in still water. The basic equation that gives the relationship between distance, rate, and time is $d = rt$.

It is usually helpful to summarize rate problems like this by using a table:

	Distance	Rate	Time
Upstream			
Downstream			

4.   An object thrown upward with an initial velocity of 32 feet/second will rise and fall according to the equation

$$s = 32t - 16t^2$$

At what times t will the object be 12 feet above the ground?

5.   The current of a river is 2 miles/hour. It takes a motorboat a total of 3 hours to travel 8 miles upstream and return 8 miles downstream. What is the speed of the boat in still water?

Answers
4. $\frac{1}{2}$ sec and $\frac{3}{2}$ sec   **5.** 6 mph

We fill in as much of the table as possible using the information given in the problem. For instance, since we let x = the speed of the boat in still water, the rate upstream (against the current) must be $x - 3$. The rate downstream (with the current) is $x + 3$.

	d	r	t
Upstream	12	$x - 3$	
Downstream	12	$x + 3$	

The last two boxes can be filled in using the relationship $d = r \cdot t$. Since the boxes correspond to t, we solve $d = r \cdot t$ for t and get

$$t = \frac{d}{r}$$

Completing the table, we have

	d	r	t
Upstream	12	$x - 3$	$\dfrac{12}{(x - 3)}$
Downstream	12	$x + 3$	$\dfrac{12}{(x + 3)}$

The total time for the trip up and back is 3 hours:

$$\text{Time upstream} + \text{Time downstream} = \text{Total time}$$

$$\frac{12}{x - 3} + \frac{12}{x + 3} = 3$$

Multiplying both sides by $(x - 3)(x + 3)$, we have

$$12(x + 3) + 12(x - 3) = 3(x^2 - 9)$$
$$12x + 36 + 12x - 36 = 3x^2 - 27$$
$$3x^2 - 24x - 27 = 0$$
$$x^2 - 8x - 9 = 0 \qquad \text{Divide both sides by 3}$$
$$(x - 9)(x + 1) = 0$$
$$x = 9 \quad \text{or} \quad x = -1$$

The speed of the motorboat in still water is 9 miles/hour. ▲

Problem Set 6.6

Number Problems

1. The sum of the squares of two consecutive odd integers is 34. Find the two integers.

2. The sum of the squares of two consecutive even integers is 100. Find the two integers.

3. The square of the sum of two consecutive integers is 81. Find the two integers.

4. Find two consecutive even integers whose sum squared is 100.

5. The sum of a number and its reciprocal is $\frac{10}{3}$. Find the number.

6. The sum of a number and twice its reciprocal is $\frac{27}{5}$. Find the number.

7. The sum of a number and its positive square root is 6. Find the number.

8. The difference of a number and twice its positive square root is 15. Find the number.

Geometry Problems

Answers

9. _____

10. _____

11. _____

12. _____

13. _____

14. _____

9. A rectangular pool, 15 feet by 30 feet, has a strip of grass of uniform width around it. If the total area of the grass and the pool is 646 square feet, find the width of the strip of grass.

10. A rectangular garden is surrounded by a path of uniform width. The area of the path is 168 square feet. If the garden measures 10 feet by 12 feet, find the width of the path.

11. The lengths of the three sides of a right triangle are given by three consecutive even integers. Find the lengths of the three sides.

12. The longest side of a right triangle is twice the shortest side. The third side measures 6 inches. Find the length of the shortest side.

13. One leg of a right triangle is 3 times the other leg. The hypotenuse is $2\sqrt{10}$ centimeters. What are the lengths of the legs?

14. The longest side of a right triangle is 2 less than twice the shortest side. The third side is 2 more than the shortest side. Find the length of all three sides.

Velocity Problems

Name _____

Class _____

Date _____

15. An object is thrown downward with an initial velocity of 5 feet/second. The relationship between the distance (s) it travels and time (t) is given by $s = 5t + 16t^2$. How long does it take the object to fall 74 feet?

Answers

15. _____

16. _____

17. _____

18. _____

16. The distance an object falls from rest is given by the equation $s = 16t^2$, where s = distance and t = time. How long does it take an object dropped from a 100-foot cliff to hit the ground?

17. An object is thrown upward with an initial velocity of 20 feet/second. The equation that gives the height (h) of the object at any time (t) is $h = 20t - 16t^2$. At what times will the object be 4 feet off the ground?

18. An object is propelled upward with an initial velocity of 32 feet/second from a height of 16 feet above the ground. The equation giving the object's height (h) at any time (t) is $h = 16 + 32t - 16t^2$. Does the object ever reach a height of 32 feet?

Distance, Rate, Time Problems

19. The current of a river is 2 miles/hour. A boat travels to a point 8 miles upstream and back again in 3 hours. What is the speed of the boat in still water?

20. A boat travels 15 miles/hour in still water. It takes twice as long for the boat to go 20 miles upstream as it does to go downstream. Find the speed of the current.

Review Problems   The following problems review material we covered in Section 2.3. Reviewing these problems will help you understand the next section.

Solve each inequality and graph the solution set.

21. $2x + 1 < 0$ or $3x - 2 > 0$ 22. $3x - 4 < 0$ or $2x - 8 > 0$

23. $x + 2 \geq 0$ and $x - 4 \leq 0$ 24. $x + 4 \geq 0$ and $x - 2 \leq 0$

Section 6.7   Quadratic Inequalities

Quadratic inequalities in one variable are inequalities of the form

$$ax^2 + bx + c < 0$$
$$ax^2 + bx + c \le 0$$
$$ax^2 + bx + c > 0$$
$$ax^2 + bx + c \ge 0$$

where a, b, and c are constants, with $a \ne 0$. The technique we will use to solve inequalities of this type involves graphing. Suppose, for example, we wish to find the solution set for the inequality $x^2 - x - 6 > 0$. We begin by factoring the left side to obtain

$$(x - 3)(x + 2) > 0$$

We have two real numbers $x - 3$ and $x + 2$ whose product $(x - 3)(x + 2)$ is greater than zero. That is, their product is positive. The only way the product can be positive is either if both factors, $(x - 3)$ and $(x + 2)$, are positive or if they are both negative. To help visualize where $x - 3$ is positive and where it is negative, we draw a real number line and label it accordingly:

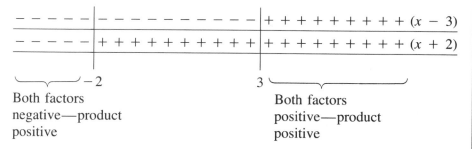

Here is a similar diagram showing where the factor $x + 2$ is positive and where it is negative:

Drawing the two number lines together and eliminating the unnecessary numbers, we have

We can see from the diagram above that the graph of the solution to $x^2 - x - 6 > 0$ is

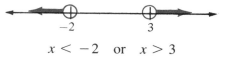

$$x < -2 \quad \text{or} \quad x > 3$$

1. Solve for x.

$$x^2 + 2x - 15 \leq 0$$

2. Solve for x.

$$2x^2 + 3x > 2$$

3. Solve.

$$x^2 + 10x + 25 < 0$$

▼ **Example 1** Solve for x: $x^2 - 2x - 8 \leq 0$.

Solution We begin by factoring:

$$x^2 - 2x - 8 \leq 0$$
$$(x - 4)(x + 2) \leq 0$$

The product $(x - 4)(x + 2)$ is negative or zero. The factors must have opposite signs. We draw a diagram showing where each factor is positive and where each factor is negative:

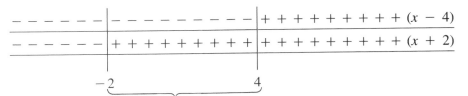

Factors have different signs—their product is negative

From the diagram we have the graph of the solution set:

$$-2 \leq x \leq 4$$ ▲

▼ **Example 2** Solve for x: $6x^2 - x \geq 2$.

Solution
$$6x^2 - x \geq 2$$
$$6x^2 - x - 2 \geq 0 \qquad \leftarrow \text{Standard form}$$
$$(3x - 2)(2x + 1) \geq 0$$

The product is positive, so the factors must agree in sign. Here is the diagram showing where that occurs:

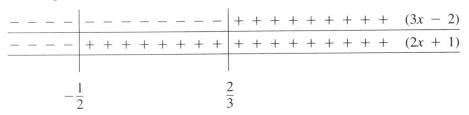

Since the factors agree in sign below $-\frac{1}{2}$ and above $\frac{2}{3}$, the graph of the solution set is

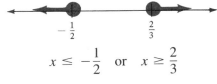

$$x \leq -\frac{1}{2} \quad \text{or} \quad x \geq \frac{2}{3}$$ ▲

▼ **Example 3** Solve $x^2 - 6x + 9 \geq 0$.

Solution
$$x^2 - 6x + 9 \geq 0$$
$$(x - 3)^2 \geq 0$$

This is a special case in which both factors are the same. Since $(x - 3)^2$ is always positive or zero, the solution set is all real numbers. That is, any real number that is used in place of x in the original inequality will produce a true statement.   ▲

Problem Set 6.7

Solve each of the following inequalities and graph the solution set.

1. $x^2 + x - 6 > 0$

2. $x^2 + x - 6 < 0$

3. $x^2 - x - 12 \leq 0$

4. $x^2 - x - 12 \geq 0$

5. $x^2 + 5x \geq -6$

6. $x^2 - 5x > 6$

7. $6x^2 < 5x - 1$

8. $4x^2 \geq -5x + 6$

9. $x^2 - 9 < 0$

10. $x^2 - 16 \geq 0$

11. $4x^2 - 9 \geq 0$

12. $9x^2 - 4 < 0$

13. $2x^2 - x - 3 < 0$

14. $3x^2 + x - 10 \geq 0$

Name _____

Class _____

Date _____

Answers

1. ←————————————————→

2. ←————————————————→

3. ←————————————————→

4. ←————————————————→

5. ←————————————————→

6. ←————————————————→

7. ←————————————————→

8. ←————————————————→

9. ←————————————————→

10. ←————————————————→

11. ←————————————————→

12. ←————————————————→

13. ←————————————————→

14. ←————————————————→

Answers

15. ⟵─────────────⟶

16. ⟵─────────────⟶

17. ⟵─────────────⟶

18. ⟵─────────────⟶

19. ⟵─────────────⟶

20. ⟵─────────────⟶

21. ⟵─────────────⟶

22. ⟵─────────────⟶

23. _____   **24.** _____

25. _____   **26.** _____

27. _____   **28.** _____

29. _____   **30.** _____

15. $x^2 - 4x + 4 \geq 0$

16. $x^2 - 4x + 4 < 0$

17. $x^2 - 10x + 25 < 0$

18. $x^2 - 10x + 25 > 0$

19. $(x - 2)(x - 3)(x - 4) > 0$

20. $(x - 2)(x - 3)(x - 4) < 0$

21. $(x + 1)(x + 2)(x + 3) \leq 0$

22. $(x + 1)(x + 2)(x + 3) \geq 0$

Review Problems   The following problems review material we covered in Section 5.2.

Write each radical in simplified form.

23. $\sqrt{48}$

24. $\sqrt{50}$

25. $\sqrt{18x^3}$

26. $\sqrt{12x^5}$

27. $\sqrt[3]{8x^3y^4}$

28. $\sqrt[3]{27x^4y^3}$

29. $\sqrt{\dfrac{2}{3}}$

30. $\sqrt{\dfrac{3}{5}}$

Chapter 6   Summary and Review

THEOREM 6.1 (ZERO-FACTOR PROPERTY) [6.1]

For all real numbers r and s, if $r \cdot s = 0$, then $r = 0$ or $s = 0$ (or both).

Examples

TO SOLVE A QUADRATIC EQUATION BY FACTORING [6.1]

Step 1: Write the equation in standard form:

$$ax^2 + bx + c = 0, \quad a \neq 0$$

Step 2: Factor the left side.

Step 3: Use the zero-factor property to set each factor equal to zero.

Step 4: Solve the resulting first-degree equations.

1. Solve $x^2 - 5x = -6$.

$$x^2 - 5x + 6 = 0$$
$$(x - 3)(x - 2) = 0$$
$$x - 3 = 0 \text{ or } x - 2 = 0$$
$$x = 3 \text{ or } \quad x = 2$$

THEOREM 6.2 [6.2]

If $a^2 = b$, where b is a real number, then

$$a = \sqrt{b} \quad \text{or} \quad a = -\sqrt{b}; \text{ that is, } a = \pm\sqrt{b}$$

2. If $(x - 3)^2 = 25$
    then $x - 3 = \pm 5$
    $$x = 3 \pm 5$$
    $$x = 8 \text{ or } x = -2$$

TO SOLVE A QUADRATIC EQUATION BY COMPLETING THE SQUARE [6.2]

Step 1: Write the equation in the form $ax^2 + bx = c$.

Step 2: If $a \neq 1$, divide through by the constant a so the coefficient of x^2 is 1.

Step 3: Complete the square on the left side by adding the square of $\frac{1}{2}$ the coefficient of x to both sides.

Step 4: Write the left side of the equation as the square of a binomial. Simplify the right side if possible.

Step 5: Apply Theorem 6.2 and solve as usual.

3. Solve $x^2 - 6x - 6 = 0$.

$$x^2 - 6x = 6$$
$$x^2 - 6x + \mathbf{9} = 6 + \mathbf{9}$$
$$(x - 3)^2 = 15$$
$$x - 3 = \pm\sqrt{15}$$
$$x = 3 \pm \sqrt{15}$$

THEOREM 6.3 (THE QUADRATIC THEOREM) [6.3]

For any quadratic equation in the form $ax^2 + bx + c = 0$, $a \neq 0$, the two solutions are

$$x = \frac{-b \pm \sqrt{b^2 - 4ac}}{2a}$$

This last expression is known as the *quadratic formula*.

4. If $2x^2 + 3x - 4 = 0$, then
    $$x = \frac{-3 \pm \sqrt{9 - 4(2)(-4)}}{2(2)}$$
    $$= \frac{-3 \pm \sqrt{41}}{4}$$

THE DISCRIMINANT [6.4]

The expression $b^2 - 4ac$ which appears under the radical sign in the quadratic formula is known as *the discriminant*.

We can classify the solutions to $ax^2 + bx + c = 0$:

5. The discriminant for
    $$x^2 + 6x + 9 = 0$$
    is $D = 36 - 4(1)(9) = 0$, which implies the equation has one rational solution.

The solutions are	When the discriminant is
Two complex numbers	Negative
One rational number	Zero
Two rational numbers	A positive perfect square
Two irrational numbers	A positive number, but not a perfect square

6. The equation $x^4 - x^2 - 12 = 0$ is quadratic in x^2. Letting $y = x^2$ we have

$$y^2 - y - 12 = 0$$
$$(y - 4)(y + 3) = 0$$
$$y = 4 \quad \text{or} \quad y = -3$$

Resubstituting x^2 for y we have

$$x^2 = 4 \quad \text{or} \quad x^2 = -3$$
$$x = \pm 2 \quad \text{or} \quad x = \pm i\sqrt{3}$$

7. Solve $x^2 - 2x - 8 > 0$. We factor and draw the sign diagram.

$$(x - 4)(x + 2) > 0$$

$$
\begin{array}{ccc}
- - - - & - - - - & + + + + \quad (x - 4) \\
\hline
- - - - & + + + + & + + + + \quad (x + 2) \\
\end{array}
$$
$$\quad -2 \qquad 4$$

The solution is

$$x < -2 \quad \text{or} \quad x > 4$$

EQUATIONS QUADRATIC IN FORM [6.5]

There are a variety of equations whose form is quadratic. We solve most of them by making a substitution so the equation becomes quadratic, and then solving that equation by factoring or the quadratic formula. For example

The equation	*is quadratic in*
$(2x - 3)^2 + 5(2x - 3) - 6 = 0$	$2x - 3$
$4x^4 - 7x^2 - 2 = 0$	x^2
$2x - 7\sqrt{x} + 3 = 0$	$\sqrt{x}$

QUADRATIC INEQUALITIES [6.7]

We solve quadratic inequalities by manipulating the inequality to get 0 on the right side and then factoring the left side. We then make a diagram that indicates where the factors are positive and where they are negative. From this sign diagram and the original inequality we graph the appropriate solution set.

COMMON MISTAKES

1. Attempting to apply the zero-factor property to numbers other than 0. For example, consider the equation

$$(x + 2)(x - 3) = 7$$

The mistake takes place when we try to solve it by setting each factor equal to 7.

$$x + 2 = 7 \quad \text{or} \quad x - 3 = 7$$
$$x = 5 \quad \text{or} \qquad x = 10$$

Neither of these two numbers is a solution to the original equation. The mistake arises when we assume that since the product of $(x + 2)$ and $(x - 3)$ is 7, one of the two factors must also be 7.

2. When both sides of an equation are squared in the process of solving the equation, a common mistake occurs when the resulting solutions are not checked in the original equation. Remember, every time we square both sides of an equation, there is the possibility we have introduced an extraneous root.

3. When squaring a quantity that has two terms involving radicals, it is a common mistake to omit the middle term in the result. For example,

$$(\sqrt{x + 3} + \sqrt{2x})^2 = (x + 3) + (2x)$$

is a common mistake. It should look like this:

$$(\sqrt{x + 3} + \sqrt{2x})^2 = (x + 3) + 2\sqrt{2x}\sqrt{x + 3} + (2x)$$

Remember: $(a + b)^2 = a^2 + 2ab + b^2$.

Chapter 6 Test

Solve the following by factoring. [6.1]

1. $x^2 - 4x = 21$

2. $25x^2 - 81 = 0$

Name _____

Class _____

Date _____

Answers

1. _____   **2.** _____

3. _____   **4.** _____

5. _____   **6.** _____

7. _____   **8.** _____

9. _____   **10.** _____

3. $(x - 4)(x + 1) = -6$

4. $\sqrt{2x + 5} = x + 1$

5. Solve $(2x + 4)^2 = -8$. [6.2]

6. Solve $x^2 - 4x = -2$ by completing the square. [6.2]

Solve by using the quadratic formula. [6.3]

7. $2x^2 - x = 3$

8. $\dfrac{1}{x - 1} = \dfrac{5}{4} - \dfrac{1}{x - 4}$

9. Determine k so that $kx^2 = 12x - 4$ has one rational solution. (6.4)

10. Use the discriminant to identify the number and type of solutions to $2x^2 - 5x = 7$. [6.4]

Answers

11. _____ 12. _____

13. _____ 14. _____

15. _____ 16. _____

17. ←——————————→

18. ←——————————→

Solve by any method. [6.5]

11. $4x^4 - 7x^2 - 2 = 0$

12. $\sqrt{2x + 1} = 1 + \sqrt{x}$

13. $(2x + 1)^2 - 5(2x + 1) + 6 = 0$ **14.** $2x - 7\sqrt{x} + 3 = 0$

15. One integer is 1 less than twice another. The sum of their squares is 34. Find the two integers. [6.6]

16. A motorboat travels at 4 miles/hour in still water. It goes 12 miles upstream and 12 miles back again in a total of 8 hours. Find the speed of the current of the river. [6.6]

Solve each inequality and graph the solution set. [6.7]

17. $x^2 - x - 6 \leq 0$

18. $2x^2 + 5x > 3$

7 Linear Equations and Inequalities

To the student:

As we have said before, mathematics is a language that can describe certain aspects of our world better than English. One important aspect of the world is the idea of a path, track, orbit, or course. Some simple paths we are familiar with are circles, cloverleaf interchanges on a highway, the sloping straight line of a sewer pipe, and the elliptical route taken by a satellite. Mathematics can be used to describe these paths very accurately. The simplest of paths—a straight line—can be described by an equation such as $3x - 2y = 5$, which we call a linear equation in two variables. In this chapter we will concern ourselves with linear equations (and inequalities) in two variables.

To make a successful attempt at Chapter 7 you should be familiar with the concepts developed in Chapter 2. The main concept is how to solve a linear equation in one variable.

Section 7.1 Graphing in Two Dimensions

Let us now consider the equation $2x - y = 5$. The equation contains two variables. A solution, therefore, must be in the form of a pair of numbers, one for x and one for y, that make the equation a true statement. One pair of numbers that works is $x = 3$ and $y = 1$, because when we substitute them for x and y in the equation we get a true statement. That is,

$$2(3) - 1 = 5$$
$$5 = 5 \qquad \text{A true statement}$$

The pair of numbers $x = 3$ and $y = 1$ can be written as $(3, 1)$. This is called an *ordered pair,* because it is a pair of numbers written in a specific order. The first number in the ordered pair is always associated with the

335

variable x, the second number with the variable y. The first number is called the *x-coordinate* (or *x*-component) of the ordered pair and the second number is called the *y-coordinate* (or *y*-component) of the ordered pair.

A *rectangular coordinate system* is made by drawing two real number lines at right angles to each other. The two number lines, called *axes*, cross each other at 0. This point is called the *origin*. Positive directions are to the right and up. Negative directions are down and to the left. The rectangular coordinate system is shown in Figure 1.

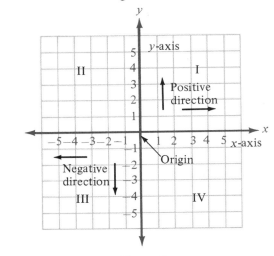

Figure 1

Note: The horizontal number line is called the *x-axis* and the vertical number line is called the *y-axis*. The two number lines divide the coordinate system into four quadrants which we number I through IV in a counterclockwise direction. Points on the axes are not considered as being in any quadrant.

To graph the ordered pair (a, b) on a rectangular coordinate system we start at the origin and move a units right or left (right if a is positive, left if a is negative). Then we move b units up or down (up if b is positive and down if b is negative). The point where we end is the graph of the ordered pair (a, b).

▼ **Example 1** Plot (graph) the ordered pairs $(2, 5)$, $(-2, 5)$, $(-2, -5)$, and $(2, -5)$.

Solution To graph the ordered pair $(2, 5)$, we start at the origin and move 2 units to the right, then 5 units up. We are now at the point whose coordinates are $(2, 5)$. We graph the other three ordered pairs in a similar manner (see Figure 2).

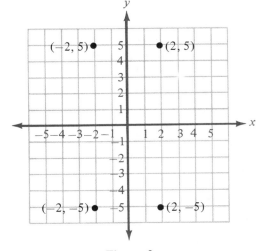

Figure 2

Practice Problems

1. Plot the ordered pairs $(1, 3)$, $(-1, 3)$, $(-1, -3)$, and $(1, -3)$.

Note: From Example 1 we see that any point in quadrant I has both its x- and y-coordinates positive $(+, +)$. Points in quadrant II have negative x-coordinates and positive y-coordinates $(-, +)$. In quadrant III both coordinates are negative $(-, -)$. In quadrant IV the form is $(+, -)$.

Answers
1. See Solutions Section for all answers in this section.

▼ **Example 2** Graph the ordered pairs $(1, -3)$, $(\frac{1}{2}, 2)$, $(3, 0)$, $(0, -2)$, $(-1, 0)$, and $(0, 5)$.

Solution

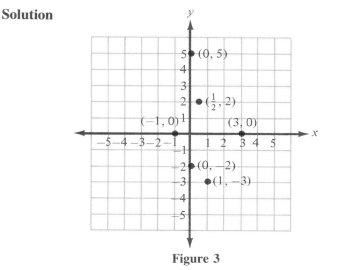

Figure 3 ▲

2. Plot the ordered pairs $(4, -2)$, $(-\frac{1}{2}, 3)$, $(1, 0)$, $(0, -5)$, $(-6, 0)$, and $(0, 4)$.

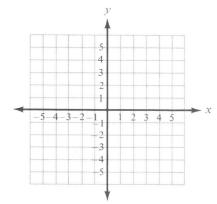

From Example 2 we see that any point on the x-axis has a y-coordinate of 0 (it has no vertical displacement), and any point on the y-axis has an x-coordinate of 0 (no horizontal displacement).

DEFINITION Any equation that can be put in the form $ax + by = c$, where a, b, and c are real numbers and a and b are not both 0, is called a *linear equation* in two variables. The graph of any equation of this form is a straight line (that is why these equations are called "linear"). The form $ax + by = c$ is called *standard form*.

To graph a linear equation in two variables, we simply graph its solution set. That is, we draw a line through all the points whose coordinates satisfy the equation.

▼ **Example 3** Graph $y = 2x - 3$.

Solution Since $y = 2x - 3$ can be put in the form $ax + by = c$, it is a linear equation in two variables. Hence, the graph of its solution set is a straight line. We can find some specific solutions by substituting numbers for x and then solving for the corresponding values of y. We are free to choose any convenient numbers for x, so let's use the numbers -1, 0, and 2:

When $x = -1$
the equation $y = 2x - 3$
becomes $y = 2(-1) - 3$
$y = -5$

The ordered pair $(-1, -5)$ is a solution.

When $x = 0$
we have $y = 2(0) - 3$
$y = -3$

The ordered pair $(0, -3)$ is also a solution.

Using $x = 2$
we have $y = 2(2) - 3$
$y = 1$

In table form

x	y
-1	-5
0	-3
2	1

3. Graph $y = 2x + 3$.

Note: When we refer to *convenient* numbers for x, we mean numbers that will be easy to work with in the equation, usually integers. For instance, if we were finding points on the line

$$y = \tfrac{1}{2}x + 3$$

it would be easier to substitute 2 or 4 for x, than 1 or 3 because we have to multiply x by $\frac{1}{2}$.

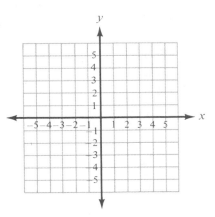

Note: It actually takes only two points to determine a straight line. We have included a third point for "insurance." If all three points do not line up in a straight line, we have made a mistake.

The ordered pair (2, 1) is another solution.
Graphing these three ordered pairs and drawing a line through them, we have the graph of $y = 2x - 3$:

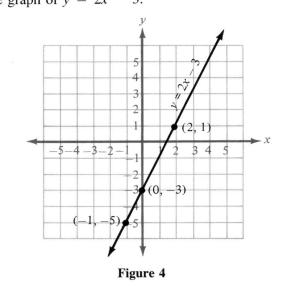

Figure 4 ▲

Two important points on the graph of a straight line, if they exist, are the points where the graph crosses the axes.

DEFINITION   The *x-intercept* of the graph of an equation is the *x*-coordinate of the point where the graph crosses the *x*-axis. The *y-intercept* is defined similarly.

Since any point on the *x*-axis has a *y*-coordinate of 0, we can find the *x*-intercept by letting $y = 0$ and solving the equation for *x*. We find the *y*-intercept by letting $x = 0$ and solving for *y*.

4. Find the *x*- and *y*-intercepts for $2x - 3y = 6$; then graph the solution set.

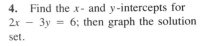

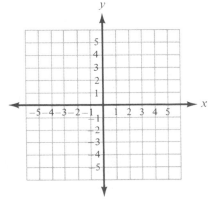

▼   **Example 4**   Find the *x*- and *y*-intercepts for $2x + 3y = 6$; then graph the solution set.

Solution   To find the *y*-intercept we let $x = 0$.

$$\text{When} \qquad x = 0$$
$$\text{we have} \quad 2(0) + 3y = 6$$
$$3y = 6$$
$$y = 2$$

The *y*-intercept is 2, and the graph crosses the *y*-axis at the point (0, 2).

$$\text{When} \qquad y = 0$$
$$\text{we have} \quad 2x + 3(0) = 6$$
$$x = 3$$

The *x*-intercept is 3, so the graph crosses the *x*-axis at the point (3, 0). We use these results to graph the solution set for $2x + 3y = 6$. The graph is shown in Figure 5 on the following page.

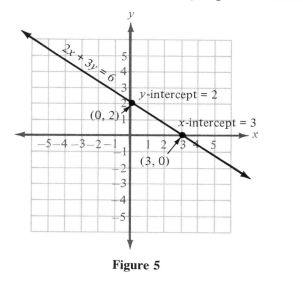

Figure 5 ▲

Note: Graphing straight lines by finding the intercepts works best when the coefficients of x and y are factors of the constant term.

▼ **Example 5** Graph the line $x = 3$ and the line $y = -2$.

Solution The line $x = 3$ is the set of all points whose x-coordinate is 3. The variable y does not appear in the equation, so the y-coordinates can be any number.

The line $y = -2$ is the set of all points whose y-coordinate is -2. The x-coordinate can be any number.

Here are the graphs:

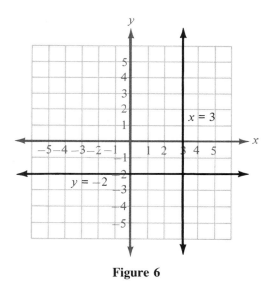

Figure 6 ▲

5. Graph the line $x = -1$ and the line $y = 4$.

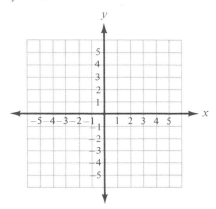

Problem Set 7.1

Graph each of the following ordered pairs on a rectangular coordinate system.

1. $(1, 2)$ **2.** $(-1, 2)$ **3.** $(-1, -2)$ **4.** $(1, -2)$

5. $(3, 4)$ **6.** $(-3, -4)$ **7.** $(5, 0)$ **8.** $(0, -3)$

9. $(0, 2)$ **10.** $(4, 0)$ **11.** $(-5, -5)$ **12.** $(-4, -1)$

13. $(\frac{1}{2}, 2)$ **14.** $(3, \frac{1}{4})$ **15.** $(5, -2)$ **16.** $(0, 4)$

Name _____

Class _____

Date _____

Answers

17. _____   18. _____

19. _____   20. _____

21. _____   22. _____

23. _____   24. _____

25. _____   26. _____

27. _____   28. _____

Odd-Numbered Answers

Even-Numbered Answers

Give the coordinates of each of the following points.

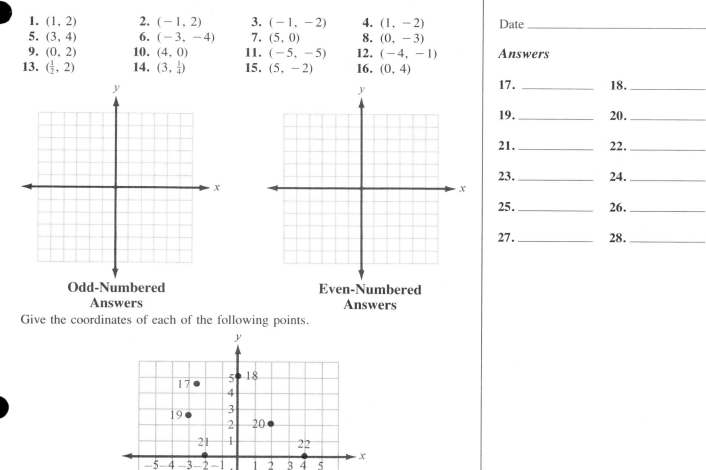

Graph each of the following linear equations by first finding the intercepts.

29. $2x - 3y = 6$ **30.** $3x - 2y = 6$

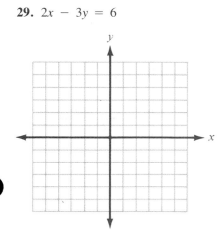
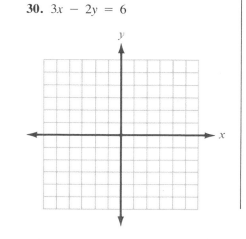

31. $y + 2x = 4$

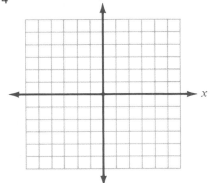

32. $y - 2x = 4$

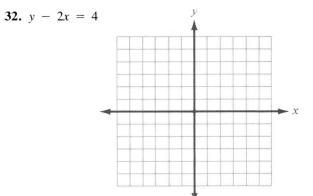

33. $4x - 5y = 20$

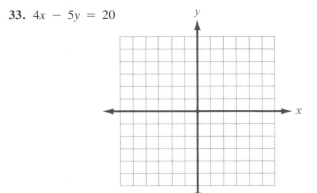

34. $4x + 5y = 20$

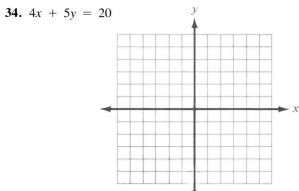

35. $3x + 5y = 15$

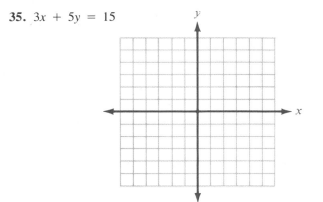

36. $5x - 3y = 15$

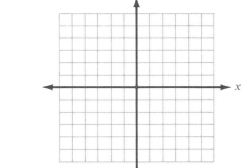

37. $y = 2x + 3$

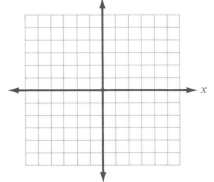

38. $y = 3x - 2$

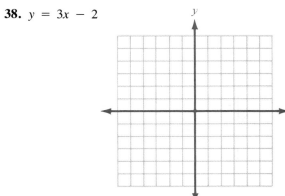

Name _____ Class _____ Date _____

Graph each of the following straight lines.

39. $2y = 4x - 8$

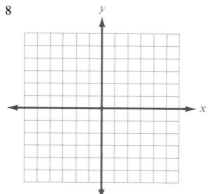

40. $2y = 4x + 8$

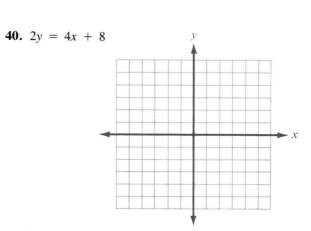

41. $2x - y = 3$

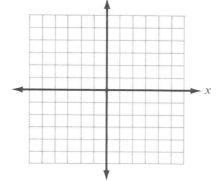

42. $3x - y = 2$

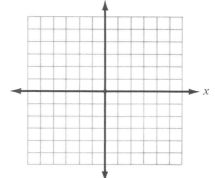

43. $y = \frac{1}{2}x + 1$

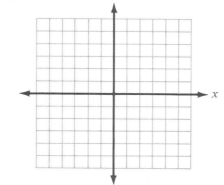

44. $y = \frac{1}{3}x + 1$

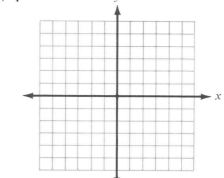

45. Graph the lines $x = -3$ and $y = 5$ on the same coordinate system.

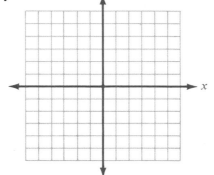

46. Graph the lines $x = 4$ and $y = -3$ on the same coordinate system.

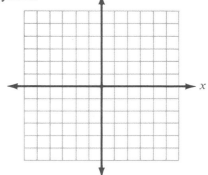

47. Complete the following ordered pairs so they are solutions to $y = |x + 2|$. Then graph the equation by connecting the points in the way that makes the most sense to you.

$$(-5, \quad) \quad (-4, \quad) \quad (-3, \quad) \quad (-2, \quad) \quad (-1, \quad) \quad (0, \quad) \quad (1, \quad)$$

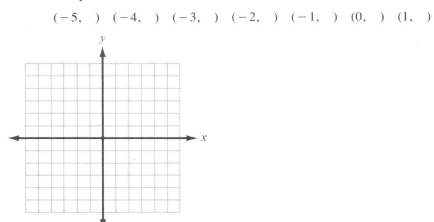

48. Complete the following ordered pairs so they are solutions to $y = |x - 2|$. Then use these points to graph $y = |x - 2|$.

$$(-1, \quad) \quad (0, \quad) \quad (1, \quad) \quad (2, \quad) \quad (3, \quad) \quad (4, \quad) \quad (5, \quad)$$

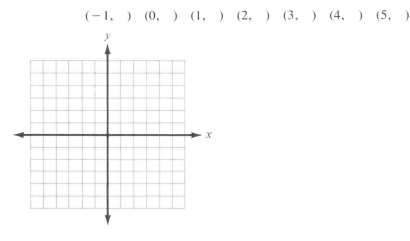

Review Problems The following problems review material we covered in Section 4.6.

Solve each equation.

49. $\dfrac{a + 8}{5} = \dfrac{5}{4}$

50. $\dfrac{a - 5}{2} = -4$

51. $\dfrac{8}{x + 2} = -\dfrac{8}{3}$

52. $\dfrac{-11}{x - 4} = -\dfrac{7}{3}$

53. $\dfrac{y^2 - 6y}{4} = -2$

54. $\dfrac{y^2 - y}{6} = 1$

Section 7.2   The Slope of a Line

In defining the slope of a straight line, we are looking for a number to associate with a straight line that does two things. First of all, we want the slope of a line to measure the "steepness" of the line. That is, in comparing two lines, the slope of the steeper line should have the larger numerical value. Secondly, we want a line that *rises* going from left to right to have a *positive* slope. We want a line that *falls* going from left to right to have a *negative* slope. (A line that neither rises nor falls going from left to right must, therefore, have 0 slope.)

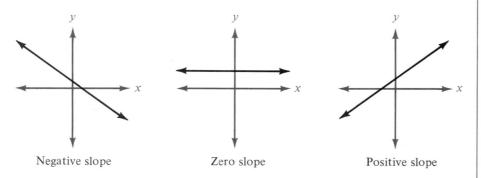

Negative slope   Zero slope   Positive slope

Geometrically, we can define the *slope* of a line as the ratio of the vertical change to the horizontal change encountered when moving from one point to another on the line. The vertical change is sometimes called the *rise*. The horizontal change is called the *run*.

▼   **Example 1**   Find the slope of the line $y = 2x - 3$.

Solution   In order to use our geometric definition, we first graph $y = 2x - 3$. We then pick any two convenient points and find the ratio of rise to run. By convenient points we mean points with integer coordinates. If we let $x = 2$ in the equation, then $y = 1$. Likewise if we let $x = 4$, then y is 5.

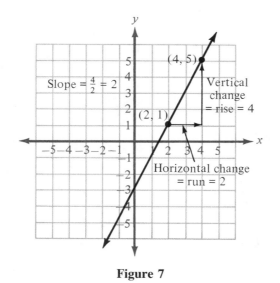

Figure 7

Our line has a slope of 2.   ▲

Practice Problems

1.   Graph the line $y = 3x - 5$ and then find the slope.

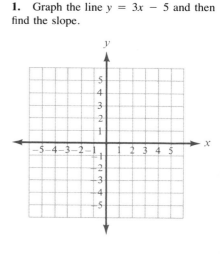

Answer
1. 3

Notice that we can measure the vertical change by subtracting the y-coordinates of the two points shown: $5 - 1 = 4$. The horizontal change is the difference of the x-coordinates: $4 - 2 = 2$. This gives us a second way of defining the slope of a line. Algebraically, we say the slope of a line between two points whose coordinates are given is the ratio of the difference in the y-coordinates to the difference in the x-coordinates. We can summarize the preceding discussion by formalizing our definition for slope.

DEFINITION The slope of the line between two points (x_1, y_1) and (x_2, y_2) is given by

$$\text{Slope} = m = \frac{\text{rise}}{\text{run}} = \frac{y_2 - y_1}{x_2 - x_1}$$

The letter m is usually used to designate slope. Our definition includes both the geometric form (rise/run) and the algebraic form $(y_2 - y_1)/(x_2 - x_1)$.

2. Find the slope of the line through $(3, 4)$ and $(1, -2)$.

▼ **Example 2** Find the slope of the line through $(-2, -3)$ and $(-5, 1)$.

Solution

$$m = \frac{y_2 - y_1}{x_2 - x_1} = \frac{1 - (-3)}{-5 - (-2)} = \frac{4}{-3} = -\frac{4}{3}$$

Looking at the graph of the line between the two points, we can see our geometric approach does not conflict with our algebraic approach.

Note: The two most common mistakes students make when first working with the formula for the slope of a line are

1. Putting the difference of the x-coordinates over the difference of the y-coordinates.
2. Subtracting in one order in the numerator and then subtracting in the opposite order in the denominator. You would make this mistake in Example 2 if you wrote $1 - (-3)$ in the numerator and then $-2 - (-5)$ in the denominator.

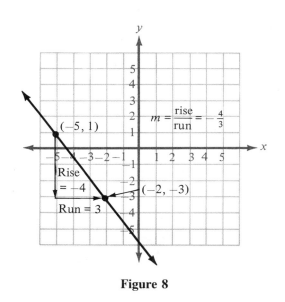

Figure 8

We should note here that it does not matter which ordered pair we call (x_1, y_1) and which we call (x_2, y_2). If we were to reverse the order of subtraction of both the x- and y-coordinates in the preceding example, we would have

$$m = \frac{-3 - 1}{-2 - (-5)} = \frac{-4}{3} = -\frac{4}{3}$$

which is the same as our previous result. ▲

Answer
2. 3

▼ **Example 3** Find the slope of the line containing $(3, -1)$ and $(3, 4)$.

Solution Using the definition for slope, we have

$$m = \frac{-1 - 4}{3 - 3} = \frac{-5}{0}$$

The expression $-5/0$ is undefined. That is, there is no real number to associate with it. In this case, we say the line has *no slope*.
The graph of our line is as follows:

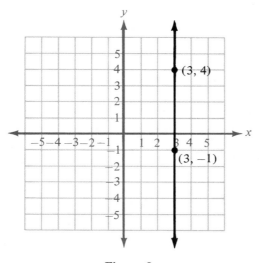

Figure 9

Our line with no slope is a vertical line. All vertical lines have no slope. (And all horizontal lines, as we mentioned earlier, have 0 slope.) ▲

Slope of Parallel and Perpendicular Lines

In geometry we call lines in the same plane that never intersect parallel. In order for two lines to be nonintersecting, they must rise or fall at the same rate. That is, the ratio of vertical change to horizontal change must be the same for each line. In other words, two lines are *parallel* if and only if they have the *same slope*.

Although it is not as obvious, it is also true that two nonvertical lines are *perpendicular* if and only if the *product of their slopes is* -1. This is the same as saying their slopes are negative reciprocals.

We can state these facts with symbols as follows.

If line l_1 has slope m_1, and line l_2 has slope m_2, then

$$l_1 \text{ and } l_2 \text{ are parallel} \Leftrightarrow m_1 = m_2$$

and

$$l_1 \text{ and } l_2 \text{ are perpendicular} \Leftrightarrow m_1 \cdot m_2 = -1$$

$$\left(\text{or } m_1 = \frac{-1}{m_2} \right)$$

To clarify this, if a line has a slope of $\frac{2}{3}$, then any line parallel to it has a slope of $\frac{2}{3}$. Any line perpendicular to it has a slope of $-\frac{3}{2}$ (the negative reciprocal of $\frac{2}{3}$).

3. Find the slope of the line through $(2, -3)$ and $(-1, -3)$.

Answer
3. 0

Although we cannot give a formal proof of the relationship between the slopes of perpendicular lines at this level of mathematics, we can offer some justification for the relationship. Figure 10 shows the graphs of two lines. One of the lines has a slope of $\frac{2}{3}$, while the other line has a slope of $-\frac{3}{2}$. As you can see, the lines are perpendicular. If you need more justification for the relationship, then you should draw some other pairs of lines with slopes that are negative reciprocals. For instance, graph a line with a slope of 2 and another line with a slope of $-\frac{1}{2}$ on the same coordinate system.

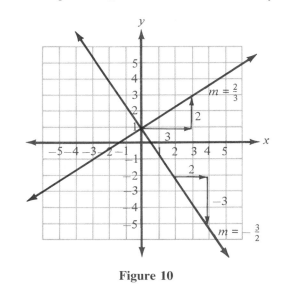

Figure 10

4. Find a if the line through $(-2, a)$ and $(2, 3)$ is parallel to a line with slope $\frac{3}{2}$.

Note: We could also have written our equation as

$$\frac{-8 - a}{-2 - 3} = \frac{5}{4}$$

and obtained the same result. Remember, it doesn't matter which point we call (x_1, y_1) and which point we call (x_2, y_2) when using the slope formula.

▼ **Example 4** Find a if the line through $(3, a)$ and $(-2, -8)$ is perpendicular to a line with slope $-\frac{4}{5}$.

Solution The slope of the line through the two points is

$$m = \frac{a - (-8)}{3 - (-2)} = \frac{a + 8}{5}$$

Since the line through the two points is perpendicular to a line with slope $-\frac{4}{5}$, we can also write its slope as $\frac{5}{4}$.

$$\frac{a + 8}{5} = \frac{5}{4}$$

Multiplying both sides by 20, we have

$$4(a + 8) = 5 \cdot 5$$
$$4a + 32 = 25$$
$$4a = -7$$
$$a = -\tfrac{7}{4}$$ ▲

Answer
4. -3

Problem Set 7.2

Find the slope of each of the following lines from the given graph.

Name _____

Class _____

Date _____

Answers

1. _____   2. _____

3. _____   4. _____

5. _____   6. _____

1.

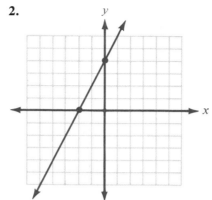

2.

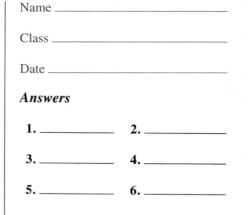

3.

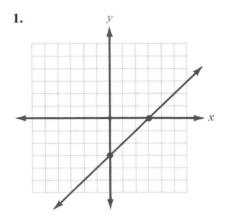

4.

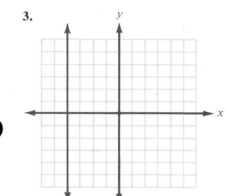

5.

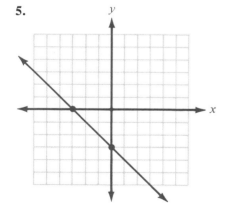

6.

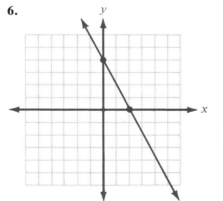

Answers

7. _____   8. _____

9. _____   10. _____

11. _____   12. _____

13. _____   14. _____

15. _____   16. _____

17. _____   18. _____

19. _____   20. _____

21. _____   22. _____

23. _____   24. _____

25. _____   26. _____

Find the slope of the line through the following pairs of points.

7. $(4, 1), (2, 5)$ **8.** $(7, 3), (2, -2)$ **9.** $(5, -1), (4, 3)$

10. $(2, -3), (5, 6)$ **11.** $(1, -2), (3, -5)$ **12.** $(4, -1), (5, -3)$

13. $(1, 7), (1, 2)$ **14.** $(-3, -4), (-3, -1)$ **15.** $(5, 4), (-1, 4)$

16. $(2, -1), (6, -1)$ **17.** $(\frac{1}{2}, 3), (\frac{2}{3}, -\frac{1}{4})$ **18.** $(\frac{3}{4}, \frac{5}{6}), (-\frac{1}{2}, \frac{1}{3})$

Solve for the indicated variable if the line through the two given points has the given slope.

19. $(5, a), (4, 2); m = 3$ **20.** $(3, a), (1, 5); m = -4$

21. $(2, 6), (3, y); m = -7$ **22.** $(-4, 9), (-5, y); m = 3$

23. $(-2, -3), (x, 5); m = -\frac{8}{3}$ **24.** $(4, 9), (x, -2); m = -\frac{7}{3}$

25. $(x, 1), (8, 9); m = \frac{1}{2}$ **26.** $(x, 4), (1, -3); m = \frac{2}{3}$

27. Find the slope of any line parallel to the line through $(\sqrt{2}, 3)$ and $(-\sqrt{8}, 1)$.

Answers

28. Find the slope of any line parallel to the line through $(2, \sqrt{27})$ and $(5, -\sqrt{3})$.

27. _____

28. _____

29. _____

30. _____

31. _____

29. Line l contains the points $(5\sqrt{2}, -6)$ and $(\sqrt{50}, 2)$. Give the slope of any line perpendicular to l.

32. _____

30. Line l contains points $(3\sqrt{6}, 4)$ and $(-3\sqrt{24}, 1)$. Give the slope of any line perpendicular to l.

31. Line l has a slope of $\frac{2}{3}$. A horizontal change of 12 will always be accompanied by how much of a vertical change?

32. For any line with slope $\frac{4}{5}$, a vertical change of 8 is always accompanied by how much of a horizontal change?

Answers

33. _____

34. _____

35. _____

36. _____

37. _____ 38. _____

39. _____ 40. _____

41. _____ 42. _____

33. The line through $(2, y^2)$ and $(1, y)$ is perpendicular to a line with slope $-\frac{1}{6}$. What are the possible values for y?

34. The line through $(7, y^2)$ and $(3, 6y)$ is parallel to a line with slope -2. What are the possible values for y?

35. A pile of sand at a construction site is in the shape of a cone. If the slope of the side of the pile is $\frac{2}{3}$ and the pile is 8 feet high, how wide is the diameter of the base of the pile?

36. The slope of the sides of one of the Great Pyramids in Egypt is 13/10. If the base of the pyramid is 750 feet, how tall is the pyramid?

Review Problems   The following problems review material we covered in Section 2.6. Reviewing these problems will help you with some parts of the next section.

Solve each formula for y.

37. $3x - 2y = 6$

38. $2x + 3y = 6$

39. $2x + 3y = 5$

40. $3x + 2y = 5$

41. $y + 2 = 5(x - 3)$

42. $y - 4 = 2(x + 3)$

Section 7.3   The Equation of a Straight Line

In the first section of this chapter we defined the y-intercept of a line to be the y-coordinate of the point where the graph crosses the y-axis. We can use this definition, along with the definition of slope from the preceding section, to derive the slope-intercept form of the equation of a straight line.

Suppose line l has slope m and y-intercept b. What is the equation of l?

Since the y-intercept is b, we know the point $(0, b)$ is on the line. If (x, y) is any other point on l, then using the definition for slope, we have

$$\frac{y - b}{x - 0} = m \qquad \text{Definition of slope}$$

$$y - b = mx \qquad \text{Multiply both sides by } x$$

$$y = mx + b \qquad \text{Add } b \text{ to both sides}$$

This last equation is known as the *slope-intercept form* of the equation of a straight line.

Slope-Intercept Form of the Equation of a Line

The equation of any line with slope m and y-intercept b is given by

$$y = mx + b$$

$$\qquad \nearrow \qquad \uparrow$$

Slope y-intercept

This form of the equation of a straight line is very useful. When the equation is in this form, the *slope* of the line is always the *coefficient of x*, and the *y-intercept* is always the *constant term*.

▼ **Example 1** Write the equation of the line with slope -2 and y-intercept 3.

   Solution   Since $m = -2$ and $b = 3$, we have

$$y = mx + b$$
$$\text{or} \quad y = -2x + 3$$

It is just as easy as it seems. The equation of the line with slope -2 and y-intercept 3 is $y = -2x + 3$.   ▲

▼ **Example 2** Give the slope and y-intercept for the line $2x - 3y = 5$.

   Solution   To use the slope-intercept form we must solve the equation for y in terms of x:

$$2x - 3y = 5$$
$$-3y = -2x + 5 \qquad \text{Add } -2x \text{ to both sides}$$
$$y = \tfrac{2}{3}x - \tfrac{5}{3} \qquad \text{Divide by } -3$$

The last equation has the form $y = mx + b$. The slope must be $m = \tfrac{2}{3}$, and the y-intercept is $b = -\tfrac{5}{3}$.   ▲

Practice Problems

1. Write the equation of the line with slope 5 and y-intercept -1.

2. Give the slope and y-intercept for the line $4x - 5y = 7$.

Answers
1. $y = 5x - 1$ **2.** $m = \tfrac{4}{5}, b = -\tfrac{7}{5}$

3. Graph the line $-3x + 2y = -6$ on the following coordinate system. Use the method shown in Example 3.

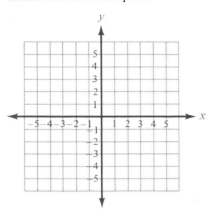

▼ **Example 3** Graph the equation $2x + 3y = 6$ using the slope and y-intercept.

Solution Although we could graph this equation using the methods developed in Section 7.1 (by finding ordered pairs that are solutions to the equation and drawing a line through their graphs), it is sometimes easier to graph a line using the slope-intercept form of the equation.

Solving the equation for y, we have

$$2x + 3y = 6$$
$$3y = -2x + 6 \qquad \text{Add } -2x \text{ to both sides}$$
$$y = -\tfrac{2}{3}x + 2 \qquad \text{Divide by 3}$$

The slope is $m = -\tfrac{2}{3}$ and the y-intercept is $b = 2$. Therefore, the point $(0, 2)$ is on the graph and the ratio rise/run going from $(0, 2)$ to any other point on the line is $-\tfrac{2}{3}$. If we start at $(0, 2)$ and move 2 units up (that's a rise of 2) and 3 units to the left (a run of -3), we will be at another point on the graph. (We could also go down 2 units and right 3 units and also be assured of ending up at another point on the line, since $2/-3$ is the same as $-2/3$.)

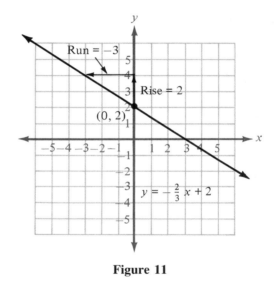

Figure 11 ▲

A second useful form of the equation of a straight line is the point-slope form.

Let line l contain the point (x_1, y_1) and have slope m. If (x, y) is any other point on l, then by the definition of slope we have

$$\frac{y - y_1}{x - x_1} = m$$

Multiplying both sides by $(x - x_1)$ gives us

$$(x - x_1) \cdot \frac{y - y_1}{x - x_1} = m(x - x_1)$$
$$y - y_1 = m(x - x_1)$$

This last equation is known as the *point-slope form* of the equation of a straight line.

Answers
3. See Solutions Section.

> **Point-Slope Form of the Equation of a Line**
>
> The equation of the line through (x_1, y_1) with slope m is given by
>
> $$y - y_1 = m(x - x_1)$$

This form of the equation of a straight line is used to find the equation of a line, given either one point on the line and the slope, or given two points on the line.

▼ **Example 4** Find the equation of the line with slope -2 that contains the point $(-4, 3)$. Write the answer in slope-intercept form.

Solution

Using $(x_1, y_1) = (-4, 3)$ and $m = -2$

$\quad$ in $\quad y - y_1 = m(x - x_1)$ $\qquad$ Point-slope form

gives us $\quad y - 3 = -2(x + 4)$ $\qquad$ Note: $x - (-4) = x + 4$

$\qquad\qquad y - 3 = -2x - 8$ $\qquad$ Multiply out right side

$\qquad\qquad\quad y = -2x - 5$ $\qquad$ Add 3 to each side

Figure 12 is the graph of the line that contains $(-4, 3)$ and has a slope of -2. Notice that the y-intercept on the graph matches that of the equation we found.

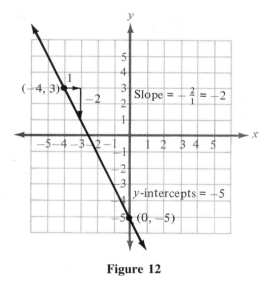

Slope $= -\frac{2}{1} = -2$

y-intercepts $= -5$

$(0, -5)$

Figure 12 $\qquad\qquad$ ▲

▼ **Example 5** Find the equation of the line that passes through the points $(-3, 3)$ and $(3, -1)$.

Solution We begin by finding the slope of the line

$$m = \frac{3 - (-1)}{-3 - 3} = \frac{4}{-6} = -\frac{2}{3}$$

Using $(x_1, y_1) = (3, -1)$ and $m = -\frac{2}{3}$ in $y - y_1 = m(x - x_1)$ yields

$y + 1 = -\frac{2}{3}(x - 3)$

$y + 1 = -\frac{2}{3}x + 2$ $\qquad$ Multiply out right side

$\quad\;\; y = -\frac{2}{3}x + 1$ $\qquad$ Add -1 to each side

4. Find the equation of the line with slope 3 that contains the point $(-1, 2)$.

5. Find the equation of the line through $(2, 5)$ and $(6, -3)$.

Answers

4. $y = 3x + 5$ $\quad$ **5.** $y = -2x + 9$

Note: We could have used the point $(-3, 3)$ instead of $(3, -1)$ and obtained the same equation. That is, using $(x_1, y_1) = (-3, 3)$ and $m = -\frac{2}{3}$ in $y - y_1 = m(x - x_1)$ gives us

$$y - 3 = -\tfrac{2}{3}(x + 3)$$
$$y - 3 = -\tfrac{2}{3}x - 2$$
$$y = -\tfrac{2}{3}x + 1$$

which is the same result we obtained using $(3, -1)$.

Figure 13 shows the graph of the line that passes through the points $(-3, 3)$ and $(3, -1)$. As you can see, the slope and y-intercept are $-\frac{2}{3}$ and 1, respectively.

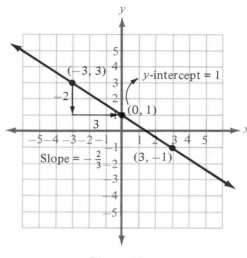

Figure 13 ▲

6. Find the equation of the line through $(3, 2)$ that is perpendicular to the graph of $3x - y = 2$.

▼ **Example 6** Give the equation of the line through $(-1, 4)$ whose graph is perpendicular to the graph of $2x - y = -3$.

Solution To find the slope of $2x - y = -3$, we solve for y:

$$2x - y = -3$$
$$y = 2x + 3$$

The slope of this line is 2. The line we are interested in is perpendicular to the line with slope 2 and must, therefore, have a slope of $-\frac{1}{2}$. Using $(x_1, y_1) = (-1, 4)$ and $m = -\frac{1}{2}$, we have

$$
\begin{aligned}
y - y_1 &= m(x - x_1) \\
y - 4 &= -\tfrac{1}{2}(x + 1) \\
y - 4 &= -\tfrac{1}{2}x - \tfrac{1}{2} && \text{Multiply out right side} \\
y &= -\tfrac{1}{2}x - \tfrac{1}{2} + 4 && \text{Add 4 to each side} \\
y &= -\tfrac{1}{2}x + \tfrac{7}{2} && -\tfrac{1}{2} + 4 = -\tfrac{1}{2} + \tfrac{8}{2} = \tfrac{7}{2}
\end{aligned}
$$

Note: Finally, we should mention again that all horizontal lines have equations of the form $y = b$ and slopes of 0. Vertical lines have no slope and have equations of the form $x = a$. These two special cases do not lend themselves well to either the slope-intercept form or the point-slope form of the equation of a line.

Our answer is in slope-intercept form. If we were to write it in standard form, we would have

$$x + 2y = 7$$ ▲

Answer

6. $y = -\dfrac{1}{3}x + 3$

Problem Set 7.3

Name _____

Class _____

Date _____

Give the equation of the line with the following slope and y-intercept.

1. $m = 2$, $b = 3$

2. $m = -4$, $b = 2$

3. $m = 1$, $b = -5$

4. $m = -5$, $b = -3$

5. $m = \frac{1}{2}$, $b = \frac{3}{2}$

6. $m = \frac{2}{3}$, $b = \frac{5}{6}$

7. $m = 0$, $b = 4$

8. $m = 0$, $b = -2$

Give the slope and y-intercept for each of the following equations. Sketch the graph using the slope and y-intercept. Give the slope of any line perpendicular to the given line.

Answers

1. _____   2. _____

3. _____   4. _____

5. _____   6. _____

7. _____   8. _____

9. $y = 3x - 2$

10. $y = 2x + 3$

11. $2x - 3y = 12$

12. $3x - 2y = 12$

13. $4x + 5y = 20$

14. $5x - 4y = 20$

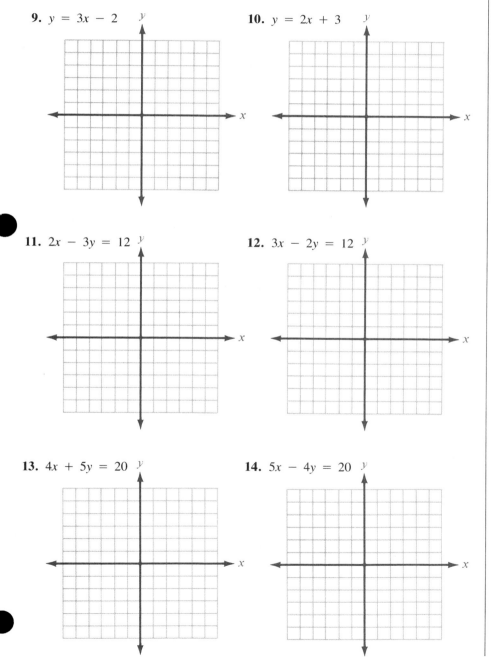

Answers

15. _____   16. _____

17. _____   18. _____

19. _____   20. _____

21. _____   22. _____

23. _____   24. _____

25. _____   26. _____

27. _____   28. _____

29. _____   30. _____

Find the equation of the line that contains the given point and has the given slope.

15. $(1,3)$; $m = 2$ **16.** $(3, -2)$; $m = 4$

17. $(5, -1)$; $m = -3$ **18.** $(6, -4)$; $m = -2$

19. $(-2, 3)$; $m = -\frac{1}{2}$ **20.** $(-1, -1)$; $m = \frac{1}{4}$

21. $(\frac{1}{2}, -\frac{3}{2})$; $m = \frac{2}{3}$ **22.** $(\frac{2}{3}, -\frac{3}{4})$; $m = -\frac{3}{2}$

Find the equation of the line that contains the given pair of points.

23. $(2, 3), (1, 5)$ **24.** $(4, 6), (2, -2)$

25. $(3, -2), (1, 5)$ **26.** $(-4, 1), (-2, 4)$

27. $(0, 5), (-3, 0)$ **28.** $(0, -7), (4, 0)$

29. $(3, 5), (-2, 5)$ **30.** $(-8, 2), (4, 2)$

31. Give the slope and y-intercept, and sketch the graph, of $y = -2$.

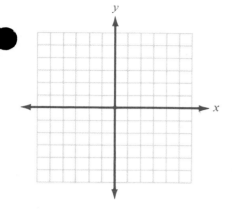

Name _____

Class _____

Date _____

Answers

33. _____

34. _____

35. _____

36. _____

32. For the line $x = -3$ sketch the graph, give the slope, and name any intercepts.

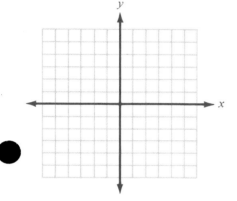

33. Find the equation of the line parallel to the graph of $3x - y = 5$ that contains the point $(-1, 4)$.

34. Find the equation of the line parallel to the graph of $2x - 4y = 5$ that contains the point $(0, 3)$.

35. Line l is perpendicular to the graph of $2x - 5y = 10$ and contains the point $(-4, -3)$. Find the equation for l.

36. Line l is perpendicular to the graph of $-3x - 5y = 2$ and contains the point $(2, -6)$. Find the equation for l.

Answers

37. _____

38. _____

39. _____

40. _____

41. _____

42 _____

43. _____

44. _____

45. _____

46. _____

37. Give the equation of the line perpendicular to $y = -4x + 2$ that has an x-intercept of -1.

38. Write the equation of the line parallel to the graph of $7x - 2y = 14$ that has an x-intercept of 5.

39. Give the equation of the line with x-intercept 3 and y-intercept -2.

40. Give the equation of the line with x-intercept $\frac{1}{2}$ and y-intercept $-\frac{1}{4}$.

Review Problems   The following problems review material we covered in Section 5.4.

Multiply.

41. $(\sqrt{x} - 3)(\sqrt{x} + 5)$ **42.** $(\sqrt{x} - 2)(\sqrt{x} - 3)$

43. $(\sqrt{5} - 2)^2$ **44.** $(\sqrt{3} + 2)^2$

Rationalize the denominator.

45. $\dfrac{\sqrt{x}}{\sqrt{x} + 2}$ **46.** $\dfrac{\sqrt{x}}{\sqrt{x} - 3}$

Section 7.4   Linear Inequalities in Two Variables

● A linear inequality in two variables is any expression that can be put in the form

$$ax + by < c$$

where a, b, and c are real numbers (a and b not both 0). The inequality symbol can be any one of the following four: $<, \leq, >, \geq$.
  Some examples of linear inequalities are

$$2x + 3y < 6 \qquad y \geq 2x + 1 \qquad x - y \leq 0$$

Although not all of these examples have the form $ax + by < c$, each one can be put in that form.
  The solution set for a linear inequality is a section of the coordinate plane. The boundary for the section is found by replacing the inequality symbol with an equal sign and graphing the resulting equation. The boundary is included in the solution set (and represented with a solid line) if the inequality symbol used originally is $\leq$ or $\geq$. The boundary is not included (and is represented with a dotted line) if the original symbol is $<$ or $>$.
  Let's look at some examples.

▼   **Example 1**   Graph the solution set for $x + y \leq 4$.

● **Solution**   The boundary for the graph is the graph of $x + y = 4$; the x- and y-intercepts are both 4. (Remember, the x-intercept is found by letting $y = 0$, and the y-intercept by letting $x = 0$.) The boundary is included in the solution set because the inequality symbol is $\leq$.
  Here is the graph of the boundary:

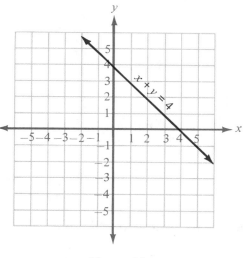

Figure 14

● The boundary separates the coordinate plane into two sections or regions—the region above the boundary and the region below the boundary. The solution set for $x + y \leq 4$ is one of these two regions along with the boundary. To find the correct region, we simply choose any convenient point that is *not* on the boundary. We then substitute

Practice Problems

1.   Graph the solution set for $x - y \geq 3$. Follow Example 1 carefully. First graph the boundary. Then shade in the correct region after testing a point not on the boundary.

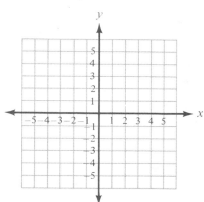

Answers
1. See Solutions Section for all answers.

the coordinates of the point into the original inequality $x + y \leq 4$. If the point we choose satisfies the inequality, then it is a member of the solution set, and we can assume that all points on the same side of the boundary as the chosen point are also in the solution set. If the coordinates of our point do not satisfy the original inequality, then the solution set lies on the other side of the boundary.

In this example, a convenient point that is not on the boundary is the origin.

$$\begin{aligned}
\text{Substituting} \quad & (0, 0) \\
\text{into} \quad & x + y \leq 4 \\
\text{gives us} \quad & 0 + 0 \leq 4 \\
& 0 \leq 4 \qquad \text{A true statement}
\end{aligned}$$

Since the origin is a solution to the inequality $x + y \leq 4$, and the origin is below the boundary, all other points below the boundary are also solutions.

Here is the graph of $x + y \leq 4$:

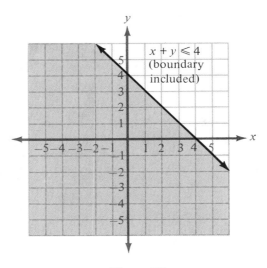

Figure 15

The region above the boundary is described by the inequality $x + y > 4$. ▲

Here is a list of steps to follow when graphing the solution set for linear inequalities in two variables.

To Graph a Linear Inequality in Two Variables

Step 1: Replace the inequality symbol with an equal sign. The resulting equation represents the boundary for the solution set.

Step 2: Graph the boundary found in step 1 using a *solid line* if the boundary is included in the solution set (that is, if the original inequality symbol was either $\leq$ or $\geq$). Use a *broken line* to graph the boundary if it is *not* included in the solution set. (It is not included if the original inequality was either $<$ or $>$.)

Step 3:   Choose any convenient point not on the boundary and substitute the coordinates into the *original* inequality. If the
resulting statement is *true*, the graph lies on the *same* side
of the boundary as the chosen point. If the resulting statement is *false*, the solution set lies on the *opposite* side of the
boundary.

▼   **Example 2**   Graph the solution set for $y < 2x - 3$.

Solution   The boundary is the graph of $y = 2x - 3$: a line with slope
2 and y-intercept -3. The boundary is not included since the original
inequality symbol is $<$. Therefore, we use a broken line to represent the
boundary.

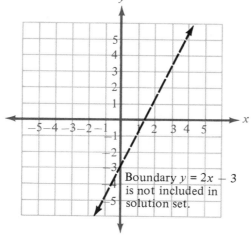

Figure 16

A convenient test point is again the origin:

$$\begin{aligned}
\text{Using} \quad & (0, 0) \\
\text{in} \quad & y < 2x - 3 \\
\text{we have} \quad & 0 < 2(0) - 3 \\
& 0 < -3 \qquad \text{A false statement}
\end{aligned}$$

Since our test point gives us a false statement and it lies above the
boundary, the solution set must lie on the other side of the boundary.

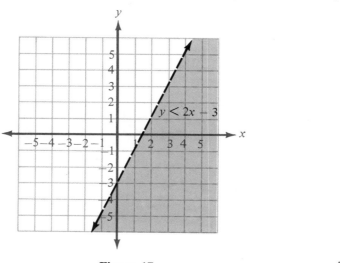

Figure 17   ▲

2.   Graph the solution set for

$$y < \frac{1}{2}x + 3$$

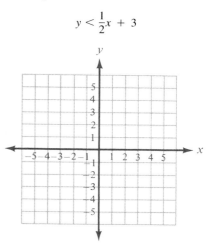

3. Graph $y > -2$.

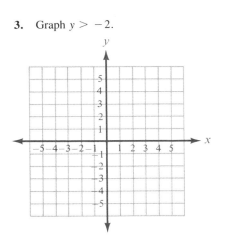

▼ **Example 3** Graph the solution set for $x \leq 5$.

Solution The boundary is $x = 5$, which is a vertical line. All points to the left have x-coordinates less than 5 and all points to the right have x-coordinates greater than 5.

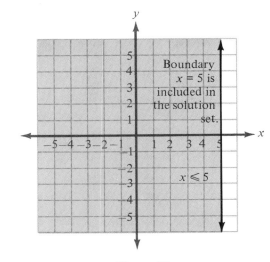

Boundary $x = 5$ is included in the solution set.

$x \leq 5$

Figure 18   ▲

Name _____ Class _____ Date _____

Problem Set 7.4

 Graph the solution set for each of the following.

1. $x + y < 5$

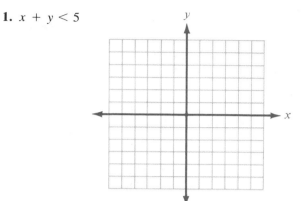

2. $x + y \leq 5$

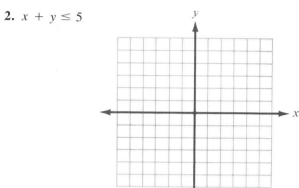

3. $x - y \geq -3$

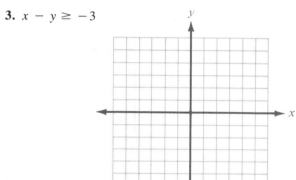

4. $x - y > -3$

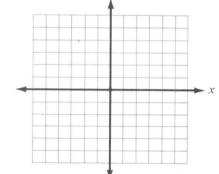

5. $2x + 3y < 6$

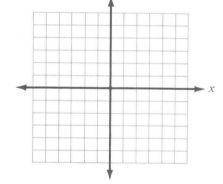

6. $2x - 3y > -6$

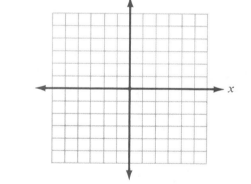

7. $x - 2y < 4$

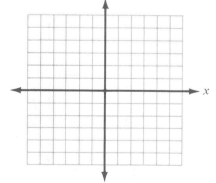

8. $x + 2y > -4$

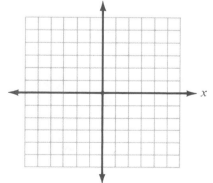

9. $2x + y < 5$

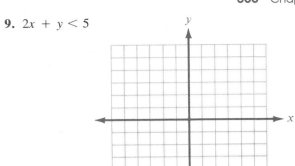

10. $2x + y < -5$

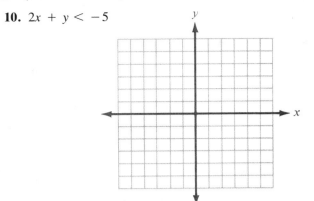

11. $3x + 5y > 7$

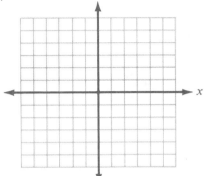

12. $3x - 5y > 7$

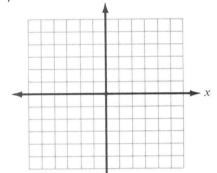

13. $y < 2x - 1$

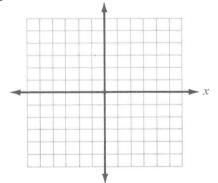

14. $y \geq 2x - 1$

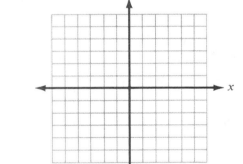

15. $y \geq -3x - 4$

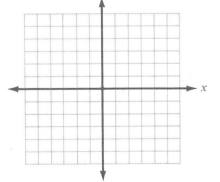

16. $y < -3x + 4$

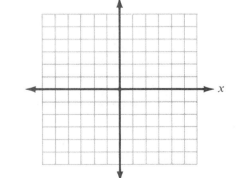

Name _____ Class _____ Date _____

17. $x > 3$

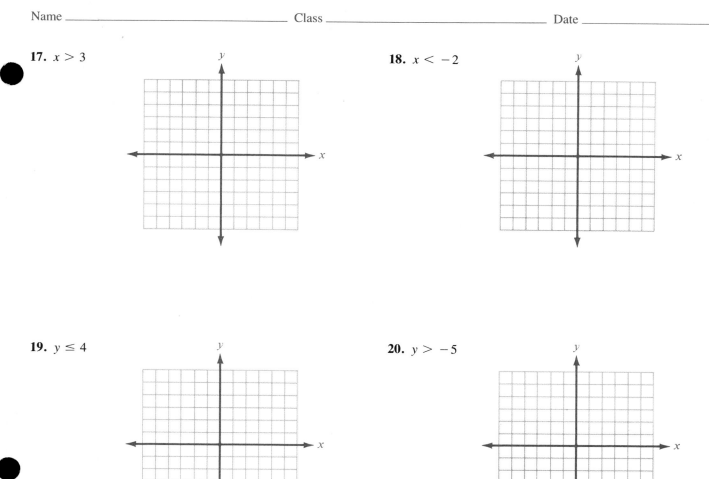

18. $x < -2$

19. $y \leq 4$

20. $y > -5$

21. Graph the inequality $y \leq |x|$ by first graphing the boundary $y = |x|$ using $x = -3, -2, -1, 0, 1, 2,$ and 3.

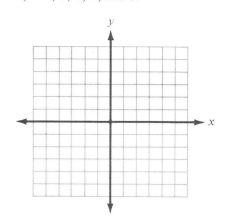

22. Graph the inequality $y > |x|$.

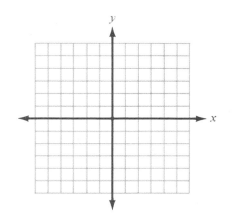

Answers

23. _____ 24. _____

25. _____ 26. _____

27. _____ 28. _____

29. _____ 30. _____

Review Problems   The following problems review material we covered in Sections 5.5 and 6.1.

Solve each equation.

23. $\sqrt{3x + 4} = 5$

24. $\sqrt{3x + 1} = -4$

25. $\sqrt{2x - 1} - 3 = 2$

26. $\sqrt{3x + 6} + 2 = 5$

27. $\sqrt{x + 15} = x + 3$

28. $\sqrt{x + 3} = x - 3$

29. $\sqrt{2x + 9} = x + 5$

30. $\sqrt{2x + 13} = x + 7$

Section 7.5 Variation

There are two main types of variation—direct variation and inverse variation. Variation problems are most common in the sciences, particularly in chemistry and physics.

Direct Variation

We say the variable y varies *directly* with the variable x if y increases as x increases (which is the same as saying y decreases as x decreases). A change in one variable produces a corresponding and similar change in the other variable. Algebraically, the relationship is written $y = Kx$ where K is a nonzero constant called the *constant of variation* (proportionality constant).

Another way of saying y varies directly with x is to say y is *directly proportional* to x.

Study the following list. It gives the mathematical equivalent of some direct-variation statements.

English phrase	Algebraic equation
y varies directly with x	$y = Kx$
s varies directly with the square of t	$s = Kt^2$
y is directly proportional to the cube of z	$y = Kz^3$
u is directly proportional to the square root of v	$u = K\sqrt{v}$

▼ **Example 1** y varies directly with x. If y is 15 when x is 5, find y when x is 7.

Solution The first sentence gives us the general relationship between x and y. The equation equivalent to the statement "y varies directly with x" is

$$y = Kx$$

The first part of the second sentence in our example gives us the information necessary to evaluate the constant K:

$$
\begin{aligned}
\text{When} \quad & y = 15 \\
\text{and} \quad & x = 5 \\
\text{the equation} \quad & y = Kx \\
\text{becomes} \quad & 15 = K \cdot 5 \\
\text{or} \quad & K = 3
\end{aligned}
$$

The equation can now be written specifically as

$$y = 3x$$

Letting $x = 7$, we have

$$
\begin{aligned}
y &= 3 \cdot 7 \\
y &= 21
\end{aligned}
$$
▲

▼ **Example 2** The distance a body falls from rest toward the earth is directly proportional to the square of the time it has been falling. If a body falls 64 feet in 2 seconds, how far will it fall in 3.5 seconds?

Practice Problems

1. y varies directly with x. If y is 24 when x is 8, find y when x is 2.

2. Use the information in Example 2 to find how far it will fall in 4 seconds.

Answers
1. 6 **2.** 256 ft

Solution   We will let d = distance and t = time. Since distance is directly proportional to the square of time, we have

$$d = Kt^2$$

Next we evaluate the constant K:

$$
\begin{aligned}
\text{When} \quad & t = 2 \\
\text{and} \quad & d = 64 \\
\text{the equation} \quad & d = Kt^2 \\
\text{becomes} \quad & 64 = K(2)^2 \\
\text{or} \quad & 64 = 4K \\
\text{and} \quad & K = 16
\end{aligned}
$$

Specifically, then, the relationship between d and t is

$$d = 16t^2$$

Finally, we find d when $t = 3.5$:

$$
\begin{aligned}
d &= 16(3.5)^2 \\
d &= 16(12.25) \\
d &= 196 \text{ feet}
\end{aligned}
$$

▲

Note: The equation $d = 16t^2$ is a specific example of the equation used in physics to find the distance a body falls from rest during a time t. In physics, the equation is $d = \frac{1}{2}gt^2$, where g is the acceleration of gravity. On earth the acceleration of gravity is $g = 32$ ft/sec^2. The equation, then, is $d = \frac{1}{2} \cdot 32t^2$ or $d = 16t^2$.

Inverse Variation

If two variables are related so that an *increase* in one produces a proportional *decrease* in the other, then the variables are said to *vary inversely*. If y varies inversely with x, then $y = K\dfrac{1}{x}$ or $y = \dfrac{K}{x}$. We can also say y is inversely proportional to x. The constant K is again called the *constant of variation or proportionality constant*.

English phrase	Algebraic equation
y is inversely proportional to x	$y = \dfrac{K}{x}$
s varies inversely with the square of t	$s = \dfrac{K}{t^2}$
y is inversely proportional to x^4	$y = \dfrac{K}{x^4}$
z varies inversely with the cube root of t	$z = \dfrac{K}{\sqrt[3]{t}}$

3. y varies inversely with the cube of x. If y is 3 when x is 2, find y when x is 3.

▼   **Example 3** y varies inversely with the square of x. If y is 4 when x is 5, find y when x is 10.

Solution   Since y is inversely proportional to the square of x, we can write

$$y = \frac{K}{x^2}$$

Evaluating K using the information given, we have

$$
\begin{aligned}
\text{When} \quad & x = 5 \\
\text{and} \quad & y = 4 \\
\text{the equation} \quad & y = \frac{K}{x^2} \\
\text{becomes} \quad & 4 = \frac{K}{5^2}
\end{aligned}
$$

Answer
3. $\frac{8}{9}$

$$\text{or} \quad 4 = \frac{K}{25}$$
$$\text{and} \quad K = 100$$

Now we write the equation again as

$$y = \frac{100}{x^2}$$

We finish by substituting $x = 10$ into the last equation:

$$y = \frac{100}{10^2}$$
$$y = \frac{100}{100}$$
$$y = 1 \qquad \blacktriangle$$

▼ **Example 4** The volume of a gas is inversely proportional to the pressure of the gas on its container. If a pressure of 48 pounds per square inch corresponds to a volume of 50 cubic feet, what pressure is needed to produce a volume of 100 cubic feet?

Solution We can represent volume with V and pressure by P:

$$V = \frac{K}{P}$$

Using $P = 48$ and $V = 50$, we have

$$50 = \frac{K}{48}$$
$$K = 50(48)$$
$$K = 2400$$

The equation that describes the relationship between P and V is

$$V = \frac{2400}{P}$$

Substituting $V = 100$ into this last equation, we get

$$100 = \frac{2400}{P}$$
$$100P = 2400$$
$$P = \frac{2400}{100}$$
$$P = 24$$

A volume of 100 cubic feet is produced by a pressure of 24 pounds per square inch. $\qquad \blacktriangle$

Joint Variation and Other Variation Combinations

Many times relationships among different quantities are described in terms of more than two variables. If the variable y varies directly with *two* other variables, say x and z, then we say y varies *jointly* with x and z. In addition to joint variation, there are many other combinations of direct and inverse variation involving more than two variables. The following table is a list of some variation statements and their equivalent mathematical form:

4. In Example 4, what pressure is needed to produce a volume of 150 cubic feet?

Note: The relationship between pressure and volume as given in this example is known as Boyle's law and applies to situations such as those encountered in a piston-cylinder arrangement. It was Robert Boyle who, in 1662, published the results of some of his experiments that showed, among other things, that the volume of a gas decreases as the pressure increases. This is known as inverse variation.

English phrase	Algebraic equation
y varies jointly with x and z	$y = Kxz$
z varies jointly with r and the square of s	$z = Krs^2$
V is directly proportional to T and inversely proportional to P	$V = \dfrac{KT}{P}$
F varies jointly with m_1 and m_2 and inversely with the square of r	$F = \dfrac{Km_1 \cdot m_2}{r^2}$

5. y varies jointly with x and the square root of z. If y is 30 when x is 2 and z is 9, find y when x is 4 and z is 4.

▼ **Example 5** y varies jointly with x and the square of z. When x is 5 and z is 3, y is 180. Find y when x is 2 and z is 4.

Solution The general equation is given by

$$y = Kxz^2$$

Substituting $x = 5$, $z = 3$, and $y = 180$, we have

$$180 = K(5)(3)^2$$
$$180 = 45K$$
$$K = 4$$

The specific equation is

$$y = 4xz^2$$

When $x = 2$ and $z = 4$, the last equation becomes

$$y = 4(2)(4)^2$$
$$y = 128$$ ▲

6. Use the information in Example 6 to find the resistance of a 300-foot cable made of the same material which is 0.25 inch thick.

▼ **Example 6** In electricity, the resistance of a cable is directly proportional to its length and inversely proportional to the square of the diameter. If a 100-foot cable 0.5 inch in diameter has a resistance of 0.2 ohm, what will be the resistance of a cable made from the same material if it is 200 feet long with a diameter of 0.25 inch?

Solution Let R = resistance, l = length, and d = diameter. The equation is

$$R = \frac{Kl}{d^2}$$

When $R = 0.2$, $l = 100$, and $d = 0.5$, the equation becomes

$$0.2 = \frac{K(100)}{(0.5)^2}$$
$$\text{or} \quad K = 0.0005$$

Using this value of K in our original equation, the result is

$$R = \frac{0.0005l}{d^2}$$

When $l = 200$ and $d = 0.25$, the equation becomes

$$R = \frac{0.0005(200)}{(0.25)^2}$$
$$R = 1.6 \text{ ohms}$$ ▲

Answers
5. 40 **6.** 2.4 ohms

Problem Set 7.5

For the following problems, *y* varies directly with *x*.

1. If *y* is 10 when *x* is 2, find *y* when *x* is 6.

2. If *y* is 20 when *x* is 5, find *y* when *x* is 3.

3. If *y* is -32 when *x* is 4, find *x* when *y* is -40.

4. If *y* is -50 when *x* is 5, find *x* when *y* is -70.

For the following problems, *r* is inversely proportional to *s*.

5. If *r* is -3 when *s* is 4, find *r* when *s* is 2.

6. If *r* is -10 when *s* is 6, find *r* when *s* is -5.

7. If *r* is 8 when *s* is 3, find *s* when *r* is 48.

8. If *r* is 12 when *s* is 5, find *s* when *r* is 30.

Name _____

Class _____

Date _____

Answers

1. _____ 2. _____

3. _____ 4. _____

5. _____ 6. _____

7. _____ 8. _____

Answers

9. _____   10. _____

11. _____   12. _____

13. _____   14. _____

15. _____   16. _____

For the following problems, *d* varies directly with the square root of *r*.

9. If $d = 10$, when $r = 25$, find *d* when $r = 16$.

10. If $d = 12$, when $r = 36$, find *d* when $r = 49$.

11. If $d = 10\sqrt{2}$, when $r = 50$, find *d* when $r = 8$.

12. If $d = 6\sqrt{3}$, when $r = 12$, find *d* when $r = 75$.

For the following problems, *y* varies inversely with the square of *x*.

13. If $y = 45$ when $x = 3$, find *y* when *x* is 5.

14. If $y = 12$ when $x = 2$, find *y* when *x* is 6.

15. If $y = 10$ when $x = 6$, find *x* when *y* is 20.

16. If $y = 13$ when $x = 4$, find *x* when *y* is 30.

For the following problems, z varies jointly with x and the square of y.

17. If z is 54 when x and y are 3, find z when $x = 2$ and $y = 4$.

18. If z is 80 when x is 5 and y is 2, find z when $x = 2$ and $y = 5$.

19. If z is 64 when $x = 1$ and $y = 4$, find x when $z = 32$ and $y = 1$.

20. If z is 27 when $x = 6$ and $y = 3$, find x when $z = 50$ and $y = 4$.

21. The length a spring stretches is directly proportional to the force applied. If a force of 5 pounds stretches a spring 3 inches, how much force is necessary to stretch the same spring 10 inches?

22. The weight of a certain material varies directly with the surface area of that material. If 8 square feet weighs half a pound, how much will 10 square feet weigh?

23. The volume of a gas is inversely proportional to the pressure. If a pressure of 36 pounds per square inch corresponds to a volume of 25 cubic feet, what pressure is needed to produce a volume of 75 cubic feet?

24. The frequency of an electromagnetic wave varies inversely with the length. If a wave of length 200 meters has a frequency of 800 kilocycles per second, what frequency will be associated with a wave of length 500 meters?

Name _____

Class _____

Date _____

Answers

17. _____ **18.** _____

19. _____ **20.** _____

21. _____ **22.** _____

23. _____ **24.** _____

Answers

25. _____ 26. _____

27. _____ 28. _____

29. _____ 30. _____

31. _____ 32. _____

33. _____ 34. _____

35. _____ 36. _____

25. The surface area of a hollow cylinder varies jointly with the height and radius of the cylinder. If a cylinder with radius 3 inches and height 5 inches has a surface area of 94 square inches, what is the surface area of a cylinder with radius 2 inches and height 8 inches?

26. The capacity of a cylinder varies jointly with the height and the square of the radius. If a cylinder with radius of 3 cm (centimeters) and a height of 6 cm has a capacity of 3 cm^3 (cubic centimeters), what will be the capacity of a cylinder with radius 4 cm and height 9 cm?

27. The resistance of a wire varies directly with the length and inversely with the square of the diameter. If 100 feet of wire with diameter 0.01 inch has a resistance of 10 ohms, what is the resistance of 60 feet of the same type of wire if its diameter is 0.02 inch?

28. The volume of a gas varies directly with its temperature and inversely with the pressure. If the volume of a certain gas is 30 cubic feet at a temperature of 300°K and a pressure of 20 pounds per square inch, what is the volume of the same gas at 340°K when the pressure is 30 pounds per square inch?

Review Problems   The following problems review material we covered in Sections 5.6 and 5.7.

Simplify.

29. $(11 - 6i) - (2 - 4i)$ **30.** $(5 + 8i) - (3 - 4i)$

Multiply.

31. $(2 + 3i)(4 - i)$ **32.** $(3 - 5i)(2 + i)$

33. $(3 - 2i)^2$ **34.** $(4 + 5i)^2$

Divide.

35. $\dfrac{2 + 3i}{2 - 3i}$ **36.** $\dfrac{2 - 3i}{2 + 3i}$

Chapter 7   Summary and Review

LINEAR EQUATIONS IN TWO VARIABLES [7.1]

A linear equation in two variables is any equation that can be put in the form $ax + by = c$. The graph of every linear equation is a straight line.

1. The equation $3x + 2y = 6$ is an example of a linear equation in two variables.

INTERCEPTS [7.1]

The x-intercept of an equation is the x-coordinate of the point where the graph crosses the x-axis. The y-intercept is the y-coordinate of the point where the graph crosses the y-axis. We find the y-intercept by substituting $x = 0$ into the equation and solving for y. The x-intercept is found by letting $y = 0$ and solving for x.

2. To find the x-intercept for $3x + 2y = 6$ we let $y = 0$ and get

$$3x = 6$$
$$x = 2$$

In this case the x-intercept is 2, and the graph crosses the x-axis at (2, 0).

THE SLOPE OF A LINE [7.2]

The slope of the line containing points (x_1, y_1) and (x_2, y_2) is given by

$$\text{Slope} = m = \frac{\text{rise}}{\text{run}} = \frac{y_2 - y_1}{x_2 - x_1}$$

Horizontal lines have 0 slope, and vertical lines have no slope.

Parallel lines have equal slopes, and perpendicular lines have slopes that are negative reciprocals.

3. The slope of the line through (6, 9) and (1, −1) is

$$m = \frac{9 - (-1)}{6 - 1} = \frac{10}{5} = 2$$

THE SLOPE-INTERCEPT FORM OF A STRAIGHT LINE [7.3]

The equation of a line with slope m and y-intercept b is given by

$$y = mx + b$$

4. The equation of the line with slope 5 and y-intercept 3 is

$$y = 5x + 3$$

THE POINT-SLOPE FORM OF A STRAIGHT LINE [7.3]

The equation of a line through (x_1, y_1) that has a slope of m can be written as

$$y - y_1 = m(x - x_1)$$

5. The equation of the line through (3, 2) with slope −4 is

$$y - 2 = -4(x - 3)$$

which can be simplified to

$$y = -4x + 14$$

LINEAR INEQUALITIES IN TWO VARIABLES [7.4]

An inequality of the form $ax + by < c$ is a linear inequality in two variables. The equation for the boundary of the solution set is given by $ax + by = c$. (This equation is found by simply replacing the inequality symbol with an equal sign.)

To graph a linear inequality, first graph the boundary. Next, choose any point not on the boundary and substitute its coordinates into the original inequality. If the resulting statement is true, the graph lies on the same side of the boundary as the test point. A false statement indicates that the solution set lies on the other side of the boundary.

6. The graph of $x - y \le 3$ is

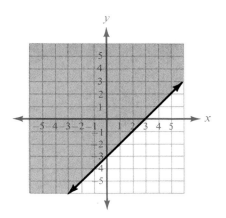

7. If y varies directly with x then

$$y = Kx$$

If also, y is 18 when x is 6, then

$$18 = K \cdot 6$$
or $$K = 3$$

So the equation can be written more specifically as

$$y = 3x$$

If we want to know what y is when x is 4, we simply substitute:

$$y = 3 \cdot 4$$
$$= 12$$

VARIATION [7.5]

If y varies directly with x (y is directly proportional to x), then we say:

$$y = Kx$$

If y varies inversely with x (y is inversely proportional to x), then we say:

$$y = \frac{K}{x}$$

If z varies jointly with x and y (z is directly proportional to both x and y), then we say:

$$z = Kxy$$

In each case, K is called the constant of variation.

COMMON MISTAKES

1. When graphing ordered pairs, the most common mistake is to associate the first coordinate with the y-axis and the second with the x-axis. If you make this mistake you would graph (3, 1) by going up 3 and to the right 1, which is just the reverse of what you should do. Remember, the first coordinate is always associated with the horizontal axis, and the second coordinate is always associated with the vertical axis.

2. The two most common mistakes students make when first working with the formula for the slope of a line are
   a. Putting the difference of the x-coordinates over the difference of the y-coordinates.
   b. Subtracting in one order in the numerator and then subtracting in the opposite order in the denominator.

3. When graphing linear inequalities in two variables remember to graph the boundary with a broken line when the inequality symbol is a $<$ symbol or a $>$ symbol. The only time you use a solid line for the boundary is when the inequality symbol is $\leq$ or $\geq$.

Chapter 7 Test

For each of the following straight lines, identify the x-intercept, y-intercept, and slope, and sketch the graph.

1. $2x + y = 6$

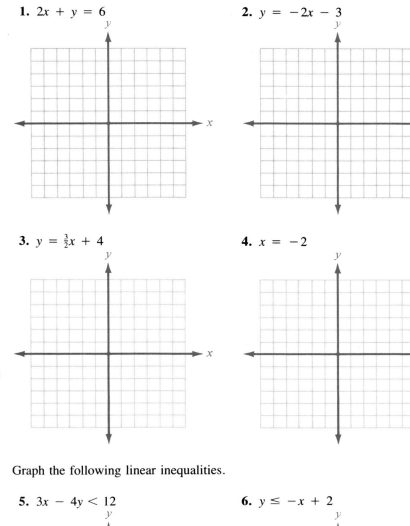

2. $y = -2x - 3$

3. $y = \frac{3}{2}x + 4$

4. $x = -2$

Graph the following linear inequalities.

5. $3x - 4y < 12$

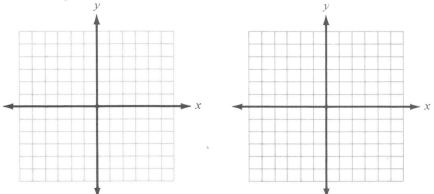

6. $y \leq -x + 2$

7. Give the equation of the line through $(-1, 3)$ that has slope $m = 2$.

8. Give the equation of the line through $(-3, 2)$ and $(4, -1)$.

Name _____

Class _____

Date _____

Answers

7. _____

8. _____

9. _____

10. _____

11. _____

12. _____

13. _____

14. _____

9. Line l contains the point $(5, -3)$ and has a graph parallel to the graph of $2x - 5y = 10$. Find the equation for l.

10. Line l contains the point $(-1, -2)$ and has a graph perpendicular to the graph of $y = 3x - 1$. Find the equation for l.

11. Give the equation of the vertical line through $(4, -7)$.

12. Quantity y varies directly with the square of x. If y is 50 when x is 5, find y when x is 3.

13. Quantity z varies jointly with x and the square root of y. If z is 15 when x is 5 and y is 36, find z when x is 2 and y is 25.

14. The maximum load (L) a horizontal beam can safely hold varies jointly with the width (w) and the square of the depth (d) and inversely with the length (l). If a 10-foot beam with width 3 and depth 4 will safely hold up to 800 pounds load, how many pounds will a 12-foot beam with width 3 and depth 4 hold?

8 Systems of Linear Equations

To the student:

In Chapter 7 we worked with linear equations in two variables. In this chapter we will extend our work with linear equations to include systems of linear equations in two and three variables.

Systems of linear equations are used extensively in many different disciplines. Systems of linear equations can be used to solve multiple-loop circuit problems in electronics, kinship patterns in anthropology, genetics problems in biology, and profit-and-cost problems in economics. There are many other applications as well.

To be successful in this chapter you should be familiar with the concepts in Chapter 7 as well as the process of solving a linear equation in one variable.

Section 8.1 Systems of Linear Equations in Two Variables

In Chapter 7 we found the graph of an equation of the form $ax + by = c$ to be a straight line. Since the graph is a straight line, the equation is said to be a linear equation. Two linear equations considered together form a *linear system* of equations. For example,

$$3x - 2y = 6$$
$$2x + 4y = 20$$

is a linear system. The solution set to the system is the set of all ordered pairs that satisfy both equations. If we graph each equation on the same set of axes, we can see the solution set (see Figure 1).

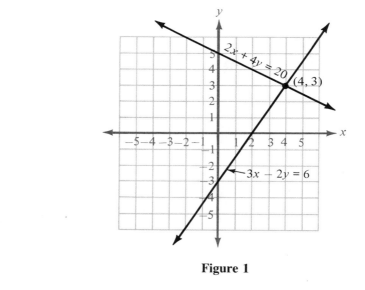

Figure 1

Note: It is important that you write solutions to systems of equations in two variables as ordered pairs, like (4, 3). That is, you should always enclose the ordered pair in parentheses.

The point (4, 3) lies on both lines and therefore must satisfy both equations. It is obvious from the graph that it is the only point that does so. The solution set for the system is $\{(4, 3)\}$.

More generally, if $a_1x + b_1y = c_1$ and $a_2x + b_2y = c_2$ are linear equations, then the solution set for the system

$$a_1x + b_1y = c_1$$
$$a_2x + b_2y = c_2$$

can be illustrated through one of the following graphs:

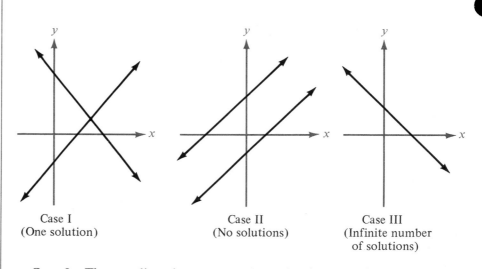

Case I
(One solution)

Case II
(No solutions)

Case III
(Infinite number
of solutions)

Case I   The two lines intersect at one and only one point. The coordinates of the point give the solution to the system. This is what usually happens.

Case II   The lines are parallel and therefore have no points in common. The solution set to the system is the empty set, $\varnothing$. In this case, we say the equations are *inconsistent*.

Case III   The lines coincide. That is, their graphs represent the same line. The solution set consists of all ordered pairs that satisfy either equation. In this case, the equations are said to be *dependent*.

In the beginning of this section we found the solution set for the system

$$3x - 2y = 6$$
$$2x + 4y = 20$$

by graphing each equation and then reading the solution set from the graph. Solving a system of linear equations by graphing is the least accurate method. If the coordinates of the point of intersection are not integers, it can be very difficult to read the solution set from the graph. There is another method of solving a linear system that does not depend on the graph. It is called the *addition method*.

▼ **Example 1** Solve the system

$$4x + 3y = 10$$
$$2x + y = 4$$

Solution If we multiply the bottom equation by -3, the coefficients of y in the resulting equation and the top equation will be opposites:

$$4x + 3y = 10 \xrightarrow{\text{No change}} 4x + 3y = 10$$
$$2x + y = 4 \xrightarrow[\text{Multiply by } -3]{} -6x - 3y = -12$$

Adding the left and right sides of the resulting equations, we have

$$4x + 3y = 10$$
$$\underline{-6x - 3y = -12}$$
$$-2x \quad\quad = -2$$

The result is a linear equation in one variable. We have eliminated the variable y from the equations by addition. (It is for this reason we call this method of solving a linear system the *addition method.*) Solving $-2x = -2$ for x, we have

$$x = 1$$

This is the x-coordinate of the solution to our system. To find the y-coordinate, we substitute $x = 1$ into any of the equations containing both the variables x and y. Let's try the second equation in our original system:

$$2(1) + y = 4$$
$$2 + y = 4$$
$$y = 2$$

This is the y-coordinate of the solution to our system. The ordered pair $(1, 2)$ is the solution to the system. ▲

▼ **Example 2** Solve the system

$$3x - 5y = -2$$
$$2x - 3y = 1$$

Solution We can eliminate either variable. Let's decide to eliminate the variable x. We can do so by multiplying the top equation by 2 and the bottom equation by -3, and then adding the left and right sides of the resulting equations:

$$3x - 5y = -2 \xrightarrow{\text{Multiply by 2}} 6x - 10y = -4$$
$$2x - 3y = 1 \xrightarrow[\text{Multiply by } -3]{} \underline{-6x + 9y = -3}$$
$$-y = -7$$
$$y = 7$$

The y-coordinate of the solution to the system is 7. Substituting this value of y into any of the equations with both x- and y-variables gives $x = 11$. The solution to the system is $(11, 7)$. It is the only ordered pair that satisfies both equations. ▲

Note: Substituting $x = 11$ into the first equation in our system we would have

$$3(11) - 5y = -2$$
$$33 - 5y = -2$$
$$-5y = -35$$
$$y = 7$$

3. Solve the system

$$2x + 7y = 3$$
$$4x + 14y = 1$$

▼ **Example 3** Solve the system

$$5x - 2y = 1$$
$$-10x + 4y = 3$$

Solution We can eliminate y by multiplying the first equation by 2 and adding the result to the second equation:

$$5x - 2y = 1 \xrightarrow{\text{Multiply by 2}} 10x - 4y = 2$$
$$-10x + 4y = 3 \xrightarrow[\text{No change}]{} \underline{-10x + 4y = 3}$$
$$0 = 5$$

The result is the false statement $0 = 5$, which indicates there is no solution to the system. The equations are said to be *inconsistent;* their graphs are parallel lines. Whenever both variables have been eliminated and the resulting statement is false, the solution set for the system will be the empty set, $\varnothing$. ▲

4. Solve the system

$$2x + 7y = 3$$
$$4x + 14y = 6$$

▼ **Example 4** Solve the system

$$4x - 3y = 2$$
$$8x - 6y = 4$$

Solution Multiplying the top equation by -2 and adding, we can eliminate the variable x:

$$4x - 3y = 2 \xrightarrow{\text{Multiply by } -2} -8x + 6y = -4$$
$$8x - 6y = 4 \xrightarrow[\text{No change}]{} \underline{8x - 6y = 4}$$
$$0 = 0$$

Both variables have been eliminated and the resulting statement $0 = 0$ is true. In this case the lines coincide and the equations are said to be *dependent.* The solution set consists of all ordered pairs that satisfy either equation. We can write the solution set as $\{(x, y)|4x - 3y = 2\}$ or $\{(x, y)|8x - 6y = 4\}$. ▲

The last two examples illustrate the two special cases in which the graphs of the equations in the system either coincide or are parallel. In both cases the left-hand sides of the equations were multiples of one another. In the case of the dependent equations, the right-hand sides were also multiples. We can generalize these observations as follows:

The equations in the system

$$a_1 x + b_1 y = c_1$$
$$a_2 x + b_2 y = c_2$$

will be inconsistent (their graphs are parallel lines) if

$$\frac{a_1}{a_2} = \frac{b_1}{b_2} \neq \frac{c_1}{c_2}$$

and will be dependent (their graphs will coincide) if

$$\frac{a_1}{a_2} = \frac{b_1}{b_2} = \frac{c_1}{c_2}$$

▼ **Example 5** Solve the system

$$\tfrac{1}{2}x - \tfrac{1}{3}y = 2$$
$$\tfrac{1}{4}x + \tfrac{2}{3}y = 6$$

Solution Although we could solve this system without clearing the equations of fractions, there is probably less chance for error if we have only integer coefficients to work with. So let's begin by multiplying both sides of the top equation by 6, and both sides of the bottom equation by 12, to clear each equation of fractions:

$$\tfrac{1}{2}x - \tfrac{1}{3}y = 2 \xrightarrow{\text{Times } 6} 3x - 2y = 12$$
$$\tfrac{1}{4}x + \tfrac{2}{3}y = 6 \xrightarrow[\text{Times } 12]{} 3x + 8y = 72$$

Now we can eliminate x by multiplying the top equation by -1 and leaving the bottom equation unchanged:

$$3x - 2y = 12 \xrightarrow{\text{Times } -1} -3x + 2y = -12$$
$$3x + 8y = 72 \xrightarrow[\text{No change}]{} \underline{3x + 8y = 72}$$
$$10y = 60$$
$$y = 6$$

We can substitute $y = 6$ into any equation that contains both x and y. Let's use $3x - 2y = 12$.

$$3x - 2(6) = 12$$
$$3x - 12 = 12$$
$$3x = 24$$
$$x = 8$$

The solution to the system is $(8, 6)$. ▲

We end this section by considering another method of solving a linear system. The method is called the *substitution* method and is shown in the following examples.

5. Solve the system

$$\frac{1}{3}x + \frac{1}{2}y = 4$$
$$\frac{2}{3}x - \frac{1}{4}y = 3$$

6. Solve the system

$$4x - 2y = -2$$
$$y = x + 3$$

by substituting the expression for y given in the second equation into the first equation.

▼ **Example 6** Solve the system

$$2x - 3y = -6$$
$$y = 3x - 5$$

Solution The second equation tells us y is $3x - 5$. Substituting the expression $3x - 5$ for y in the first equation, we have

$$2x - 3(3x - 5) = -6$$

The result of the substitution is the elimination of the variable y. Solving the resulting linear equation in x as usual, we have

$$2x - 9x + 15 = -6$$
$$-7x + 15 = -6$$
$$-7x = -21$$
$$x = 3$$

Putting $x = 3$ into the second equation in the original system, we have

$$y = 3(3) - 5$$
$$= 9 - 5$$
$$= 4$$

The solution to the system is $(3, 4)$. ▲

7. Solve by substitution

$$5x - 3y = -4$$
$$x + 2y = 7$$

▼ **Example 7** Solve by substitution:

$$2x + 3y = 5$$
$$x - 2y = 6$$

Solution In order to use the substitution method we must solve one of the two equations for x or y. We can solve for x in the second equation by adding $2y$ to both sides:

$$x - 2y = 6$$
$$x = 2y + 6 \qquad \text{Add } 2y \text{ to both sides}$$

Substituting the expression $2y + 6$ for x in the first equation of our system, we have

$$2(2y + 6) + 3y = 5$$
$$4y + 12 + 3y = 5$$
$$7y + 12 = 5$$
$$7y = -7$$
$$y = -1$$

Using $y = -1$ in either equation in the original system, we find $x = 4$. The solution is $(4, -1)$. ▲

Note: Both the substitution method and the addition method can be used to solve any system of linear equations in two variables. However, systems like the one in Example 6 are easier to solve using the substitution method, since one of the variables is already written in terms of the other. A system like the one in Example 2 is easier to solve using the addition method, since solving for one of the variables would lead to an expression involving fractions. The system in Example 7 could be solved easily by either method, since solving the second equation for x is a one-step process.

Problem Set 8.1

Name _____

Class _____

Date _____

Solve each of the following systems by the addition method.

1. $x + y = 5$
   $3x - y = 3$

2. $x - y = 4$
   $-x + 2y = -3$

Answers

1. _____   2. _____

3. _____   4. _____

5. _____   6. _____

7. _____   8. _____

9. _____   10. _____

3. $3x + y = 4$
   $4x + y = 5$

4. $6x - 2y = -10$
   $6x + 3y = -15$

5. $3x - 2y = 6$
   $6x - 4y = 12$

6. $4x + 5y = -3$
   $-8x - 10y = 3$

7. $x + 2y = 0$
   $2x - 6y = 5$

8. $x + 3y = 3$
   $2x - 9y = 1$

9. $2x + y = 5$
   $5x + 3y = 11$

10. $5x + 2y = 11$
    $7x + y = 10$

Answers

11. _____ 12. _____

13. _____ 14. _____

15. _____ 16. _____

17. _____ 18. _____

11. $4x + 3y = 14$
$9x - 2y = 14$

12. $7x - 6y = 13$
$6x - 5y = 11$

13. $2x - 5y = 3$
$-4x + 10y = 3$

14. $3x - 2y = 1$
$-6x + 4y = -2$

15. $\frac{1}{2}x + \frac{1}{3}y = 13$
$\frac{1}{5}x + \frac{1}{8}y = 5$

16. $\frac{1}{2}x + \frac{1}{3}y = \frac{2}{3}$
$\frac{1}{3}x + \frac{1}{5}y = \frac{7}{15}$

17. $\frac{1}{3}x + \frac{1}{5}y = 2$
$\frac{1}{3}x - \frac{1}{2}y = -\frac{1}{3}$

18. $\frac{1}{2}x - \frac{1}{3}y = \frac{5}{6}$
$-\frac{1}{5}x + \frac{1}{4}y = -\frac{9}{20}$

Solve each of the following systems by the substitution method.

19. $y = x + 3$
$x + y = 3$

20. $y = x - 5$
$2x - 6y = -2$

Answers

19. _____   **20.** _____

21. $x - y = 4$
$2x - 3y = 6$

22. $x + y = 3$
$2x + 3y = -4$

21. _____   **22.** _____

23. _____   **24.** _____

25. _____   **26.** _____

27. _____   **28.** _____

23. $y = 3x - 2$
$y = 4x - 4$

24. $y = 5x - 2$
$y = -2x + 5$

25. $7x - y = 24$
$x = 2y + 9$

26. $3x - y = -8$
$y = 6x + 3$

27. $2x - y = 5$
$4x - 2y = 10$

28. $5x - 4y = 3$
$-10x + 8y = -6$

29. _____ 30. _____

31a. _____

b. _____

32a. _____

b. _____

c. _____

33. _____ 34. _____

35. _____ 36. _____

37. _____ 38. _____

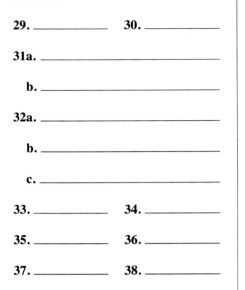

29. Multiply both sides of the second equation in the following system by 100 and then solve as usual.

$$x + y = 10,000$$
$$.06x + .05y = 560$$

30. Multiply both sides of the second equation in the following system by 10 and then solve as usual.

$$x + y = 12$$
$$.20x + .50y = .30(12)$$

31. One telephone company charges 25 cents for the first minute and 15 cents for each additional minute for a certain long-distance phone call. If the number of additional minutes after the first minute is x and the cost, in cents, for the call is y, then the equation that gives the total cost, in cents, for the call is $y = 15x + 25$.
   a. If a second phone company charges 22 cents for the first minute and 16 cents for each additional minute, write the equation that gives the total cost (y) of a call in terms of the number of additional minutes (x).
   b. After how many additional minutes will the two companies charge an equal amount? (What is the x-coordinate of the point of intersection of the two lines?)

32. In a certain city a taxi ride costs 75¢ for the first $\frac{1}{7}$ of a mile and 10¢ for every additional $\frac{1}{7}$ of a mile after the first seventh. If x is the number of additional sevenths of a mile, then the total cost y of a taxi ride is $y = 10x + 75$.
   a. How much does it cost to ride a taxi for 10 miles in this city?
   b. Suppose a taxi ride in another city costs 50¢ for the first $\frac{1}{7}$ of a mile, and 15¢ for each additional $\frac{1}{7}$ of a mile. Write an equation that gives the total cost y, in cents, to ride x sevenths of a mile past the first seventh, in this city.
   c. Solve the two equations given above simultaneously (as a system of equations) and explain in words what your solution represents.

Review Problems   The following problems review material we covered in Section 5.3.

Combine the following radicals. (Assume all variables are positive.)

33. $5\sqrt{3} + 2\sqrt{3}$

34. $8\sqrt{2} - 6\sqrt{2}$

35. $2x\sqrt{5} - 7x\sqrt{5}$

36. $5x\sqrt{7} - 3x\sqrt{7}$

37. $3\sqrt{8} + 5\sqrt{18}$

38. $5\sqrt{12} + 3\sqrt{27}$

Section 8.2 Systems of Linear Equations in Three Variables

A solution to an equation in three variables such as

$$2x + y - 3z = 6$$

is an ordered triple of numbers (x, y, z). For example, the ordered triples $(0, 0, -2)$, $(2, 2, 0)$, and $(0, 9, 1)$ are solutions to the equation $2x + y - 3z = 6$, since they produce a true statement when their coordinates are replaced for x, y, and z in the equation.

DEFINITION The solution set for a system of three linear equations in three variables is the set of ordered triples that satisfy all three equations.

▼ **Example 1** Solve the system

$$
\begin{aligned}
x + y + z &= 6 &\quad (1)\\
2x - y + z &= 3 &\quad (2)\\
x + 2y - 3z &= -4 &\quad (3)
\end{aligned}
$$

Solution We want to find the ordered triple (x, y, z) that satisfies all three equations. We have numbered the equations so it will be easier to keep track of where they are and what we are doing.

There are many ways to proceed. The main idea is to take two different pairs of equations and eliminate the same variable from each pair. We begin by adding equations (1) and (2) to eliminate the y-variable. The resulting equation is numbered (4):

$$
\begin{array}{ll}
x + y + z = 6 & (1)\\
\underline{2x - y + z = 3} & (2)\\
3x \phantom{{}- y} + 2z = 9 & (4)
\end{array}
$$

Adding twice equation (2) to equation (3) will also eliminate the variable y. The resulting equation is numbered (5):

$$
\begin{array}{ll}
4x - 2y + 2z = 6 & \text{Twice (2)}\\
\underline{x + 2y - 3z = -4} & (3)\\
5x \phantom{{}- 2y} - z = 2 & (5)
\end{array}
$$

Equations (4) and (5) form a linear system in two variables. By multiplying equation (5) by 2 and adding the result to equation (4), we will succeed in eliminating the variable z from the new pair of equations:

$$
\begin{array}{ll}
3x + 2z = 9 & (4)\\
\underline{10x - 2z = 4} & \text{Twice (5)}\\
13x \phantom{{}+ 2z} = 13 &\\
x = 1 &
\end{array}
$$

Substituting $x = 1$ into equation (4), we have

$$
\begin{aligned}
3(1) + 2z &= 9\\
2z &= 6\\
z &= 3
\end{aligned}
$$

Practice Problems

1. Solve the system

$$
\begin{aligned}
x + 2y + z &= 2\\
x + y - z &= 6\\
x - y + 2z &= -7
\end{aligned}
$$

Answer
1. $(1, 2, -3)$

Using $x = 1$ and $z = 3$ in equation (1) gives us

$$1 + y + 3 = 6$$
$$y + 4 = 6$$
$$y = 2$$

The solution set for the system is the ordered triple $\{(1, 2, 3)\}$. ▲

2. Solve the system

$$3x - 2y + z = 2$$
$$3x + y + 3z = 7$$
$$x + 4y - z = 4$$

▼ **Example 2** Solve the system

$$2x + y - z = 3 \quad (1)$$
$$3x + 4y + z = 6 \quad (2)$$
$$2x - 3y + z = 1 \quad (3)$$

Solution It is easiest to eliminate z from the equations. The equation produced by adding (1) and (2) is

$$5x + 5y = 9 \quad (4)$$

The equation that results from adding (1) and (3) is

$$4x - 2y = 4 \quad (5)$$

Equations (4) and (5) form a linear system in two variables. We can eliminate the variable y from this system as follows:

$$5x + 5y = 9 \xrightarrow{\text{Multiply by 2}} 10x + 10y = 18$$
$$4x - 2y = 4 \xrightarrow[\text{Multiply by 5}]{} \underline{20x - 10y = 20}$$
$$30x = 38$$
$$x = \tfrac{38}{30}$$
$$x = \tfrac{19}{15}$$

Substituting $x = \tfrac{19}{15}$ into equation (5) or equation (4) and solving for y gives

$$y = \tfrac{8}{15}$$

Using $x = \tfrac{19}{15}$ and $y = \tfrac{8}{15}$ in equation (1), (2), or (3) and solving for z results in

$$z = \tfrac{1}{15}$$

The ordered triple that satisfies all three equations is $(\tfrac{19}{15}, \tfrac{8}{15}, \tfrac{1}{15})$. ▲

3. Solve the system

$$3x + 5y - 2z = 1$$
$$6x + 10y - 4z = 2$$
$$x - 8y + z = 4$$

▼ **Example 3** Solve the system

$$2x + 3y - z = 5 \quad (1)$$
$$4x + 6y - 2z = 10 \quad (2)$$
$$x - 4y + 3z = 5 \quad (3)$$

Solution Multiplying equation (1) by -2 and adding the result to equation (2) looks like this

$$-4x - 6y + 2z = -10 \qquad -2 \text{ times (1)}$$
$$\underline{4x + 6y - 2z = 10} \qquad (2)$$
$$0 = 0$$

All three variables have been eliminated, and we are left with a true statement. As was the case in Section 8.1, this implies that the two equations are dependent. There is either no solution to the system or there is an infinite number of solutions. ▲

Note: The last page of this section contains a discussion of the geometric interpretations associated with systems of equations in three variables.

Answers
2. $(1, 1, 1)$ **3.** No unique solution, it is a dependent system.

▼ **Example 4**   Solve the system

$$x - 5y + 4z = 8 \quad (1)$$
$$3x + y - 2z = 7 \quad (2)$$
$$-9x - 3y + 6z = 5 \quad (3)$$

Solution   Multiplying equation (2) by 3 and adding the result to equation (3) produces

$$\begin{array}{rl} 9x + 3y - 6z = 21 & \text{3 times (2)} \\ -9x - 3y + 6z = 5 & \text{(3)} \\ \hline 0 = 26 & \end{array}$$

In this case all three variables have been eliminated, and we are left with a false statement. The two equations are inconsistent; there are no ordered triples that satisfy both equations. The solution set for the system is the empty set, $\varnothing$. If equations (2) and (3) have no ordered triples in common, then certainly (1), (2), and (3) do not either.   ▲

▼ **Example 5**   Solve the system

$$x + 3y = 5 \quad (1)$$
$$6y + z = 12 \quad (2)$$
$$x - 2z = -10 \quad (3)$$

Solution   It may be helpful to rewrite the system as

$$\begin{array}{rcll} x + 3y & = 5 & (1) \\ 6y + z & = 12 & (2) \\ x - 2z & = -10 & (3) \end{array}$$

Equation (2) does not contain the variable x. If we multiply equation (3) by -1 and add the result to equation (1), we will be left with another equation that does not contain the variable x:

$$\begin{array}{rcll} x + 3y & = 5 & (1) \\ -x + 2z & = 10 & -1 \text{ times (3)} \\ \hline 3y + 2z & = 15 & (4) \end{array}$$

Equations (2) and (4) form a linear system in two variables. Multiplying equation (2) by -2 and adding to equation (4) eliminates the variable z:

$$\begin{array}{rcl} 6y + z = 12 \xrightarrow{\text{Multiply by } -2} & -12y - 2z = -24 \\ 3y + 2z = 15 \xrightarrow[\text{No change}]{} & \underline{3y + 2z = 15} \\ & -9y = -9 \\ & y = 1 \end{array}$$

Using $y = 1$ in equation (4) and solving for z, we have

$$z = 6$$

Substituting $y = 1$ into equation (1) gives

$$x = 2$$

The ordered triple that satisfies all three equations is $(2, 1, 6)$.   ▲

4.   Solve the system

$$3x - y + 2z = 4$$
$$6x - 2y + 4z = 2$$
$$5x - 3y + 7z = 5$$

5.   Solve the system

$$x + 2y = 0$$
$$3y + z = -3$$
$$2x - z = 5$$

Answers
4. No solution, it is an inconsistent system.   **5.** $(4, -2, 3)$

The Geometry Behind Equations in Three Variables

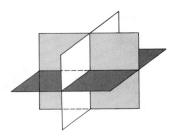

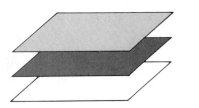

Case 1 The three planes have exactly one point in common. In this case we get one solution to our system, as in Examples 1, 2, and 5.

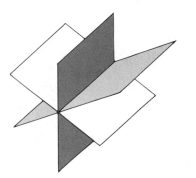

Case 2 The three planes have no points in common because they are all parallel to each other. The system they represent is an inconsistent system.

Case 3 The three planes intersect in a line. Any point on the line is a solution to the system of equations represented by the planes, so there is an infinite number of solutions to the system. This is an example of a dependent system.

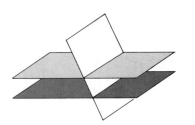

Case 4 Two of the planes are parallel, while the third plane intersects each of the parallel planes. In this case the three planes have no points in common. There is no solution to the system; it is an inconsistent system.

We can graph an ordered triple on a coordinate system with three axes. The graph will be a point in space. The coordinate system is drawn in perspective; you have to imagine that the x-axis comes out of the paper and is perpendicular to both the y-axis and the z-axis. To graph the point $(3, 4, 5)$ we move 3 units in the x-direction, 4 units in the y-direction and then 5 units in the z-direction, as shown in Figure 2.

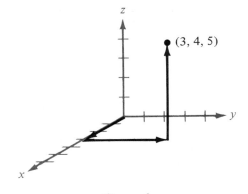

Figure 2

Although in actual practice it is sometimes difficult to graph equations in three variables, if we were to graph a linear equation in three variables we would find that the graph was a plane in space. A system of three equations in three variables is represented by three planes in space.

There are a number of possible ways in which these three planes can intersect, some of which are shown in the margin on this page. And there are still other possibilities that are not among those shown in the margin.

In Example 3, we found that equations 1 and 2 were dependent equations. They represent the same plane. That is, they have all their points in common. But the system of equations that they came from has either no solution or an infinite number of solutions. It all depends on the third plane. If the third plane coincides with the first two, then the solution to the system is a plane. If the third plane is parallel to the first two, then there is no solution to the system. And finally, if the third plane intersects the first two, then the solution to the system is that line of intersection.

In Example 4 we found that trying to eliminate a variable from the second and third equation resulted in a false statement. This means that the two planes represented by these equations are parallel. It makes no difference where the third plane is; there is no solution to the system in Example 4. (If we were to graph the three planes from Example 4, we would obtain a diagram similar to Case 2 or Case 4 in the margin.

If, in the process of solving a system of linear equations in three variables, we eliminate all the variables from a pair of equations and are left with a false statement, we will say the system is inconsistent. If we eliminate all the variables and are left with a true statement, then we will say the system is a dependent one.

Problem Set 8.2

Solve the following systems.

1. $x + y + z = 4$
$\quad x - y + 2z = 1$
$\quad x - y - 3z = -4$

2. $x - y - 2z = -1$
$\quad x + y + z = 6$
$\quad x + y - z = 4$

3. $x + y + z = 6$
$\quad x - y + 2z = 7$
$\quad 2x - y - 4z = -9$

4. $x + y + z = 0$
$\quad x + y - z = 6$
$\quad x - y + 2z = -7$

5. $x + 2y + z = 3$
$\quad 2x - y + 2z = 6$
$\quad 3x + y - z = 5$

6. $2x + y - 3z = -14$
$\quad x - 3y + 4z = 22$
$\quad 3x + 2y + z = 0$

Answers

7. _____ 8. _____

9. _____ 10. _____

11. _____ 12. _____

7. $2x - y - 3z = 1$
$x + 2y + 4z = 3$
$4x - 2y - 6z = 2$

8. $3x + 2y + z = 3$
$x - 3y + z = 4$
$-6x - 4y - 2z = 1$

9. $2x - y + 3z = 4$
$x + 2y - z = 2$
$4x + 3y + 2z = 9$

10. $6x - 2y + z = 5$
$3x + y + 3z = 7$
$x + 4y - z = 4$

11. $x + y = 9$
$y + z = 7$
$x - z = 2$

12. $x - y = -3$
$x + z = 2$
$y - z = 7$

13. $2x + y = 2$
$y + z = 3$
$4x - z = 0$

14. $2x + y = 6$
$3y - 2z = -8$
$x + z = 5$

Name _____

Class _____

Date _____

Answers

13. _____   **14.** _____

15. _____   **16.** _____

17. _____   **18.** _____

15. $3x + 4y = 15$
$2x - 5z = -3$
$4y - 3z = 9$

16. $6x - 4y = 2$
$3y + 3z = 9$
$2x - 5z = -8$

17. $2x - y + 2z = -8$
$3x - y - 4z = 3$
$x + 2y - 3z = 9$

18. $2x + 2y + 4z = 2$
$2x - y - z = 0$
$3x + y + 2z = 2$

Answers

19. _____

20a. _____

b. _____

c. _____

21. _____ 22. _____

23. _____ 24. _____

25. _____ 26. _____

19. In the following diagram of an electrical circuit, x, y, and z represent the amount of current (in amperes) flowing across the 5-ohm, 20-ohm, and 10-ohm resistors, respectively. (In circuit diagrams resistors are represented by $\sim\!\!\!\sim$ and potential differences by $\dashv\vdash$.)

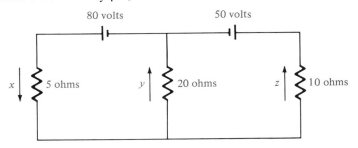

The system of equations used to find the three currents x, y, and z is

$$x - y - z = 0$$
$$5x + 20y = 80$$
$$20y - 10z = 50$$

Solve the system for all variables.

20. If a car rental company charges \$10 a day and 8¢ a mile to rent one of its cars, then the cost z, in dollars, to rent a car for x days and drive y miles can be found from the equation

$$z = 10x + .08y$$

a. How much does it cost to rent a car for 2 days and drive it 200 miles under these conditions?

b. A second company charges \$12 a day and 6¢ a mile for the same car. Write an equation that gives the cost z, in dollars, to rent a car from this company for x days and drive it y miles.

c. A car is rented from each of the companies mentioned above for 2 days. To find the mileage at which the cost of renting the cars from each of the two companies will be equal, solve the following system for y.

$$z = 10x + .08y$$
$$z = 12x + .06y$$
$$x = 2$$

Review Problems   The following problems review material we covered in Sections 6.1 and 6.3. Reviewing these problems will help you with some of the material in the next section.

Solve by factoring.

21. $x^2 - 2x - 8 = 0$ **22.** $x^2 - 5x - 6 = 0$

23. $6x^2 - 13x + 6 = 0$ **24.** $9x^2 + 6x - 8 = 0$

Solve using the quadratic formula.

25. $x^2 + x + 1 = 0$ **26.** $x^2 + x - 1 = 0$

Section 8.3   Introduction to Determinants

In this section we will expand and evaluate determinants. The purpose of this section is simply to be able to find the value of a given determinant. As we will see in the next section, determinants are very useful in solving systems of linear equations. Before we apply determinants to systems of linear equations, however, we must practice calculating the value of some determinants.

DEFINITION   The value of the 2 × 2 (2 by 2) determinant

$$\begin{vmatrix} a & c \\ b & d \end{vmatrix}$$

is given by

$$\begin{vmatrix} a & c \\ b & d \end{vmatrix} = ad - bc$$

From the preceding definition we see that a determinant is simply a square array of numbers with two vertical lines enclosing it. The value of a 2 × 2 determinant is found by cross-multiplying on the diagonals, a diagram of which looks like

$$\begin{vmatrix} a & c \\ b & d \end{vmatrix} = ad - bc$$

▼ **Example 1**   Find the value of the following 2 × 2 determinants:

a. $\begin{vmatrix} 1 & 2 \\ 3 & 4 \end{vmatrix} = 1(4) - 3(2) = 4 - 6 = -2$

b. $\begin{vmatrix} 3 & 5 \\ -2 & 7 \end{vmatrix} = 3(7) - (-2)5 = 21 + 10 = 31$ ▲

▼ **Example 2**   Solve for x if

$$\begin{vmatrix} x^2 & 2 \\ x & 1 \end{vmatrix} = 8$$

Solution   We expand the determinant on the left side to get

$$x^2(1) - x(2) = 8$$
$$x^2 - 2x = 8$$
$$x^2 - 2x - 8 = 0$$
$$(x - 4)(x + 2) = 0$$
$$x - 4 = 0 \quad \text{or} \quad x + 2 = 0$$
$$x = 4 \quad \text{or} \quad x = -2 \quad ▲$$

We now turn our attention to 3 × 3 determinants. A 3 × 3 determinant is also a square array of numbers, the value of which is given by the following definition.

Practice Problems

1.   Find the value of each determinant.

a. $\begin{vmatrix} 2 & 1 \\ 4 & 3 \end{vmatrix}$

b. $\begin{vmatrix} 4 & -2 \\ 0 & 3 \end{vmatrix}$

2.   Solve for x if

$$\begin{vmatrix} -3 & x \\ 2 & x \end{vmatrix} = 20$$

Answers
1a. 2   **b.** 12   **2.** -4

DEFINITION   The value of the 3×3 determinant

$$\begin{vmatrix} a_1 & b_1 & c_1 \\ a_2 & b_2 & c_2 \\ a_3 & b_3 & c_3 \end{vmatrix}$$

is given by

$$\begin{vmatrix} a_1 & b_1 & c_1 \\ a_2 & b_2 & c_2 \\ a_3 & b_3 & c_3 \end{vmatrix} = a_1 b_2 c_3 + a_3 b_1 c_2 + a_2 b_3 c_1 - a_3 b_2 c_1 - a_1 b_3 c_2 - a_2 b_1 c_3$$

At first glance, the expansion of a 3×3 determinant looks a little complicated. There are actually two different methods used to find the six products given above that simplify matters somewhat.

METHOD I

We begin by writing the determinant with the first two columns repeated on the right:

$$\begin{vmatrix} a_1 & b_1 & c_1 \\ a_2 & b_2 & c_2 \\ a_3 & b_3 & c_3 \end{vmatrix} \begin{matrix} a_1 & b_1 \\ a_2 & b_2 \\ a_3 & b_3 \end{matrix}$$

The positive products in the definition come from multiplying down the three full diagonals:

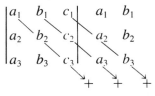

The negative products come from multiplying up the three full diagonals:

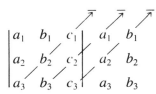

▼   **Example 3**   Find the value of

$$\begin{vmatrix} 1 & 3 & -2 \\ 2 & 0 & 1 \\ 4 & -1 & 1 \end{vmatrix}$$

Solution   Repeating the first two columns and then finding the products up the diagonals and the products down the diagonals as given in Method I, we have

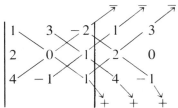

Note: Check the products found by multiplying up and down the diagonals given here with the products given in the definition of a 3×3 determinant to see that they match.

3.   Find the value of

$$\begin{vmatrix} 2 & 0 & -1 \\ 3 & 1 & 2 \\ 5 & -2 & 1 \end{vmatrix}$$

Answer
3. 21

$$= 1(0)(1) + 3(1)(4) + (-2)(2)(-1)$$
$$- 4(0)(-2) - (-1)(1)(1) - 1(2)(3)$$
$$= 0 + 12 + 4 - 0 - (-1) - (6)$$
$$= 11$$ ▲

METHOD 2

The second method of evaluating a 3 × 3 determinant is called *expansion by minors*.

DEFINITION The *minor* for an element in a 3 × 3 determinant is the determinant consisting of the elements remaining when the row and column to which the element belongs are deleted. For example, in the determinant

$$\begin{vmatrix} a_1 & b_1 & c_1 \\ a_2 & b_2 & c_2 \\ a_3 & b_3 & c_3 \end{vmatrix}$$

$$\text{Minor for element } a_1 = \begin{vmatrix} b_2 & c_2 \\ b_3 & c_3 \end{vmatrix}$$

$$\text{Minor for element } b_2 = \begin{vmatrix} a_1 & c_1 \\ a_3 & c_3 \end{vmatrix}$$

$$\text{Minor for element } c_3 = \begin{vmatrix} a_1 & b_1 \\ a_2 & b_2 \end{vmatrix}$$

Before we can evaluate a 3 × 3 determinant by Method 2, we must first define what is known as the sign array for a 3 × 3 determinant.

DEFINITION The *sign array* for a 3 × 3 determinant is a 3 × 3 array of signs in the following pattern:

$$\begin{vmatrix} + & - & + \\ - & + & - \\ + & - & + \end{vmatrix}$$

The sign array begins with a + sign in the upper left-hand corner. The signs then alternate between + and − across every row and down every column.

Note: If you have read this far and are confused, hang on. After you have done a couple of examples you will find expansion by minors to be a fairly simple process. It just takes a lot of writing to explain it.

To Evaluate a 3 × 3 Determinant by Expansion of Minors

We can evaluate a 3 × 3 determinant by expanding across any row or down any column as follows:

Step 1: Choose a row or column to expand about.

Step 2: Write the product of each element in the row or column chosen in Step 1 with its minor.

Step 3: Connect the three products in Step 2 with the signs in the corresponding row or column in the sign array.

We will use the same determinant as in Example 3 to illustrate the procedure.

4. Expand across the first row:

$$\begin{vmatrix} 2 & 0 & -1 \\ 3 & 1 & 2 \\ 5 & -2 & 1 \end{vmatrix}$$

Note: This method of evaluating a determinant is actually more valuable than our first method, because it will work with any size determinant from 3×3 to 4×4 to any higher order determinant. Method 1 only works on 3×3 determinants. It cannot be used on a 4×4 determinant.

5. Expand down column 2:

$$\begin{vmatrix} 0 & 4 & -2 \\ 3 & 1 & 1 \\ 1 & -2 & 0 \end{vmatrix}$$

▼ **Example 4** Expand across the first row:

$$\begin{vmatrix} 1 & 3 & -2 \\ 2 & 0 & 1 \\ 4 & -1 & 1 \end{vmatrix}$$

Solution The products of the three elements in row 1 with their minors are

$$1\begin{vmatrix} 0 & 1 \\ -1 & 1 \end{vmatrix} \qquad 3\begin{vmatrix} 2 & 1 \\ 4 & 1 \end{vmatrix} \qquad (-2)\begin{vmatrix} 2 & 0 \\ 4 & -1 \end{vmatrix}$$

Connecting these three products with the signs from the first row of the sign array, we have

$$+1\begin{vmatrix} 0 & 1 \\ -1 & 1 \end{vmatrix} - 3\begin{vmatrix} 2 & 1 \\ 4 & 1 \end{vmatrix} + (-2)\begin{vmatrix} 2 & 0 \\ 4 & -1 \end{vmatrix}$$

We complete the problem by evaluating each of the three 2×2 determinants and then simplifying the resulting expression:

$$+1[0 - (-1)] - 3(2 - 4) + (-2)(-2 - 0)$$
$$= 1(1) - 3(-2) + (-2)(-2)$$
$$= 1 + 6 + 4$$
$$= 11$$

The results of Examples 3 and 4 match. It makes no difference which method we use—the value of a 3×3 determinant is unique. ▲

▼ **Example 5** Expand down column 2:

$$\begin{vmatrix} 2 & 3 & -2 \\ 1 & 4 & 1 \\ 1 & 5 & -1 \end{vmatrix}$$

Solution We connect the products of elements in column 2 and their minors with the signs from the second column in the sign array:

$$\begin{vmatrix} 2 & 3 & -2 \\ 1 & 4 & 1 \\ 1 & 5 & -1 \end{vmatrix} = -3\begin{vmatrix} 1 & 1 \\ 1 & -1 \end{vmatrix} + 4\begin{vmatrix} 2 & -2 \\ 1 & -1 \end{vmatrix} - 5\begin{vmatrix} 2 & -2 \\ 1 & 1 \end{vmatrix}$$
$$= -3(-1 - 1) + 4[-2 - (-2)] - 5[2 - (-2)]$$
$$= -3(-2) + 4(0) - 5(4)$$
$$= 6 + 0 - 20$$
$$= -14$$
▲

Problem Set 8.3

Find the value of the following 2×2 determinants.

1. $\begin{vmatrix} 1 & 0 \\ 2 & 3 \end{vmatrix}$

2. $\begin{vmatrix} 5 & 4 \\ 3 & 2 \end{vmatrix}$

3. $\begin{vmatrix} 2 & 1 \\ 3 & 4 \end{vmatrix}$

4. $\begin{vmatrix} 4 & 1 \\ 5 & 2 \end{vmatrix}$

Answers

5. $\begin{vmatrix} 0 & 1 \\ 1 & 0 \end{vmatrix}$

6. $\begin{vmatrix} 1 & 0 \\ 0 & 1 \end{vmatrix}$

7. $\begin{vmatrix} -3 & 2 \\ 6 & -4 \end{vmatrix}$

8. $\begin{vmatrix} 8 & -3 \\ -2 & 5 \end{vmatrix}$

1. _____   2. _____

3. _____   4. _____

5. _____   6. _____

7. _____   8. _____

9. _____   10. _____

11. _____   12. _____

13. _____   14. _____

Solve each of the following for x.

9. $\begin{vmatrix} 1 & 2x \\ 2 & -3x \end{vmatrix} = 21$

10. $\begin{vmatrix} -5 & 4x \\ 1 & -x \end{vmatrix} = 27$

11. $\begin{vmatrix} 2x & -4 \\ 2 & x \end{vmatrix} = -8x$

12. $\begin{vmatrix} 3x & 2 \\ 2 & x \end{vmatrix} = -11x$

13. $\begin{vmatrix} x^2 & 3 \\ x & 1 \end{vmatrix} = 10$

14. $\begin{vmatrix} x^2 & -2 \\ x & 1 \end{vmatrix} = 35$

Answers

15. _____   16. _____

17. _____   18. _____

19. _____   20. _____

21. _____   22. _____

Find the value of each of the following 3×3 determinants by using Method I of this section.

15. $\begin{vmatrix} 1 & 2 & 0 \\ 0 & 2 & 1 \\ 1 & 1 & 1 \end{vmatrix}$ 16. $\begin{vmatrix} -1 & 0 & 2 \\ 3 & 0 & 1 \\ 0 & 1 & 3 \end{vmatrix}$

17. $\begin{vmatrix} 1 & 2 & 3 \\ 3 & 2 & 1 \\ 1 & 1 & 1 \end{vmatrix}$ 18. $\begin{vmatrix} -1 & 2 & 0 \\ 3 & -2 & 1 \\ 0 & 5 & 4 \end{vmatrix}$

Find the value of each determinant by using Method 2 and expanding across the first row.

19. $\begin{vmatrix} 0 & 1 & 2 \\ 1 & 0 & 1 \\ -1 & 2 & 0 \end{vmatrix}$ 20. $\begin{vmatrix} 3 & -2 & 1 \\ 0 & -1 & 0 \\ 2 & 0 & 1 \end{vmatrix}$

21. $\begin{vmatrix} 3 & 0 & 2 \\ 0 & -1 & -1 \\ 4 & 0 & 0 \end{vmatrix}$ 22. $\begin{vmatrix} 1 & 1 & 1 \\ 1 & -1 & 1 \\ 1 & 1 & -1 \end{vmatrix}$

Find the value of each of the following determinants.

23. $\begin{vmatrix} 2 & -1 & 0 \\ 1 & 0 & -2 \\ 0 & 1 & 2 \end{vmatrix}$

24. $\begin{vmatrix} 5 & 0 & -4 \\ 0 & 1 & 3 \\ -1 & 2 & -1 \end{vmatrix}$

25. $\begin{vmatrix} 1 & 3 & 7 \\ -2 & 6 & 4 \\ 3 & 7 & -1 \end{vmatrix}$

26. $\begin{vmatrix} 2 & 1 & 5 \\ 6 & -3 & 4 \\ 8 & 9 & -2 \end{vmatrix}$

27. Show that the following determinant equation is another way to write the slope-intercept form of the equation of a line.

$$\begin{vmatrix} y & x \\ m & 1 \end{vmatrix} = b$$

28. Show that the following determinant equation is another way to write the equation $F = \frac{9}{5}C + 32$.

$$\begin{vmatrix} C & F & 1 \\ 5 & 41 & 1 \\ -10 & 14 & 1 \end{vmatrix} = 0$$

The following problems review material we covered in Section 6.5.

Answers

29. _____   30. _____

31. _____   32. _____

33. _____   34. _____

Solve each equation.

29. $x^4 - 2x^2 - 8 = 0$

30. $x^4 - 8x^2 - 9 = 0$

31. $2x - 5\sqrt{x} + 3 = 0$

32. $3x - 8\sqrt{x} + 4 = 0$

33. $\sqrt{x + 5} = \sqrt{x} + 1$

34. $\sqrt{x + 1} = 1 - \sqrt{2x}$

Section 8.4 Cramer's Rule

We begin this section with a look at how determinants can be used to solve a system of linear equations in two variables. The method we use is called Cramer's Rule. We state it here as a theorem without proof.

Theorem 8.2 (Cramer's Rule) The solution to the system

$$a_1x + b_1y = c_1$$
$$a_2x + b_2y = c_2$$

is given by

$$x = \frac{D_x}{D}, \qquad y = \frac{D_y}{D}$$

where

$$D = \begin{vmatrix} a_1 & b_1 \\ a_2 & b_2 \end{vmatrix} \qquad D_x = \begin{vmatrix} c_1 & b_1 \\ c_2 & b_2 \end{vmatrix} \qquad D_y = \begin{vmatrix} a_1 & c_1 \\ a_2 & c_2 \end{vmatrix} \qquad (D \neq 0)$$

The determinant D is made up of the coefficients of x and y in the original system. The terms D_x and D_y are found by replacing the coefficients of x or y by the constant terms in the original system. Notice also that Cramer's rule does not apply if $D = 0$. In this case the equations are either inconsistent or dependent.

▼ **Example 1** Use Cramer's rule to solve

$$2x - 3y = 4$$
$$4x + 5y = 3$$

Solution We begin by calculating the determinants D, D_x, and D_y:

$$D = \begin{vmatrix} 2 & -3 \\ 4 & 5 \end{vmatrix} = 2(5) - 4(-3) = 22$$

$$D_x = \begin{vmatrix} 4 & -3 \\ 3 & 5 \end{vmatrix} = 4(5) - 3(-3) = 29$$

$$D_y = \begin{vmatrix} 2 & 4 \\ 4 & 3 \end{vmatrix} = 2(3) - 4(4) = -10$$

$$x = \frac{D_x}{D} = \frac{29}{22} \quad \text{and} \quad y = \frac{D_y}{D} = \frac{-10}{22} = -\frac{5}{11}$$

The solution set for the system is $\{(\frac{29}{22}, -\frac{5}{11})\}$. ▲

Cramer's rule can be applied to systems of linear equations in three variables also.

Practice Problems

1. Use Cramer's rule to solve

$$3x - 5y = 2$$
$$2x + 4y = 1$$

Answer
1. $(\frac{13}{22}, -\frac{1}{22})$

Theorem 8.3 (Also Cramer's Rule) The solution set to the system

$$a_1x + b_1y + c_1z = d_1$$
$$a_2x + b_2y + c_2z = d_2$$
$$a_3x + b_3y + c_3z = d_3$$

is given by

$$x = \frac{D_x}{D}, \qquad y = \frac{D_y}{D}, \qquad \text{and } z = \frac{D_z}{D}$$

where

$$D = \begin{vmatrix} a_1 & b_1 & c_1 \\ a_2 & b_2 & c_2 \\ a_3 & b_3 & c_3 \end{vmatrix} \qquad D_x = \begin{vmatrix} d_1 & b_1 & c_1 \\ d_2 & b_2 & c_2 \\ d_3 & b_3 & c_3 \end{vmatrix} \qquad (D \neq 0)$$

$$D_y = \begin{vmatrix} a_1 & d_1 & c_1 \\ a_2 & d_2 & c_2 \\ a_3 & d_3 & c_3 \end{vmatrix} \qquad D_z = \begin{vmatrix} a_1 & b_1 & d_1 \\ a_2 & b_2 & d_2 \\ a_3 & b_3 & d_3 \end{vmatrix}$$

Again the determinant D consists of the coefficients of x, y, and z in the original system. The determinants D_x, D_y, and D_z are found by replacing the coefficients of x, y, and z respectively with the constant terms from the original system. If $D = 0$, there is no unique solution to the system.

2. Use Cramer's rule to solve

$$x + 2y + z = 2$$
$$x + y - z = 6$$
$$x - y + z = -4$$

▼ **Example 2** Use Cramer's rule to solve

$$x + y + z = 6$$
$$2x - y + z = 3$$
$$x + 2y - 3z = -4$$

Solution This is the same system used in Example 1 in Section 8.2, so we can compare Cramer's rule with our previous methods of solving a system in three variables. We begin by setting up and evaluating D, D_x, D_y, and D_z. (Recall that there are a number of ways to evaluate a 3×3 determinant. Since we have four of these determinants, we can use both Methods 1 and 2 from the previous section.) We evaluate D using Method 1 from Section 8.3.

Note: When we are solving a system of linear equations by Cramer's rule, it is best to find the determinant D first. If $D = 0$, then there is no unique solution to the system and we may not want to go further.

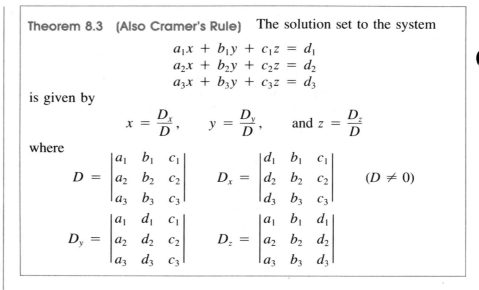

$$= 3 + 1 + 4 - (-1) - (2) - (-6) = 13$$

We evaluate D_x using Method 2 from Section 8.3 and expanding across row 1:

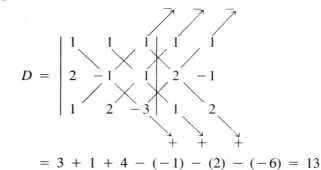

$$D_x = \begin{vmatrix} 6 & 1 & 1 \\ 3 & -1 & 1 \\ -4 & 2 & -3 \end{vmatrix} = 6\begin{vmatrix} -1 & 1 \\ 2 & -3 \end{vmatrix} - 1\begin{vmatrix} 3 & 1 \\ -4 & -3 \end{vmatrix} + 1\begin{vmatrix} 3 & -1 \\ -4 & 2 \end{vmatrix}$$

$$= 6(1) - 1(-5) + 1(2)$$
$$= 13$$

Find D_y by expanding across row 2:

$$D_y = \begin{vmatrix} 1 & 6 & 1 \\ 2 & 3 & 1 \\ 1 & -4 & -3 \end{vmatrix} = -2 \begin{vmatrix} 6 & 1 \\ -4 & -3 \end{vmatrix} + 3 \begin{vmatrix} 1 & 1 \\ 1 & -3 \end{vmatrix} - 1 \begin{vmatrix} 1 & 6 \\ 1 & -4 \end{vmatrix}$$

$$= -2(-14) + 3(-4) - 1(-10)$$
$$= 26$$

Note: We are solving each of these determinants by expanding about different rows or columns just to show the different ways these determinants can be evaluated.

Find D_z by expanding down column 1:

$$D_z = \begin{vmatrix} 1 & 1 & 6 \\ 2 & -1 & 3 \\ 1 & 2 & -4 \end{vmatrix} = 1 \begin{vmatrix} -1 & 3 \\ 2 & -4 \end{vmatrix} - 2 \begin{vmatrix} 1 & 6 \\ 2 & -4 \end{vmatrix} + 1 \begin{vmatrix} 1 & 6 \\ -1 & 3 \end{vmatrix}$$

$$= 1(-2) - 2(-16) + 1(9)$$
$$= 39$$

$$x = \frac{D_x}{D} = \frac{13}{13} = 1 \qquad y = \frac{D_y}{D} = \frac{26}{13} = 2 \qquad z = \frac{D_z}{D} = \frac{39}{13} = 3$$

The solution set is $\{(1, 2, 3)\}$. ▲

▼ **Example 3** Use Cramer's rule to solve

$$\begin{array}{rcr} x + y & = & -1 \\ 2x - z & = & 3 \\ y + 2z & = & -1 \end{array}$$

3. Use Cramer's rule to solve

$$\begin{array}{rcr} x + y & = & 3 \\ 2x - z & = & 3 \\ y + 2z & = & 9 \end{array}$$

Solution It is helpful to rewrite the system using zeros for the coefficients of those variables not shown:

$$\begin{array}{rcr} x + y + 0z & = & -1 \\ 2x + 0y - z & = & 3 \\ 0x + y + 2z & = & -1 \end{array}$$

The four determinants used in Cramer's rule are

$$D = \begin{vmatrix} 1 & 1 & 0 \\ 2 & 0 & -1 \\ 0 & 1 & 2 \end{vmatrix} = -3$$

$$D_x = \begin{vmatrix} -1 & 1 & 0 \\ 3 & 0 & -1 \\ -1 & 1 & 2 \end{vmatrix} = -6$$

$$D_y = \begin{vmatrix} 1 & -1 & 0 \\ 2 & 3 & -1 \\ 0 & -1 & 2 \end{vmatrix} = 9$$

$$D_z = \begin{vmatrix} 1 & 1 & -1 \\ 2 & 0 & 3 \\ 0 & 1 & -1 \end{vmatrix} = -3$$

$$x = \frac{D_x}{D} = \frac{-6}{-3} = 2, \qquad y = \frac{D_y}{D} = \frac{9}{-3} = -3, \qquad z = \frac{D_z}{D} = \frac{-3}{-3} = 1$$

The solution set is $\{(2, -3, 1)\}$. ▲

Answer
3. $(4, -1, 5)$

Finally, we should mention the possible situations that can occur when the determinant D is 0, when we are using Cramer's rule.

If $D = 0$ and at least one of the other determinants, D_x or D_y (or D_z) are not 0 then the system is inconsistent. In this case, there is no solution to the system.

On the other hand, if $D = 0$ and both D_x and D_y (and D_z in a system of three equations in three variables) are 0, then the system is a dependent one.

Problem Set 8.4

Solve each of the following systems using Cramer's rule.

1. $2x - 3y = 3$
$4x - 2y = 10$

2. $3x + y = -2$
$-3x + 2y = -4$

3. $5x - 2y = 4$
$-10x + 4y = 1$

4. $-4x + 3y = -11$
$5x + 4y = 6$

5. $4x - 7y = 3$
$5x + 2y = -3$

6. $3x - 4y = 7$
$6x - 2y = 5$

7. $9x - 8y = 4$
$2x + 3y = 6$

8. $4x - 7y = 10$
$-3x + 2y = -9$

Name _____

Class _____

Date _____

Answers

1. _____   **2.** _____

3. _____   **4.** _____

5. _____   **6.** _____

7. _____   **8.** _____

Answers

9. _____ 10. _____

11. _____ 12. _____

13. _____ 14. _____

9.
$$x + y - z = 2$$
$$-x + y + z = 3$$
$$x + y + z = 4$$

10.
$$-x - y + z = 1$$
$$x - y + z = 3$$
$$x + y - z = 4$$

11.
$$x + y + z = 4$$
$$x - y - z = 2$$
$$2x + 2y - z = 2$$

12.
$$-x + y + 3z = 6$$
$$x + y + 2z = 7$$
$$2x + 3y + z = 4$$

13.
$$3x - y + 2z = 4$$
$$6x - 2y + 4z = 8$$
$$x - 5y + 2z = 1$$

14.
$$2x - 3y + z = 1$$
$$3x - y - z = 4$$
$$4x - 6y + 2z = 3$$

15. $2x - y + 3z = 4$
$\quad\ \ x - 5y - 2z = 1$
$\quad -4x - 2y + z = 3$

16. $4x - y + 5z = 1$
$\quad\ 2x + 3y + 4z = 5$
$\quad\ \ x + y + 3z = 2$

Name _____

Class _____

Date _____

Answers

15. _____   16. _____

17. _____   18. _____

19. _____   20. _____

17. $-x - 2y = 1$
$\quad\ \ x + 2z = 11$
$\quad\ 2y + z = 0$

18. $\quad x + y = 2$
$\quad -x + z = 0$
$\quad\ 2x + z = 3$

19. $\ x - y = 2$
$\quad 3x + z = 11$
$\quad\ \ y - 2z = -3$

20. $4x + 5y = -1$
$\quad\ 2y + 3z = -5$
$\quad\ \ x + 2z = -1$

Answers

21. _____

22a. _____

b. _____

c. _____

23. _____

24. _____

25. _____

26. _____

21. If a company has fixed costs of $100 per week and each item it produces costs $10 to manufacture, then the total cost (y) per week to produce x items is

$$y = 10x + 100$$

If the company sells each item it manufactures for $12, then the total amount of money (y) the company brings in for selling x items is

$$y = 12x$$

Use Cramer's rule to solve the system

$$y = 10x + 100$$
$$y = 12x$$

for x to find the number of items the company must sell per week in order to break even.

22. Suppose a company has fixed costs of $200 per week, and each item it produces costs $20 to manufacture.

a. Write an equation that gives the total cost per week, y, to manufacture x items.

b. If each item sells for $25, write an equation that gives the total amount of money, y, the company brings in for selling x items.

c. Use Cramer's rule to find the number of items the company must sell each week to break even.

Review Problems   The following problems review material we covered in Section 4.6. They are taken from the book *Academic Algebra,* written by William J. Milne and published by the American Book Company in 1901.

23. Find a fraction whose value is $\frac{4}{7}$ and whose denominator is 15 greater than its numerator.

24. Find a fraction whose value is $\frac{2}{3}$ and whose numerator is 3 greater than half of its denominator.

25. Three pipes empty into a cistern. One can fill the cistern in 5 hours, another in 6 hours, and the third in 10 hours. How long will it take three pipes together to fill it?

26. A cistern can be filled by one pipe in 20 minutes, by another in 15 minutes, and it can be emptied by a third in 10 minutes. If the three pipes are running at the same time, how long will it take to fill the cistern?

Section 8.5   Word Problems

Many times word problems involve more than one unknown quantity. If a problem is stated in terms of two unknowns and we represent each unknown quantity with a different variable, then we must write the relationship between the variables with two equations. The two equations written in terms of the two variables form a system of linear equations which we solve using the methods developed in this section. If we find a problem that relates three unknown quantities, then we need three different equations in order to form a linear system we can solve.

▼ **Example 1**   One number is 2 more than 3 times another. Their sum is 26. Find the two numbers.

Solution   If we let x and y represent the two numbers, then the translation of the first sentence in the problem into an equation would be

$$y = 3x + 2$$

The second sentence gives us a second equation:

$$x + y = 26$$

The linear system that describes the situation is

$$x + y = 26$$
$$y = 3x + 2$$

Substituting the expression for y from the second equation into the first and solving for x yields

$$x + (3x + 2) = 26$$
$$4x + 2 = 26$$
$$4x = 24$$
$$x = 6$$

Using $x = 6$ in $y = 3x + 2$ gives the second number:

$$y = 3(6) + 2$$
$$y = 20$$

The two numbers are 6 and 20. Their sum is 26, and the second is 2 more than 3 times the first.   ▲

▼ **Example 2**   Suppose 850 tickets were sold for the game for a total of $1,100. If adult tickets cost $1.50 and children's tickets cost $1.00, how many of each kind of ticket were sold?

Solution   If we let $x =$ the number of adult tickets and $y =$ the number of children's tickets, then

$$x + y = 850$$

since a total of 850 tickets were sold. Since each adult ticket costs $1.50 and each children's ticket costs $1.00 and the total amount of money paid for tickets was $1,100, a second equation is

$$1.50x + 1.00y = 1,100$$

Practice Problems

1. A number is 1 less than twice another. Their sum is 14. Find the two numbers.

2. There were 750 tickets sold for a basketball game for a total of $1,090. If adult tickets cost $2.00 and children's tickets cost $1.00, how many of each kind were sold?

Answers
1. 5, 9   **2.** 340 adult; 410 children

The same information can also be obtained by summarizing the problem with a table. One such table follows. Notice that the two equations we obtained previously are given by the two rows of the table.

	Adult Tickets	Children's Tickets	Total
Number	x	y	850
Value	$1.50x$	$1.00y$	1100

Whether we use a table to summarize the information in the problem, or just talk our way through the problem, the system of equations that describes the situation is

$$\begin{aligned} x + y &= 850 \\ 1.50x + 1.00y &= 1100 \end{aligned}$$

If we multiply the second equation by 10 to clear it of decimals, we have the system

$$\begin{aligned} x + y &= 850 \\ 15x + 10y &= 11{,}000 \end{aligned}$$

Multiplying the first equation by -10 and adding the result to the second equation eliminates the variable y from the system:

$$\begin{aligned} -10x - 10y &= -8{,}500 \\ \underline{15x + 10y} &= \underline{11{,}000} \\ 5x &= 2{,}500 \\ x &= 500 \end{aligned}$$

The number of adult tickets sold was 500. To find the number of children's tickets, we substitute $x = 500$ into $x + y = 850$ to get

$$\begin{aligned} 500 + y &= 850 \\ y &= 350 \end{aligned}$$

The number of children's tickets sold was 350.   ▲

3. A person invests $12,000 in two accounts. One account earns 6% annually and the other earns 7%. If the total interest in a year is $790, how much was invested in each account?

▼ **Example 3** Suppose a person invests a total of $10,000 in two accounts. One account earns 8% annually and the other earns 9% annually. If the total interest earned from both accounts in a year is $860, how much is invested in each account?

Solution The form of the solution to this problem is very similar to that of Example 2. We let x equal the amount invested at 9% and y be the amount invested at 8%. Since the total investment is $10,000, one relationship between x and y can be written as

$$x + y = 10{,}000$$

The total interest earned from both accounts is $860. The amount of interest earned on x dollars at 9% is $0.09x$, while the amount of interest earned on y dollars at 8% is $0.08y$. This relationship is represented by the equation

$$0.09x + 0.08y = 860$$

The two equations we have just written can also be found by first summarizing the information from the problem in a table. Again, the two rows of the table yield the two equations just written. Here is the table.

	Dollars at 9%	Dollars at 8%	Total
Number	x	y	10,000
Interest	0.09x	·0.08y	860

The system of equations that describes this situation is given by

$$x + \quad y = 10,000$$
$$0.09x + 0.08y = \quad 860$$

Multiplying the second equation by 100 will clear it of decimals. The system that results after doing so is

$$x + \quad y = 10,000$$
$$9x + 8y = 86,000$$

We can eliminate y from this system by multiplying the first equation by -8 and adding the result to the second equation.

$$-8x - 8y = -80,000$$
$$\underline{\quad 9x + 8y = \quad 86,000}$$
$$x = \quad 6,000$$

The amount of money invested at 9% is $6,000. Since the total investment was $10,000, the amount invested at 8% must be $4,000.

▲

▼ **Example 4**   How much 20% alcohol solution and 50% alcohol solution must be mixed to get 12 gallons of 30% alcohol solution?

Solution   To solve this problem we must first understand that a 20% alcohol solution is 20% alcohol and 80% water.

Let x = the number of gallons of 20% alcohol solution needed, and y = the number of gallons of 50% alcohol solution needed. Since we must end up with a total of 12 gallons of solution, one equation for the system is

$$x + y = 12$$

The amount of alcohol in the x gallons of 20% solution is 0.20x, while the amount of alcohol in the y gallons of 50% solution is 0.50y. Since the total amount of alcohol in the 20% and 50% solutions must add up to the amount of alcohol in the 12 gallons of 30% solution, the second equation in our system can be written as

$$0.20x + 0.50y = 0.30(12)$$

Again, let's make a table that summarizes the information we have to this point in the problem.

	20% Solution	50% Solution	Final Solution
Total Number of Gallons	x	y	12
Gallons of Alcohol	0.20x	0.50y	0.30(12)

4.   How much 30% alcohol solution and 70% alcohol solution must be mixed to get 16 gallons of 60% solution?

Answer
4. 4 gallons 30%; 12 gallons 70%

Our system of equations is

$$x + y = 12$$
$$0.20x + 0.50y = 0.30(12) = 3.6$$

Multiplying the second equation by 10 gives us an equivalent system

$$x + y = 12$$
$$2x + 5y = 36$$

Multiplying the top equation by -2 to eliminate the x-variable, we have

$$
\begin{array}{r}
-2x - 2y = -24 \\
\underline{2x + 5y = 36} \\
3y = 12 \\
y = 4
\end{array}
$$

Substituting $y = 4$ into $x + y = 12$, we solve for x:

$$x + 4 = 12$$
$$x = 8$$

It takes 8 gallons of 20% alcohol solution and 4 gallons of 50% alcohol solution to produce 12 gallons of 30% alcohol solution. ▲

5. A boat can travel 20 miles downstream in 2 hours. The same boat can travel 18 miles upstream in 3 hours. What is the speed of the boat in still water, and what is the speed of the current?

▼ **Example 5** It takes 2 hours for a boat to travel 28 miles downstream. The same boat can travel 18 miles upstream in 3 hours. What is the speed of the boat in still water and the speed of the current of the river?

Solution Let x = the speed of the boat in still water and y = the speed of the current. Using a table as we did in Section 4.6, we have

	d	r	t
Upstream	18	$x - y$	3
Downstream	28	$x + y$	2

Since $d = r \cdot t$, the system we need to solve the problem is

$$18 = (x - y) \cdot 3$$
$$28 = (x + y) \cdot 2$$

which is equivalent to

$$6 = x - y$$
$$14 = x + y$$

Adding the two equations, we have

$$20 = 2x$$
$$x = 10$$

Substituting $x = 10$ into $14 = x + y$, we see that

$$y = 4$$

The speed of the boat in still water is 10 mph and the speed of the current is 4 mph. ▲

Answer
5. Boat 8 mph; current 2 mph

▼ **Example 6** A coin collection consists of 14 coins with a total value of $1.35. If the coins are nickels, dimes, and quarters, and the number of nickels is three less than twice the number of dimes, how many of each coin are there in the collection?

Solution Since we have three types of coins we will have to use three variables. Let's let x = the number of nickels, y = the number of dimes, and z = the number of quarters. Since the total number of coins is 14, we have our first equation

$$x + y + z = 14$$

Since the number of nickels is three less than twice the number of dimes, we have a second equation.

$$x = 2y - 3 \quad \text{which is equivalent to} \quad x - 2y = -3$$

Our last equation is obtained by considering the value of each coin and the total value of the collection. Let's write the equation in terms of cents, so we won't have to clear it of decimals later.

$$5x + 10y + 25z = 135$$

Here is our system, with the equations numbered for reference:

$$
\begin{aligned}
x + \quad y + \quad z &= 14 \quad &(1) \\
x - \quad 2y \quad\quad &= -3 \quad &(2) \\
5x + 10y + 25z &= 135 \quad &(3)
\end{aligned}
$$

Let's begin by eliminating x from the first and second equations, and the first and third equations. Adding -1 times the second equation to the first equation gives us an equation in only y and z. We call this equation (4).

$$3y + z = 17 \quad (4)$$

Adding -5 times equation (1) to equation (3) gives us

$$5y + 20z = 65 \quad (5)$$

We can eliminate z from equations (4) and (5) by adding -20 times (4) to (5). Here is the result:

$$
\begin{aligned}
-55y &= -275 \\
y &= 5
\end{aligned}
$$

Substituting $y = 5$ into equation (4) gives us $z = 2$. Substituting $y = 5$ and $z = 2$ into equation (1) gives us $x = 7$. The collection consists of 7 nickels, 5 dimes, and 2 quarters. ▲

6. A collection of nickels, dimes, and quarters consists of 15 coins with a total value of $1.10. If the number of nickels is one less than 4 times the number of dimes, how many of each coin is contained in the collection?

Note: Although we have solved each system of equations in this section by the addition method or the substitution method, we could have used Cramer's rule also. Cramer's rule applies to any system of linear equations with a unique solution.

Answer
6. 11 nickels, 3 dimes, 1 quarter

Problem Set 8.5

Name _____

Class _____

Date _____

Number Problems

1. One number is 3 more than twice another. The sum of the numbers is 18. Find the two numbers.

2. The sum of two numbers is 32. One of the numbers is 4 less than 5 times the other. Find the two numbers.

3. The difference of two numbers is 6. Twice the smaller is 4 more than the larger. Find the two numbers.

4. The larger of two numbers is 5 more than twice the smaller. If the smaller is subtracted from the larger, the result is 12. Find the two numbers.

5. The sum of three numbers is 8. Twice the smallest is 2 less than the largest, while the sum of the largest and smallest is 5. Use a linear system in three variables to find the three numbers.

6. The sum of three numbers is 14. The largest is 4 times the smallest, while the sum of the smallest and twice the largest is 18. Use a linear system in three variables to find the three numbers.

Answers

1. _____   2. _____

3. _____   4. _____

5. _____   6. _____

Ticket and Interest Problems

7. A total of 925 tickets were sold for the game for a total of $1150. If adult tickets sold for $2.00 and children's tickets sold for $1.00, how many of each kind of ticket were sold?

8. If tickets for the show cost $2.00 for adults and $1.50 for children, how many of each kind of ticket were sold if a total of 300 tickets were sold for $525?

9. Mr. Jones has $20,000 to invest. He invests part at 6% and the rest at 7%. If he earns $1280 interest after one year, how much did he invest at each rate?

10. A man invests $17,000 in two accounts. One account earns 5% interest per year and the other 6.5%. If his yearly yield in interest is $970, how much does he invest at each rate?

11. Susan invests twice as much money at 7.5% as she does at 6%. If her total interest after a year is $840, how much does she have invested at each rate?

12. A woman earns $1350 interest from two accounts in a year. If she has three times as much invested at 7% as she does at 6%, how much does she have in each account?

Mixture Problems

Name _____

Class _____

Date _____

Answers

13. How many gallons of 20% alcohol solution and 50% alcohol solution must be mixed to get 9 gallons of 30% alcohol solution?

14. How many ounces of 30% hydrochloric acid solution and 80% hydrochloric acid solution must be mixed to get 10 ounces of 50% hydrochloric acid solution?

15. A mixture of 16% disinfectant solution is to be made from 20% and 14% disinfectant solutions. How much of each solution should be used if 15 gallons of the 16% solution are needed?

16. How much 25% antifreeze and 50% antifreeze should be combined to give 40 gallons of 30% antifreeze?

13. _____ **14.** _____

15. _____ **16.** _____

17. _____ **18.** _____

Rate Problems

17. It takes a boat 2 hours to travel 24 miles downstream and 3 hours to travel 18 miles upstream. What is the speed of the boat in still water and of the current of the river?

18. A boat on a river travels 20 miles downstream in only 2 hours. It takes the same boat 6 hours to travel 12 miles upstream. What are the speed of the boat and the speed of the current?

19. An airplane flying with the wind can cover a certain distance in 2 hours. The return trip against the wind takes $2\frac{1}{2}$ hours. How fast is the plane and what is the speed of the air, if the distance is 600 miles?

20. An airplane covers a distance of 1500 miles in 3 hours when it flies with the wind and $3\frac{1}{3}$ hours when it flies against the wind. What is the speed of the plane in still air?

Coin Problems

21. A collection of nickels, dimes, and quarters consists of 9 coins with a total value of $1.20. If the number of dimes is equal to the number of nickels, find the number of each type of coin.

22. A coin collection consists of 12 coins with a total value of $1.20. If the collection consists only of nickels, dimes, and quarters, and the number of dimes is two more than twice the number of nickels, how many of each type of coin are in the collection?

Review Problems   The following problems review material we covered in Section 6.7.

Solve each inequality and graph the solution set.

23. $x^2 - 2x - 8 \leq 0$ **24.** $x^2 - x - 12 < 0$

25. $2x^2 + 5x - 3 > 0$ **26.** $3x^2 - 5x - 2 \leq 0$

Chapter 8 Summary and Review

● SYSTEMS OF LINEAR EQUATIONS [8.1, 8.2]

A system of linear equations consists of two or more linear equations considered simultaneously. The solution set to a linear system in two variables is the set of ordered pairs that satisfy both equations. The solution set to a linear system in three variables consists of all the ordered triples that satisfy each equation in the system.

1. The solution to the system

$$x + 2y = 4$$
$$x - y = 1$$

is the ordered pair (2, 1). It is the only ordered pair that satisfies both equations.

TO SOLVE A SYSTEM BY THE ADDITION METHOD [8.1]

Step 1: Look the system over to decide which variable will be easiest to eliminate.
Step 2: Use the multiplication property of equality on each equation separately to ensure the coefficients of the variable to be eliminated are opposites.
Step 3: Add the left and right sides of the system produced in Step 2 and solve the resulting equation.
Step 4: Substitute the solution from Step 3 back into any equation with both x and y variables and solve.
Step 5: Check your solutions in both equations if necessary.

2. We can eliminate the y variable from the system in Example 1 by multiplying both sides of the second equation by 2 and adding the result to the first equation

$$x + 2y = 4 \xrightarrow{\text{No change}} x + 2y = 4$$
$$x - y = 1 \xrightarrow{\text{times 2}} \dfrac{2x - 2y = 2}{3x \quad = 6}$$
$$x = 2$$

Substituting $x = 2$ into either of the original two equations gives $y = 1$. The solution is (2, 1).

● TO SOLVE A SYSTEM BY THE SUBSTITUTION METHOD [8.1]

Step 1: Solve either of the equations for one of the variables (this step is not necessary if one of the equations has the correct form already).
Step 2: Substitute the results of Step 1 into the other equation and solve.
Step 3: Substitute the results of Step 2 into an equation with both x and y variables and solve. (The equation produced in Step 1 is usually a good one to use.)
Step 4: Check your solution if necessary.

3. We can apply the substitution method to the system in Example 1 by first solving the second equation for x to get

$$x = y + 1$$

Substituting this expression of x into the first equation we have

$$y + 1 + 2y = 4$$
$$3y + 1 = 4$$
$$3y = 3$$
$$y = 1$$

Using $y = 1$ in either of the original equations gives $x = 2$.

INCONSISTENT AND DEPENDENT EQUATIONS [8.1, 8.2]

Two linear equations that have no solutions in common are said to be *inconsistent*, while two linear equations that have all their solutions in common are said to be *dependent*.

4. If the two lines are parallel, then the system will be inconsistent and the solution is $\varnothing$. If the two lines coincide, then the system is dependent.

2 × 2 DETERMINANTS [8.3]

The value of a 2 × 2 determinant is as follows:

$$\begin{vmatrix} a & c \\ b & d \end{vmatrix} = ad - bc$$

5. $\begin{vmatrix} 3 & 4 \\ -2 & 5 \end{vmatrix} = 15 - (-8) = 23$

6. Expanding $\begin{vmatrix} 1 & 3 & -2 \\ 2 & 0 & 1 \\ 4 & -1 & 1 \end{vmatrix}$

across the first row gives us

$$1\begin{vmatrix} 0 & 1 \\ -1 & 1 \end{vmatrix} - 3\begin{vmatrix} 2 & 1 \\ 4 & 1 \end{vmatrix} - 2\begin{vmatrix} 2 & 0 \\ 4 & -1 \end{vmatrix}$$

$$= 1(1) - 3(-2) - 2(-2)$$

$$= 11$$

7. For the system $\quad x + y = 6$
$\qquad\qquad\qquad 3x - 2y = -2$

we have

$$D = \begin{vmatrix} 1 & 1 \\ 3 & -2 \end{vmatrix} = -5$$

$$x = \frac{-10}{-5} = 2$$

$$D_x = \begin{vmatrix} 6 & 1 \\ -2 & -2 \end{vmatrix} = -10$$

$$y = \frac{-20}{-5} = 4$$

$$D_y = \begin{vmatrix} 1 & 6 \\ 3 & -2 \end{vmatrix} = -20$$

8. For the system

$$x + y = -1$$
$$2x - z = 3$$
$$y + 2z = -1$$

$$D = \begin{vmatrix} 1 & 1 & 0 \\ 2 & 0 & -1 \\ 0 & 1 & 2 \end{vmatrix} = -3$$

$$x = \frac{-6}{-3} = 2$$

$$D_x = \begin{vmatrix} -1 & 1 & 0 \\ 3 & 0 & -1 \\ -1 & 1 & 2 \end{vmatrix} = -6$$

$$y = \frac{9}{-3} = -3$$

$$D_y = \begin{vmatrix} 1 & -1 & 0 \\ 2 & 3 & -1 \\ 0 & -1 & 2 \end{vmatrix} = 9$$

$$z = \frac{-3}{-3} = 1$$

$$D_z = \begin{vmatrix} 1 & 1 & -1 \\ 2 & 0 & 3 \\ 0 & 1 & -1 \end{vmatrix} = -3$$

3×3 DETERMINANTS [8.3]

The definition of a 3×3 determinant is

$$\begin{vmatrix} a_1 & b_1 & c_1 \\ a_2 & b_2 & c_2 \\ a_3 & b_3 & c_3 \end{vmatrix} = \begin{matrix} a_1b_2c_3 + a_3b_1c_2 + a_2b_3c_1 \\ - a_3b_2c_1 - a_1b_3c_2 - a_2b_1c_3 \end{matrix}$$

There are two methods of finding the six products in the expansion of a 3×3 determinant. One method involves a cross-multiplication scheme. The other method involves expanding the determinant by minors.

CRAMER'S RULE FOR A LINEAR SYSTEM IN TWO VARIABLES [8.4]

The solution to the system

$$a_1x + b_1y = c_1$$
$$a_2x + b_2y = c_2$$

is given by

$$x = \frac{D_x}{D} \quad \text{and} \quad y = \frac{D_y}{D} \qquad (D \neq 0)$$

where

$$D = \begin{vmatrix} a_1 & b_1 \\ a_2 & b_2 \end{vmatrix}, \qquad D_x = \begin{vmatrix} c_1 & b_1 \\ c_2 & b_2 \end{vmatrix}, \qquad \text{and } D_y = \begin{vmatrix} a_1 & c_1 \\ a_2 & c_2 \end{vmatrix}$$

CRAMER'S RULE FOR A LINEAR SYSTEM IN THREE VARIABLES [8.4]

The solution to the system

$$a_1x + b_1y + c_1z = d_1$$
$$a_2x + b_2y + c_2z = d_2$$
$$a_3x + b_3y + c_3z = d_3$$

is given by

$$x = \frac{D_x}{D}, \qquad y = \frac{D_y}{D}, \qquad \text{and } z = \frac{D_z}{D} \qquad (D \neq 0)$$

where

$$D = \begin{vmatrix} a_1 & b_1 & c_1 \\ a_2 & b_2 & c_2 \\ a_3 & b_3 & c_3 \end{vmatrix} \qquad D_y = \begin{vmatrix} a_1 & d_1 & c_1 \\ a_2 & d_2 & c_2 \\ a_3 & d_3 & c_3 \end{vmatrix}$$

$$D_x = \begin{vmatrix} d_1 & b_1 & c_1 \\ d_2 & b_2 & c_2 \\ d_3 & b_3 & c_3 \end{vmatrix} \qquad D_z = \begin{vmatrix} a_1 & b_1 & d_1 \\ a_2 & b_2 & d_2 \\ a_3 & b_3 & d_3 \end{vmatrix}$$

Chapter 8 Test

Name _____

Class _____

Date _____

Solve the following systems by the addition method. [8.1]

1. $2x - 5y = -8$
    $3x + y = 5$

2. $4x - 7y = -2$
    $-5x + 6y = -3$

Answers

1. _____

2. _____

3. _____

Solve the following systems by the substitution method. [8.1]

3. $2x - 5y = 14$
    $y = 3x + 8$

4. $6x - 3y = 0$
    $x + 2y = 5$

4. _____

5. _____

6. _____

7. _____

5. Solve the system. [8.2]

$$2x - y + z = 9$$
$$x + y - 3z = -2$$
$$3x + y - z = 6$$

Evaluate each determinant. [8.3]

6. $\begin{vmatrix} 3 & -5 \\ -4 & 2 \end{vmatrix}$

7. $\begin{vmatrix} 1 & 0 & -3 \\ 2 & 1 & 0 \\ 0 & 5 & 4 \end{vmatrix}$

Answers

8. _____

9. _____

10. _____

11. _____

12. _____

Use Cramer's rule to solve. [8.4]

8. $5x - 4y = 2$
$-2x + y = 3$

9. $2x + 4y = 3$
$-4x - 8y = -6$

10. $2x - y + 3z = 2$
$x - 4y - z = 6$
$3x - 2y + z = 4$

11. John invests twice as much money at 6% as he does at 5%. If his investments earn a total of $680 in one year, how much does he have invested at each rate? [8.5]

12. For a woman of average height and weight between the ages of 19 and 22, the Food and Nutrition Board of the National Academy of Sciences has determined the Recommended Daily Allowance (RDA) of ascorbic acid to be 45 mg (milligrams). They also determined the RDA for niacin to be 14 mg for the same woman.

Each ounce of cereal I contains 10 mg of ascorbic acid and 4 mg of niacin, while each ounce of cereal II contains 15 mg of ascorbic acid and 2 mg of niacin. How many ounces of each cereal must the average woman between the ages of 19 and 22 consume in order to have the RDAs for both ascorbic acid and niacin? [8.5]

The following table is a summary of the information given.

	Cereal I	Cereal II	Recommended Daily Allowance (RDA)
Ascorbic acid	10 mg	15 mg	45 mg
Niacin	4 mg	2 mg	14 mg

The Conic Sections

To the student:

This chapter is concerned with four special types of graphs and their associated equations. The four types of graphs are called parabolas, circles, ellipses, and hyperbolas. They are called *conic sections* because each can be found by slicing a cone with a plane as is shown in Figure 1.

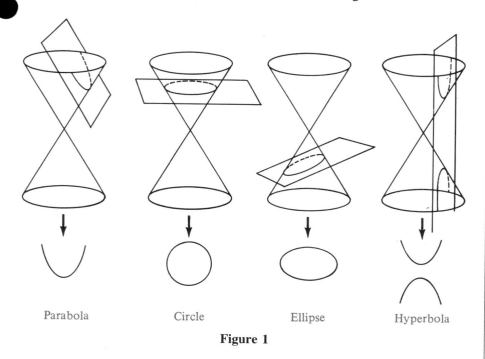

| Parabola | Circle | Ellipse | Hyperbola |

Figure 1

There are many applications associated with conic sections. The planets orbit the sun in elliptical orbits. Many of the comets that come in contact with the gravitational field surrounding the earth travel in parabolic or hyperbolic paths. Flashlight and searchlight mirrors have elliptical or parabolic shapes because of the way surfaces with those shapes reflect light. The arches of many bridges are in the shape of parabolas. Objects fired into the air travel in parabolic paths.

Section 9.1 Graphing Parabolas

The solution set to the equation

$$y = x^2 - 3$$

will consist of ordered pairs. One method of graphing the solution set is to find a number of ordered pairs that satisfy the equation and graph them. We can obtain some ordered pairs that are solutions to $y = x^2 - 3$ by use of a table as follows:

x	$y = x^2 - 3$	y	Solutions
-3	$y = (-3)^2 - 3 = 9 - 3 = 6$	6	$(-3, 6)$
-2	$y = (-2)^2 - 3 = 4 - 3 = 1$	1	$(-2, 1)$
-1	$y = (-1)^2 - 3 = 1 - 3 = -2$	-2	$(-1, -2)$
0	$y = \quad 0^2 - 3 = 0 - 3 = -3$	-3	$(0, -3)$
1	$y = \quad 1^2 - 3 = 1 - 3 = -2$	-2	$(1, -2)$
2	$y = \quad 2^2 - 3 = 4 - 3 = 1$	1	$(2, 1)$
3	$y = \quad 3^2 - 3 = 9 - 3 = 6$	6	$(3, 6)$

Graphing these solutions on a rectangular coordinate system indicates the shape of the graph of $y = x^2 - 3$. (See Figure 2.)

Note: Although it is always possible to graph parabolas by making a table of values of x and y that satisfy the equation, there are other methods that are faster and, in some cases, more accurate. In the rest of this section we will be looking at one such method.

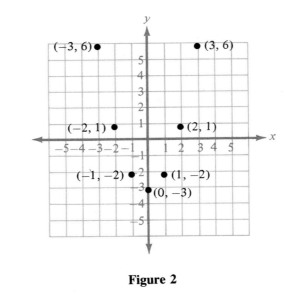

Figure 2

If we were to find more solutions by extending the table to include values of x between those we have already, we would see they follow the same pattern. Connecting the points on the graph with a smooth curve we have the graph of the second-degree equation $y = x^2 - 3$. (See Figure 3.)

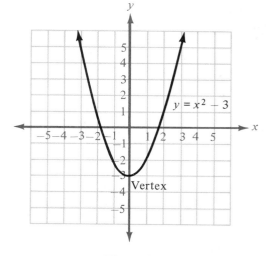

$$y = x^2 - 3$$

Vertex

Figure 3

This graph is an example of a *parabola*. All equations of the form $y = ax^2 + bx + c$, $a \neq 0$, have parabolas for graphs.

The important points associated with the graph of a parabola are the highest (or lowest) point on the graph and the x-intercepts. The y-intercepts can also be useful.

Intercepts for Parabolas

The graph of the equation $y = ax^2 + bx + c$ will cross the y-axis at $y = c$, since substituting $x = 0$ into $y = ax^2 + bx + c$ yields $y = c$.

Since the graph will cross the x-axis when $y = 0$, the x-intercepts are those values of x that are solutions to the quadratic equation $0 = ax^2 + bx + c$.

The Vertex of a Parabola

The highest or lowest point on a parabola is called the *vertex*. The vertex for the graph of $y = ax^2 + bx + c$ will always occur when

$$x = \frac{-b}{2a}$$

To see this we must transform the right side of $y = ax^2 + bx + c$ into an expression that contains x in just one of its terms. This is accomplished by completing the square on the first two terms. Here is what it looks like:

$$y = ax^2 + bx + c$$

$$y = a\left(x^2 + \frac{b}{a}x\right) + c$$

$$y = a\left[x^2 + \frac{b}{a}x + \left(\frac{b}{2a}\right)^2\right] + c - a\left(\frac{b}{2a}\right)^2$$

$$y = a\left(x + \frac{b}{2a}\right)^2 + \frac{4ac - b^2}{4a}$$

It may not look like it, but this last line indicates that the vertex of the graph of $y = ax^2 + bx + c$ has an x-coordinate of $-b/2a$. Since a, b, and

Note: What we are doing here is attempting to explain why the vertex of a parabola always has an x-coordinate of $-b/2a$. But the explanation may not be easy to understand the first time you see it. It may be helpful to look over the examples in this section and the notes that accompany these examples, and then come back and read over this discussion again.

c are constants, the only quantity that is varying in the last expression is the x in $(x + b/2a)^2$. Since the quantity $(x + b/2a)^2$ is the square of $x + b/2a$, the smallest it will ever be is 0, and that will happen when $x = -b/2a$.

We can use the vertex point along with the x- and y-intercepts to sketch the graph of any equation of the form $y = ax^2 + bx + c$. Here is a summary of the preceding information.

Graphing Parabolas

The graph of $y = ax^2 + bx + c$ will have

   1. a y-intercept at $y = c$
   2. x-intercepts (if they exist) at

$$x = \frac{-b \pm \sqrt{b^2 - 4ac}}{2a}$$

   3. a vertex when $x = -b/2a$

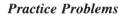

Practice Problems

1. Graph $y = x^2 - 2x - 3$.

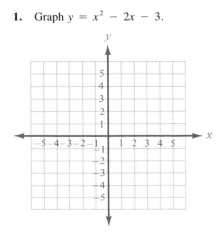

▼ **Example 1**   Sketch the graph of $y = x^2 - 6x + 5$.

Solution   To find the x-intercepts we let $y = 0$ and solve for x:

$$0 = x^2 - 6x + 5$$
$$0 = (x - 5)(x - 1)$$
$$x = 5 \quad \text{or} \quad x = 1$$

To find the coordinates of the vertex we first find

$$x = \frac{-b}{2a} = \frac{-(-6)}{2(1)} = 3$$

The x-coordinate of the vertex is 3. To find the y-coordinate we substitute 3 for x in our original equation:

$$y = 3^2 - 6(3) + 5 = 9 - 18 + 5 = -4$$

The graph crosses the x-axis at 1 and 5 and has its vertex at $(3, -4)$. Plotting these points and connecting them with a smooth curve, we have the graph shown in Figure 4. The graph is a parabola that opens up, so we say the graph is *concave up*. The vertex is the lowest point on the graph.

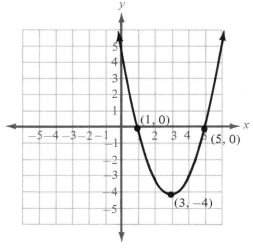

Figure 4

Answer
1. See Solutions Section for all answers in this section.

Another way to locate the vertex of this parabola is by completing the square on the first two terms on the right side of the equation $y = x^2 - 6x + 5$. In this case, we would do so by adding 9 to and subtracting 9 from the right side of the equation. This amounts to adding 0 to the equation, so we know we haven't changed its solutions. This is what it looks like:

$$y = (x^2 - 6x \quad\ ) + 5$$
$$y = (x^2 - 6x + \mathbf{9}) + 5 - \mathbf{9}$$
$$y = (x - 3)^2 - 4$$

You may have to look at this last equation awhile to see this, but when $x = 3$, then $y = (x - 3)^2 - 4 = 0^2 - 4 = -4$ is the smallest y will ever be. And that is why the vertex is at $(3, -4)$. As a matter of fact, this is the same kind of reasoning we used when we derived the formula $x = -b/2a$ for the x-coordinate of the vertex. ▲

▼ **Example 2** Graph $y = -x^2 - 2x + 3$.

2. Graph $y = -x^2 + 2x + 8$.

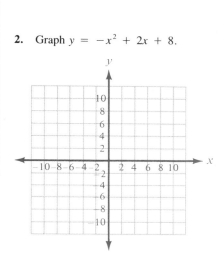

Solution   To find the x-intercepts, we let $y = 0$:

$$0 = -x^2 - 2x + 3$$
$$0 = x^2 + 2x - 3 \qquad \text{Multiply each side by } -1$$
$$0 = (x + 3)(x - 1)$$
$$x = -3 \quad \text{or} \quad x = 1$$

The x-coordinate of the vertex is given by

$$x = \frac{-b}{2a} = \frac{-(-2)}{2(-1)} = \frac{2}{-2} = -1$$

To find the y-coordinate of the vertex, we substitute -1 for x in our original equation to get

$$y = -(-1)^2 - 2(-1) + 3 = -1 + 2 + 3 = 4$$

Our parabola has x-intercepts at -3 and 1, and a vertex at $(-1, 4)$. Figure 5 shows the graph. We say the graph is *concave down* since it opens downward.

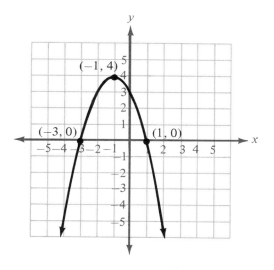

Figure 5

Again, we could have obtained the coordinates of the vertex by completing the square on the first two terms of the right side of our equation. To do so we must first factor -1 from the first two terms. (Remember, the leading coefficient must be 1 in order to complete the square.) When we complete the square, we add 1 inside the parentheses, which actually decreases the right side of the equation by -1 since everything in the parentheses is multiplied by -1. To make up for it, we add 1 outside the parentheses.

$$y = -1(x^2 + 2x \quad\;\;) + 3$$
$$y = -1(x^2 + 2x + \mathbf{1}) + 3 + \mathbf{1}$$
$$y = -1(x + 1)^2 + 4$$

The last line tells us that the *largest* value of y will be 4, and that will occur when $x = -1$. ▲

3. Graph $y = 2x^2 - 4x + 1$.

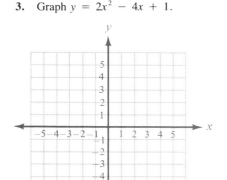

Note: To find the coordinates of the vertex by completing the square we would use the following procedure:

$$y = 3(x^2 - 2x \quad\;\;) + 1$$
$$y = 3(x^2 - 2x + \mathbf{1}) + 1 - \mathbf{3}$$
$$y = 3(x - 1)^2 - 2$$

From the last line we see that the vertex occurs at $(1, -2)$.

▼ **Example 3** Graph $y = 3x^2 - 6x + 1$.

Solution To find the x-intercepts, we let $y = 0$ and solve for x:

$$0 = 3x^2 - 6x + 1$$

Since the right side of this equation does not factor, we can look at the discriminant to see what kind of solutions are possible. The discriminant for this equation is

$$b^2 - 4ac = 36 - 4(3)(1) = 24$$

Since the discriminant is a positive number but not a perfect square, the equation will have irrational solutions. This means that the x-intercepts are irrational numbers and will have to be approximated with decimals using the quadratic formula. Rather than use the quadratic formula, let's find some other points on the graph.

The x-coordinate of the vertex is

$$x = \frac{-b}{2a} = \frac{-(-6)}{2(3)} = 1$$

To find the y-coordinate of the vertex, we let $x = 1$:

$$y = 3(1)^2 - 6(1) + 1 = 3 - 6 + 1 = -2$$

The vertex is $(1, -2)$. If we can find two points, one on each side of the vertex, we can sketch the graph. Let's let $x = 0$ and $x = 2$ since each of these numbers is the same distance from $x = 1$, and $x = 0$ will give us the y-intercept.

When $x = 0$ When $x = 2$
$$y = 3(0)^2 - 6(0) + 1 \qquad\qquad y = 3(2)^2 - 6(2) + 1$$
$$= 0 - 0 + 1 \qquad\qquad\qquad\qquad = 12 - 12 + 1$$
$$= 1 \qquad\qquad\qquad\qquad\qquad\quad\;\; = 1$$

The two points just found are $(0, 1)$ and $(2, 1)$. Plotting these two points along with the vertex $(1, -2)$, we have the graph shown in Figure 6.

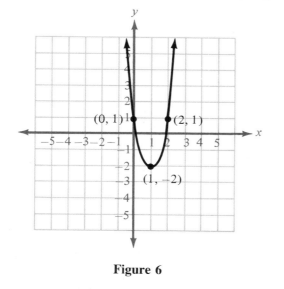

Figure 6   ▲

▼ **Example 4** Graph $y = -2x^2 + 6x - 5$.

Solution Letting $y = 0$, we have

$$0 = -2x^2 + 6x - 5$$

Again, the right side of this equation does not factor. The discriminant is $b^2 - 4ac = 36 - 4(-2)(-5) = -4$, which indicates that the solutions are complex numbers. This means that our original equation does not have x-intercepts. The graph does not cross the x-axis.

Let's find the vertex. Using our formula for the x-coordinate of the vertex, we have:

$$x = \frac{-b}{2a} = \frac{-6}{2(-2)} = \frac{6}{4} = \frac{3}{2}$$

To find the y-coordinate, we let $x = \frac{3}{2}$:

$$y = -2\left(\frac{3}{2}\right)^2 + 6\left(\frac{3}{2}\right) - 5$$

$$= \frac{-18}{4} + \frac{18}{2} - 5$$

$$= \frac{-18 + 36 - 20}{4}$$

$$= -\frac{1}{2}$$

The vertex is $\left(\frac{3}{2}, -\frac{1}{2}\right)$. Since this is the only point we have so far, we must find two others. Let's let $x = 3$ and $x = 0$, since each point is the same distance from $x = \frac{3}{2}$ and on either side:

When $x = 3$
$$y = -2(3)^2 + 6(3) - 5$$
$$= -18 + 18 - 5$$
$$= -5$$

When $x = 0$
$$y = -2(0)^2 + 6(0) - 5$$
$$= 0 + 0 - 5$$
$$= -5$$

4. Graph $y = -x^2 + 4x - 5$.

Note: Completing the square to find the vertex looks like this:

$$y = -2(x^2 - 3x \qquad) - 5$$
$$y = -2\left(x^2 - 3x + \frac{9}{4}\right) - 5 + \frac{9}{2}$$
$$y = -2\left(x - \frac{3}{2}\right)^2 - \frac{1}{2}$$

The vertex is at $\left(\frac{3}{2}, -\frac{1}{2}\right)$.

Note: We see from the examples of this section that the graph of $y = ax^2 + bx + c$ is concave up whenever $a > 0$ and concave down whenever $a < 0$.

The two additional points on the graph are $(3, -5)$ and $(0, -5)$. Figure 7 shows the graph.

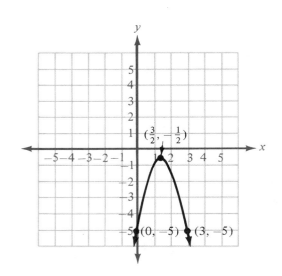

Figure 7

The graph is concave-down. The vertex is the highest point on the graph. ▲

Name _____ Class _____ Date _____

Problem Set 9.1

For each of the following equations, give the x-intercepts and the coordinates of the vertex and sketch the graph.

1. $y = x^2 + 2x - 3$

2. $y = x^2 - 2x - 3$

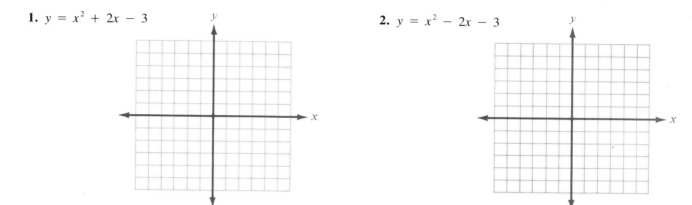

3. $y = -x^2 - 4x + 5$

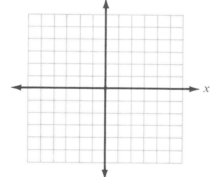

4. $y = -x^2 + 4x - 5$

5. $y = x^2 - 1$

6. $y = x^2 - 4$

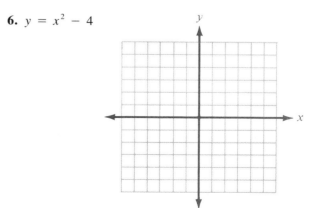

7. $y = -x^2 + 9$

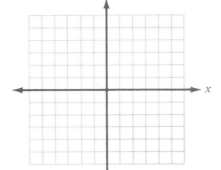

8. $y = -x^2 + 1$

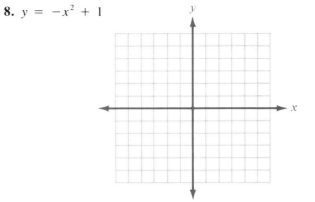

9. $y = 2x^2 - 4x - 6$

10. $y = 2x^2 + 4x - 6$

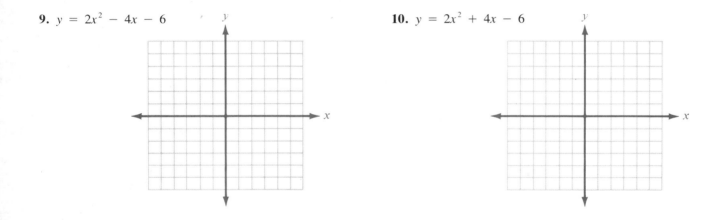

11. $y = x^2 - 2x - 4$

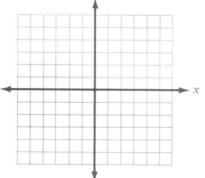

12. $y = x^2 - 2x - 2$

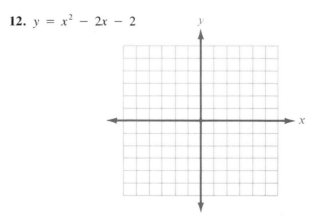

Name _____ Class _____ Date _____

Find the vertex and any two convenient points to sketch the graphs of the following.

13. $y = x^2 - 4x - 4$

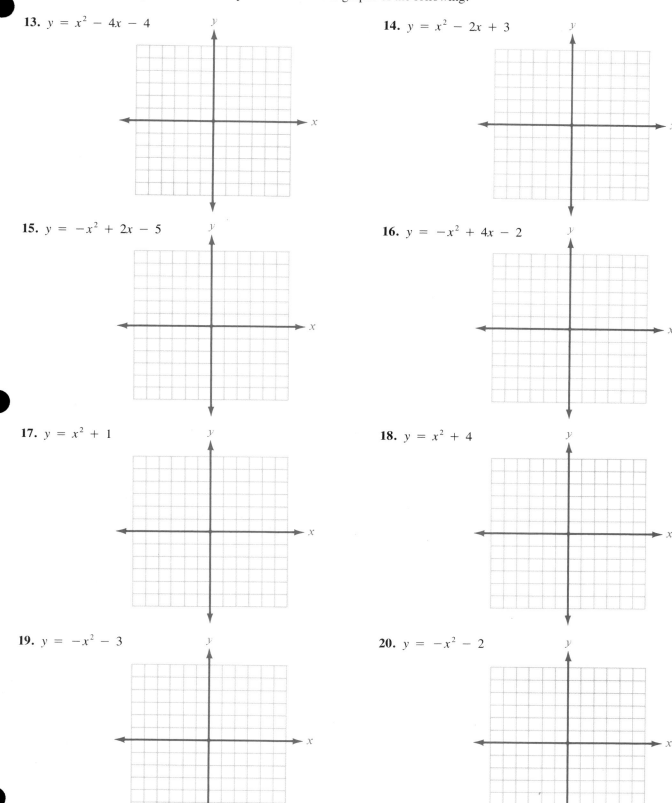

14. $y = x^2 - 2x + 3$

15. $y = -x^2 + 2x - 5$

16. $y = -x^2 + 4x - 2$

17. $y = x^2 + 1$

18. $y = x^2 + 4$

19. $y = -x^2 - 3$

20. $y = -x^2 - 2$

Answers

23. _____

24a. _____

  b. _____

25. _____

26. _____

27. _____

28. _____

29. _____

30. _____

31. _____

32. _____

21. $y = 3x^2 + 4x + 1$ **22.** $y = 2x^2 + 4x + 3$

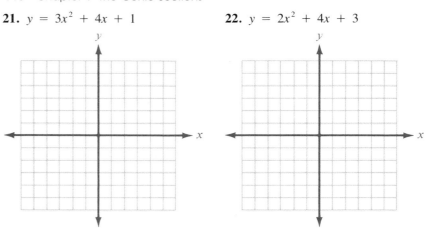

23. An arrow is shot straight up into the air with an initial velocity of 128 feet/second. If h is the height of the arrow at any time t, then the equation that gives h in terms of t is $h = 128t - 16t^2$. Find the maximum height attained by the arrow.

24. A company finds that its weekly profit P, obtained by selling x items is given by the equation $P = -2x^2 + 160x + 1,000$.

  a. How many items must they sell to obtain their maximum profit?
  b. What is their maximum profit?

Review Problems   The following problems review material we covered in Section 6.2. Reviewing these problems will help you in the next section.

Add a last term to each of the following so that the trinomial that results is a perfect square trinomial. In each case write the binomial square that it is equal to.

25. $x^2 + 6x$ **26.** $x^2 - 6x$

27. $x^2 - 10x$ **28.** $x^2 + 4x$

29. $x^2 + 8x$ **30.** $x^2 - 14x$

31. $x^2 + 3x$ **32.** $x^2 + 5x$

Section 9.2   The Circle

Before we find the general equation of a circle, we must first derive what is known as the *distance formula*.

Suppose (x_1, y_1) and (x_2, y_2) are any two points in the first quadrant. (Actually, we could choose the two points to be anywhere on the coordinate plane. It is just more convenient to have them in the first quadrant.) We can name the points P_1 and P_2, respectively, and draw the diagram shown in Figure 8.

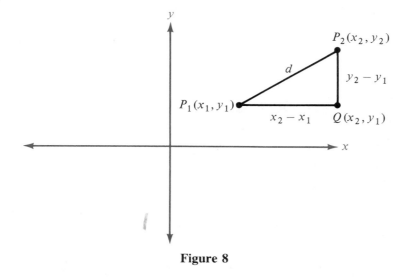

Figure 8

Notice the coordinates of point Q. The x-coordinate is x_2 since Q is directly below point P_2. The y-coordinate of Q is y_1 since Q is directly across from point P_1. It is evident from the diagram that the length of P_2Q is $y_2 - y_1$ and the length of P_1Q is $x_2 - x_1$. Using the Pythagorean theorem, we have

$$(P_1P_2)^2 = (P_1Q)^2 + (P_2Q)^2$$

or

$$d^2 = (x_2 - x_1)^2 + (y_2 - y_1)^2$$

Taking the square root of both sides, we have

$$d = \sqrt{(x_2 - x_1)^2 + (y_2 - y_1)^2}$$

We know this is the positive square root, since d is the distance from P_1 to P_2 and must therefore be positive. This formula is called the *distance formula*.

▼   **Example 1**   Find the distance between $(3, 5)$ and $(2, -1)$.

Solution   If we let $(3, 5)$ be (x_1, y_1) and $(2, -1)$ be (x_2, y_2) and apply the distance formula, we have

$$\begin{aligned} d &= \sqrt{(2 - 3)^2 + (-1 - 5)^2} \\ &= \sqrt{(-1)^2 + (-6)^2} \\ &= \sqrt{1 + 36} \\ &= \sqrt{37} \end{aligned}$$

▲

Practice Problems

1.   Find the distance between $(-4, 1)$ and $(2, 5)$.

Note: The choice of $(3, 5)$ as (x_1, y_1) and $(2, -1)$ as (x_2, y_2) is arbitrary. We could just as easily have reversed them.

Answer
1. $2\sqrt{13}$

2. Find x if the distance from $(x, 2)$ to $(3, -1)$ is $\sqrt{10}$.

▼ **Example 2** Find x if the distance from $(x, 5)$ to $(3, 4)$ is $\sqrt{2}$.

Solution Using the distance formula, we have

$$\sqrt{2} = \sqrt{(x-3)^2 + (5-4)^2}$$
$$2 = (x-3)^2 + 1^2$$
$$2 = x^2 - 6x + 9 + 1$$
$$0 = x^2 - 6x + 8$$
$$0 = (x-4)(x-2)$$
$$x = 4 \quad \text{or} \quad x = 2$$

The two solutions are 4 and 2, which indicates there are two points, $(4, 5)$ and $(2, 5)$, which are $\sqrt{2}$ units from $(3, 4)$. ▲

We can use the distance formula to derive the equation of a circle.

Theorem 9.1 The equation of the circle with center at (a, b) and radius r is given by

$$(x-a)^2 + (y-b)^2 = r^2$$

PROOF By definition, all points on the circle are a distance r from the center (a, b). If we let (x, y) represent any point on the circle, then (x, y) is r units from (a, b). Applying the distance formula, we have

$$r = \sqrt{(x-a)^2 + (y-b)^2}$$

Squaring both sides of this equation gives the equation of the circle:

$$(x-a)^2 + (y-b)^2 = r^2$$

We can use Theorem 9.1 to find the equation of a circle given its center and radius, or to find its center and radius given the equation.

3. Find the equation of the circle with center at $(4, -3)$ having a radius of 2.

▼ **Example 3** Find the equation of the circle with center at $(-3, 2)$ having a radius of 5.

Solution We have $(a, b) = (-3, 2)$ and $r = 5$. Applying Theorem 9.1 yields

$$[x - (-3)]^2 + (y - 2)^2 = 5^2$$
$$(x + 3)^2 + (y - 2)^2 = 25 \qquad ▲$$

4. Give the equations of the circle with radius 5 whose center is at the origin.

▼ **Example 4** Give the equation of the circle with radius 3 whose center is at the origin.

Solution The coordinates of the center are $(0, 0)$, and the radius is 3. The equation must be

$$(x - 0)^2 + (y - 0)^2 = 3^2$$
$$x^2 + y^2 = 9 \qquad ▲$$

We can see from Example 4 that the equation of any circle with its center at the origin and radius r will be

$$x^2 + y^2 = r^2$$

Answers
2. 4, 2 **3.** $(x - 4)^2 + (y + 3)^2 = 4$
4. $x^2 + y^2 = 25$

▼ **Example 5** Find the center and radius, and sketch the graph, of the circle whose equation is

$$(x - 1)^2 + (y + 3)^2 = 4$$

Solution Writing the equation in the form

$$(x - a)^2 + (y - b)^2 = r^2$$

we have

$$(x - 1)^2 + [y - (-3)]^2 = 2^2$$

The center is at $(1, -3)$ and the radius is 2. (See Figure 9.)

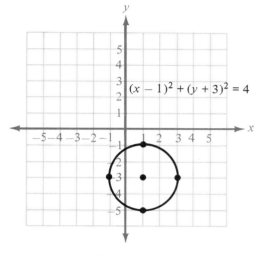

Figure 9

▼ **Example 6** Sketch the graph of $x^2 + y^2 = 9$.

Solution Since the equation can be written in the form

$$(x - 0)^2 + (y - 0)^2 = 3^2$$

it must have its center at $(0, 0)$ and a radius of 3. (See Figure 10.)

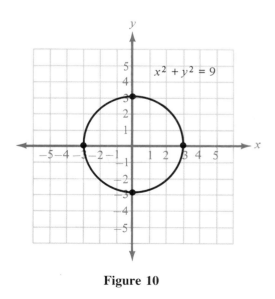

Figure 10 ▲

5. Find the center and radius of the circle whose equation is

$$(x - 3)^2 + (y - 4)^2 = 9$$

and then sketch the graph.

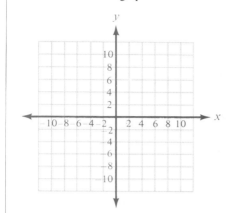

▲

6. Graph $x^2 + y^2 = 25$.

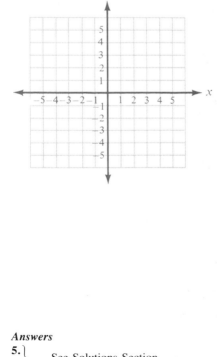

Answers

5.⎫
6.⎭ See Solutions Section.

7. Graph

$$x^2 + y^2 - 6x + 4y - 3 = 0$$

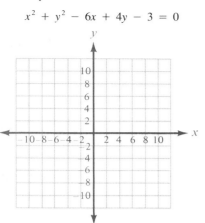

Note: Remember, when we complete the square, we take half the coefficient of the linear term and square it. Half of 6 is 3, the square of which is 9. Half of 4 is 2, the square of which is 4.

▼ **Example 7** Sketch the graph of $x^2 + y^2 + 6x - 4y - 12 = 0$.

Solution To sketch the graph we must find the center and radius. The center and radius can be identified if the equation has the form

$$(x - a)^2 + (y - b)^2 = r^2$$

The original equation can be written in this form by completing the squares on x and y:

$$x^2 + y^2 + 6x - 4y - 12 = 0$$
$$x^2 + 6x \qquad + y^2 - 4y \qquad = 12$$
$$x^2 + 6x + \mathbf{9} + y^2 - 4y + \mathbf{4} = 12 + \mathbf{9} + \mathbf{4}$$
$$(x + 3)^2 + (y - 2)^2 = 25$$
$$(x + 3)^2 + (y - 2)^2 = 5^2$$

From the last line it is apparent that the center is at $(-3, 2)$ and the radius is 5. (See Figure 11.)

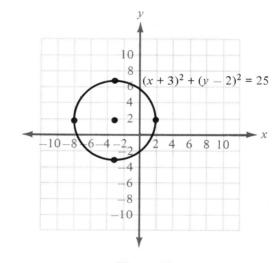

Figure 11

Problem Set 9.2

Find the distance between the following points.

1. (3, 7) and (6, 3)

2. (4, 7) and (8, 1)

3. (0, 9) and (5, 0)

4. (−3, 0) and (0, 4)

5. (3, −5) and (−2, 1)

6. (−8, 9) and (−3, −2)

7. (−1, −2) and (−10, 5)

8. (−3, −8) and (−1, 6)

9. Find x so the distance between $(x, 2)$ and $(1, 5)$ is $\sqrt{13}$.

10. Find x so the distance between $(−2, 3)$ and $(x, 1)$ is 3.

11. Find y so the distance between $(7, y)$ and $(8, 3)$ is 1.

12. Find y so the distance between $(3, −5)$ and $(3, y)$ is 9.

Write the equation of the circle with the given center and radius.

13. Center (2, 3); $r = 4$

14. Center (3, −1); $r = 5$

15. Center (3, −2); $r = 3$

16. Center (−2, 4); $r = 1$

17. Center (−5, −1); $r = \sqrt{5}$

18. Center (−7, −6); $r = \sqrt{3}$

19. Center (0, −5); $r = 1$

20. Center (0, −1); $r = 7$

21. Center (0, 0); $r = 2$

22. Center (0, 0); $r = 5$

Name _____

Class _____

Date _____

Answers

1. _____ 2. _____

3. _____ 4. _____

5. _____ 6. _____

7. _____ 8. _____

9. _____ 10. _____

11. _____ 12. _____

13. _____

14. _____

15. _____

16. _____

17. _____

18. _____

19. _____

20. _____

21. _____

22. _____

Give the center and radius, and sketch the graph, of each of the following circles.

23. $x^2 + y^2 = 4$

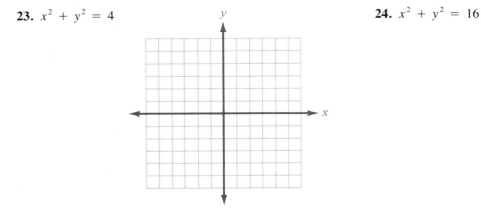

24. $x^2 + y^2 = 16$

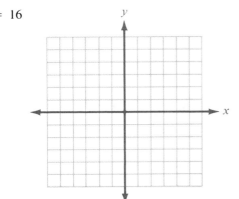

25. $(x - 1)^2 + (y - 3)^2 = 25$

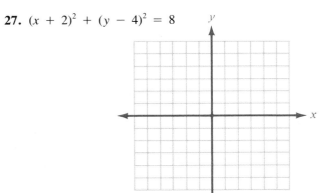

26. $(x - 4)^2 + (y - 1)^2 = 36$

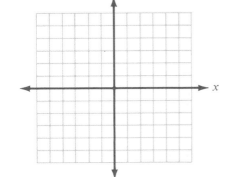

27. $(x + 2)^2 + (y - 4)^2 = 8$

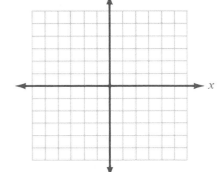

28. $(x - 3)^2 + (y + 1)^2 = 12$

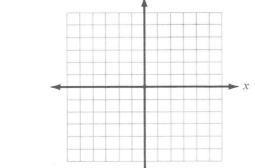

29. $(x + 1)^2 + (y + 1)^2 = 1$

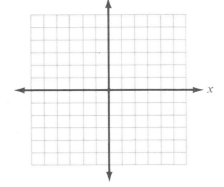
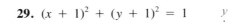

30. $(x + 3)^2 + (y + 2)^2 = 9$

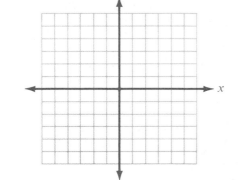

Name _____ Class _____ Date _____

31. $x^2 + y^2 - 6y = 7$

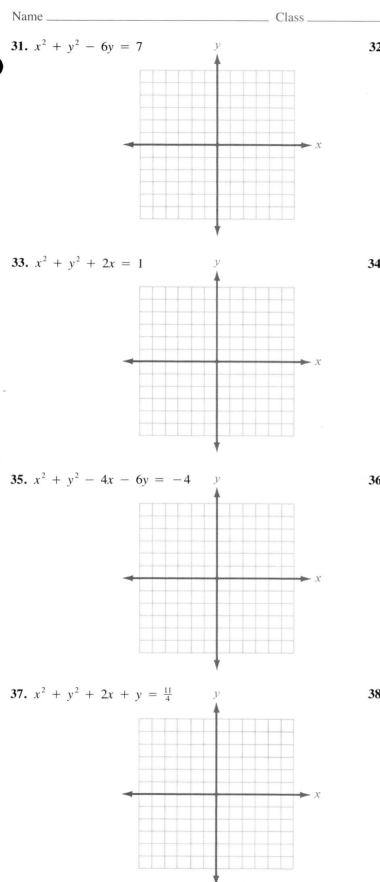

32. $x^2 + y^2 - 4y = 5$

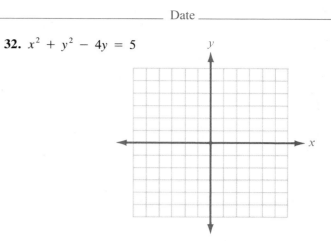

33. $x^2 + y^2 + 2x = 1$

34. $x^2 + y^2 + 10x = 0$

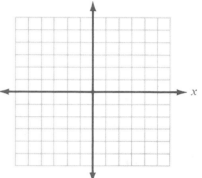

35. $x^2 + y^2 - 4x - 6y = -4$

36. $x^2 + y^2 - 4x + 2y = 4$

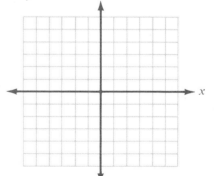

37. $x^2 + y^2 + 2x + y = \frac{11}{4}$

38. $x^2 + y^2 - 6x - y = -\frac{1}{4}$

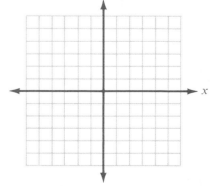

Answers

39. _____

40. _____

41. _____

42. _____

43. _____

44. _____

45. _____

46. _____

47. _____

48. _____

49. _____

50. _____

39. Find the equation of the circle with center at the origin that contains the point $(3, 4)$.

40. Find the equation of the circle with center at the origin and x-intercepts 3 and -3.

41. Find the equation of the circle with y-intercepts 4 and -4, and center at the origin.

42. A circle with center at $(-1, 3)$ passes through the point $(4, 3)$. Find the equation.

43. A circle with center at $(2, 5)$ passes through the point $(-1, 4)$. Find the equation.

44. A circle with center at $(-3, -4)$ contains the point $(2, -1)$. Find the equation.

Review Problems   The following problems review material we covered in Section 7.2.

Find the slope of the line that contains the following pairs of points.

45. $(-4, -1)$ and $(-2, 5)$ **46.** $(-2, -3)$ and $(-5, 1)$

47. Find y if the slope of the line through $(5, y)$ and $(4, 2)$ is 3.

48. Find x if the slope of the line through $(4, 9)$ and $(x, -2)$ is $-7/3$.

A line has a slope of 2/3. Find the slope of any line:

49. parallel to it.   **50.** perpendicular to it.

Section 9.3   Ellipses and Hyperbolas

This section is concerned with the graphs of ellipses and hyperbolas. To simplify matters somewhat we will only consider those graphs that are centered about the origin.

Suppose we want to graph the equation

$$\frac{x^2}{25} + \frac{y^2}{9} = 1$$

We can find the y-intercepts by letting $x = 0$, and the x-intercepts by letting $y = 0$:

When $x = 0$

$$\frac{0^2}{25} + \frac{y^2}{9} = 1$$
$$y^2 = 9$$
$$y = \pm 3$$

When $y = 0$

$$\frac{x^2}{25} + \frac{0^2}{9} = 1$$
$$x^2 = 25$$
$$x = \pm 5$$

The graph crosses the y-axis at $(0, 3)$ and $(0, -3)$ and the x-axis at $(5, 0)$ and $(-5, 0)$. Graphing these points and then connecting them with a smooth curve gives the graph shown in Figure 12.

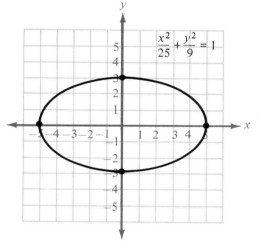

Figure 12

A graph of this type is called an *ellipse*. If we were to find some other ordered pairs that satisfy our original equation, we would find that their graphs lie on the ellipse. Also, the coordinates of any point on the ellipse will satisfy the equation. We can generalize these results as follows.

The Ellipse

The graph of any equation of the form

$$\frac{x^2}{a^2} + \frac{y^2}{b^2} = 1$$

will be an ellipse. The ellipse will cross the x-axis at $(a, 0)$ and $(-a, 0)$. It will cross the y-axis at $(0, b)$ and $(0, -b)$. When a and b are equal, the ellipse will be a circle.

Note: We can find other ordered pairs on the graph by substituting in values for x (or y) and then solving for y (or x). For example if we let $x = 3$ then

$$\frac{3^2}{25} + \frac{y^2}{9} = 1$$
$$\frac{9}{25} + \frac{y^2}{9} = 1$$
$$0.36 + \frac{y^2}{9} = 1$$
$$\frac{y^2}{9} = 0.64$$
$$y^2 = 5.76$$
$$y = \pm 2.4$$

This would give us the two ordered pairs $(3, -2.4)$ and $(3, 2.4)$.

Note: This form of the equation of an ellipse is called the *standard form*.

The most convenient method for graphing an ellipse is to locate the intercepts.

Practice Problems

1. Graph $25x^2 + 4y^2 = 100$. (*Hint:* First, divide both sides by 100.)

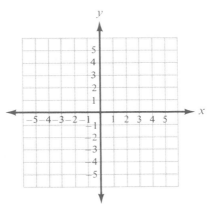

Note: When the equation is written in standard form, the x-intercepts are the positive and negative square roots of the number below x^2. The y-intercepts are the square roots of the number below y^2.

▼ **Example 1** Sketch the graph of $4x^2 + 9y^2 = 36$.

Solution To write the equation in the form

$$\frac{x^2}{a^2} + \frac{y^2}{b^2} = 1$$

we must divide both sides by 36:

$$\frac{4x^2}{36} + \frac{9y^2}{36} = \frac{36}{36}$$

$$\frac{x^2}{9} + \frac{y^2}{4} = 1$$

The graph crosses the x-axis at $(3, 0)$, $(-3, 0)$ and the y-axis at $(0, 2)$, $(0, -2)$. (See Figure 13.)

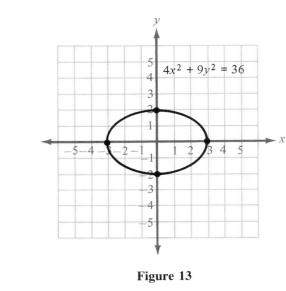

Figure 13 ▲

Consider the equation

$$\frac{x^2}{9} - \frac{y^2}{4} = 1$$

If we were to find a number of ordered pairs that are solutions to the equation and connect their graphs with a smooth curve, we would have Figure 14. This graph is an example of a *hyperbola*. Notice that the graph has x-intercepts at $(3, 0)$ and $(-3, 0)$. The graph has no y-intercepts and hence does not cross the y-axis, since substituting $x = 0$ into the equation yields

$$\frac{0^2}{9} - \frac{y^2}{4} = 1$$

$$-y^2 = 4$$

$$y^2 = -4$$

for which there is no real solution. We can, however, use the number below

Answer
1. See Solutions Section for all answers in this section.

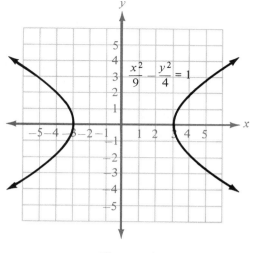

Figure 14

y^2 to help sketch the graph. If we draw a rectangle that has its sides parallel to the x- and y-axes and that passes through the x-intercepts and the points on the y-axis corresponding to the square roots of the number below y, $+2$ and -2, it looks like the rectangle in Figure 15.

The lines that connect opposite corners of the rectangle are called *asymptotes*. The graph of the hyperbola

$$\frac{x^2}{9} - \frac{y^2}{4} = 1$$

will approach these lines. Figure 15 is the graph.

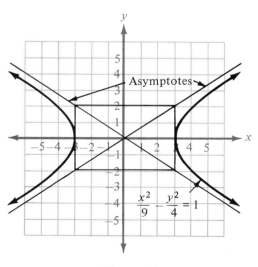

Figure 15

2. Graph the equation

$$\frac{x^2}{25} - \frac{y^2}{9} = 1$$

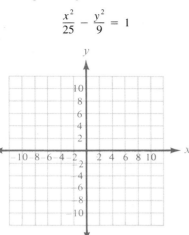

▼ **Example 2**   Graph the equation $\dfrac{y^2}{9} - \dfrac{x^2}{16} = 1$.

Solution   In this case the y-intercepts are 3 and -3, and the x-intercepts do not exist. We can use the square root of the number below x^2, however, to find the asymptotes associated with the graph. The sides of the rectangle used to draw the asymptotes must pass through 3 and -3 on the y-axis, and 4 and -4 on the x-axis. (See Figure 16.)

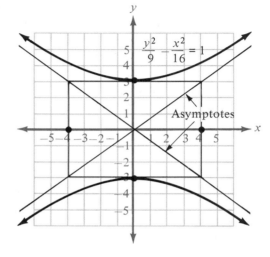

Figure 16   ▲

Here is a summary of what we have for hyperbolas.

The Hyperbola

The graph of the equation

$$\frac{x^2}{a^2} - \frac{y^2}{b^2} = 1$$

will be a hyperbola centered at the origin. The graph will have x-intercepts at $-a$ and a.

The graph of the equation

$$\frac{y^2}{a^2} - \frac{x^2}{b^2} = 1$$

will be a hyperbola centered at the origin. The graph will have y-intercepts at $-a$ and a.

As an aid in sketching either of the preceding equations, the asymptotes can be found by drawing a line through opposite corners of the rectangle whose sides pass through $-a$, a, $-b$, and b on the axes.

Name _____ Class _____ Date _____

Problem Set 9.3

Graph each of the following. Be sure to label both the x- and y-intercepts.

1. $\dfrac{x^2}{9} + \dfrac{y^2}{16} = 1$

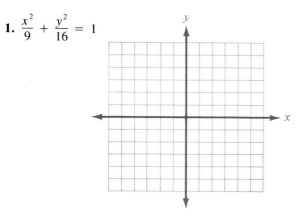

2. $\dfrac{x^2}{25} + \dfrac{y^2}{4} = 1$

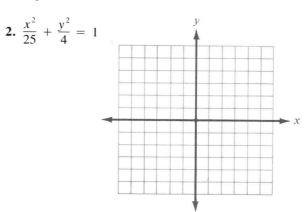

3. $\dfrac{x^2}{16} + \dfrac{y^2}{9} = 1$

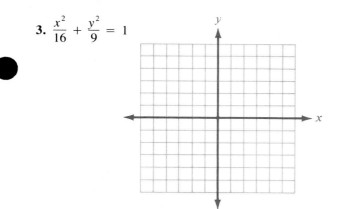

4. $\dfrac{x^2}{4} + \dfrac{y^2}{25} = 1$

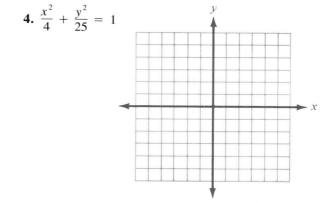

5. $\dfrac{x^2}{3} + \dfrac{y^2}{4} = 1$

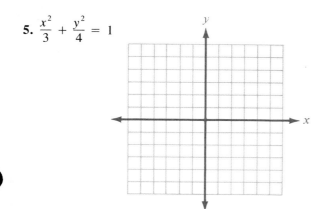

6. $\dfrac{x^2}{4} + \dfrac{y^2}{3} = 1$

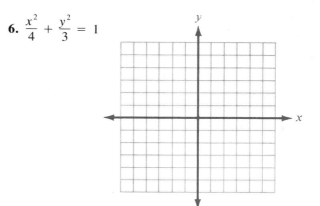

7. $4x^2 + 25y^2 = 100$

8. $4x^2 + 9y^2 = 36$

9. $x^2 + 8y^2 = 16$

10. $12x^2 + y^2 = 36$

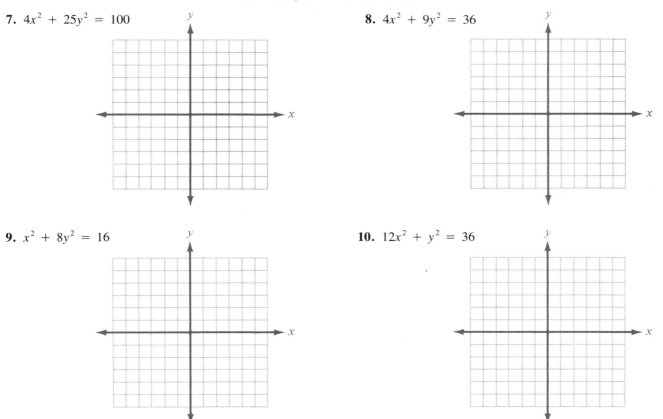

Graph each of the following. Show all intercepts and the asymptotes in each case.

11. $\dfrac{x^2}{9} - \dfrac{y^2}{16} = 1$

12. $\dfrac{x^2}{25} - \dfrac{y^2}{4} = 1$

13. $\dfrac{x^2}{16} - \dfrac{y^2}{9} = 1$

14. $\dfrac{x^2}{4} - \dfrac{y^2}{25} = 1$

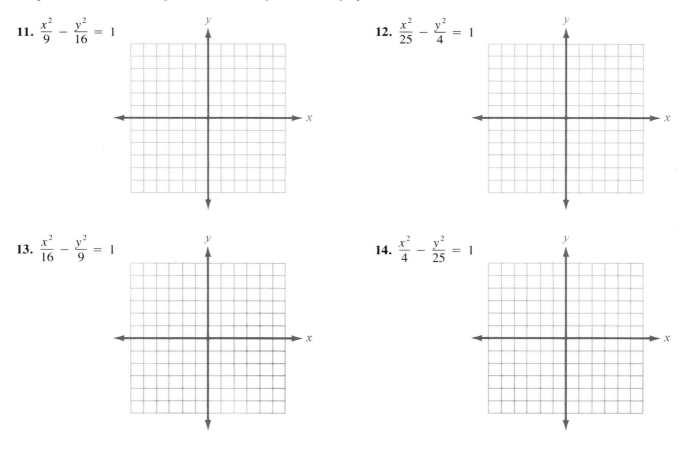

Name _____ Class _____ Date _____

15. $\dfrac{y^2}{9} - \dfrac{x^2}{16} = 1$

16. $\dfrac{y^2}{25} - \dfrac{x^2}{4} = 1$

17. $\dfrac{y^2}{36} - \dfrac{x^2}{4} = 1$

18. $\dfrac{y^2}{4} - \dfrac{x^2}{36} = 1$

19. $x^2 - 4y^2 = 4$

20. $y^2 - 4x^2 = 4$

21. $16y^2 - 9x^2 = 144$

22. $4y^2 - 25x^2 = 100$

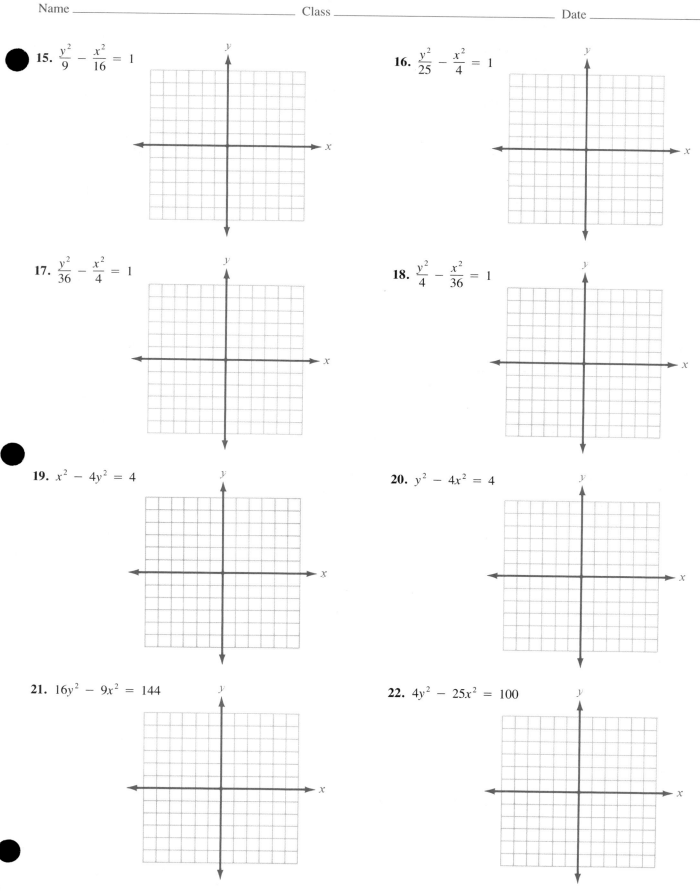

23. Give the equation of the two asymptotes in the graph you found in Problem 15.

24. Give the equation of the two asymptotes in the graph you found in Problem 16.

25. For the ellipses you have graphed in this section, the longer line segment connecting opposite intercepts is called the *major axis* of the ellipse. Give the length of the major axis of the ellipse you graphed in Problem 3.

26. For the ellipses you have graphed in this section, the shorter line segment connecting opposite intercepts is called the *minor axis* of the ellipse. Give the length of the minor axis of the ellipse you graphed in Problem 3.

Review Problems The following problems review material we covered in Section 7.4. Reviewing these problems will help you with the next section.

Graph each inequality.

27. $x + y < 5$

28. $x - y < 5$

29. $y \geq 2x - 1$

30. $y \leq 2x + 1$

31. $2x - 3y > 6$

32. $3x + 2y > 6$

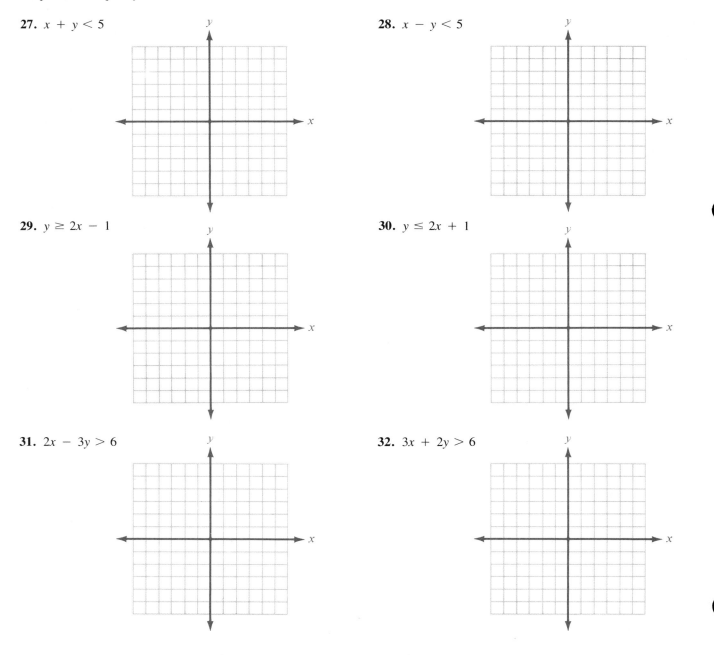

Section 9.4   Second-Degree Inequalities

In Section 7.4 we graphed linear inequalities by first graphing the boundary and then choosing a test point not on the boundary to indicate the region used for the solution set. The problems in this section are very similar. We will use the same general methods for graphing the inequalities in this section that we used in Section 7.4.

▼ **Example 1**   Graph $x^2 + y^2 < 16$.

Solution   The boundary is $x^2 + y^2 = 16$, which is a circle with center at the origin and a radius of 4. Since the inequality sign is $<$, the boundary is not included in the solution set and must therefore be represented with a broken line. The graph of the boundary is shown in Figure 17.

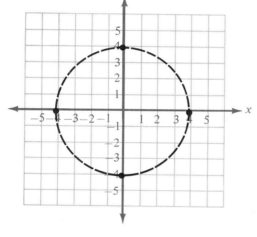

Figure 17

The solution set for $x^2 + y^2 < 16$ is either the region inside the circle or the region outside the circle. To see which region represents the solution set, we choose a convenient point not on the boundary and test it in the original inequality. The origin $(0, 0)$ is a convenient point. Since the origin satisfies the inequality $x^2 + y^2 < 16$, all points in the same region will also satisfy the inequality. The graph of the solution set is shown in Figure 18.

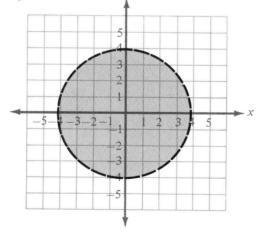

Figure 18

▲

Practice Problems

1. Graph $x^2 + y^2 > 9$.

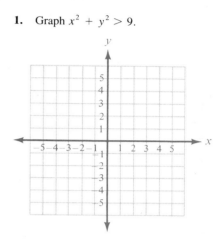

2. Graph $y \geq x^2 + 3$.

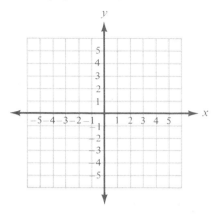

Example 2 Graph the inequality $y \leq x^2 - 2$.

Solution The parabola $y = x^2 - 2$ is the boundary and is included in the solution set. Using $(0, 0)$ as the test point, we see that $0 \leq 0^2 - 2$ is a false statement, which means that the region containing $(0, 0)$ is not in the solution set. (See Figure 19.)

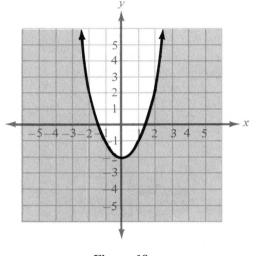

Figure 19

3. Graph $16x^2 - 9y^2 > 144$.

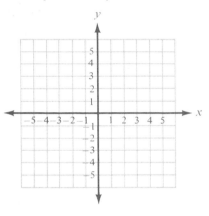

Example 3 Graph $4y^2 - 9x^2 < 36$.

Solution The boundary is the hyperbola $4y^2 - 9x^2 = 36$ and is not included in the solution set. Testing $(0, 0)$ in the original inequality yields a true statement, which means that the region containing the origin is the solution set. (See Figure 20.)

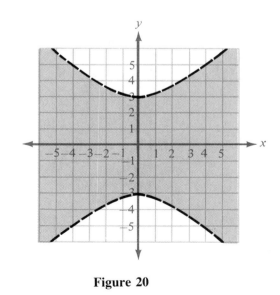

Figure 20

We now turn our attention to systems of inequalities. To solve a system of inequalities by graphing, we simply graph each inequality on the same set of axes. The solution set for the system is the region common to both graphs—the intersection of the individual solution sets.

▼ **Example 4**   Graph the solution set for the system

$$x^2 + y^2 \leq 9$$

$$\frac{x^2}{4} + \frac{y^2}{25} \geq 1$$

Solution   The boundary for the top equation is a circle with center at the origin and a radius of 3. The solution set lies inside the boundary. The boundary for the second equation is an ellipse. In this case the solution set lies outside the boundary. (See Figure 21.)

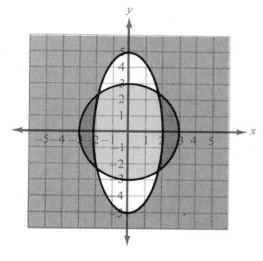

Figure 21

The solution set for the system is the intersection of the two individual solution sets.   ▲

4.   Graph the solution set for the system

$$x^2 + y^2 \geq 9$$

$$\frac{x^2}{4} + \frac{y^2}{25} \leq 1$$

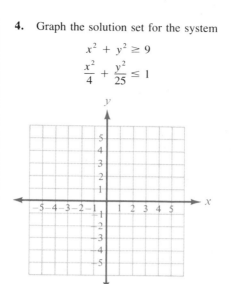

Name _____ Class _____ Date _____

Problem Set 9.4

Graph each of the following inequalities.

1. $x^2 + y^2 > 49$

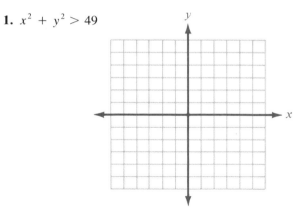

2. $x^2 + y^2 \geq 49$

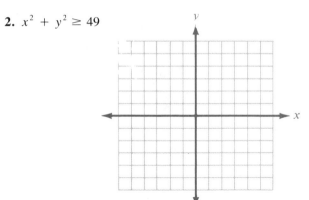

3. $x^2 + y^2 \leq 49$

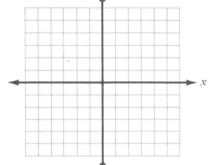

4. $x^2 + y^2 < 49$

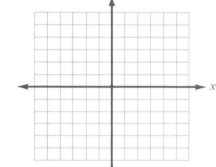

5. $(x - 2)^2 + (y + 3)^2 < 16$

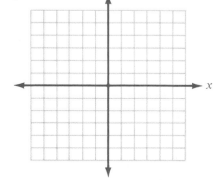

6. $(x + 3)^2 + (y - 2)^2 \geq 25$

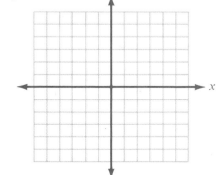

7. $y \leq x^2 - 4$

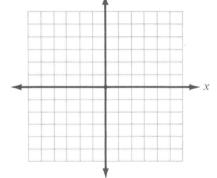

8. $y \geq x^2 + 3$

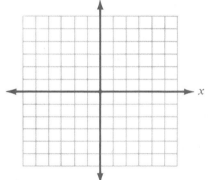

9. $y < x^2 - 6x + 7$

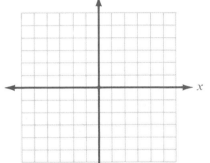

10. $y \geq x^2 + 2x - 8$

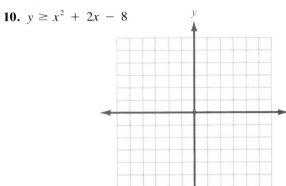

11. $\dfrac{x^2}{9} + \dfrac{y^2}{25} < 1$

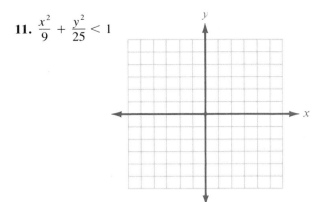

12. $\dfrac{x^2}{9} - \dfrac{y^2}{25} > 1$

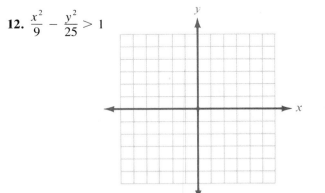

13. $\dfrac{x^2}{25} - \dfrac{y^2}{9} \geq 1$

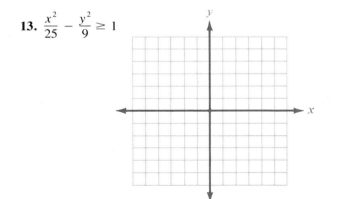

14. $\dfrac{x^2}{25} - \dfrac{y^2}{9} \leq 1$

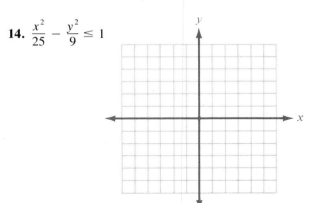

15. $4x^2 + 25y^2 \leq 100$

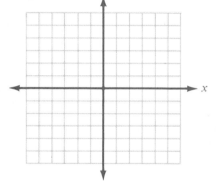

16. $25x^2 - 4y^2 > 100$

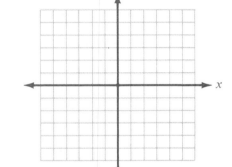

Name _____ Class _____ Date _____

Graph the solution sets to the following systems.

17. $x^2 + y^2 < 9$
$\quad\quad y \geq x^2 - 1$

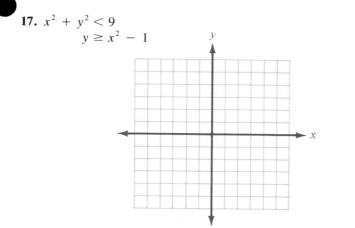

18. $x^2 + y^2 \leq 16$
$\quad\quad y < x^2 + 2$

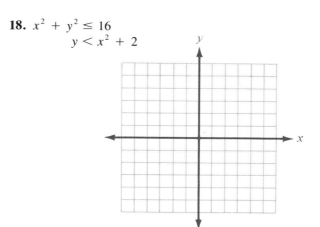

19. $\dfrac{x^2}{9} + \dfrac{y^2}{25} \leq 1$

$\quad \dfrac{x^2}{4} - \dfrac{y^2}{9} > 1$

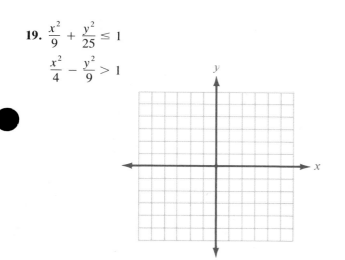

20. $\dfrac{x^2}{4} + \dfrac{y^2}{16} \geq 1$

$\quad \dfrac{x^2}{9} - \dfrac{y^2}{25} < 1$

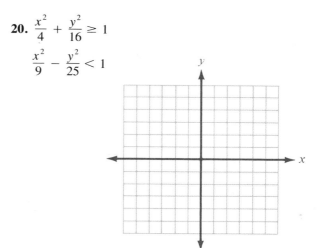

21. $4x^2 + 9y^2 \leq 36$
$\quad\quad y > x^2 + 2$

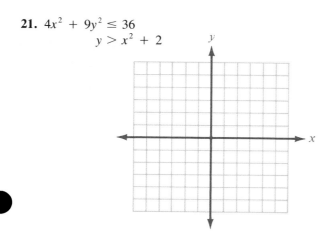

22. $9x^2 + 4y^2 \geq 36$
$\quad\quad y < x^2 + 1$

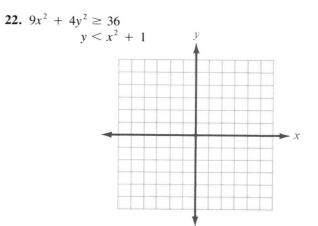

Answers

23. _____   24. _____

25. _____   26. _____

27. _____   28. _____

Review Problems   The following problems review material we covered in Section 8.1. Reviewing these problems will help you understand the next section.

Solve each system by the addition method.

23. $4x + 3y = 10$
$\quad\ 2x + \ \ y = 4$

24. $3x - 5y = -2$
$\quad\ 2x - 3y = 1$

Solve each system by the substitution method.

25. $x + y = 3$
$\qquad\ y = x + 3$

26. $x + y = 6$
$\qquad\ y = x - 4$

27. $2x - 3y = -6$
$\qquad\ \ y = 3x - 5$

28. $7x - y = 24$
$\qquad\ x = 2y + 9$

Section 9.5 Nonlinear Systems

Each system of equations in this section contains at least one second-degree equation. The most convenient method of solving a system that contains one or two second-degree equations is by substitution, although the addition method can be used at times.

▼ **Example 1** Solve the system

$$x^2 + y^2 = 4$$
$$x - 2y = 4$$

Solution In this case the substitution method is the most convenient. Solving the second equation for x in terms of y, we have

$$x - 2y = 4$$
$$x = 2y + 4$$

We now substitute $2y + 4$ for x in the first equation in our original system and proceed to solve for y:

$$(2y + 4)^2 + y^2 = 4$$
$$4y^2 + 16y + 16 + y^2 = 4$$
$$5y^2 + 16y + 12 = 0$$
$$(5y + 6)(y + 2) = 0$$
$$5y + 6 = 0 \quad \text{or} \quad y + 2 = 0$$
$$y = -\tfrac{6}{5} \quad \text{or} \quad y = -2$$

These are the y-coordinates of the two solutions to the system. Substituting $y = -\tfrac{6}{5}$ into $x - 2y = 4$ and solving for x gives us $x = \tfrac{8}{5}$. Using $y = -2$ in the same equation yields $x = 0$. The two solutions to our system are $(\tfrac{8}{5}, -\tfrac{6}{5})$ and $(0, -2)$. Although graphing the system is not necessary, it does help us visualize the situation. (See Figure 22.)

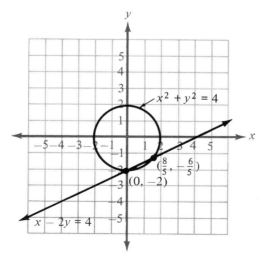

Figure 22 ▲

Practice Problems

1. Solve the system
$$x^2 + y^2 = 9$$
$$x - y = 3$$

Answer
1. $(3, 0)$, $(0, -3)$

2. Solve the system

$$16x^2 - 4y^2 = 64$$
$$x^2 + y^2 = 4$$

▼ **Example 2** Solve the system

$$16x^2 - 4y^2 = 64$$
$$x^2 + y^2 = 9$$

Solution Since each equation is of the second degree in both x and y, it is easier to solve this system by eliminating one of the variables by addition. To eliminate y we multiply the bottom equation by 4 and add the results to the top equation:

$$
\begin{aligned}
16x^2 - 4y^2 &= 64 \\
\underline{4x^2 + 4y^2} &= \underline{36} \\
20x^2 &= 100
\end{aligned}
$$

$$x^2 = 5$$
$$x = \pm\sqrt{5}$$

The x-coordinates of the points of intersection are $\sqrt{5}$ and $-\sqrt{5}$. We substitute each back into the second equation in the original system and solve for y:

When
$$x = \sqrt{5}$$
$$(\sqrt{5})^2 + y^2 = 9$$
$$5 + y^2 = 9$$
$$y^2 = 4$$
$$y = \pm 2$$

When
$$x = -\sqrt{5}$$
$$(-\sqrt{5})^2 + y^2 = 9$$
$$5 + y^2 = 9$$
$$y^2 = 4$$
$$y = \pm 2$$

The four points of intersection are $(\sqrt{5}, 2)$, $(\sqrt{5}, -2)$, $(-\sqrt{5}, 2)$, and $(-\sqrt{5}, -2)$. Graphically the situation is as shown in Figure 23.

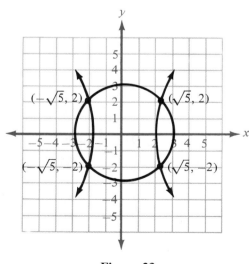

Figure 23

Answer
2. $(2, 0)$, $(-2, 0)$

▼ **Example 3** Solve the system

$$x^2 - 2y = 2$$
$$y = x^2 - 3$$

Solution We can solve this system using the substitution method. Replacing y in the first equation with $x^2 - 3$ from the second equation, we have

$$x^2 - 2(x^2 - 3) = 2$$
$$-x^2 + 6 = 2$$
$$x^2 = 4$$
$$x = \pm 2$$

Using either $+2$ or -2 in the equation $y = x^2 - 3$ gives us $y = 1$. The system has two solutions: $(2, 1)$ and $(-2, 1)$. ▲

▼ **Example 4** The sum of the squares of two numbers is 34. The difference of their squares is 16. Find the two numbers.

Solution Let x and y be the two numbers. The sum of their squares is $x^2 + y^2$ and the difference of their squares is $x^2 - y^2$. (We can assume here that x^2 is the larger number.) The system of equations that describes the situation is

$$x^2 + y^2 = 34$$
$$x^2 - y^2 = 16$$

We can eliminate y by simply adding the two equations. The result of doing so is

$$2x^2 = 50$$
$$x^2 = 25$$
$$x = \pm 5$$

Substituting $x = 5$ into either equation in the system gives $y = \pm 3$. Using $x = -5$ gives the same results, $y = \pm 3$. The four pairs of numbers that are solutions to the original problem are

$$\{5, 3\} \qquad \{-5, 3\} \qquad \{5, -3\} \qquad \{-5, -3\} \qquad ▲$$

3. Solve the system

$$x^2 + y^2 = 4$$
$$y = x^2 - 4$$

4. One number is two less than the square of another number. The sum of the squares of the two numbers is 58. Find the two numbers.

Problem Set 9.5

Solve each of the following systems of equations.

1. $x^2 + y^2 = 9$
$\quad 2x + y = 3$

2. $x^2 + y^2 = 9$
$\quad x + 2y = 3$

3. $x^2 + y^2 = 16$
$\quad x + 2y = 8$

4. $x^2 + y^2 = 16$
$\quad x - 2y = 8$

5. $x^2 + y^2 = 25$
$\quad x^2 - y^2 = 25$

6. $x^2 - y^2 = 4$
$\quad 2x^2 + y^2 = 5$

7. $x^2 + y^2 = 9$
$\quad y = x^2 - 3$

8. $x^2 + y^2 = 4$
$\quad y = x^2 - 2$

Name _____

Class _____

Date _____

Answers

1. _____

2. _____

3. _____

4. _____

5. _____

6. _____

7. _____

8. _____

Answers

9. _____

10. _____

11. _____

12. _____

13. _____

14. _____

15. _____

16. _____

9. $x^2 + y^2 = 16$
$y = x^2 - 4$

10. $x^2 + y^2 = 1$
$y = x^2 - 1$

11. $3x + 2y = 10$
$y = x^2 - 5$

12. $4x + 2y = 10$
$y = x^2 - 10$

13. $4x^2 - 9y^2 = 36$
$4x^2 + 9y^2 = 36$

14. $4x^2 + 25y^2 = 100$
$4x^2 - 25y^2 = 100$

15. $x - y = 4$
$x^2 + y^2 = 16$

16. $x + y = 2$
$x^2 - y^2 = 4$

17. The sum of the squares of two numbers is 89. The difference of the numbers is 3. Find the numbers.

Answers

17. _____

18. _____

19. _____

20. _____

18. The difference of the squares of two numbers is 35. The sum of their squares is 37. Find the numbers.

19. One number is 3 less than the square of another. Their sum is 9. Find the numbers.

20. The square of one number is 2 less than twice the square of another. The sum of the squares of the two numbers is 25. Find the numbers.

Answers

21. _____

22. _____

23. _____

24. _____

25. _____

26. _____

Review Problems   The following problems review material we covered in Section 7.3.

21. Give the equation of the line with slope -3 and y-intercept 5.

22. Give the slope and y-intercept of the line $2x - 3y = 6$.

23. Find the equation of the line with slope 5 that contains the point $(3, -2)$.

24. Find the equation of the line through $(1, 3)$ and $(-1, -5)$.

25. Find the equation of the line with x-intercept 3 and y-intercept -2.

26. Find the equation of the line through $(-1, 4)$ whose graph is perpendicular to the graph of $y = 2x + 3$.

Chapter 9   Summary and Review

CONIC SECTIONS [9.1]

Each of the four conic sections can be obtained by slicing a cone with a plane at different angles as shown in Figure 24.

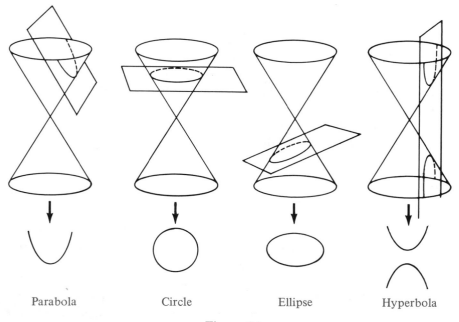

Parabola   Circle   Ellipse   Hyperbola

Figure 24

Examples

THE PARABOLA [9.1]

The graph of any equation of the form

$$y = ax^2 + bx + c \qquad a \neq 0$$

is a parabola. The graph is concave up if $a > 0$, and concave down if $a < 0$. The highest or lowest point on the graph is called the *vertex* and will always occur at (h, k) when the equation has been written in the form $y = a(x - h)^2 + k$ by completing the square on x.

1. The graph of $y = x^2 - 4$ will be a parabola. It will cross the x-axis at 2 and -2, and the vertex will be $(0, -4)$.

DISTANCE FORMULA [9.2]

The distance between the two points (x_1, y_1) and (x_2, y_2) is given by the formula

$$d = \sqrt{(x_2 - x_1)^2 + (y_2 - y_1)^2}$$

2. The distance between $(5, 2)$ and $(-1, 1)$ is

$$d = \sqrt{(5 + 1)^2 + (2 - 1)^2}$$
$$= \sqrt{37}$$

THE CIRCLE [9.2]

The graph of any equation of the form

$$(x - a)^2 + (y - b)^2 = r^2$$

will be a circle having its center at (a, b) and a radius of r.

3. The graph of the circle $(x - 3)^2 + (y + 2)^2 = 25$ will have its center at $(3, -2)$ and the radius will be 5.

4. The ellipse $\frac{x^2}{9} + \frac{y^2}{4} = 1$ will cross the x-axis at 3 and -3, and will cross the y-axis at 2 and -2.

5. The hyperbola $\frac{x^2}{4} - \frac{y^2}{9} = 1$ will cross the x-axis at 2 and -2. It will not cross the y-axis.

6. The graph of the inequality

$$x^2 + y^2 < 9$$

is all points inside the circle with center at the origin and radius 3. The circle itself is not part of the solution and is therefore shown with a broken curve.

7. We can solve the system

$$x^2 + y^2 = 4$$
$$x = 2y + 4$$

by substituting $2y + 4$ from the second equation for x in the first equation, giving us

$$(2y + 4)^2 + y^2 = 4$$
$$4y^2 + 16y + 16 + y^2 = 4$$
$$5y^2 + 16y + 12 = 0$$
$$(5y + 6)(y + 2) = 0$$
$$y = -\frac{6}{5} \quad \text{or} \quad y = -2$$

Substituting these values of y into the second equation in our system gives $x = \frac{8}{5}$ and $x = 0$. The solutions to the system are

$$\left(\frac{8}{5}, -\frac{6}{5}\right) \quad \text{and} \quad (0, -2)$$

THE ELLIPSE [9.3]

Any equation that can be put in the form

$$\frac{x^2}{a^2} + \frac{y^2}{b^2} = 1$$

will have an ellipse for its graph. The x-intercepts will be at a and $-a$, the y-intercepts at b and $-b$.

THE HYPERBOLA [9.3]

The graph of an equation that can be put in either of the forms

$$\frac{x^2}{a^2} - \frac{y^2}{b^2} = 1 \quad \text{or} \quad \frac{y^2}{b^2} - \frac{x^2}{a^2} = 1$$

will be a hyperbola. The x-intercepts, if they exist, will be a and $-a$. The y-intercepts, if they occur, will be at b and $-b$. There are two straight lines called asymptotes associated with the graph of every hyperbola. Although the asymptotes are not part of the hyperbola, they are useful in sketching the graph.

NONLINEAR INEQUALITIES IN TWO VARIABLES [9.4]

We graph nonlinear inequalities in two variables in much the same way that we graphed linear inequalities. That is, we begin by graphing the boundary, using a solid curve if the boundary is included in the solution (this happens when the inequality symbol is $\geq$ or $\leq$), or a broken curve if the boundary is not included in the solution (when the inequality symbol is $>$ or $<$). After we have graphed the boundary, we choose a test point that is not on the boundary and try it in the original inequality. A true statement indicates we are in the region of the solution. A false statement indicates we are not in the region of the solution.

SYSTEMS OF NONLINEAR EQUATIONS [9.5]

A system of nonlinear is two equations, at least one of which is not linear, considered at the same time. The solution set for the system consists of all ordered pairs that satisfy both equations. In most cases we use the substitution method to solve these systems; however, the addition method can be used if the like variables are raised to the same power in both equations. It is sometimes helpful to graph each equation in the system on the same set of axes in order to anticipate the number and approximate position of the solution.

Chapter 9 Test

Name _____

Class _____

Date _____

1. Sketch the graph of each of the following. Give the coordinates of the vertex in each case. [9.1]

    a. $y = x^2 - 2x - 3$ **b.** $y = -x^2 + 2x + 8$

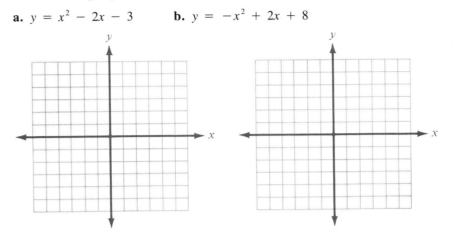

Answers

2. _____

3. _____

4. _____

5. _____

6. _____

2. Find the distance between the points $(3, -7)$ and $(4, 2)$. [9.2]

3. Find x so that $(x, 2)$ is $2\sqrt{5}$ units from $(-1, 4)$. [9.2]

4. Give the equation of the circle with center at $(-2, 4)$ and radius 3. [9.2]

5. Give the equation of the circle with center at the origin that contains the point $(-3, -4)$. [9.2]

6. Find the center and radius of the circle $x^2 + y^2 - 10x + 6y = 5$. [9.2]

Answers

11. _____

12. _____

Graph each of the following. [9.3, 9.4]

7. $4x^2 - y^2 = 16$

8. $\dfrac{x^2}{25} + \dfrac{y^2}{4} = 1$

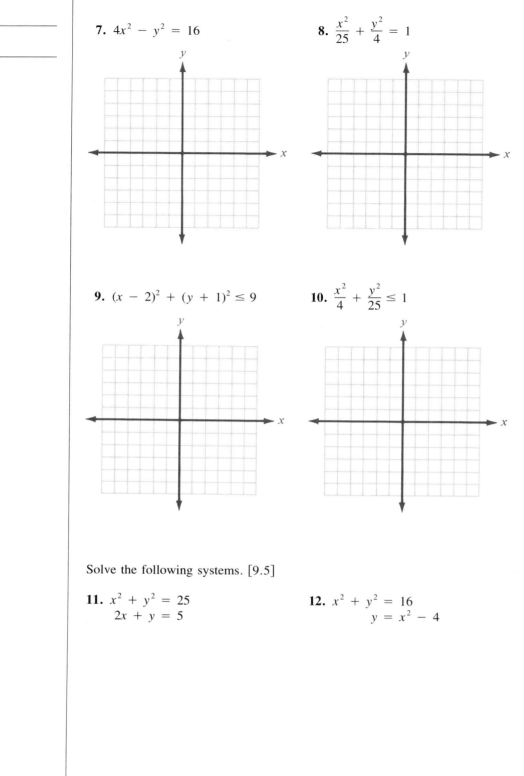

9. $(x - 2)^2 + (y + 1)^2 \leq 9$

10. $\dfrac{x^2}{4} + \dfrac{y^2}{25} \leq 1$

Solve the following systems. [9.5]

11. $x^2 + y^2 = 25$
$\quad\;\; 2x + y = 5$

12. $x^2 + y^2 = 16$
$\qquad\quad y = x^2 - 4$

$\bullet$10 Relations and Functions

To the student:

In this chapter we will study two main concepts, relations and functions. Relations and functions have many applications in the real world. The idea of a relation is already familiar to us on an intuitive level. When we say "the price of gasoline is increasing because there is more demand for it this year," we are expressing a relationship between the price of gasoline and the demand for it. We are implying the price of gasoline is a function of the demand for it. Mathematics becomes a part of this problem when we express, with an equation, the exact relationship between the two quantities.

Actually, we have been working with functions and relations for some time now, we just haven't said so. Any time we have used an equation containing two variables we have been using a relation.

Section 10.1 Relations and Functions

We begin this section with the definition of a relation. It is apparent from the definition that we have worked with relations many times previously in this book.

DEFINITION A *relation* is any set of ordered pairs. The set of all first coordinates is called the *domain* of the relation, and the set of all second coordinates is said to be the *range* of the relation.

There are two ways to specify the ordered pairs in a relation. One method

477

is simply to list them. The other method is to give the rule (equation) for obtaining them.

Practice Problems

1. For the relation $\{(3, 5), \left(-\frac{1}{4}, 2\right),$ $(\sqrt{2}, -5\}, (0, 0)\}$, find

a. the domain
b. the range

2. List some members of the relation

$$\{(x, y)|y = 2x - 3\}$$

▼ **Example 1** The set $\{(1, 2), (-3, \frac{1}{2}), (\pi, -4), (0, 1)\}$ is a relation. The domain for this relation is $(1, -3, \pi, 0\}$ and the range is $\{2, \frac{1}{2}, -4, 1\}$. ▲

▼ **Example 2** The set of ordered pairs given by $\{(x, y)|x + y = 5\}$ is an example of a relation. In this case we have written the relation in terms of the equation used to obtain the ordered pairs in the relation. This relation is the set of all ordered pairs whose coordinates have a sum of 5. Some members of this relation are (1, 4), (0, 5), (5, 0), (−1, 6), and $(\frac{1}{2}, \frac{9}{2})$. It is impossible to list all the members of this relation since there are an infinite number of ordered pairs that are solutions to the equation $x + y = 5$. The domain, although not given directly, is the set of real numbers; the range is also. ▲

DEFINITION   A *function* is a relation in which no two different ordered pairs have the same first coordinates. The *domain* and *range* of a function are the sets of first and second coordinates, respectively.

A function is simply a relation that does not repeat any first coordinates.

3. Which of the following two relations is also a function?

a. $\{(7, 2), (8, 1), (3, 2)\}$
b. $\{(5, 3), (2, 0), (5, 1)\}$

▼ **Example 3** The relation $\{(2, 3), (5, 2), (6, 3)\}$ is also a function, since no two ordered pairs have the same first coordinates. The relation $\{(1, 7), (3, 7), (1, 5)\}$ is not a function since two of its ordered pairs, (1, 7) and (1, 5), have the same first coordinates. ▲

Vertical Line Test

If the ordered pairs of a relation are given in terms of an equation rather than a list, we can use the graph of the relation to determine if the relation is a function or not. Any two ordered pairs with the same first coordinates will lie along a vertical line parallel to the y-axis. Therefore, if a vertical line crosses the graph of a relation in more than one place, the relation cannot be a function. If no vertical line can be found that crosses the graph in more than one place, the relation must be a function. Testing to see if a relation is a function by observing if a vertical line crosses the graph of the relation in more than one place is called the *vertical line test*.

4. Use the vertical line test to see which of the following is a function.

▼ **Example 4** Use the vertical line test to see which of the following are functions: (a) $y = x^2 - 2$; (b) $x^2 + y^2 = 9$.

Solution   The graph of each relation is given in Figure 1. The equation $y = x^2 - 2$ is a function, since there are no vertical lines that cross its graph in more than one place. The equation $x^2 + y^2 = 9$ does not represent a function, since we can find a vertical line that crosses its graph in more than one place.

Answers
1a. Domain = $\{3, -\frac{1}{4}, \sqrt{2}, 0\}$
b. Range = $\{5, 2, -5, 0\}$
2. $(0, -3), (1, -1), (2, 1), (\frac{1}{2}, -2),$ $(-2, -7), (-10, -23)$
3. a **4.** $y = x^2 + 1$ is a function

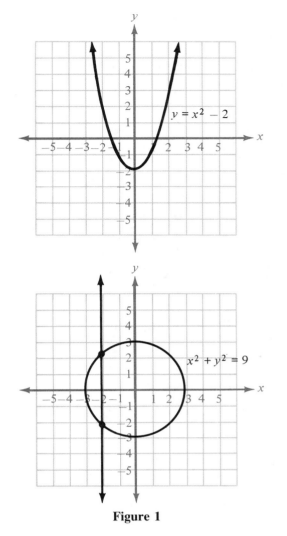

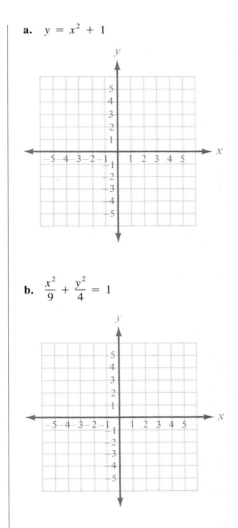

a. $y = x^2 + 1$

b. $\dfrac{x^2}{9} + \dfrac{y^2}{4} = 1$

Figure 1 ▲

The Domain and Range of a Function

When a function (or relation) is given in terms of an equation, the domain is the set of all possible replacements for the variable x. If the domain of a function (or relation) is not specified, it is assumed to be all real numbers that do not give undefined terms in the equation. That is, we cannot use values of x in the domain that will produce 0 in a denominator or the square root of a negative number.

▼ **Example 5**   Specify the domain for $y = \dfrac{1}{x - 3}$.

Solution   The domain can be any real number that does not produce an undefined term. If $x = 3$, the denominator on the right side will be 0. Hence, the domain is all real numbers except 3. ▲

▼ **Example 6**   Give the domain for $y = \sqrt{x - 4}$.

Solution   Since the domain must consist of real numbers, the quantity under the radical will have to be greater than or equal to 0:

$$x - 4 \geq 0$$
$$x \geq 4$$

The domain in this case is $\{x \mid x \geq 4\}$. ▲

5. Specify the domain for
$$y = \dfrac{1}{x + 2}$$

6. Give the domain for $y = \sqrt{x + 5}$.

Answers
5. $x \neq -2$ **6.** $x \geq -5$

The graph of a function (or relation) is sometimes helpful in determining the domain and range.

7. Give the domain and range for
$$16x^2 + 9y^2 = 144$$
from its graph.

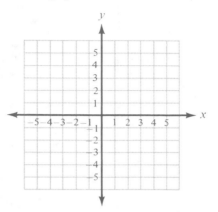

▼ **Example 7**   Give the domain and range for $9x^2 + 4y^2 = 36$.

Solution   The graph is the ellipse shown in Figure 2.

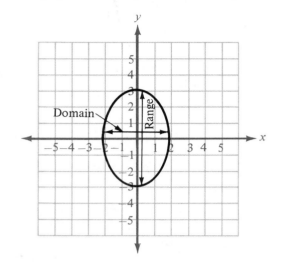

Figure 2

From the graph we have

$$\text{Domain} = \{x \mid -2 \le x \le 2\}$$
$$\text{Range} = \{y \mid -3 \le y \le 3\}$$

Note also that by applying the vertical line test we see the relation is not a function.

8. Use the graph of $y = x^2 + 1$ to find its domain and range.

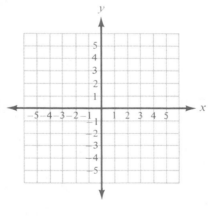

▼ **Example 8**   Give the domain and range for $y = x^2 - 3$.

Solution   The graph is the parabola shown in Figure 3.

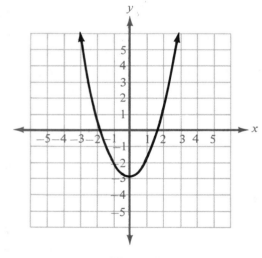

Figure 3

The domain is all real numbers, and the range is the set $\{y \mid y \ge -3\}$. Since no vertical line will cross the graph in more than one place, the graph represents a function.

Answers
7. Domain $= \{x \mid -3 \le x \le 3\}$;
range $= \{y \mid -4 \le y \le 4\}$
8. Domain $= \{$real numbers$\}$;
range $= \{y \mid y \ge 1\}$

Problem Set 10.1

For each of the following relations, give the domain and range and indicate which are also functions.

1. {(1, 3), (2, 5), (4, 1)}

2. {(3, 1), (5, 7), (2, 3)}

3. {(−1, 3), (1, 3), (2, −5)}

4. {(3, −4), (−1, 5), (3, 2)}

5. {(7, −1), (3, −1), (7, 4)}

6. {(5, −2), (3, −2), (5, −1)}

7. {(4, 3), (3, 4), (3, 5)}

8. {(4, 1), (1, 4), (−1, −4)}

9. {(5, −3), (−3, 2), (2, −3)}

10. {(2, 4), (3, 4), (4, 4)}

Which of the following graphs represent functions?

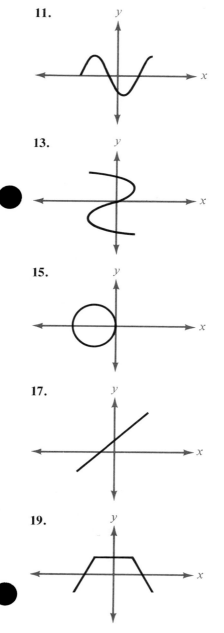

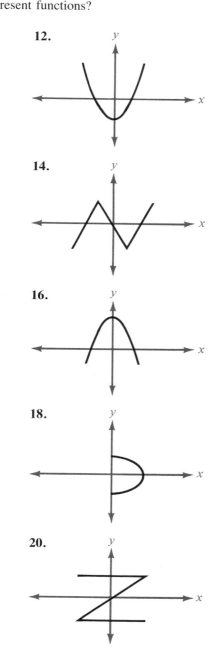

Answers

21. _____

22. _____

23. _____

24. _____

25. _____

26. _____

27. _____

28. _____

29. _____

30. _____

31. _____

32. _____

33. _____

34. _____

35. *See graph* _____

36. *See graph* _____

Give the domain for each of the following functions.

21. $y = \sqrt{x + 3}$

22. $y = \sqrt{x + 4}$

23. $y = \sqrt{2x - 1}$

24. $y = \sqrt{3x - 2}$

25. $y = \sqrt{1 - 4x}$

26. $y = \sqrt{2 + 3x}$

27. $y = \dfrac{x + 2}{x - 5}$

28. $y = \dfrac{x - 3}{x + 4}$

29. $y = \dfrac{3}{2x^2 + 5x - 3}$

30. $y = \dfrac{-1}{3x^2 - 5x + 2}$

31. $y = \dfrac{-3}{x^2 - x - 6}$

32. $y = \dfrac{4}{x^2 - 2x - 8}$

33. $y = \dfrac{4}{x^2 - 4}$

34. $y = \dfrac{2}{x^2 - 9}$

Graph each of the following relations. Use the graph to find the domain and range, and indicate which relations are also functions.

35. $x^2 + 4y^2 = 16$

36. $4x^2 + y^2 = 16$

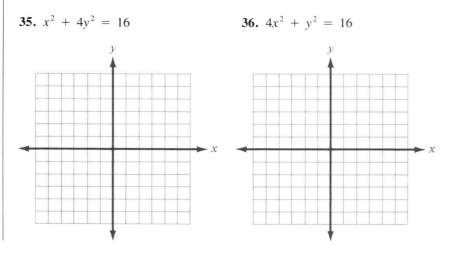

Name _____ Class _____ Date _____

37. $(x - 2)^2 + (y + 1)^2 = 9$

38. $(x + 3)^2 + (y - 4)^2 = 25$

39. $x^2 + y^2 - 4x = 12$

40. $x^2 + y^2 + 6x = 16$

41. $y = x^2 - x - 12$

42. $y = x^2 + 2x - 8$

43. $\dfrac{x^2}{4} - \dfrac{y^2}{9} = 1$

44. $\dfrac{x^2}{9} - \dfrac{y^2}{4} = 1$

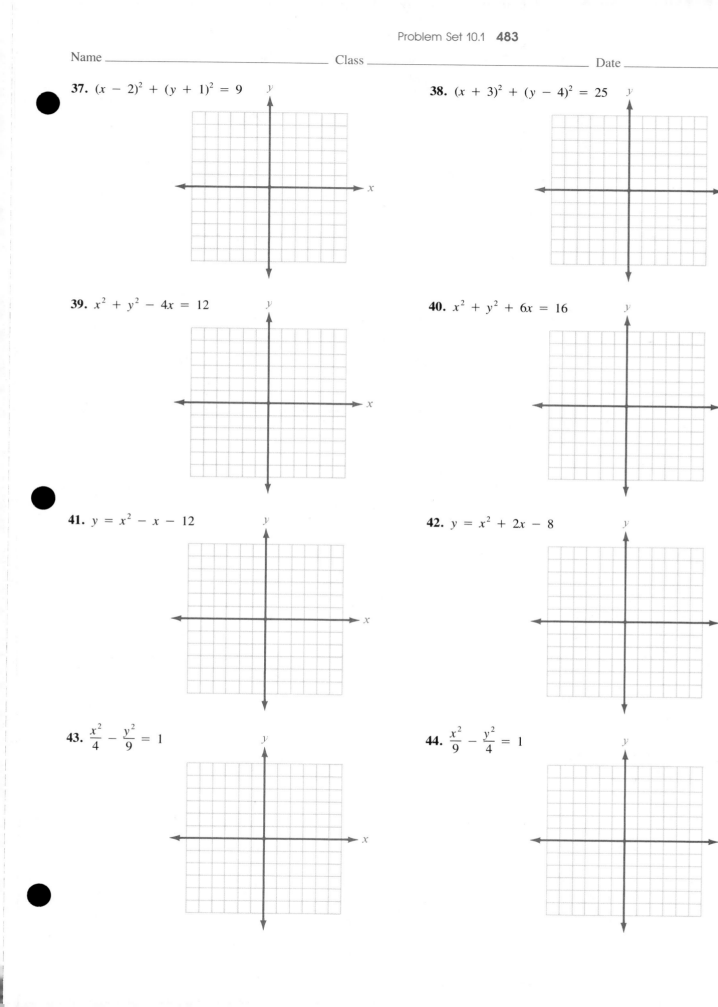

Answers

45a. _____

b. _____

c. _____

d. _____

e. _____

46a. _____

b. _____

c. _____

d. _____

47. _____

48. _____

49. _____

50. _____

45. A ball is thrown straight up into the air from ground level. The relationship between the height (h) of the ball at any time (t) is illustrated by the following graph:

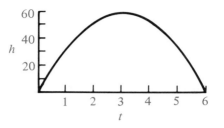

The horizontal axis represents time (t) and the vertical axis represents height (h).

a. Is this graph the graph of a function?
b. Identify the domain and range.
c. At what time does the ball reach its maximum height?
d. What is the maximum height of the ball?
e. At what time does the ball hit the ground?

46. The following graph shows the relationship between a company's profits, P, and the number of items it sells, x. (P is in dollars.)

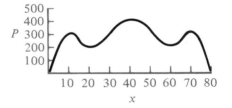

a. Is this graph the graph of a function?
b. Identify the domain and range.
c. How many items must the company sell to make their maximum profit?
d. What is their maximum profit?

Review Problems   The following problems review material we covered in Section 8.2.

Solve each system.

47. $x + y + z = 6$
$2x - y + z = 3$
$x + 2y - 3z = -4$

48. $x + y + z = 6$
$x - y + 2z = 7$
$2x - y - z = 0$

49. $3x + 4y = 15$
$2x - 5z = -3$
$4y - 3z = 9$

50. $x + 3y = 5$
$6y + z = 12$
$x - 2z = -10$

Section 10.2   Function Notation

Consider the function

$$y = 3x - 2$$

Up to this point we have expressed the functions we have worked with as y in terms of x. There is an alternative to expressing y in terms of x called *function notation*. The notation $f(x)$ is read "f of x" and can be used instead of the letter y when writing functions. That is, the equations $y = 3x - 2$ and $f(x) = 3x - 2$ are equivalent. The symbols $f(x)$ and y are interchangeable when we are working with functions. If we wanted to find the value of y when x is 4 in the equation $y = 3x - 2$, we would have to say, "If $x = 4$, then $y = 3(4) - 2 = 10$." With function notation we simply write $f(4) = 3(4) - 2 = 10$. The following table illustrates the equivalence of the notations y and $f(x)$:

y in terms of x	Function notation
$y = x^2 - 3$	$f(x) = x^2 - 3$
If $x = 2$, then $y = 2^2 - 3 = 1$	$f(2) = (2)^2 - 3 = 1$
If $x = -4$, then $y = (-4)^2 - 3 = 13$	$f(-4) = (-4)^2 - 3 = 13$
If $x = 0$, then $y = 0^2 - 3 = -3$	$f(0) = 0^2 - 3 = -3$

Note: The notation $f(x)$ does *not* mean "f times x." It is a special kind of notation that does not imply multiplication.

▼ **Example 1**   If $f(x) = 3x^2 + 2x - 1$, find $f(0), f(3), f(5),$ and $f(-2)$.

Solution   Since $f(x) = 3x^2 + 2x - 1$, we have

$$f(0) = 3(0)^2 + 2(0) - 1 = 0 + 0 - 1 = -1$$
$$f(3) = 3(3)^2 + 2(3) - 1 = 27 + 6 - 1 = 32$$
$$f(5) = 3(5)^2 + 2(5) - 1 = 75 + 10 - 1 = 84$$
$$f(-2) = 3(-2)^2 + 2(-2) - 1 = 12 - 4 - 1 = 7$$ ▲

In the preceding example the function f is defined by the equation $f(x) = 3x^2 + 2x - 1$. We could just as easily have said $y = 3x^2 + 2x - 1$. That is, $y = f(x)$. Saying $f(-2) = 7$ is exactly the same as saying y is 7 when x is -2. If $f(-2) = 7$, then the ordered pair $(-2, 7)$ belongs to the function f; and conversely, if the ordered pair $(-2, 7)$ belongs to f, then $f(-2) = 7$. We can generalize this discussion by saying

$$(a, b) \in f \quad \text{if and only if} \quad f(a) = b$$

where $\in$ is read "belongs to."

▼ **Example 2**   If the function f is given by

$$f = \{(-2, 0), (3, -1), (2, 4), (3, 5)\}$$

then $f(-2) = 0, f(3) = -1, f(2) = 4,$ and $f(3) = 5$.   ▲

▼ **Example 3**   If $f(x) = 4x - 1$ and $g(x) = x^2 + 2$, then

$$f(5) = 4(5) - 1 = 19 \qquad \text{and} \qquad g(5) = 5^2 + 2 = 27$$
$$f(-2) = 4(-2) - 1 = -9 \qquad \text{and} \qquad g(-2) = (-2)^2 + 2 = 6$$
$$f(0) = 4(0) - 1 = -1 \qquad \text{and} \qquad g(0) = 0^2 + 2 = 2$$

Practice Problems

1. If $f(x) = 4x^2 - 3$, find

    a. $f(0)$
    b. $f(3)$
    c. $f(5)$
    d. $f(-2)$

2. If $f = \{(-4, 1), (2, -3), (7, 9)\}$ find

    a. $f(-4)$
    b. $f(2)$
    c. $f(7)$

3. If $f(x) = 2x + 1$ and $g(x) = x^2 - 3$, find

    a. $f(5)$
    b. $g(5)$
    c. $f(-2)$
    d. $g(-2)$
    e. $f(a)$
    f. $g(a)$

Answers
1a. -3 b. 33   c. 97   d. 13
2a. 1   b. -3 c. 9
3a. 11   b. 22   c. -3 d. 1
e. $2a + 1$ f. $a^2 - 3$

$$f(z) = 4z - 1 \qquad \text{and} \quad g(z) = z^2 + 2$$
$$f(a) = 4a - 1 \qquad \text{and} \quad g(a) = a^2 + 2$$

The ordered pairs $(5, 19)$, $(-2, -9)$, $(0, -1)$, $(z, 4z - 1)$, and $(a, 4a - 1)$ belong to the function f, while the ordered pairs $(5, 27)$, $(-2, 6)$, $(0, 2)$, $(z, z^2 + 2)$, and $(a, a^2 + 2)$ belong to the function g. ▲

4. If $f(x) = 3x^2$ and $g(x) = 4x + 1$, find

a. $f[g(2)]$

b. $g[f(2)]$

c. $f[g(x)]$

d. $g[f(x)]$

▼ **Example 4** If $f(x) = 2x^2$ and $g(x) = 3x - 1$, find **(a)** $f[g(2)]$; **(b)** $g[f(2)]$; **(c)** $f[g(x)]$; and **(d)** $g[f(x)]$.

Solutions

a. Since $g(2) = 3(2) - 1 = 5$,
$$f[g(2)] = f(5) = 2(5)^2 = 50$$

b. Since $f(2) = 2(2)^2 = 8$,
$$g[f(2)] = g(8) = 3(8) - 1 = 23$$

c. Substituting $3x - 1$ for $g(x)$ in the expression $f[g(x)]$, we have
$$\begin{aligned} f[g(x)] &= f(3x - 1) \\ &= 2(3x - 1)^2 \\ &= 2(9x^2 - 6x + 1) \\ &= 18x^2 - 12x + 2 \end{aligned}$$

d. Substituting $2x^2$ for $f(x)$ in the expression $g[f(x)]$, we have
$$\begin{aligned} g[f(x)] &= g(2x^2) \\ &= 3(2x^2) - 1 \\ &= 6x^2 - 1 \end{aligned}$$

The last two expressions in Example 4, $f[g(x)]$ and $g[f(x)]$, are called the *composition* of f with g and the *composition* of g with f, respectively. ▲

5. If $f(x) = 5x - 2$, find
$$\frac{f(x + h) - f(x)}{h}$$

Note: The expression
$$\frac{f(x + h) - f(x)}{h}$$
is a very important formula used in calculus. We are using it here just for practice.

▼ **Example 5** If $f(x) = 2x - 3$, find $\dfrac{f(x + h) - f(x)}{h}$.

Solution The expression $f(x + h)$ is given by
$$\begin{aligned} f(x + h) &= 2(x + h) - 3 \\ &= 2x + 2h - 3 \end{aligned}$$

Using this result gives us
$$\begin{aligned} \frac{f(x + h) - f(x)}{h} &= \frac{(2x + 2h - 3) - (2x - 3)}{h} \\ &= \frac{2h}{h} \\ &= 2 \end{aligned}$$
▲

6. If $f(x) = 3x + 2$, find
$$\frac{f(x) - f(a)}{x - a}$$

▼ **Example 6** If $f(x) = 2x - 4$, find $\dfrac{f(x) - f(a)}{x - a}$.

Solution
$$\begin{aligned} \frac{f(x) - f(a)}{x - a} &= \frac{(2x - 4) - (2a - 4)}{x - a} \\ &= \frac{2x - 2a}{x - a} \\ &= \frac{2(x - a)}{x - a} \\ &= 2 \end{aligned}$$
▲

Answers
4a. 243   **b.** 49   **c.** $48x^2 + 24x + 3$
d. $12x^2 + 1$ **5.** 5   **6.** 3

Problem Set 10.2

Name _____

Class _____

Date _____

Let $f(x) = 2x - 5$ and $g(x) = x^2 + 3x + 4$. Evaluate the following.

1. $f(2)$

2. $g(3)$

3. $f(-3)$

4. $g(-2)$

5. $f(0)$

6. $f(5)$

7. $g(-1)$

8. $f(-4)$

9. $g(-3)$

10. $g(2)$

11. $g(4) + f(4)$

12. $f(2) - g(3)$

13. $f(3) - g(2)$

14. $g(-1) + f(-1)$

Answers

1. _____   2. _____

3. _____   4. _____

5. _____   6. _____

7. _____   8. _____

9. _____   10. _____

11. _____   12. _____

13. _____   14. _____

15. _____   16. _____

17. _____   18. _____

19. _____   20. _____

21. _____   22. _____

23. _____   24. _____

If $f = \{(1, 4), (-2, 0), (3, \frac{1}{2}), (\pi, 0)\}$ and $g = \{(1, 1), (-2, 2), (\frac{1}{2}, 0)\}$, find each of the following values of f and g.

15. $f(1)$

16. $g(1)$

17. $g(\frac{1}{2})$

18. $f(3)$

19. $g(-2)$

20. $f(\pi)$

21. $f(-2) + g(-2)$

22. $g(1) + f(1)$

23. $f(-2) - g(1) + f(3)$

24. $g(1) + g(-2) + f(-2)$

Answers

Let $f(x) = 3x^2 - 4x + 1$ and $g(x) = 2x - 1$. Evaluate each of the following.

25. _____   26. _____

25. $f(0)$ **26.** $g(0)$

27. _____   28. _____

29. _____   30. _____

27. $g(-4)$ **28.** $f(1)$

31. _____   32. _____

33. _____   34. _____

29. $f(a)$ **30.** $g(z)$

35. _____   36. _____

37. _____   38. _____

31. $f(a + 3)$ **32.** $g(a - 2)$

39. _____   40. _____

41. _____   42. _____

33. $f[g(2)]$ **34.** $g[f(2)]$

43. _____   44. _____

35. $g[f(-1)]$ **36.** $f[g(-2)]$

37. $g[f(0)]$ **38.** $f[g(0)]$

39. $f[g(x)]$ **40.** $g[f(x)]$

For each of the following functions, evaluate the quantity $\dfrac{f(x + h) - f(x)}{h}$.

41. $f(x) = 2x + 3$ **42.** $f(x) = 3x - 2$

43. $f(x) = x^2$ **44.** $f(x) = x^2 - 3$

45. $y = -4x - 1$

46. $y = -x + 4$

47. $y = 3x^2 - 2$

48. $y = 4x^2 + 3$

49. $f(x) = 2x^2 + 3x + 4$

50. $f(x) = 4x^2 + 3x + 2$

For each of the following functions evaluate the quantity $\dfrac{f(x) - f(a)}{x - a}$.

51. $f(x) = 3x$

52. $f(x) = -2x$

53. $f(x) = 4x - 5$

54. $f(x) = 3x + 1$

55. $f(x) = x^2$

56. $f(x) = 2x^2$

57. $y = 5x - 3$

58. $y = -2x + 7$

59. $y = x^2 + 1$

60. $y = x^2 - 1$

Name _____

Class _____

Date _____

Answers

45. _____   46. _____

47. _____   48. _____

49. _____   50. _____

51. _____   52. _____

53. _____   54. _____

55. _____   56. _____

57. _____   58. _____

59. _____   60. _____

61. Suppose the total cost C of manufacturing x items is given by the equation $C(x) = 2x^2 + 5x + 100$. If the notation $C(x)$ is used in the same way we have been using $f(x)$, then $C(10) = 2(10)^2 + 5(10) + 100 = 350$ is the total cost, in dollars, of manufacturing 10 items. Find the total cost of producing 1 item, 5 items, and 20 items.

62. Suppose the profit P a company makes by selling x items is given by $P(x) = -x^3 + 100x^2$. Find the profit made if 0 items are sold and if 50 items are sold.

63. Suppose $f(x) = x^2 - 5x + 6$. Find the values of x for which $f(x) = 0$.

64. Let $f(x) = x^2 - x - 9$, and find the values of x for which $f(x) = 3$.

65. Let $f(x) = 3x - 5$ and $g(x) = 7x + 1$, and find the value of x for which $f(x) = g(x)$.

66. Use the functions $f(x)$ and $g(x)$ as given in Problem 65 and find the value of x for which $f(x) = -g(x)$.

Review Problems   The following problems review material we covered in Section 8.3.

Find the value of each determinant.

67. $\begin{vmatrix} 2 & 3 \\ 5 & 1 \end{vmatrix}$

68. $\begin{vmatrix} 6 & 1 \\ 2 & 0 \end{vmatrix}$

69. $\begin{vmatrix} -3 & 5 \\ -2 & -7 \end{vmatrix}$

70. $\begin{vmatrix} 4 & -3 \\ -1 & -8 \end{vmatrix}$

71. $\begin{vmatrix} 2 & 3 & -2 \\ 1 & 4 & 1 \\ 1 & 5 & -1 \end{vmatrix}$

72. $\begin{vmatrix} 1 & 2 & 0 \\ 1 & 1 & 1 \\ 0 & 2 & 1 \end{vmatrix}$

Section 10.3   Algebra with Functions

If we are given two functions, f and g, with a common domain, we can define four other functions as follows.

DEFINITION

$$(f + g)(x) = f(x) + g(x)$$

The function $f + g$ is the sum of the functions f and g.

$$(f - g)(x) = f(x) - g(x)$$

The function $f - g$ is the difference of the functions f and g.

$$(fg)(x) = f(x)g(x)$$

The function fg is the product of the functions f and g.

$$\frac{f}{g}(x) = \frac{f(x)}{g(x)}$$

The function f/g is the quotient of the functions f and g, where $g(x) \neq 0$.

▼ **Example 1**   If $f(x) = 4x^2 + 3x + 2$ and $g(x) = 2x^2 - 5x - 6$, write the formula for the functions $f + g$, $f - g$, fg, and f/g.

Solution   The function $f + g$ is defined by

$$
\begin{aligned}
(f + g)(x) &= f(x) + g(x) \\
&= (4x^2 + 3x + 2) + (2x^2 - 5x - 6) \\
&= 6x^2 - 2x - 4
\end{aligned}
$$

The function $f - g$ is defined by

$$
\begin{aligned}
(f - g)(x) &= f(x) - g(x) \\
&= (4x^2 + 3x + 2) - (2x^2 - 5x - 6) \\
&= 4x^2 + 3x + 2 - 2x^2 + 5x + 6 \\
&= 2x^2 + 8x + 8
\end{aligned}
$$

The function fg is defined by

$$
\begin{aligned}
(fg)(x) &= f(x)g(x) \\
&= (4x^2 + 3x + 2)(2x^2 - 5x - 6) \\
&= 8x^4 - 20x^3 - 24x^2 \\
&\quad\quad + 6x^3 - 15x^2 - 18x \\
&\quad\quad\quad\quad + 4x^2 - 10x - 12 \\
&= 8x^4 - 14x^3 - 35x^2 - 28x - 12
\end{aligned}
$$

The function f/g is defined by

$$
\begin{aligned}
\left(\frac{f}{g}\right)(x) &= \frac{f(x)}{g(x)} \\
&= \frac{4x^2 + 3x + 2}{2x^2 - 5x - 6}
\end{aligned}
$$

▲

Practice Problems

1. If $f(x) = 3x^2 + 4$ and $g(x) = 2x - 1$, write the formula for

a. $f + g$

b. $f - g$

c. fg

d. f/g

Answers

1a. $3x^2 + 2x + 3$ b. $3x^2 - 2x + 5$

c. $6x^3 - 3x^2 + 8x - 4$ d. $\dfrac{3x^2 + 4}{2x - 1}$

2. Let $f(x) = 3x + 2$, $g(x) = 3x^2 - 10x - 8$, and $h(x) = x - 4$. Find

a. $f + g$

b. fh

c. fg

d. g/f

▼ **Example 2** Let $f(x) = 4x - 3$, $g(x) = 4x^2 - 7x + 3$, and $h(x) = x - 1$. Find $f + g$, fh, fg, and g/f.

Solution The function $f + g$, the sum of functions f and g, is defined by

$$(f + g)(x) = f(x) + g(x)$$
$$= (4x - 3) + (4x^2 - 7x + 3)$$
$$= 4x^2 - 3x$$

The function fh, the product of functions f and h, is defined by

$$(fh)(x) = f(x)h(x)$$
$$= (4x - 3)(x - 1)$$
$$= 4x^2 - 7x + 3$$
$$= g(x)$$

The product of the functions f and g, fg, is given by

$$(fg)(x) = f(x)g(x)$$
$$= (4x - 3)(4x^2 - 7x + 3)$$
$$= 16x^3 - 28x^2 + 12x - 12x^2 + 21x - 9$$
$$= 16x^3 - 40x^2 + 33x - 9$$

The quotient of the functions g and f, g/f, is defined as

$$\frac{g}{f}(x) = \frac{g(x)}{f(x)}$$
$$= \frac{4x^2 - 7x + 3}{4x - 3}$$

Factoring the numerator, we can reduce to lowest terms:

$$\frac{g}{f}(x) = \frac{(4x - 3)(x - 1)}{4x - 3}$$
$$= x - 1$$
$$= h(x)$$ ▲

3. Use the functions defined in Practice Problem 2 to find

a. $(f + g)(2)$

b. $(fh)(-1)$

c. $(fg)(0)$

d. $\frac{g}{f}(5)$

▼ **Example 3** If f, g, and h are the same functions defined in Example 2, evaluate $(f + g)(2)$, $(fh)(-1)$, $(fg)(0)$, and $(g/f)(5)$.

Solution We use the formulas for $f + g$, fh, fg, and g/f found in Example 2:

$$(f + g)(2) = 4(2)^2 - 3(2)$$
$$= 16 - 6$$
$$= 10$$
$$(fh)(-1) = 4(-1)^2 - 7(-1) + 3$$
$$= 4 + 7 + 3$$
$$= 14$$
$$(fg)(0) = 16(0)^3 - 40(0)^2 + 33(0) - 9$$
$$= 0 - 0 + 0 - 9$$
$$= -9$$

$$\frac{g}{f}(5) = 5 - 1$$
$$= 4$$ ▲

Answers
2a. $3x^2 - 7x - 6$ **b.** $g(x)$
c. $9x^3 - 24x^2 - 44x - 16$ **d.** $h(x)$
3a. -8 **b.** 5 **c.** -16 **d.** 1

Problem Set 10.3

Name _____

Class _____

Date _____

Let $f(x) = 4x - 3$ and $g(x) = 2x + 5$. Write a formula for each of the following functions.

1. $f + g$

2. $f - g$

3. $g - f$

4. $g + f$

5. fg

6. f/g

7. g/f

8. ff

If the functions f, g, and h are defined by $f(x) = 3x - 5$, $g(x) = x - 2$, and $h(x) = 3x^2 - 11x + 10$, write a formula for each of the following functions.

9. $g + f$

10. $f + h$

11. $g + h$

12. $f - g$

13. $g - f$

14. $h - g$

15. fg

16. gf

17. fh

18. gh

19. h/f

20. h/g

21. f/h

22. g/h

23. $f + g + h$

24. $h - g + f$

25. $h + fg$

26. $h - fg$

Answers

1. _____

2. _____

3. _____

4. _____

5. _____

6. _____

7. _____

8. _____

9. _____

10. _____

11. _____

12. _____

13. _____

14. _____

15. _____

16. _____

17. _____

18. _____

19. _____

20. _____

21. _____

22. _____

23. _____

24. _____

25. _____

26. _____

27. _____

28. _____

29. _____

30. _____

31. _____

32. _____

33. _____

34. _____

35. _____

36. _____

37. _____

38. _____

39a. _____

  b. _____

  c. _____

40a. _____

  b. _____

  c. _____

41. _____

42. _____

43. _____

44. _____

Let $f(x) = 2x + 1$, $g(x) = 4x + 2$, and $h(x) = 4x^2 + 4x + 1$, and find the following.

27. $(f + g)(2)$ **28.** $(f - g)(-1)$

29. $(fg)(3)$ **30.** $(f/g)(-3)$

31. $(h/g)(1)$ **32.** $(hg)(1)$

33. $(fh)(0)$ **34.** $(h - g)(-4)$

35. $(f + g + h)(2)$ **36.** $(h - f + g)(0)$

37. $(h + fg)(3)$ **38.** $(h - fg)(5)$

39. Suppose a phone company charges 33¢ for the first minute and 24¢ for each additional minute to place a long-distance call out of state between 5 P.M. and 11 P.M. If x is the number of additional minutes and $f(x)$ is the cost of the call, then $f(x) = 24x + 33$.

  a. How much does it cost to talk for 10 minutes?
  b. What does $f(5)$ represent in this problem?
  c. If a call costs $1.29, how long was it?

40. The same phone company mentioned in Problem 39 charges 52¢ for the first minute and 36¢ for each additional minute to place an out-of-state call between 8 A.M. and 5 P.M.

  a. Let $g(x)$ be the total cost of an out-of-state call between 8 A.M. and 5 P.M. and write an equation for $g(x)$.
  b. Find $g(5)$.
  c. Find the difference in price between a 10-minute call made between 8 A.M. and 5 P.M. and the cost of the same call made between 5 P.M. and 11 P.M.

Review Problems   The following problems review material we covered in Section 8.4.

Solve each system by using Cramer's rule.

41. $4x - 7y = 3$
$5x + 2y = -3$

42. $9x - 8y = 4$
$2x + 3y = 6$

43. $3x + 4y = 15$
$2x - 5z = -3$
$4y - 3z = 9$

44. $x + 3y = 5$
$6y + z = 12$
$x - 2z = -10$

Section 10.4   Classification of Functions

● Much of the work we have done in previous chapters has involved functions. All linear equations in two variables, except those with vertical lines for graphs, are functions. The parabolas we worked with in Chapter 9 are graphs of functions.

Constant Functions

Any function that can be written in the form

$$f(x) = c$$

where c is a real number, is called a *constant function*. The graph of every constant function is a horizontal line.

Practice Problems

▼ **Example 1**   The function $f(x) = 3$ is an example of a constant function. Since all ordered pairs belonging to f have a y-coordinate of 3, the graph is the horizontal line given by $y = 3$. Remember, y and $f(x)$ are equivalent—that is, $y = f(x)$.   ▲

1. Graph the constant function $f(x) = 3$.

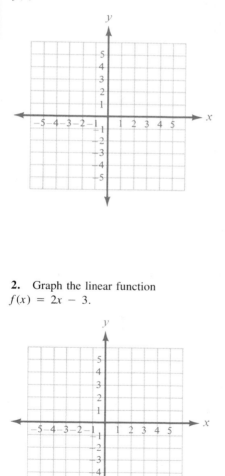

Linear Functions

● Any function that can be written in the form

$$f(x) = ax + b$$

where a and b are real numbers, $a \neq 0$, is called a *linear function*. The graph of every linear function is a straight line. In the past we have written linear functions in the form

$$y = mx + b$$

▼ **Example 2**   The function $f(x) = 2x - 3$ is an example of a linear function. The graph of this function is a straight line with slope 2 and y-intercept -3.   ▲

2. Graph the linear function $f(x) = 2x - 3$.

Quadratic Functions

A *quadratic function* is any function that can be written in the form

$$f(x) = ax^2 + bx + c$$

where a, b, and c are real numbers and $a \neq 0$. The graph of every quadratic function is a parabola. We considered parabolic graphs in Section 9.1. At that time the quadratic functions were written as
● $y = ax^2 + bx + c$ using y instead of $f(x)$.

Answers
1. }
        See Solutions Section.
2. }

3. Graph the quadratic function
$f(x) = 2x^2 - 4x - 6$.

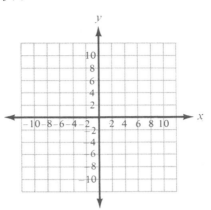

4. If $f(x) = 4^x$, find

a. $f(0)$

b. $f(1)$

c. $f(2)$

d. $f(3)$

e. $f(-1)$

f. $f(-2)$

5. Graph $y = 3^x$.

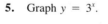

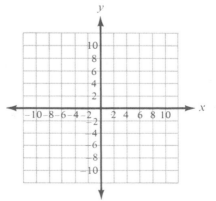

Answers
3. See Solutions Section.
4a. 1   **b.** 4   **c.** 16   **d.** 64   **e.** $\frac{1}{4}$ **f.** $\frac{1}{16}$
5. See Solutions Section.

▼ **Example 3**   The function $f(x) = 2x^2 - 4x - 6$ is an example of a quadratic function. Its graph is a parabola.   ▲

There are many other classifications of functions. One such classification we have not worked with previously is the exponential function. Our introduction to exponential functions, along with the material on inverse functions in the next section, will lay the groundwork necessary to get started in Chapter 11.

Exponential Functions

An *exponential function* is any function that can be written in the form

$$f(x) = b^x$$

where b is a positive real number other than 1.

Each of the following is an exponential function:

$$f(x) = 2^x, \qquad y = 3^x, \qquad f(x) = \left(\tfrac{1}{4}\right)^x$$

The first step in becoming familiar with exponential functions is to find some values for specific exponential functions.

▼ **Example 4**   If the exponential functions f and g are defined by

$$f(x) = 2^x \quad \text{and} \quad g(x) = 3^x$$

then

$$f(0) = 2^0 = 1 \qquad\qquad g(0) = 3^0 = 1$$
$$f(1) = 2^1 = 2 \qquad\qquad g(1) = 3^1 = 3$$
$$f(2) = 2^2 = 4 \qquad\qquad g(2) = 3^2 = 9$$
$$f(3) = 2^3 = 8 \qquad\qquad g(3) = 3^3 = 27$$

$$f(-2) = 2^{-2} = \frac{1}{2^2} = \frac{1}{4} \qquad g(-2) = 3^{-2} = \frac{1}{3^2} = \frac{1}{9}$$

$$f(-3) = 2^{-3} = \frac{1}{2^3} = \frac{1}{8} \qquad g(-3) = 3^{-3} = \frac{1}{3^3} = \frac{1}{27} \qquad ▲$$

We will now turn our attention to the graphs of exponential functions. Since the notation y is easier to use when graphing, and $y = f(x)$, for convenience we will write the exponential functions as

$$y = b^x$$

▼ **Example 5**   Sketch the graph of the exponential function

$$y = 2^x$$

Solution   Using the results of Example 4 in addition to some other convenient values of x, we have the following table:

x	y
-3	1/8
-2	1/4
-1	1/2
0	1
1	2
2	4
3	8

Graphing the ordered pairs given in the table and connecting them with a smooth curve, we have the graph of $y = 2^x$ shown in Figure 4.

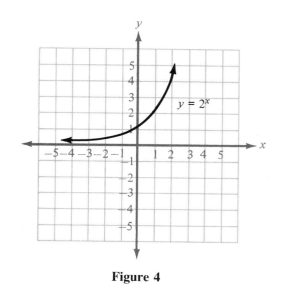

Figure 4

Notice that the graph does not cross the x-axis. It *approaches* the x-axis—in fact, we can get it as close to the x-axis as we want without its actually intersecting the x-axis. In order for the graph of $y = 2^x$ to intersect the x-axis, we would have to find a value of x that would make $2^x = 0$. Because no such value of x exists, the graph of $y = 2^x$ cannot intersect the x-axis.   ▲

▼ **Example 6**   Sketch the graph of $y = (\frac{1}{3})^x$.

Solution   We can make a table that will give some ordered pairs that satisfy the equation:

x	$y = \left(\dfrac{1}{3}\right)^x$	y
-3	$y = \left(\dfrac{1}{3}\right)^{-3} = 3^3 = 27$	27
-2	$y = \left(\dfrac{1}{3}\right)^{-2} = 3^2 = 9$	9
-1	$y = \left(\dfrac{1}{3}\right)^{-1} = 3^1 = 3$	3
0	$y = \left(\dfrac{1}{3}\right)^{0} = 1$	1
1	$y = \left(\dfrac{1}{3}\right)^{1} = \dfrac{1}{3}$	$\dfrac{1}{3}$
2	$y = \left(\dfrac{1}{3}\right)^{2} = \dfrac{1}{9}$	$\dfrac{1}{9}$
3	$y = \left(\dfrac{1}{3}\right)^{3} = \dfrac{1}{27}$	$\dfrac{1}{27}$

6.   Graph $y = \left(\dfrac{1}{2}\right)^x$.

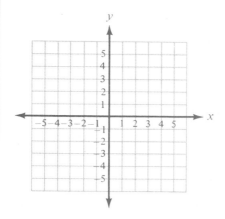

Using the ordered pairs from the table, we have the graph shown in Figure 5.

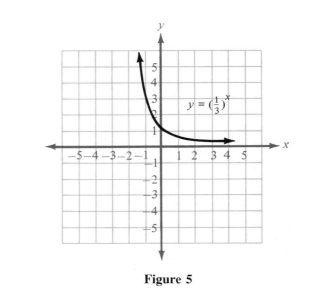

Figure 5

The graphs of all exponential functions have two things in common: (1) each crosses the y-axis at $(0, 1)$, since $b^0 = 1$; and (2) none can cross the x-axis, since $b^x = 0$ is impossible because of the restrictions on b.

Name _____ Class _____ Date _____

Problem Set 10.4

Sketch the graph of each of the following functions. Identify each as a constant function, linear function, or quadratic function.

1. $f(x) = x^2 - 3$

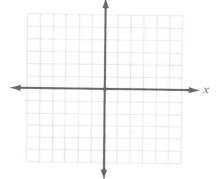

2. $g(x) = 2x^2$

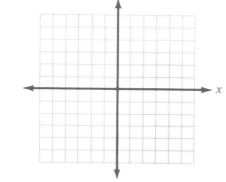

3. $g(x) = 4x - 1$

4. $f(x) = 3x + 2$

5. $f(x) = 5$

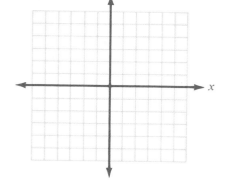

6. $f(x) = -3$

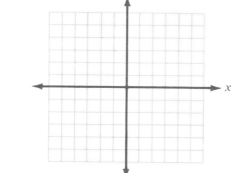

7. $f(x) = x^2 + 4x - 5$

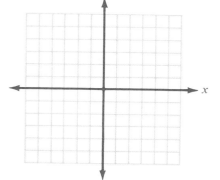

8. $f(x) = -x^2 - 4x + 5$

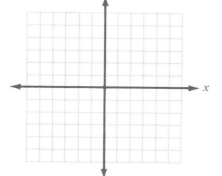

Answers

9. _____   10. _____

11. _____   12. _____

13. _____   14. _____

15. _____   16. _____

17. _____   18. _____

19. _____   20. _____

21. _____   22. _____

23. _____   24. _____

25. _____   26. _____

Let $f(x) = 3^x$ and $g(x) = (\frac{1}{2})^x$ and evaluate each of the following.

9. $f(-2)$ **10.** $f(4)$

11. $g(2)$ **12.** $g(-2)$

13. $g(0)$ **14.** $f(0)$

15. $g(-1)$ **16.** $g(-4)$

17. $f(-3)$ **18.** $f(-1)$

19. $f(2) + g(-2)$ **20.** $f(2) - g(-2)$

21. $g(-3) + f(2)$ **22.** $g(2) + f(-1)$

23. $f(0) + g(0)$ **24.** $g(-3) + f(3)$

25. $f(-2) + g(3)$ **26.** $g(0) - f(0)$

Name _____ Class _____ Date _____

Graph each of the following functions.

27. $y = 4^x$

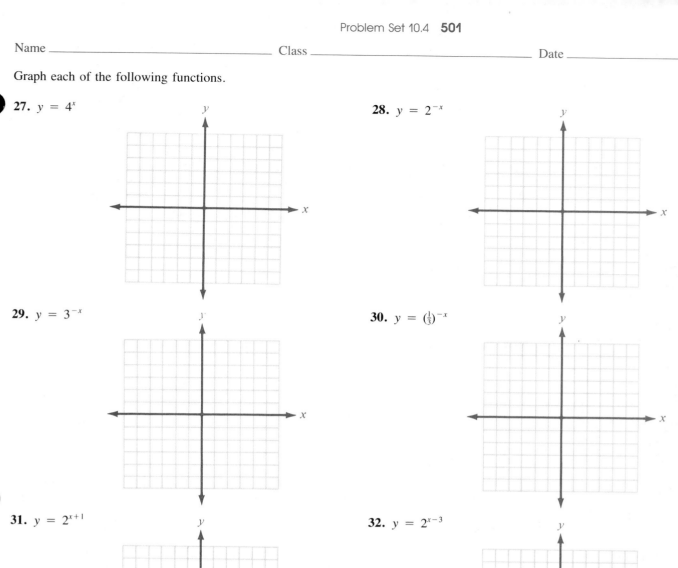

28. $y = 2^{-x}$

29. $y = 3^{-x}$

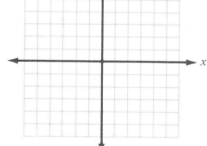

30. $y = \left(\frac{1}{3}\right)^{-x}$

31. $y = 2^{x+1}$

32. $y = 2^{x-3}$

33. $y = 2^{2x}$

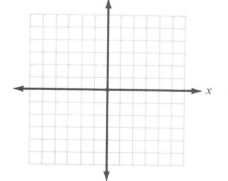

34. $y = 3^{2x}$

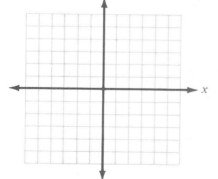

The base b in an exponential function is restricted to positive numbers other than 1. To see why this is done, graph each of the following if possible.

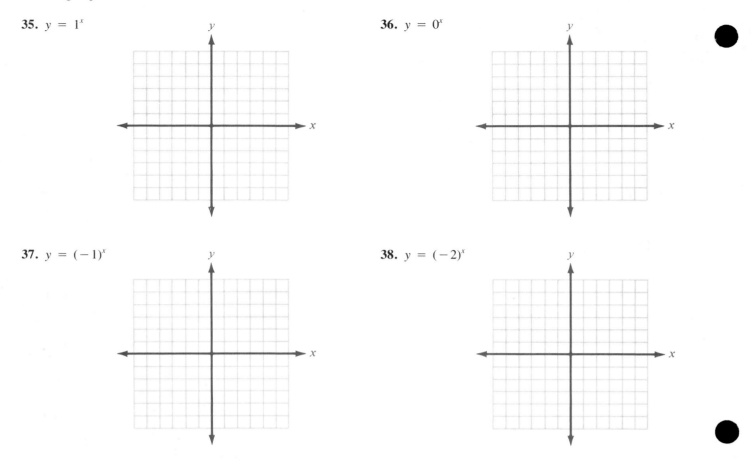

35. $y = 1^x$

36. $y = 0^x$

37. $y = (-1)^x$

38. $y = (-2)^x$

39. Suppose it takes 1 day for a certain strain of bacteria to reproduce by dividing in half. If there are 100 bacteria present to begin with, then the total number present after x days will be $f(x) = 100 \cdot 2^x$. Find the total number present after 1 day, 2 days, 3 days, and 4 days. How many days must elapse before there are over 100,000 bacteria present?

40. Suppose it takes 12 hours for a certain strain of bacteria to reproduce by dividing in half. If there are 50 bacteria present to begin with, then the total number present after x days will be $f(x) = 50 \cdot 4^x$. Find the total number present after 1 day, 2 days, and 3 days.

Review Problems
The following problems review material we covered in Section 9.2.

Find the distance between the following points.

41. $(0, 4)$ $(3, 0)$ **42.** $(2, -5)$ $(-4, 3)$

43. Find x so the distance between $(x, 3)$ and $(1, 6)$ is $\sqrt{13}$.

44. Find y so the distance between $(2, y)$ and $(1, 2)$ is $\sqrt{2}$.

Give the center and radius of each of the following circles.

45. $x^2 + y^2 = 25$ **46.** $x^2 + y^2 = 9$

47. $x^2 + y^2 + 6x - 4y = 3$ **48.** $x^2 + y^2 - 8x + 2y = 8$

Section 10.5   The Inverse of a Function

Suppose the function f is given by

$$f = \{(1, 4), (2, 5), (3, 6), (4, 7)\}$$

The inverse of f, written f^{-1}, is obtained by reversing the order of the coordinates in each ordered pair in f. The inverse of f is the relation given by

$$f^{-1} = \{(4, 1), (5, 2), (6, 3), (7, 4)\}$$

It is obvious that the domain of f is now the range of f^{-1}, and the range of f is now the domain of f^{-1}. Every function (or relation) has an inverse that is obtained from the original function by interchanging the components of each ordered pair.

Suppose a function f is defined with an equation instead of a list of ordered pairs. We can obtain the equation of the inverse f^{-1} by interchanging the role of x and y in the equation for f.

Practice Problems

▼ **Example 1**   If the function f is defined by $f(x) = 2x - 3$, find the equation that represents the inverse of f.

1.   If $f(x) = 4x + 1$, find the equation for the inverse of f.

Solution   Since the inverse of f is obtained by interchanging the components of all the ordered pairs belonging to f, and each ordered pair in f satisfies the equation $y = 2x - 3$, we simply exchange x and y in the equation $y = 2x - 3$ to get the formula for f^{-1}:

$$x = 2y - 3$$

We now solve this equation for y in terms of x:

$$x + 3 = 2y$$

$$\frac{x + 3}{2} = y$$

$$y = \frac{x + 3}{2}$$

The last line gives the equation that defines the function f^{-1}. We can write this equation with function notation as

$$f^{-1}(x) = \frac{x + 3}{2}$$

Let's compare the graphs of f and f^{-1} as given in Example 1. (See Figure 6.)

The graphs of f and f^{-1} have symmetry about the line $y = x$. This is a reasonable result, since the one function was obtained from the other by interchanging x and y in the equation. The ordered pairs (a, b) and (b, a) always have symmetry about the line $y = x$.   ▲

Answer

1. $f^{-1}(x) = \dfrac{x - 1}{4}$

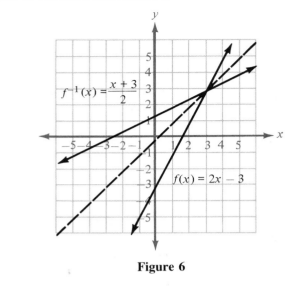

Figure 6

2. Graph $y = x^2 + 1$ and its inverse. Give the equation for the inverse.

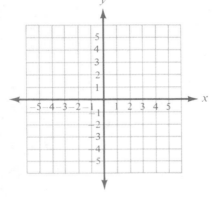

▼ **Example 2** Graph the function $y = x^2 - 2$ and its inverse. Give the equation for the inverse.

Solution We can obtain the graph of the inverse of $y = x^2 - 2$ by graphing $y = x^2 - 2$ by the usual methods, and then reflecting the graph about the line $y = x$. The equation that corresponds to the inverse of $y = x^2 - 2$ is obtained by interchanging x and y to get $x = y^2 - 2$. (See Figure 7.)

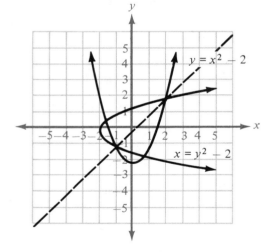

Figure 7

We can solve the equation $x = y^2 - 2$ for y in terms of x as follows:

$$x = y^2 - 2$$
$$x + 2 = y^2$$
$$y = \pm\sqrt{x + 2}$$

Using function notation, we can write the function and its inverse as

$$f(x) = x^2 - 2, \qquad f^{-1}(x) = \pm\sqrt{x + 2}$$

Comparing the graphs from Examples 1 and 2, we observe that the inverse of a function is not always a function. In Example 1, both f and f^{-1} have graphs that are straight lines and therefore both represent

Answer
2. See Solutions Section.

functions. In Example 2, the inverse of function f is not a function, since a vertical line crosses the graph of f^{-1} in more than one place.

▼ **Example 3**   Graph the relation

$$\frac{x^2}{9} + \frac{y^2}{25} = 1$$

and its inverse. Write an equation for the inverse.

Solution   The graph of

$$\frac{x^2}{9} + \frac{y^2}{25} = 1$$

is an ellipse that crosses the x-axis at $(3, 0)$ and $(-3, 0)$ and the y-axis at $(0, 5)$ and $(0, -5)$. Exchanging x and y in the equation, we obtain the equation of the inverse shown in Figure 8.

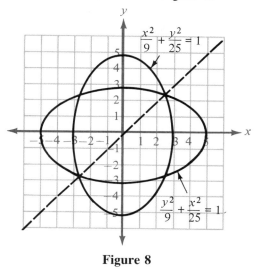

Figure 8

$\dfrac{x^2}{9} + \dfrac{y^2}{25} = 1$ and $\dfrac{y^2}{9} + \dfrac{x^2}{25} = 1$ are inverse relations.   ▲

▼ **Example 4**   Graph the function $y = 2^x$ and its inverse $x = 2^y$.

Solution   We graphed $y = 2^x$ in the preceding section. We simply reflect its graph about the line $y = x$ to obtain the graph of its inverse $x = 2^y$. (See Figure 9.)

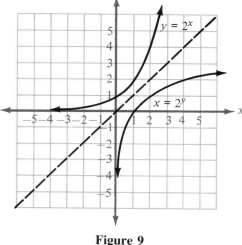

Figure 9   ▲

3.   Graph $\dfrac{x^2}{4} + \dfrac{y^2}{16} = 1$ and its inverse. Write an equation for the inverse.

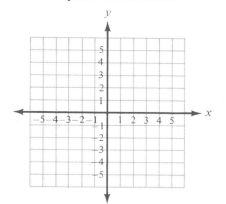

4.   Graph the function $y = 3^x$ and its inverse $x = 3^y$.

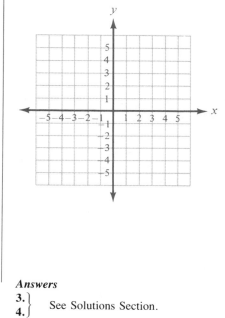

Answers
3.⎫
4.⎭   See Solutions Section.

Problem Set 10.5

For each of the following functions, find the equation of the inverse. Write the inverse using the notation $f^{-1}(x)$.

1. $f(x) = 3x - 1$

2. $f(x) = 2x - 5$

3. $f(x) = 1 - 3x$

4. $f(x) = 3 - 4x$

5. $f(x) = x^2 + 4$

6. $f(x) = 3x^2$

7. $f(x) = \dfrac{x - 3}{4}$

8. $f(x) = \dfrac{x + 7}{2}$

9. $f(x) = \frac{1}{2}x - 3$

10. $f(x) = \frac{1}{3}x + 1$

11. $f(x) = -x^2 + 3$

12. $f(x) = 4 - x^2$

Name _____

Class _____

Date _____

Answers

1. _____

2. _____

3. _____

4. _____

5. _____

6. _____

7. _____

8. _____

9. _____

10. _____

11. _____

12. _____

For each of the following relations, sketch the graph of the relation and its inverse, and write an equation for the inverse.

13. $y = 2x - 1$

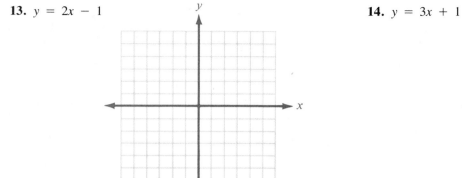

14. $y = 3x + 1$

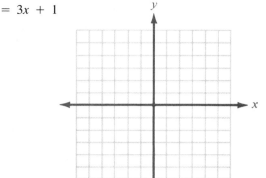

15. $y = x^2 - 3$

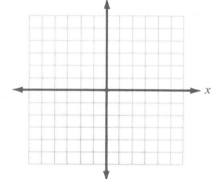

16. $y = x^2 + 1$

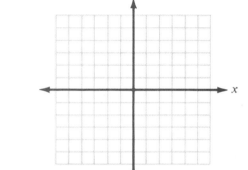

17. $y = x^2 - 2x - 3$

18. $y = x^2 + 2x - 3$

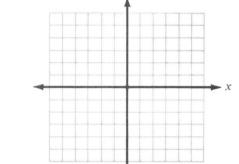

19. $y = 3^x$

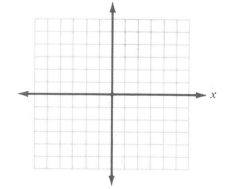

20. $y = \left(\dfrac{1}{2}\right)^x$

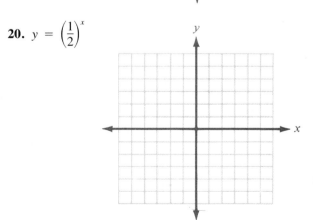

Name _____ Class _____ Date _____

21. $y = 4$

22. $y = -2$

23. $4x^2 - 9y^2 = 36$

24. $9x^2 + 4y^2 = 36$

25. $y = \frac{1}{2}x + 2$

26. $y = \frac{1}{3}x - 1$

27. $x^2 + y^2 = 16$

28. $x^2 - y^2 = 16$

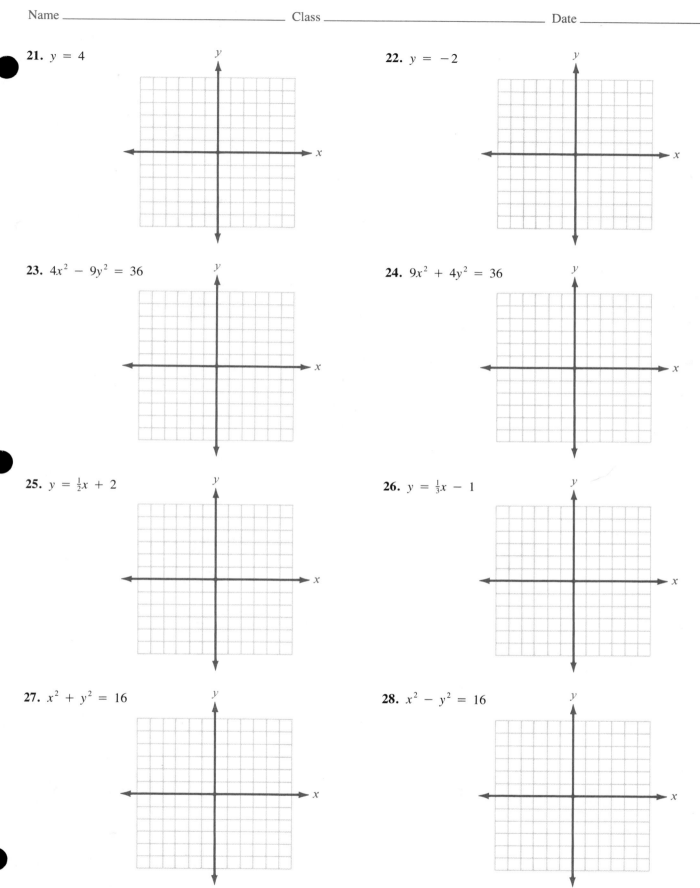

Answers

29a. _____

  b. _____

  c. _____

  d. _____

30a. _____

  b. _____

  c. _____

  d. _____

31. _____

32. _____

33. _____

34. _____

35. _____

36. _____

37. _____

38. _____

29. If $f(x) = 3x - 2$, then $f^{-1}(x) = \dfrac{x + 2}{3}$. Use these two functions to find

    a. $f(2)$ **c.** $f[f^{-1}(2)]$

    b. $f^{-1}(2)$ **d.** $f^{-1}[f(2)]$

30. If $f(x) = \frac{1}{2}x + 5$, then $f^{-1}(x) = 2x - 10$. Use these two functions to find

    a. $f(-4)$ **c.** $f[f^{-1}(-4)]$

    b. $f^{-1}(-4)$ **d.** $f^{-1}[f(-4)]$

31. Let $f(x) = \dfrac{1}{x}$, and find $f^{-1}(x)$.

32. Let $f(x) = \dfrac{a}{x}$, and find $f^{-1}(x)$. (a is a real number constant.)

Review Problems   The following problems review material we covered in Section 9.5.

Solve each system.

33. $x^2 + y^2 = 9$
     $x - 2y = 3$

34. $x^2 - y^2 = 9$
     $x + 2y = 3$

35. $x^2 + y^2 = 16$
    $4x^2 + y^2 = 16$

36. $x^2 + y^2 = 25$
     $x^2 - y^2 = 25$

37. $x^2 + y^2 = 4$
          $y = x^2 - 2$

38. $x^2 + y^2 = 49$
          $y = x^2 - 7$

Chapter 10   Summary and Review

Examples

RELATIONS AND FUNCTIONS [10.1]

A *relation* is any set of ordered pairs. The set of all first coordinates is called the *domain* of the relation. The set of all second coordinates is the *range* of the relation.

A *function* is a relation in which no two different ordered pairs have the same first coordinate.

If the domain for a relation or a function is not specified, it is assumed to be all real numbers for which the relation (or function) is defined. Since we are only concerned with real number functions, a function is not defined for those values of x that give 0 in the denominator or the square root of a negative number.

1. The relation $\{(8, 1), (6, 1), (-3, 0)\}$ is also a function since no ordered pairs have the same first coordinates. The domain is $\{8, 6, -3\}$ and the range is $\{1, 0\}$.

VERTICAL LINE TEST [10.1]

If a vertical line crosses the graph of a relation in more than one place, then the relation is not a function. If no vertical line can cross the graph of a relation in more than one place, then the relation is a function.

2. The graph of any circle, ellipse, or hyperbola found in this chapter will fail the vertical line test: A vertical line can always be found that crosses the graph in more than one place.

FUNCTION NOTATION [10.2]

The notation $f(x)$ is read "*f* of *x*." It is defined to be the value of the function f at x. The value of $f(x)$ is the value of y associated with a given value of x. The expressions $f(x)$ and y are equivalent. That is, $y = f(x)$.

3. If $f(x) = 5x - 3$ then
$$f(0) = 5(0) - 3 = -3$$
$$f(1) = 5(1) - 3 = 2$$
$$f(-2) = 5(-2) - 3 = -13$$
$$f(a) = 5a - 3$$

ALGEBRA WITH FUNCTIONS [10.3]

If f and g are any two functions with a common domain, then:

The sum of f and g, written $f + g$, is defined by
$$(f + g)(x) = f(x) + g(x)$$

The difference of f and g, written $f - g$, is defined by
$$(f - g)(x) = f(x) - g(x)$$

The product of f and g, written fg, is defined by
$$(fg)(x) = f(x)g(x)$$

The quotient of f and g, written f/g, is defined by
$$\left(\frac{f}{g}\right)(x) = \frac{f(x)}{g(x)} \qquad g(x) \neq 0$$

4. If $f(x) = 4x$ and $g(x) = x^2 - 3$, then

$$(f + g)(x) = x^2 + 4x - 3$$

$$(f - g)(x) = -x^2 + 4x + 3$$

$$(fg)(x) = 4x^3 - 12x$$

$$\frac{f}{g}(x) = \frac{4x}{x^2 - 3}$$

CLASSIFICATION OF FUNCTIONS [10.4]

Constant function:	$f(x) = c$	(c = Constant)
Linear function:	$f(x) = ax + b$	($a \neq 0$)
Quadratic function:	$f(x) = ax^2 + bx + c$	($a \neq 0$)
Exponential function:	$f(x) = b^x$	($b > 0, b \neq 1$)

5. Functions

Constant:	$f(x) = 5$
Linear:	$f(x) = 3x - 2$
Quadratic:	$f(x) = x^2 - 5x + 6$
Exponential:	$f(x) = 2^x$

THE INVERSE OF A FUNCTION [10.5]

The inverse of a function is obtained by reversing the order of the coordinates of the ordered pairs belonging to the function.

The inverse of a function is not necessarily a function.

6. The inverse of $f(x) = 2x - 3$ is

$$f^{-1}(x) = \frac{x + 3}{2}$$

THE GRAPH OF THE INVERSE OF A FUNCTION [10.5]

The graph of f^{-1} can be obtained from the graph of f by simply reflecting the graph of f across the line $y = x$. That is, the graphs of f and f^{-1} are symmetrical about the line $y = x$.

COMMON MISTAKES

1. The most common mistake made when working with functions is to interpret the notation $f(x)$ as meaning the product of f and x. The notation $f(x)$ does *not* mean f times x. It is the value of the function f at x and is equivalent to y.

2. Another common mistake occurs when the expression $f^{-1}(x)$ is interpreted as meaning the reciprocal of x. The notation $f^{-1}(x)$ is used to denote the *inverse* of $f(x)$:

$$f^{-1}(x) \neq \frac{1}{f(x)}$$

$$f^{-1}(x) = \text{Inverse of } f$$

Chapter 10 Test

Name _____

Class _____

Date _____

Specify the domain and range for the following relations and indicate which relations are also functions.

1. $\{(-3, 1), (2, 1), (3, 5), (0, 3)\}$ **2.** $\{(-2, 0), (-3, 0), (-2, 1)\}$

3. $y = x^2 - 9$ **4.** $4x^2 + 9y^2 = 36$

Indicate any restrictions on the domain of the following.

5. $y = \sqrt{x - 4}$ **6.** $y = \dfrac{4}{\sqrt{3 - x}}$

7. $y = \dfrac{6}{x + 1}$ **8.** $y = \dfrac{x - 1}{x^2 - 2x - 8}$

Answers

1. _____
2. _____
3. _____
4. _____
5. _____
6. _____
7. _____
8. _____
9. _____
10. _____
11. _____
12. _____
13. _____
14. _____

Let $f(x) = x - 2$, $g(x) = 3x + 4$, and $h(x) = 3x^2 - 2x - 8$, and find the following.

9. $f(3) + g(2)$ **10.** $h(0) + g(0)$

11. $(f + g)(x)$ **12.** $(h/g)(x)$

13. $(f + g + h)(-3)$ **14.** $(h + fg)(1)$

Graph each of the following exponential functions.

15. $y = 2^x$

16. $y = 3^{-x}$

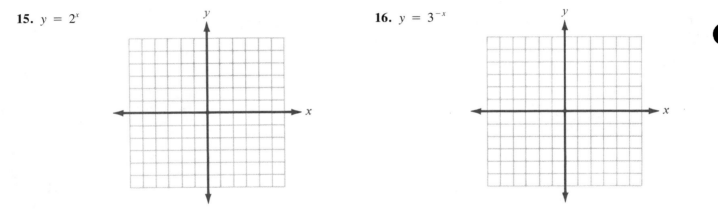

Find an equation for the inverse of each of the following functions. Sketch the graph of f and f^{-1} on the same set of axes.

17. $f(x) = 2x - 3$

18. $f(x) = x^2 - 4$

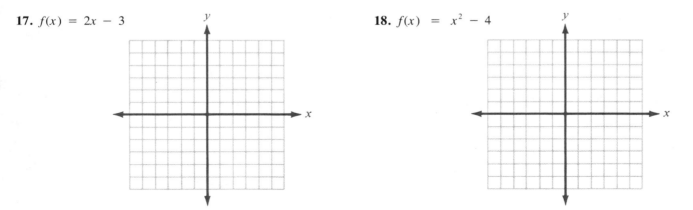

Logarithms

To the student:

This chapter is mainly concerned with applications of a new notation for exponents. Logarithms are exponents. The properties of logarithms are actually the properties of exponents. As it turns out, writing exponents with the new notation, logarithms, allows us to solve some problems we would otherwise be unable to solve. Logarithms used to be used extensively to simplify tedious calculations. Since hand-held calculators are so common now, logarithms are seldom used in connection with computations. Nevertheless, there are many other applications of logarithms to both science and higher mathematics. For example, the pH of a liquid is defined in terms of logarithms. (That's the same pH that is given on the label of many hair conditioners.) The Richter scale for measuring earthquake intensity is a logarithmic scale, as is the decibel scale used for measuring the intensity of sound.

We will begin this chapter with the definition of logarithms and the three main properties of logarithms. The rest of the chapter involves applications of the definition and properties. Understanding the last two sections in Chapter 10 will be very useful in getting started in this chapter.

Section 11.1 Logarithms Are Exponents

We can exchange x and y in the equation of an exponential function to get the equation of its inverse. The equation of the inverse of an exponential function must have the form

$$x = b^y \qquad (b > 0, b \neq 1)$$

515

The problem with this expression is that y is not written explicitly in terms of x. That is, we would like to be able to write the equation $x = b^y$ as an equivalent equation with just y on the left side. One way to do so is with the following definition.

DEFINITION The expression $y = \log_b x$ is read "y is the logarithm to the base b of x," and is equivalent to the expression

$$x = b^y \qquad (b > 0, \ b \neq 1)$$

We say y is the number we raise b to in order to get x.

Notation: When an expression is in the form $x = b^y$, it is said to be in *exponential form*. On the other hand, if an expression is in the form $y = \log_b x$, it is said to be in *logarithmic form*.

The following table illustrates the two forms:

Exponential form		Logarithmic form
$8 = 2^3$	$\Leftrightarrow$	$\log_2 8 = 3$
$25 = 5^2$	$\Leftrightarrow$	$\log_5 25 = 2$
$.1 = 10^{-1}$	$\Leftrightarrow$	$\log_{10} .1 = -1$
$\frac{1}{8} = 2^{-3}$	$\Leftrightarrow$	$\log_2 \frac{1}{8} = -3$
$r = z^s$	$\Leftrightarrow$	$\log_z r = s$

As the table indicates, logarithms are exponents. That is, $\log_2 8$ is 3 *because* 3 is the exponent to which we raise 2 in order to get 8. *Logarithms are exponents.*

▼ **Example 1** Solve for x: $\log_3 x = -2$.

Solution In exponential form the equation looks like this:

$$x = 3^{-2}$$
$$\text{or} \quad x = \tfrac{1}{9}$$

The solution set is $\{\tfrac{1}{9}\}$. ▲

▼ **Example 2** Solve $\log_x 4 = 3$.

Solution Again, we use the definition of logarithms to write the expression in exponential form:

$$4 = x^3$$

Taking the cube root of both sides, we have

$$\sqrt[3]{4} = \sqrt[3]{x^3}$$
$$x = \sqrt[3]{4}$$

The solution set is $\{\sqrt[3]{4}\}$. ▲

▼ **Example 3** Solve $\log_8 4 = x$.

Solution We write the expression again in exponential form:

$$4 = 8^x$$

Note: The ability to change from logarithmic form to exponential form is the most important thing to know about logarithms to begin with.

Practice Problems

1. Solve for x: $\log_2 x = 3$.

2. Solve $\log_x 5 = 2$.

3. Solve $\log_9 27 = x$.

Answers
1. 8 2. $\sqrt{5}$ 3. $\tfrac{3}{2}$

Since both 4 and 8 can be written as powers of 2, we write them in terms of powers of 2:

$$2^2 = (2^3)^x$$
$$2^2 = 2^{3x}$$

The only way the left and right sides of this last line can be equal is if the exponents are equal—that is, if

$$2 = 3x$$
$$\text{or} \quad x = \tfrac{2}{3}$$

The solution is $\tfrac{2}{3}$. We check as follows:

$$\log_8 4 = \tfrac{2}{3} \Leftrightarrow 4 = 8^{2/3}$$
$$4 = (\sqrt[3]{8})^2$$
$$4 = 2^2$$
$$4 = 4$$

The solution checks when used in the original equation. ▲

Graphing logarithmic functions can be done using the graphs of exponential functions and the fact that the graphs of inverse functions have symmetry about the line $y = x$. Here's an example to illustrate.

▼ **Example 4** Graph the equation $y = \log_2 x$.

Solution   The equation $y = \log_2 x$ is, by definition, equivalent to the exponential equation

$$x = 2^y$$

which is the equation of the inverse of the function

$$y = 2^x$$

The graph of $y = 2^x$ was given in Figure 4 in Chapter 10. We simply reflect the graph of $y = 2^x$ about the line $y = x$ to get the graph of $x = 2^y$, which is also the graph of $y = \log_2 x$. (See Figure 1.)

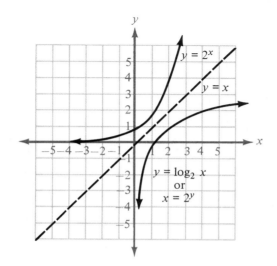

Figure 1

Note: The first step in each of these first three examples is the same. In each case the first step in solving the equation is to put the equation in exponential form.

4. Graph the equation

$$y = \log_3 x$$

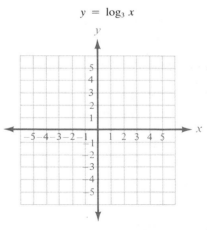

Note: From the graph of $y = \log_2 x$ it is apparent that $x > 0$ since the graph does not appear to the left of the y-axis. In general, the only variable in the expression $y = \log_b x$ that can be negative is y.

Answer
4. See Solutions Section.

It is apparent from the graph that $y = \log_2 x$ is a function, since no vertical line will cross its graph in more than one place. The same is true for all logarithmic equations of the form

$$y = \log_b x$$

where b is a positive number other than 1.

If b is a positive real number other than 1, then each of the following is a consequence of the definition of a logarithm:

Two Special Identities

$$(1)\ b^{\log_b x} = x \quad \text{and} \quad (2)\ \log_b b^x = x$$

The justifications for these identities are similar. Let's consider only the first one. Consider the expression

$$y = \log_b x$$

By definition, it is equivalent to

$$x = b^y$$

Substituting $\log_b x$ for y in the last line gives us

$$x = b^{\log_b x}$$

The last examples in this section show how these two special properties can be used to simplify expressions involving logarithms.

▼ **Example 5** Simplify $\log_2 8$.

Solution Substitute 2^3 for 8:

$$\log_2 8 = \log_2 2^3$$
$$= 3$$ ▲

▼ **Example 6** Simplify $\log_{10} 10{,}000$.

Solution 10,000 can be written as 10^4:

$$\log_{10} 10{,}000 = \log_{10} 10^4$$
$$= 4$$ ▲

▼ **Example 7** Simplify $\log_b b$ ($b > 0$, $b \neq 1$).

Solution Since $b^1 = b$, we have

$$\log_b b = \log_b b^1$$
$$= 1$$ ▲

▼ **Example 8** Simplify $\log_b 1$ ($b > 0$, $b \neq 1$).

Solution Since $1 = b^0$, we have

$$\log_b 1 = \log_b b^0$$
$$= 0$$ ▲

▼ **Example 9** Simplify $\log_4 (\log_5 5)$.

Solution Since $\log_5 5 = 1$,

$$\log_4 (\log_5 5) = \log_4 1$$
$$= 0$$ ▲

5. Simplify $\log_3 27$.

6. Simplify $\log_{10} 1000$.

7. Simplify $\log_6 6$.

8. Simplify $\log_3 1$.

9. Simplify $\log_2 (\log_8 8)$.

Answers
5. 3 **6.** 3 **7.** 1 **8.** 0 **9.** 0

Problem Set 11.1

Name _____

Class _____

Date _____

Write each of the following expressions in logarithmic form.

1. $2^4 = 16$

2. $3^2 = 9$

3. $125 = 5^3$

4. $16 = 4^2$

5. $.01 = 10^{-2}$

6. $.001 = 10^{-3}$

7. $2^{-5} = \frac{1}{32}$

8. $4^{-2} = \frac{1}{16}$

9. $\left(\frac{1}{2}\right)^{-3} = 8$

10. $\left(\frac{1}{3}\right)^{-2} = 9$

11. $27 = 3^3$

12. $81 = 3^4$

Write each of the following expressions in exponential form.

13. $\log_{10} 100 = 2$

14. $\log_2 8 = 3$

15. $\log_2 64 = 6$

16. $\log_2 32 = 5$

17. $\log_8 1 = 0$

18. $\log_9 9 = 1$

19. $\log_{10} .001 = -3$

20. $\log_{10} .0001 = -4$

21. $\log_6 36 = 2$

22. $\log_7 49 = 2$

23. $\log_5 \frac{1}{25} = -2$

24. $\log_3 \frac{1}{81} = -4$

Answers

1. _____   2. _____

3. _____   4. _____

5. _____   6. _____

7. _____   8. _____

9. _____   10. _____

11. _____   12. _____

13. _____   14. _____

15. _____   16. _____

17. _____   18. _____

19. _____   20. _____

21. _____   22. _____

23. _____   24. _____

Answers

Solve each of the following equations for x:

25. _____   26. _____

27. _____   28. _____

29. _____   30. _____

31. _____   32. _____

33. _____   34. _____

35. _____   36. _____

25. $\log_3 x = 2$

26. $\log_4 x = 3$

27. $\log_5 x = -3$

28. $\log_2 x = -4$

29. $\log_2 16 = x$

30. $\log_3 27 = x$

31. $\log_8 2 = x$

32. $\log_{25} 5 = x$

33. $\log_x 4 = 2$

34. $\log_x 16 = 4$

35. $\log_x 5 = 3$

36. $\log_x 8 = 2$

Name _____ Class _____ Date _____

Sketch the graph of each of the following logarithmic equations.

37. $y = \log_3 x$

38. $y = \log_{1/2} x$

39. $y = \log_{1/3} x$

40. $y = \log_4 x$

41. $y = \log_5 x$

42. $y = \log_{1/5} x$

43. $y = \log_{10} x$

44. $y = \log_{1/4} x$

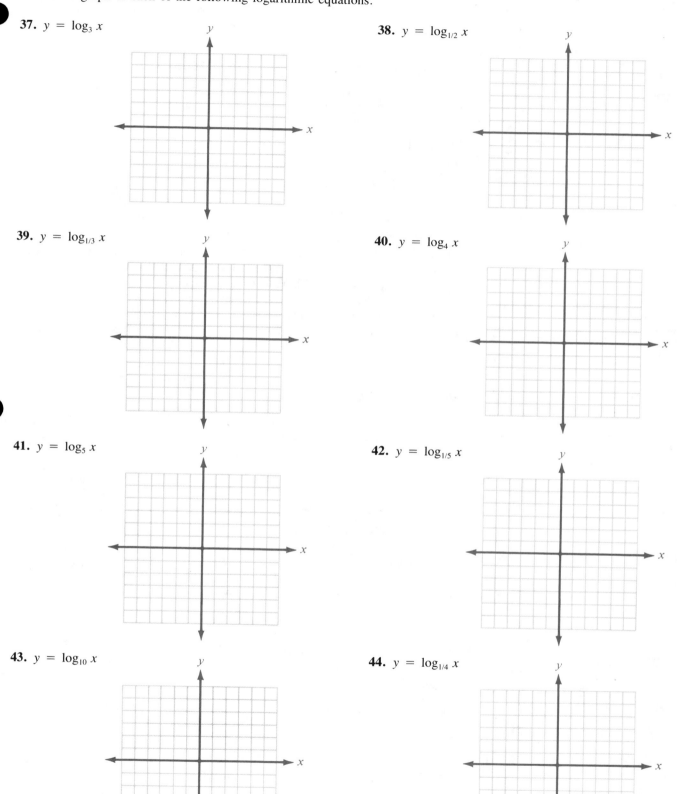

Answers

45. _____   46. _____

47. _____   48. _____

49. _____   50. _____

51. _____   52. _____

53. _____   54. _____

55. _____   56. _____

57. _____   58. _____

59. _____   60. _____

61. _____   62. _____

63. _____   64. _____

65. _____   66. _____

67. _____   68. _____

45. $\log_2 16$

46. $\log_3 9$

47. $\log_{25} 125$

48. $\log_9 27$

49. $\log_{10} 1000$

50. $\log_{10} 10,000$

51. $\log_3 3$

52. $\log_4 4$

53. $\log_5 1$

54. $\log_{10} 1$

55. $\log_3 (\log_6 6)$

56. $\log_5 (\log_3 3)$

57. $\log_4 [\log_2 (\log_2 16)]$

58. $\log_4 [\log_3 (\log_2 8)]$

59. The formula $M = 0.21(\log_{10} a - \log_{10} b)$ is used in the food processing industry to find the number of minutes M of heat processing a certain food should undergo at 250°F to reduce the probability of survival of *C. botulinum* spores. The letter a represents the number of spores per can before heating, and b represents the total number of spores per can after heating. Find M if $a = 1$ and $b = 10^{-12}$.

60. The formula $N = 10 \log_{10} \dfrac{P_1}{P_2}$ is used in radio electronics to find the ratio of the acoustic powers of two electric circuits in terms of their electric powers. Find N if P_1 is 50 and P_2 is 1/2.

Review Problems The following problems review material we covered in Sections 2.2 and 6.1.

Solve each equation.

61. $5(2x + 1) - 4 = 5x - 9$

62. $3(4x - 1) + 5 = 8x + 10$

63. $9 - 2(3x + 7) = 5 - 4x$

64. $7 - 3(4x + 9) = 4 - 4x$

65. $x^2 + 2x = 8$

66. $x^2 - 2x = 3$

67. $\dfrac{5}{x} - \dfrac{3}{x^2} = -2$

68. $2 + \dfrac{1}{x} = \dfrac{15}{x^2}$

Section 11.2   Properties of Logarithms

For the following three properties, x, y, and b are all positive real numbers, $b \neq 1$, and r is any real number.

Property 1 $\log_b (xy) = \log_b x + \log_b y$
In words: The logarithm of a *product* is the *sum* of the logarithms.

Property 2 $\log_b \left(\dfrac{x}{y} \right) = \log_b x - \log_b y$

In words: The logarithm of a *quotient* is the *difference* of the logarithms.

Property 3 $\log_b x^r = r \log_b x$
In words: The logarithm of a number raised to a *power* is the *product* of the power and the logarithm of the number.

PROOF OF PROPERTY 1   To prove property 1 we simply apply the first identity for logarithms given at the end of the preceding section.

$$b^{\log_b xy} = xy = (b^{\log_b x})(b^{\log_b y}) = b^{\log_b x + \log_b y}$$

Since the first and last expressions are equal and the bases are the same, the exponents $\log_b xy$ and $\log_b x + \log_b y$ must be equal. Therefore,

$$\log_b xy = \log_b x + \log_b y$$

The proofs of properties 2 and 3 proceed in much the same manner, so we will omit them here. The examples that follow show how the three properties can be used.

▼ **Example 1**   Expand using the properties of logarithms: $\log_5 \dfrac{3xy}{z}$.

Solution   Applying property 2, we can write the quotient of $3xy$ and z in terms of a difference:

$$\log_5 \frac{3xy}{z} = \log_5 3xy - \log_5 z$$

Applying property 1 to the product $3xy$, we write it in terms of addition:

$$\log_5 \frac{3xy}{z} = \log_5 3 + \log_5 x + \log_5 y - \log_5 z \qquad \blacktriangle$$

▼ **Example 2**   Expand using the properties of logarithms:

$$\log_2 \frac{x^4}{\sqrt{y} \cdot z^3}$$

Solution   We write $\sqrt{y}$ as $y^{1/2}$ and apply the properties:

$$\log_2 \frac{x^4}{\sqrt{y} \cdot z^3} = \log_2 \frac{x^4}{y^{1/2} z^3} \qquad \sqrt{y} = y^{1/2}$$

$$= \log_2 x^4 - \log_2 (y^{1/2} \cdot z^3) \qquad \text{Property 2}$$

$$= \log_2 x^4 - (\log_2 y^{1/2} + \log_2 z^3) \qquad \text{Property 1}$$

Practice Problems

1. Expand using the properties of logarithms:

$$\log_3 \frac{5a}{b}$$

2. Expand $\log_{10} \dfrac{x^2}{\sqrt[3]{y}}$.

Answers
1. $\log_3 5 + \log_3 a - \log_3 b$
2. $2 \log_{10} x - \frac{1}{3} \log_{10} y$

$$= \log_2 x^4 - \log_2 y^{1/2} - \log_2 z^3 \qquad \text{Remove parentheses}$$

$$= 4 \log_2 x - \frac{1}{2} \log_2 y - 3 \log_2 z \qquad \text{Property 3} \quad \blacktriangle$$

We can also use the three properties to write an expression in expanded form as just one logarithm.

3. Write as a single logarithm:

$$3 \log_4 x + \log_4 y - 2 \log_4 z$$

▼ **Example 3** Write as a single logarithm:

$$2 \log_{10} a + 3 \log_{10} b - \frac{1}{3} \log_{10} c$$

Solution We begin by applying property 3:

$$2 \log_{10} a + 3 \log_{10} b - \frac{1}{3} \log_{10} c$$

$$= \log_{10} a^2 + \log_{10} b^3 - \log_{10} c^{1/3} \qquad \text{Property 3}$$
$$= \log_{10} (a^2 \cdot b^3) - \log_{10} c^{1/3} \qquad \text{Property 1}$$
$$= \log_{10} \frac{a^2 b^3}{c^{1/3}} \qquad\qquad\qquad \text{Property 2}$$
$$= \log_{10} \frac{a^2 b^3}{\sqrt[3]{c}} \qquad\qquad\qquad c^{1/3} = \sqrt[3]{c} \quad \blacktriangle$$

The properties of logarithms along with the definition of logarithms are useful in solving equations that involve logarithms.

4. Solve for x:

$$\log_2 (x + 3) + \log_2 x = 2$$

▼ **Example 4** Solve for x: $\log_2 (x + 2) + \log_2 x = 3$.

Solution Applying property 1 to the left side of the equation allows us to write it as a single logarithm:

$$\log_2 (x + 2) + \log_2 x = 3$$
$$\log_2 [(x + 2)(x)] = 3$$

The last line can be written in exponential form using the definition of logarithms:

$$(x + 2)(x) = 2^3$$

Solve as usual:

$$x^2 + 2x = 8$$
$$x^2 + 2x - 8 = 0$$
$$(x + 4)(x - 2) = 0$$
$$x + 4 = 0 \quad \text{or} \quad x - 2 = 0$$
$$x = -4 \quad \text{or} \quad\quad x = 2$$

In the previous section we noted the fact that x in the expression $y = \log_b x$ cannot be a negative number. Since substitution of $x = -4$ into the original equation gives

$$\log_2 (-2) + \log_2 (-4) = 3$$

which contains logarithms of negative numbers, we cannot use -4 as a solution. The solution set is $\{2\}$. $\quad \blacktriangle$

Answers

3. $\log_4 \dfrac{x^3 y}{z^2}$ **4.** 1

Problem Set 11.2

Name _____

Class _____

Date _____

Use the three properties of logarithms given in this section to expand each expression as much as possible.

1. $\log_3 4x$

2. $\log_2 5x$

3. $\log_6 \dfrac{5}{x}$

4. $\log_3 \dfrac{x}{5}$

5. $\log_2 y^5$

6. $\log_7 y^3$

7. $\log_9 \sqrt[3]{z}$

8. $\log_8 \sqrt{z}$

9. $\log_6 x^2 y^3$

10. $\log_{10} x^2 y^4$

11. $\log_5 \sqrt{x} \cdot y^4$

12. $\log_8 \sqrt[3]{xy^6}$

13. $\log_b \dfrac{xy}{z}$

14. $\log_b \dfrac{3x}{y}$

15. $\log_{10} \dfrac{4}{xy}$

16. $\log_{10} \dfrac{5}{4y}$

17. $\log_{10} \dfrac{x^2 y}{\sqrt{z}}$

18. $\log_{10} \dfrac{\sqrt{x} \cdot y}{z^3}$

19. $\log_{10} \dfrac{x^3 \sqrt{y}}{z^4}$

20. $\log_{10} \dfrac{x^4 \sqrt[3]{y}}{\sqrt{z}}$

21. $\log_b \sqrt[3]{\dfrac{x^2 y}{z^4}}$

22. $\log_b \sqrt[4]{\dfrac{x^4 y^3}{z^5}}$

Answers

1. _____

2. _____

3. _____

4. _____

5. _____

6. _____

7. _____

8. _____

9. _____

10. _____

11. _____

12. _____

13. _____

14. _____

15. _____

16. _____

17. _____

18. _____

19. _____

20. _____

21. _____

22. _____

Answers

Write each expression as a single logarithm.

23. _____   24. _____

23. $\log_b x + \log_b z$ **24.** $\log_b x - \log_b z$

25. _____   26. _____

27. _____   28. _____

29. _____   30. _____

25. $2 \log_3 x - 3 \log_3 y$ **26.** $4 \log_2 x + 5 \log_2 y$

31. _____   32. _____

33. _____   34. _____

27. $\frac{1}{2} \log_{10} x + \frac{1}{3} \log_{10} y$ **28.** $\frac{1}{3} \log_{10} x - \frac{1}{4} \log_{10} y$

29. $3 \log_2 x + \frac{1}{2} \log_2 y - \log_2 z$ **30.** $2 \log_3 x + 3 \log_3 y - \log_3 z$

31. $\frac{1}{2} \log_2 x - 3 \log_2 y - 4 \log_2 z$ **32.** $3 \log_{10} x - \log_{10} y - \log_{10} z$

33. $\frac{3}{2} \log_{10} x - \frac{3}{4} \log_{10} y - \frac{4}{5} \log_{10} z$ **34.** $3 \log_{10} x - \frac{4}{3} \log_{10} y - 5 \log_{10} z$

Solve each of the following equations.

35. $\log_2 x + \log_2 3 = 1$

36. $\log_2 x - \log_2 3 = 1$

37. $\log_3 x - \log_3 2 = 2$

38. $\log_3 x + \log_3 2 = 2$

39. $\log_3 x + \log_3 (x - 2) = 1$

40. $\log_6 x + \log_6 (x - 1) = 1$

41. $\log_3 (x + 3) - \log_3 (x - 1) = 1$ **42.** $\log_4 (x - 2) - \log_4 (x + 1) = 1$

Name _____

Class _____

Date _____

Answers

35. _____ **36.** _____

37. _____ **38.** _____

39. _____ **40.** _____

41. _____ **42.** _____

Answers

43. _____ 44. _____

45. _____ 46. _____

47. _____ 48. _____

49. _____ 50. _____

51. _____ 52. _____

53. _____ 54. _____

55. _____ 56. _____

43. $\log_2 x + \log_2 (x - 2) = 3$ **44.** $\log_4 x + \log_4 (x + 6) = 2$

45. $\log_8 x + \log_8 (x - 3) = \dfrac{2}{3}$ **46.** $\log_{27} x + \log_{27} (x + 8) = \dfrac{2}{3}$

47. $\log_5 \sqrt{x} + \log_5 \sqrt{6x + 5} = 1$ **48.** $\log_2 \sqrt{x} + \log_2 \sqrt{6x + 5} = 1$

Review Problems   The following problems review material we covered in Section 3.1. Reviewing these problems will help you with the next section.

Write each number in scientific notation.

49. 394,000,000   **50.** 2760

51. 0.0391   **52.** 0.000276

Write each number in expanded form.

53. 5.23×10^{-3} **54.** 7.48×10^{-2}

55. 5.03×10^4 **56.** 6.89×10^3

Section 11.3   Common Logarithms and Computations

In the past, logarithms have been very useful in simplifying calculations. With the widespread availability of hand-held calculators, the importance of logarithms in calculations has been decreased considerably. Working through arithmetic problems using logarithms is, however, good practice with logarithms.

DEFINITION   A *common logarithm* is a logarithm with a base of 10. Since common logarithms are used so frequently, it is customary, in order to save time, to omit notating the base. That is,

$$\log_{10} x = \log x$$

When the base is not shown, it is assumed to be 10.

Common logarithms of powers of 10 are very simple to evaluate. We need only recognize that $\log 10 = \log_{10} 10 = 1$ and apply the third property of logarithms: $\log_b x^r = r \log_b x$.

Note: Remember, when the base is not written it is assumed to be 10.

$$
\begin{aligned}
\log 1000 &= \log 10^3 &&= 3 \log 10 &&= 3(1) &&= 3 \\
\log 100 &= \log 10^2 &&= 2 \log 10 &&= 2(1) &&= 2 \\
\log 10 &= \log 10^1 &&= 1 \log 10 &&= 1(1) &&= 1 \\
\log 1 &= \log 10^0 &&= 0 \log 10 &&= 0(1) &&= 0 \\
\log .1 &= \log 10^{-1} &&= -1 \log 10 &&= -1(1) &&= -1 \\
\log .01 &= \log 10^{-2} &&= -2 \log 10 &&= -2(1) &&= -2 \\
\log .001 &= \log 10^{-3} &&= -3 \log 10 &&= -3(1) &&= -3
\end{aligned}
$$

For common logarithms of numbers that are not powers of 10, we have to resort to a table. The table in Appendix E at the back of the book gives common logarithms of numbers between 1.00 and 9.99. To find the common logarithm of, say, 2.76, we read down the left-hand column until we get to 2.7, then across until we are below the 6 in the top row (or above the 6 in the bottom row):

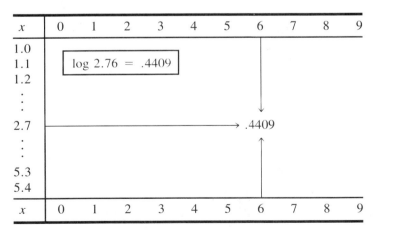

The table contains only logarithms of numbers between 1.00 and 9.99. Check the following logarithms in the table to be sure you know how to use the table:

$$
\begin{aligned}
\log 7.02 &= .8463 \\
\log 1.39 &= .1430 \\
\log 6.00 &= .7782 \\
\log 9.99 &= .9996
\end{aligned}
$$

Note: Remember, a number is written in scientific notation when it is written as the product of a number between 1 and 10 and a power of 10. For example, $39,800 = 3.98 \times 10^4$ in scientific notation.

Practice Problems

1. Find log 27,600.

2. Find log 952.

3. Find log .00391.

4. Find log .00952.

Note: It is not necessary to show the intermediate steps we have shown in these examples. As a matter of fact, it is better if we don't. With a little practice the steps can be eliminated.

5. Find x if log $x = 3.9786$.

To find the common logarithm of a number that is not between 1.00 and 9.99, we simply write the number in scientific notation, apply property 1 of logarithms, and use the table. The following examples illustrate the procedure.

▼ **Example 1**   Use the table of logarithms to find log 2760.

Solution $\log 2760 = \log (2.76 \times 10^3)$
$= \log 2.76 + \log 10^3$
$= .4409 + 3$
$= 3.4409$

The 3 in the answer is called the *characteristic,* and its main function is to keep track of the decimal point. The decimal part of this logarithm is called the *mantissa.* It is found from the table.   ▲

Here's more of the same.

▼ **Example 2**   Find log 843.

Solution $\log 843 = \log (8.43 \times 10^2)$
$= \log 8.43 + \log 10^2$
$= .9258 + 2$
$= 2.9258$ ▲

▼ **Example 3**   Find log .0391.

Solution $\log .0391 = \log (3.91 \times 10^{-2})$
$= \log 3.91 + \log 10^{-2}$
$= .5922 + (-2)$

Now there are two ways to proceed from here. We could add .5922 and -2 to get -1.4078. (If you were using a calculator to find log .0391, this is the answer you would see.) The problem with -1.4078 is that the mantissa is negative. Our table contains only positive numbers. If we have to use log .0391 again, and it is written as -1.4078, we will not be able to associate it with an entry in the table. It is most common, when using a table, to write the characteristic -2 as $8 + (-10)$ and proceed as follows:

$$\log .0391 = .5922 + 8 + (-10)$$
$$= 8.5922 - 10$$ ▲

▼ **Example 4**   Find log .00523.

Solution $\log .00523 = \log (5.23 \times 10^{-3})$
$= \log 5.23 + \log 10^{-3}$
$= .7185 + (-3)$
$= .7185 + 7 + (-10)$
$= 7.7185 - 10$ ▲

▼ **Example 5**   Find x if log $x = 3.8774$.

Solution   We are looking for the number whose logarithm is 3.8774. The mantissa is .8774, which appears in the table across from 7.5 and under (or above) 4.

Answers
1. 4.4409   **2.** 2.9786   **3.** 7.5922 − 10
4. 7.9786 − 10   **5.** 9520

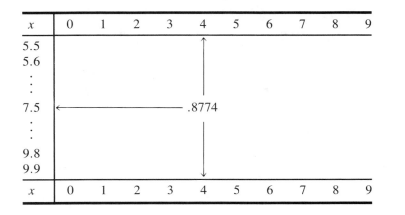

The characteristic is 3 and came from the exponent of 10. Putting these together, we have

$$\log x = 3.8774$$
$$\log x = .8774 + 3$$
$$x = 7.54 \times 10^3$$
$$x = 7540$$

The number 7540 is called the *antilogarithm* or just *antilog* of 3.8774. That is, 7540 is the number whose logarithm is 3.8774. ▲

▼ **Example 6** Find x if $\log x = 7.5821 - 10$.

Solution The mantissa is .5821, which comes from 3.82 in the table. The characteristic is $7 + (-10)$ or -3, which comes from a power of 10:

$$\log x = 7.5821 - 10$$
$$\log x = .5821 + 7 + (-10)$$
$$\log x = .5821 + (-3)$$
$$x = 3.82 \times 10^{-3}$$
$$x = .00382$$

The antilog of $7.5821 - 10$ is .00382. That is, the logarithm of .00382 is $7.5821 - 10$. ▲

Calculator Note: To find antilogs on a calculator, you use the key labeled

$\boxed{10^x}$. (On some calculators you may have to use the logarithm key, $\boxed{\log}$ and the inverse key to do this. Look up *antilogarithms* in the manual that came with your calculator to see which key you should use.) If your calculator uses the 10^x key, then the sequence of keys to use to work Example 5 is

$$3.8774 \quad \boxed{10^x}$$

To work Example 6 on a calculator you would use this sequence

The following examples illustrate how logarithms are used as an aid in computations.

6. Find x if

$$\log x = 8.4099 - 10$$

7. Use logarithms to find (952)(39,100).

Note: We apply property 1 for logarithms to write the log of a product as the sum of the logs.

Note: The answer 1.71×10^8 is not exactly equal to (3780)(45,200). It is an approximation. If we want to be more accurate, we would have to use a table with more significant digits.

8. Use logarithms to find $\sqrt{3780}$.

9. Use logarithms to find

$$\frac{(478)^3(5.62)}{\sqrt{9050}}$$

▼ **Example 7** Use logarithms to find (3780)(45,200).

Solution We will let n represent the answer to this problem:

$$n = (3780)(45,200)$$

Since these two numbers are equal, so are their logarithms. We therefore take the common logarithm of both sides:

$$
\begin{aligned}
\log n &= \log (3780)(45,200) \\
&= \log 3780 + \log 45,200 \\
&= 3.5775 + 4.6551 \\
\log n &= 8.2326
\end{aligned}
$$

The number 8.2326 is the logarithm of the answer. The mantissa is .2326, which is not in the table. Since .2326 is closest to .2330, and .2330 is the logarithm of 1.71, we write

$$n = 1.71 \times 10^8 \qquad ▲$$

▼ **Example 8** Use logarithms to find $\sqrt[3]{875}$.

Solution

$$
\begin{aligned}
\text{If} \quad n &= \sqrt[3]{875}, \\
\text{then} \quad n &= (875)^{1/3} \\
\text{and} \quad \log n &= \log 875^{1/3} \\
&= \tfrac{1}{3} \log 875 \\
&= \tfrac{1}{3}(2.9420) \\
\log n &= .9807 \\
n &= 9.56
\end{aligned}
$$

A good approximation to the cube root of 875 is 9.56. ▲

▼ **Example 9** Use logarithms to find $\dfrac{(34.5)^2\sqrt{1080}}{(2.76)^3}$.

Solution

$$
\begin{aligned}
\text{If} \quad n &= \frac{(34.5)^2\sqrt{1080}}{(2.76)^3} \\
\text{then} \quad \log n &= \log\left[\frac{(34.5)^2\sqrt{1080}}{(2.76)^3}\right] \\
&= 2 \log 34.5 + \frac{1}{2} \log 1080 - 3 \log 2.76 \\
&= 2(1.5378) + \frac{1}{2}(3.0334) - 3(.4409) \\
&= 3.0756 + 1.5167 - 1.3227 \\
\log n &= 3.2696 \\
n &= 1.86 \times 10^3 \\
&= 1860 \qquad ▲
\end{aligned}
$$

Answers
7. 3.72×10^7 **8.** 61.5
9. 6.45×10^6

Problem Set 11.3

Use the table in Appendix E to find the following.

1. log 378

2. log 426

3. log 37.8

4. log 42,600

5. log 3780

6. log .4260

7. log .0378

8. log .0426

9. log 37,800

10. log 4900

11. log 600

12. log 900

13. log 2010

14. log 10,200

15. log .00971

16. log .0312

17. log .0314

18. log .00052

19. log .399

20. log .111

Find x in the following equations.

21. log $x = 2.8802$

22. log $x = 4.8802$

23. log $x = 7.8802 - 10$

24. log $x = 6.8802 - 10$

25. log $x = 3.1553$

26. log $x = 5.5911$

27. log $x = 4.6503 - 10$

28. log $x = 8.4330 - 10$

29. log $x = 2.9628 - 10$

30. log $x = 5.8000 - 10$

Name _____

Class _____

Date _____

Answers

1. _____   2. _____

3. _____   4. _____

5. _____   6. _____

7. _____   8. _____

9. _____   10. _____

11. _____   12. _____

13. _____   14. _____

15. _____   16. _____

17. _____   18. _____

19. _____   20. _____

21. _____   22. _____

23. _____   24. _____

25. _____   26. _____

27. _____   28. _____

29. _____   30. _____

Answers

Use logarithms to evaluate the following.

31. _____   32. _____

31. (378)(24.5)   **32.** (921)(2630)

33. _____   34. _____

35. _____   36. _____

37. _____   38. _____

33. $\dfrac{496}{391}$ **34.** $\dfrac{512}{216}$

39. _____   40. _____

35. $\sqrt{401}$ **36.** $\sqrt[3]{92.3}$

37. $\sqrt[3]{1030}$ **38.** $\sqrt{.641}$

39. $\dfrac{(2390)(28.4)}{176}$ **40.** $\dfrac{(32.9)(5760)}{11.1}$

41. $(296)^2(459)$

42. $(3250)(24.2)^3$

Name _____

Class _____

Date _____

Answers

41. _____   **42.** _____

43. _____   **44.** _____

45. _____   **46.** _____

47. _____   **48.** _____

43. $\sqrt{526}(1080)$

44. $(32.7)\sqrt{.580}$

45. $45^{3.1}$

46. $72^{1.8}$

47. $\dfrac{(895)^3\sqrt{41.1}}{17.8}$

48. $\dfrac{(925)^2\sqrt{1.99}}{243}$

Answers

49. _____   50. _____

51. _____   52. _____

53. _____   54. _____

55. _____   56. _____

57. _____   58. _____

59. _____   60. _____

49. The weight W of a sphere with diameter d can be found by using the formula

$$W = \frac{\pi}{6}d^3w$$

where w is the weight of a cubic unit of material. Use logarithms to find W if $D = 2.98$ in, $w = 3.03$ lb, and $\pi = 3.14$.

50. The following formula is used in hydraulics:

$$d = 2.57 \sqrt[5]{\frac{flQ^2}{h}}$$

Use logarithms to find d, when $f = 0.022$, $l = 2{,}820$, $h = 133$, and $Q = 12.5$.

51. The area A of a triangle in which all three sides are of equal length l (equilateral) is given by the formula

$$A = \frac{l^2}{4}\sqrt{3}$$

Find A when $l = 276$. (Use logarithms.)

52. The formula $H = \dfrac{PLAN}{33{,}000}$ is used to compute the horsepower of a steam or gas engine. In this formula, H is the horsepower; P, the average effective pressure on the piston, in pounds per square inch; L, the distance the piston travels per stroke, in feet; A, the area of cross-section of the cylinder, in square inches; and N, the number of working strokes per minute. Find H, when $P = 62.8$ pounds; $L = 2.63$ feet; $A = 18.4$ square inches; and $N = 92.4$.

Review Problems   The following problems review material we covered in Sections 2.3 and 6.7.

Solve each inequality.

53. $-3x < 21$

54. $-2x > -12$

55. $6(3x - 2) \le 4 - (2x - 4)$

56. $5(2x - 4) \ge 7 - (3x + 1)$

57. $(2x - 3)(x + 4) > 0$

58. $(3x - 5)(x + 2) < 0$

59. $x^2 - 8x + 15 \le 0$

60. $x^2 - 8x + 12 \ge 0$

Section 11.4   Exponential Equations and Change of Base

Logarithms are very important in solving equations in which the variable appears as an exponent. The equation

$$5^x = 12$$

is an example of one such equation. Equations of this form are called *exponential equations*. Since the quantities 5^x and 12 are equal, so are their common logarithms. We begin our solution by taking the logarithm of both sides:

$$\log 5^x = \log 12$$

We now apply property 3 for logarithms, $\log x^r = r \log x$, to turn x from an exponent into a coefficient:

$$x \log 5 = \log 12$$

Dividing both sides by log 5 gives us

$$x = \frac{\log 12}{\log 5}$$

If we want a decimal approximation to the solution, we can find log 12 and log 5 in the table of logarithms and divide:

$$x = \frac{1.0792}{.6990}$$
$$= 1.5439$$

The complete problem looks like this:

$$5^x = 12$$
$$\log 5^x = \log 12$$
$$x \log 5 = \log 12$$
$$x = \frac{\log 12}{\log 5}$$
$$= \frac{1.0792}{.6990}$$
$$= 1.5439$$

Note: A very common mistake can occur in the third-from-the-last step. Many times the expression

$$\frac{\log 12}{\log 5}$$

is mistakenly simplified as $\log 12 - \log 5$. There is no property of logarithms that allows us to do this. The only property of logarithms that deals with division is property 2, which is *this:*

$$\log_b \frac{x}{y} = \log_b x - \log_b y \qquad \text{(Right)}$$

not this:

$$\frac{\log_b x}{\log_b y} = \log_b x - \log_b y \qquad \text{(Wrong)}$$

The second statement is simply not a property of logarithms, although it is sometimes mistaken for one.

Practice Problems

1. Solve for x: $12^{x+2} = 20$.

Here is another example of solving an exponential equation using logarithms.

▼ **Example 1** Solve for x: $25^{2x+1} = 15$.

Solution Taking the logarithm of both sides and then writing the exponent $(2x + 1)$ as a coefficient, we proceed as follows:

$$25^{2x+1} = 15$$
$$\log 25^{2x+1} = \log 15 \qquad \text{Take the log of both sides}$$
$$(2x + 1) \log 25 = \log 15 \qquad \text{Property 3}$$
$$2x + 1 = \frac{\log 15}{\log 25} \qquad \text{Divide by log 25}$$
$$2x = \frac{\log 15}{\log 25} - 1 \qquad \text{Add } -1 \text{ to both sides}$$
$$x = \frac{1}{2}\left(\frac{\log 15}{\log 25} - 1\right) \qquad \text{Multiply both sides by } \tfrac{1}{2}$$

Using the table of common logarithms, we can write a decimal approximation to the answer:

$$x = \frac{1}{2}\left(\frac{1.1761}{1.3979} - 1\right)$$
$$= \frac{1}{2}(.8413 - 1)$$
$$= \frac{1}{2}(-.1587)$$
$$= -.0793 \qquad \blacktriangle$$

There is a fourth property of logarithms we have not yet considered. This last property allows us to change from one base to another and is therefore called the *change-of-base property*.

Property 4 (Change of Base) If a and b are both positive numbers other than 1, and if $x > 0$, then

$$\log_a x = \frac{\log_b x}{\log_b a}$$
$$\qquad\quad \uparrow \qquad\quad \uparrow$$
$$\qquad \text{Base } a \quad \text{Base } b$$

The logarithm on the left side has a base of a, while both logarithms on the right side have a base of b. This allows us to change from base a to any other base b that is a positive number other than 1. Here is a proof of property 4 for logarithms.

PROOF We begin by writing the identity

$$a^{\log_a x} = x$$

Taking the logarithm base b of both sides and setting the exponent $\log_a x$ as a coefficient, we have

$$\log_b a^{\log_a x} = \log_b x$$

$$\log_a x \log_b a = \log_b x$$

Dividing both sides by $\log_b a$, we have the desired result:

$$\frac{\log_a x \log_b a}{\log_b a} = \frac{\log_b x}{\log_b a}$$

$$\log_a x = \frac{\log_b x}{\log_b a}$$

We can use this property to find logarithms we do not have a table for. The next two examples illustrate the use of this property.

▼ **Example 2**   Find $\log_8 24$.

2. Find $\log_6 14$.

Solution   Since we do not have a table for base-8 logarithms, we can change this expression to an equivalent expression that only contains base-10 logarithms:

$$\log_8 24 = \frac{\log 24}{\log 8}$$

Don't be confused. We did not just drop the base, we changed to base 10. We could have written the last line like this:

$$\log_8 24 = \frac{\log_{10} 24}{\log_{10} 8}$$

Looking up $\log 24$ and $\log 8$ in the table of logarithms, we write

$$\log_8 24 = \frac{1.3802}{.9031}$$

$$= 1.5283 \qquad ▲$$

Calculator Note: To work Example 2 with a calculator, use the following sequence:

$$24 \;\boxed{\log}\; \boxed{\div}\; 8 \;\boxed{\log}\; \boxed{=}$$

▼ **Example 3**   Find $\log_{20} 342$.

3. Find $\log_{12} 478$.

Solution   Changing to base 10 using property 4, we proceed as follows:

$$\log_{20} 342 = \frac{\log 342}{\log 20}$$

$$= \frac{2.5340}{1.3010}$$

$$= 1.9477$$

The decimal approximation to $\log_{20} 342$ is 1.9477.   ▲

Problem Set 11.4

Name _____

Class _____

Date _____

Solve each exponential equation. Use the table of logarithms to write the answer in decimal form.

1. $3^x = 5$

2. $4^x = 3$

3. $5^x = 3$

4. $3^x = 4$

5. $5^{-x} = 12$

6. $7^{-x} = 8$

7. $12^{-x} = 5$

8. $8^{-x} = 7$

9. $8^{x+1} = 4$

10. $9^{x+1} = 3$

11. $4^{x-1} = 4$

12. $3^{x-1} = 9$

13. $3^{2x+1} = 2$

14. $2^{2x+1} = 3$

15. $3^{1-2x} = 2$

16. $2^{1-2x} = 3$

17. $15^{3x-4} = 10$

18. $10^{3x-4} = 15$

19. $6^{5-2x} = 4$

20. $9^{7-3x} = 5$

Answers

1. _____   2. _____

3. _____   4. _____

5. _____   6. _____

7. _____   8. _____

9. _____   10. _____

11. _____   12. _____

13. _____   14. _____

15. _____   16. _____

17. _____   18. _____

19. _____   20. _____

Use the change-of-base property and the table of logarithms to find a decimal approximation to each of the following logarithms.

21. $\log_8 16$ **22.** $\log_9 27$ **23.** $\log_{16} 8$

24. $\log_{27} 9$ **25.** $\log_7 15$ **26.** $\log_3 12$

27. $\log_{15} 7$ **28.** $\log_{12} 3$ **29.** $\log_{12} 11$

30. $\log_{14} 15$ **31.** $\log_{11} 12$ **32.** $\log_{15} 14$

33. $\log_8 240$ **34.** $\log_6 180$ **35.** $\log_4 321$

36. $\log_5 462$

37. The formula $A = P(1 + r)^n$ shows how to find the amount of money A that will be in an account if P dollars is invested at interest rate r for n years if the interest is compounded yearly. Use logarithms to solve this formula for n.

38. If P dollars is invested in an account that pays an annual rate of interest r, that is compounded semiannually, the amount of money in the account at the end of n years is given by the formula

$$A = P\left(1 + \frac{r}{2}\right)^{2n}$$

Use logarithms to solve this formula for n.

Review Problems   The following problems review material we covered in Section 8.5. They are taken from the book *Algebra for the Practical Man*, written by J. E. Thompson and published by D. Van Nostrand Company in 1931.

39. A man spent $112.80 for 108 geese and ducks, each goose costing 14 dimes and each duck 6 dimes. How many of each did he buy?

40. If 15 lb of tea and 10 lb of coffee together cost $15.50, while 25 lb of tea and 13 lb of coffee at the same prices cost $24.55, find the price per pound of each.

41. A number of oranges at the rate of three for ten cents and apples at fifteen cents a dozen cost, together, $6.80. Five times as many oranges and one fourth as many apples at the same rates would have cost $25.45. How many of each were bought?

42. An estate is divided among three persons, A, B and C. A's share is three times that of B and B's share is twice that of C. If A receives $9000 more than C, how much does each receive?

Section 11.5 Word Problems

There are many practical applications of exponential equations and logarithms. Many times an exponential equation will describe a situation arising in nature. Logarithms are then used to solve the exponential equation. Many of the problems in this section deal with expressions and equations that have been derived or defined in some other discipline. We will not attempt to derive them here. We will simply accept them as they are and use them to solve some problems.

In chemistry the pH of a solution is defined in terms of logarithms as

$$pH = -\log(H_3O^+)$$

where (H_3O^+) is the concentration of the hydronium ion, H_3O^+, in solution. An acid solution has a pH lower than 7, and a basic solution has a pH above 7. (This is from chemistry. We don't need to worry here about *why* it's this way. We just want to work some problems involving logarithms.)

▼ **Example 1** Find the pH of a solution in which $(H_3O^+) = 5.1 \times 10^{-3}$.

Solution Using the preceding definition, we write

$$\begin{aligned} pH &= -\log(H_3O^+) \\ &= -\log(5.1 \times 10^{-3}) \\ &= -[.7076 + (-3)] \\ &= -.7076 + 3 \\ &\approx 2.29 \end{aligned}$$

According to our previous discussion, this solution would be considered an acid solution, since its pH is less than 7. ▲

▼ **Example 2** What is (H_3O^+) for a solution with a pH of 9.3?

Solution We substitute 9.3 for pH in the definition of pH and proceed as follows:

$$\begin{aligned} 9.3 &= -\log(H_3O^+) \\ \log(H_3O^+) &= -9.3 \end{aligned}$$

It is impossible to look up -9.3 in the table of logarithms because it is negative. We can get around this problem by adding and subtracting 10 to the -9.3:

$$\begin{aligned} \log(H_3O^+) &= -9.3 + 10 - 10 \quad \text{(Actually adding 0)} \\ &= .7 - 10 \end{aligned}$$

The closest thing to .7 in the table is .6998, which is the logarithm of 5.01:

$$(H_3O^+) = 5.01 \times 10^{-10}$$

The concentration of H_3O^+ is 5.01×10^{-10}. (This quantity is usually given in moles/liter. We have left off the units to make things simpler.) ▲

Practice Problems

1. Find the pH of a solution in which $(H_3O^+) = 4.8 \times 10^{-3}$.

2. What is (H_3O^+) for a solution with a pH of 8.1?

Note: You can use the 10^x key on your calculator to find x if $\log x = -9.3$ without changing -9.3 to a positive number. But if you are using a table, you must proceed as we are showing in Example 2.

Answers
1. 2.32 **2.** 7.94×10^{-9}

Carbon-14 dating is used extensively in science to find the age of fossils. If at one time a nonliving substance contains an amount A_0 of carbon-14, then t years later it will contain an amount A of carbon-14, where

$$A = A_0 \cdot 2^{-t/5600}$$

3. How much carbon-14 will the substance in Example 3 contain after 1000 years?

▼ **Example 3** If a nonliving substance has 3 grams of carbon-14, how much carbon-14 will be present 500 years later?

Solution The original amount of carbon-14, A_0, is 3 grams. The number of years, t, is 500. Substituting these quantities into the preceding equation, we have the expression

$$A = (3)2^{-500/5600}$$
$$= (3)2^{-5/56}$$

In order to evaluate this expression we must use logarithms. We begin by taking the logarithm of both sides:

$$\log A = \log \left[(3)2^{-5/56}\right]$$
$$= \log 3 - \tfrac{5}{56} \log 2$$
$$= .4771 - \tfrac{5}{56}(.3010)$$
$$= .4771 - .0269$$
$$\log A = .4502$$
$$A = 2.82$$

The amount remaining after 500 years is 2.82 grams. ▲

If an amount of money P (P for principal) is invested in an account that pays a rate r of interest compounded annually, then the total amount of money A (the original amount P plus all the interest) in the account after t years is given by the equation

$$A = P(1 + r)^t$$

4. How much money will accumulate over 10 years if $5000 is invested in an account that pays 8% interest per year?

▼ **Example 4** How much money will accumulate over 20 years if a person invests $5000 in an account that pays 6% interest per year?

Solution The original amount P is $5000, the rate of interest r is .06 (6% = .06), and the length of time t is 20 years. We substitute these values into the equation and solve for A:

$$A = 5000(1 + .06)^{20}$$
$$A = 5000(1.06)^{20}$$
$$\log A = \log \left[5000(1.06)^{20}\right]$$
$$\log A = \log 5000 + 20 \log 1.06$$
$$= 3.6990 + 20(.0253)$$
$$= 3.6990 + .5060$$
$$\log A = 4.2050$$
$$A = 1.60 \times 10^4$$
$$= 16,000$$

The original $5000 will more than triple to become $16,000 in 20 years at 6% annual interest. ▲

▼ **Example 5** How long does it take for $5000 to double if it is deposited in an account that yields 5% per year?

Solution The original amount P is $5000, *the total amount after t years is* $A = $10,000$, and the interest rate r is .05. Substituting into

$$A = P(1 + r)^t$$

we have

$$10,000 = 5000(1 + .05)^t$$
$$= 5000(1.05)^t$$

This is an exponential equation. We solve by taking the logarithm of both sides:

$$\log 10,000 = \log [(5000)(1.05)^t]$$
$$\log 10,000 = \log 5000 + t \log 1.05$$
$$4 = 3.6990 + t(.0212)$$

Subtract 3.6990 from both sides:

$$.3010 = .0212t$$

Dividing both sides by .0212, we have

$$t = 14.20$$

It takes a little over 14 years for $5000 to double if it earns 5% per year. ▲

5. How long does it take for $5000 to double if it is invested in an account that pays 11% per year?

Answer
5. 6.64 years

Problem Set 11.5

For problems 1 through 8 find the pH of the solution using the formula $pH = -\log (H_3O^+)$.

1. $(H_3O^+) = 4 \times 10^{-3}$

2. $(H_3O^+) = 3 \times 10^{-4}$

3. $(H_3O^+) = 5 \times 10^{-6}$

4. $(H_3O^+) = 6 \times 10^{-5}$

5. $(H_3O^+) = 4.2 \times 10^{-5}$

6. $(H_3O^+) = 2.7 \times 10^{-7}$

7. $(H_3O^+) = 8.6 \times 10^{-2}$

8. $(H_3O^+) = 5.3 \times 10^{-4}$

For problems 9 through 12 find (H_3O^+) for solutions with the given pH.

9. pH $= 3.4$

10. pH $= 5.7$

11. pH $= 6.5$

12. pH $= 2.1$

Name _____

Class _____

Date _____

Answers

1. _____   2. _____

3. _____   4. _____

5. _____   6. _____

7. _____   8. _____

9. _____   10. _____

11. _____   12. _____

Answers

13a. _____

b. _____

c. _____

d. _____

14a. _____

b. _____

c. _____

d. _____

15. _____   16. _____

13. A nonliving substance contains 3 micrograms of carbon-14. How much carbon-14 will be left at the end of

    a. 5000 years?
    b. 10,000 years?
    c. 56,000 years?
    d. 112,000 years?

14. A nonliving substance contains 5 micrograms of carbon-14. How much carbon-14 will be left at the end of

    a. 500 years?
    b. 5000 years?
    c. 56,000 years?
    d. 112,000 years?

15. At one time a certain nonliving substance contained 10 micrograms of carbon-14. How many years later did the same substance contain only 5 micrograms of carbon-14?

16. At one time a certain nonliving substance contained 20 micrograms of carbon-14. How many years later did the same substance contain only 5 micrograms of carbon-14?

17. How much money is in an account after 10 years if $5000 was deposited originally at 6% per year?

Name _____

Class _____

Date _____

Answers

17. _____   18. _____

19. _____   20. _____

21. _____   22. _____

18. If you put $2000 in an account that earns 5% interest annually, how much will you have in the account at the end of 10 years?

19. If you deposit $2000 in an account that earns 7.5% annually, how much will you have in the account after 10 years?

20. Suppose $15,000 is deposited in an account that yields 10% per year. How much is in the account 5 years later?

21. If $4000 is in an account that earns 5% per year, how long does it take before the account has $8000 in it?

22. If $4000 is deposited in an account that yields 7% annually, how long does it take the account to reach $8000?

Answers

23. _____ 24. _____

25. _____

26. _____

27. _____

28. _____

29. _____

30. _____

31. _____

32. _____

23. How long does it take to double $10,000 if it is in an account that earns 6% per year?

24. How long does it take to double $10,000 if it is in an account that earns 10% per year?

Review Problems The following problems review material we covered in Sections 2.4 and 2.5.

Solve each equation.

25. $|3x - 5| = 2$

26. $|3x + 1| = 5$

27. $|7x - 8| + 9 = 1$

28. $|5x - 3| + 5 = 12$

Solve each inequality.

29. $|x - 4| > 5$

30. $|x + 3| < 2$

31. $|2x - 1| \leq 3$

32. $|2x + 1| \geq 5$

Chapter 11   Summary and Review

DEFINITION OF LOGARITHMS [11.1]

If b is a positive number not equal to 1, then the expression

$$y = \log_b x$$

is equivalent to $x = b^y$. That is, in the expression $y = \log_b x$, y is the number to which we raise b in order to get x. Expressions written in the form $y = \log_b x$ are said to be in *logarithmic form*. Expressions like $x = b^y$ are in *exponential form*.

1. The definition allows us to write expressions like

$$y = \log_3 27$$

equivalently in exponential form as

$$3^y = 27$$

which makes it apparent that y is 3.

TWO SPECIAL IDENTITIES [11.1]

For $b > 0$, $b \neq 1$, the following two expressions hold for all positive real numbers x:

1. $b^{\log_b x} = x$
2. $\log_b b^x = x$

2. Examples of the two special properties are

$$5^{\log_5 12} = 12$$

and

$$\log_8 8^3 = 3$$

PROPERTIES OF LOGARITHMS [11.2]

If x, y, and b are positive real numbers, $b \neq 1$, and r is any real number, then

1. $\log_b (xy) = \log_b x + \log_b y$
2. $\log_b \left(\dfrac{x}{y} \right) = \log_b x - \log_b y$
3. $\log_b x^r = r \log_b x$

3. We can rewrite the expression

$$\log_{10} \frac{45^6}{273}$$

using the properties of logarithms, as

$$6 \log_{10} 45 - \log_{10} 273$$

COMMON LOGARITHMS [11.3]

Common logarithms are logarithms with a base of 10. To save time in writing, we omit the base when working with common logarithms. That is,

$$\log x = \log_{10} x$$

4. $\log_{10} 10{,}000 = \log 10{,}000$
$\qquad\qquad\quad = \log 10^4$
$\qquad\qquad\quad = 4$

NOTATION [11.3]

In the expression

$$\log 4240 = 3.6274$$

the 3 is called the *characteristic* and the decimal .6274 is called the *mantissa*.

5. For common logarithms, the characteristic is the power of 10 needed to put the number in scientific notation, and the mantissa is found in the table of logarithms.

CHANGE OF BASE [11.4]

If x, a, and b are positive real numbers, $a \neq 1$ and $b \neq 1$, then

$$\log_a x = \frac{\log_b x}{\log_b a}$$

6. $\log_6 475 = \dfrac{\log 475}{\log 6}$

$\qquad\qquad = \dfrac{2.6767}{.7782}$

$\qquad\qquad = 3.44$

COMMON MISTAKES

The most common mistakes that occur with logarithms come from trying to apply the three properties of logarithms to situations in which they don't apply. For example, a very common mistake looks like this:

$$\frac{\log 3}{\log 2} = \log 3 - \log 2 \qquad \text{Mistake}$$

This is not a property of logarithms. In order to write the expression $\log 3 - \log 2$, we would have to start with

$$\log \frac{3}{2} \quad \text{not} \quad \frac{\log 3}{\log 2}$$

There is a difference.

Chapter 11 Test

Name _____

Class _____

Date _____

Solve for x. [11.1]

1. $\log_4 x = 3$

2. $\log_x 5 = 2$

Graph each of the following. [11.1]

3. $y = \log_2 x$

4. $y = \log_{1/2} x$

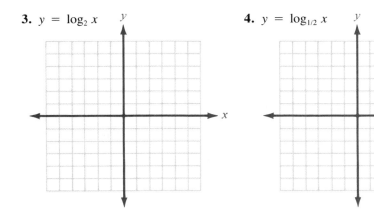

Evaluate each of the following. [11.1, 11.3, 11.4]

5. $\log_8 4$

6. $\log_7 21$

7. $\log 23{,}400$

8. $\log .0123$

Find x in each of the following. [11.3]

9. $\log x = 4.8476$

10. $\log x = 7.3522 - 10$

Answers

1. _____

2. _____

3. *See graph* _____

4. *See graph* _____

5. _____

6. _____

7. _____

8. _____

9. _____

10. _____

Answers

11. _____

12. _____

13. _____

14. _____

15. _____

16. _____

17. _____

18. _____

19. _____

20. _____

Use logarithms to find an approximate answer for the following computations. [11.3]

11. $(2.34)(6080)$

12. $3^{2.5}$

13. $\sqrt[4]{23}$

14. $\dfrac{(352)(41.5)^2}{(2.31)^3}$

Use the properties of logarithms as an aid in solving the following. [11.2, 11.4]

15. $5 = 3^x$

16. $4^{2x-1} = 8$

17. $\log_5 x - \log_5 3 = 1$

18. $\log_2 x + \log_2 (x - 7) = 3$

19. Find the total amount of money in an account if $4000 was deposited 5 years ago at 5% annual interest. [11.5]

20. Give the pH of a solution in which $(H_3O^+) = 3 \times 10^{-4}$. [11.5]

Intermediate Algebra—Final Exam

Name _____

Class _____

Date _____

1. Write in symbols.
"The sum of x and y is greater than the product of x and y."

2. Give the opposite, reciprocal, and absolute value of $-\frac{4}{7}$.

Answers

1. _____

3. Graph.
$\{x \mid x > -2 \text{ and } x < 3\}$

4. Apply the distributive property to $3(x + 5)$.

2. _____

3. ◄————————————————————►

5. Simplify.
$-4 - |-3| + 7$

6. Multiply.
$-2(3)(-5)$

4. _____

5. _____

7. Solve for x.
$2(5x - 1) - x = 7x + 2$

8. Solve and graph.
$-3x - 2 < 7$

6. _____

7. _____

8. ◄————————————————————►

9. _____

9. Solve for a.
$|3a - 2| = 7$

10. Solve and graph.
$|2x + 1| \le 7$

10. ◄————————————————————►

11. _____

12. _____

11. Solve for h.
$A = \frac{1}{2}(b + B)h$

12. A rectangle is twice as long as it is wide. The perimeter is 60 feet. Find the dimensions.

13. _____

14. _____

15. _____

16. _____

13. Simplify.
$(-2x^3)(4x^5)$

14. Simplify and write your answer with a positive exponent.
$\dfrac{x^{-3}}{x^{-7}}$

15. Simplify.
$2x - 5[4 - (3x + 1)]$

16. Multiply.
$(3x - 5)(2x + 1)$

Answers

17. _____

18. _____

19. _____

20. _____

21. _____

22. _____

23. _____

24. _____

25. _____

26. _____

17. Multiply.

$(4a - 3)(4a + 3)$

18. Divide.

$3x^2 - 8x - 1$ by $x - 3$

19. Factor out the greatest common factor.

$25a^3b^4 - 30a^2b^2 + 15a^4b^3$

20. Factor.

$4x^2 - 7xy + 3y^2$

21. Factor.

$x^3 + 8$

22. Reduce to lowest terms.

$\dfrac{y^2 - 5y + 6}{y^2 - 4}$

23. Multiply.

$\dfrac{x - 5}{x^2 - 9} \cdot \dfrac{x + 3}{x^2 - 10x + 25}$

24. Add.

$\dfrac{3}{x^2 - 25} + \dfrac{2}{x^2 - 4x - 5}$

25. Simplify.

$\dfrac{\frac{1}{x} + \frac{1}{2}}{\frac{1}{x} - \frac{1}{2}}$

26. Solve for x.

$\dfrac{x}{3} + 1 = \dfrac{1}{2}$

27. One number is three times another. The sum of their reciprocals is $\frac{4}{3}$. Find the numbers.

28. Simplify.
$27^{2/3}$

29. Write in simplified form.
$\sqrt{12x^4y^5}$

30. Add.
$4\sqrt{20} + 3\sqrt{45}$

31. Rationalize the denominator.
$$\frac{4}{\sqrt{7} - \sqrt{5}}$$

32. Solve for x.
$\sqrt{3x + 2} + 3 = 5$

33. Write in terms of i.
$\sqrt{-48}$

34. Multiply.
$(2 - 5i)(2 + 5i)$

35. Solve for x.
$x^2 - x - 6 = 0$

36. Solve for x.
$(3x - 2)^2 = 36$

Name _____

Class _____

Date _____

Answers

27. _____

28. _____

29. _____

30. _____

31. _____

32. _____

33. _____

34. _____

35. _____

36. _____

Answers

37. _____

38. _____

39. _____

40. *See graph* _____

41. _____

42. _____

43. *See graph* _____

44. _____

45. _____

46. _____

37. Solve for x.

$$3x^2 + 6x - 2 = 0$$

38. Find K so that the equation $x^2 + Kx = -25$ has exactly one rational solution.

39. The sum of the squares of two consecutive integers is 41. Find the two integers.

40. Graph.

$$y = 2x + 3$$

41. Find the slope of the line through $(4, -1)$ and $(-2, -5)$.

42. Find the equation of the line with slope 3 that contains the point $(2, 4)$.

43. Graph.

$$x - y \geq 3.$$

44. y varies inversely with the square of x. If y is 2 when x is 5, find y when x is 10.

45. Solve the system.

$$3x - 4y = 1$$
$$2x + y = 8$$

46. Solve the system.

$$x + 2y + z = 3$$
$$2x - y + 2z = 6$$
$$3x + y - z = 5$$

47. Find the value of the determinant.

$$\begin{vmatrix} 3 & -1 & 2 \\ 1 & 0 & -1 \\ 5 & 1 & 1 \end{vmatrix}$$

48. Use Cramer's rule to solve.

$$3x - 2y = 5$$
$$4x + 3y = 2$$

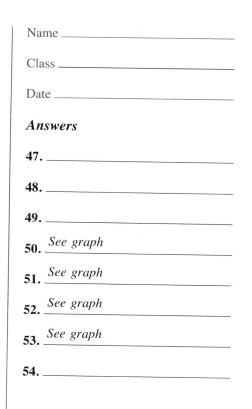

Name _____

Class _____

Date _____

Answers

47. _____

48. _____

49. _____

50. *See graph* _____

51. *See graph* _____

52. *See graph* _____

53. *See graph* _____

54. _____

49. How much 30% alcohol solution and 70% alcohol solution must be mixed to get 16 gallons of 60% solution?

50. Graph.

$$y = x^2 - 2x - 3$$

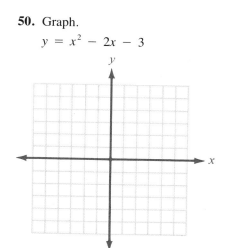

51. Sketch the graph of the circle.

$$x^2 + y^2 - 6x + 4y - 3 = 0$$

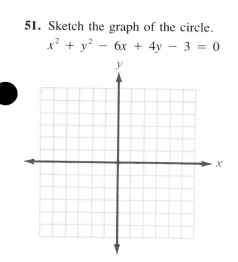

52. Graph.

$$25x^2 + 4y^2 = 100$$

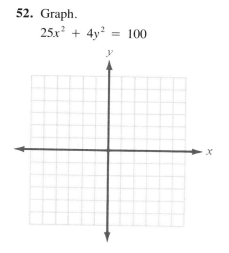

53. Graph.

$$16x^2 - 9y^2 > 144$$

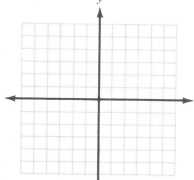

54. Solve the system.

$$x^2 + y^2 = 9$$
$$x - y = 3$$

Answers

55. _____

56. _____

57. _____

58. *See graph* _____

59. _____

60. _____

61. _____

62. _____

63. _____

64. _____

55. Specify the domain for the following.

$$y = \frac{3}{x - 2}$$

56. If $f(x) = 2x^2 - 3x + 1$, find $f(0)$.

57. Let $f(x) = 2x - 5$, and $g(x) = 2x^2 - 3x - 5$, and find g/f.

58. Graph.

$$y = 3^x$$

59. If $f(x) = 3x + 2$, find $f^{-1}(x)$.

60. Solve for x.

$$\log_9 27 = x$$

61. Write as a single logarithm.

$$3 \log_{10} x - 5 \log_{10} y$$

62. Use logarithms to find the following.

$$\sqrt[3]{756}$$

63. Find.

$$\log_7 23$$

64. If $pH = -\log (H_3O^+)$, find the pH of a solution in which $(H_3O^+) = 4.2 \times 10^{-5}$.

Appendix A:
Synthetic Division

Synthetic division is a short form of long division with polynomials. We will consider synthetic division only for those cases in which the divisor is of the form $x + k$, where k is a constant.

Let's begin by looking over an example of long division with polynomials as done in Section 3.6:

$$
\begin{array}{r}
3x^2 - 2x + 4 \\
x + 3 \overline{)3x^3 + 7x^2 - 2x - 4} \\
\underline{3x^3 + 9x^2} \\
-2x^2 - 2x \\
\underline{-2x^2 - 6x} \\
4x - 4 \\
\underline{4x + 12} \\
-16
\end{array}
$$

We can rewrite the problem without showing the variable, since the variable is written in descending powers and similar terms are in alignment. It looks like this:

$$
\begin{array}{r}
3 \quad -2 \quad +4 \\
1 + 3 \overline{)3 \quad\quad 7 \quad -2 \quad -4} \\
\underline{(3) + 9} \\
-2 \, (-2) \\
\underline{(-2) - 6} \\
4 \, (-4) \\
\underline{(4) \quad 12} \\
-16
\end{array}
$$

We have used parentheses to enclose the numbers that are repetitions of the numbers above them. We can compress the problem by eliminating all repetitions:

$$
\begin{array}{r}
3 \quad -2 \quad\quad 4 \\
1 + 3 \overline{)3 \quad\quad 7 \quad -2 \quad -4} \\
\underline{9 \quad -6 \quad\quad 12} \\
3 \quad -2 \quad\quad 4 \quad -16
\end{array}
$$

The top line is the same as the first three terms of the bottom line, so we eliminate the top line. Also, the 1 that was the coefficient of x in the original problem can be eliminated, since we will only consider division problems where the divisor is of the form $x + k$. The following is the most compact form of the original division problem:

$$
\begin{array}{r}
+ 3 \overline{)3 \quad\quad 7 \quad -2 \quad -4} \\
\underline{9 \quad -6 \quad\quad 12} \\
3 \quad -2 \quad\quad 4 \quad -16
\end{array}
$$

If we check over the problem, we find that the first term in the bottom row is exactly the same as the first term in the top row—and it always will be in problems of this type. Also, the last three terms in the bottom row come from multiplication by $+3$ and then subtraction. We can get an equivalent result by multiplying by -3 and adding. The problem would then look like this:

$$
\begin{array}{r|rrrr}
-3 & 3 & 7 & -2 & -4 \\
& \downarrow & -9 & 6 & -12 \\
\hline
& 3 & -2 & 4 & -16
\end{array}
$$

We have used the brackets ⌐ ⌐ to separate the divisor and the remainder. This last expression is synthetic division. It is an easy process to remember. Simply change the sign of the constant term in the divisor, then bring down the first term of the dividend. The process is then just a series of multiplications and additions, as indicated in the following diagram by the arrows:

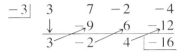

$$-3 \overline{\begin{array}{cccc} 3 & 7 & -2 & -4 \end{array}}$$

The last term on the bottom row is always the remainder.

Here are some additional examples of synthetic division with polynomials.

Practice Problems

1. Divide $x^3 + 2x^2 - 8x + 1$ by $x + 2$.

▼ **Example 1**   Divide $x^4 - 2x^3 + 4x^2 - 6x + 2$ by $x - 2$.

Solution   We change the sign of the constant term in the divisor to get $+2$ and then complete the procedure:

$$+2 \overline{\begin{array}{ccccc} 1 & -2 & 4 & -6 & 2 \\ & 2 & 0 & 8 & 4 \\ \hline 1 & 0 & 4 & 2 & \lfloor 6 \end{array}}$$

From the last line we have the answer:

$$1x^3 + 0x^2 + 4x + 2 + \frac{6}{x - 2}$$

or

$$\frac{x^4 - 2x^3 + 4x^2 - 6x + 2}{x - 2} = x^3 + 4x + 2 + \frac{6}{x - 2} \qquad ▲$$

2. Divide: $\dfrac{2x^3 - 5x^2 + 3}{x - 3}$.

▼ **Example 2**   Divide: $\dfrac{3x^3 - 4x + 5}{x + 4}$.

Solution   Since we cannot skip any powers of the variable in the polynomial $3x^3 - 4x + 5$, we rewrite it as $3x^3 + 0x^2 - 4x + 5$ and proceed as we did in Example 1:

$$-4 \overline{\begin{array}{cccc} 3 & 0 & -4 & 5 \\ & -12 & 48 & -176 \\ \hline 3 & -12 & 44 & \lfloor -171 \end{array}}$$

From the synthetic division, we have

$$\frac{3x^3 - 4x + 5}{x + 4} = 3x^2 - 12x + 44 - \frac{171}{x + 4} \qquad ▲$$

3. Divide: $\dfrac{x^3 + 8}{x + 2}$.

▼ **Example 3**   Divide: $\dfrac{x^3 - 1}{x - 1}$.

Solution   Writing the numerator as $x^3 + 0x^2 + 0x - 1$ and using synthetic division, we have

$$+1 \overline{\begin{array}{cccc} 1 & 0 & 0 & -1 \\ & 1 & 1 & 1 \\ \hline 1 & 1 & 1 & \lfloor 0 \end{array}}$$

which indicates

$$\frac{x^3 - 1}{x - 1} = x^2 + x + 1 \qquad ▲$$

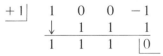

Answers

1. $x^2 - 8 + \dfrac{17}{x + 2}$

2. $2x^2 + x + 3 + \dfrac{12}{x - 3}$

3. $x^2 - 2x + 4$

Problem Set A

Use synthetic division to find the following quotients.

1. $\dfrac{x^2 - 5x + 6}{x + 2}$

2. $\dfrac{x^2 + 8x - 12}{x - 3}$

3. $\dfrac{3x^2 - 4x + 1}{x - 1}$

4. $\dfrac{4x^2 - 2x - 6}{x + 1}$

5. $\dfrac{x^3 + 2x^2 + 3x + 4}{x - 2}$

6. $\dfrac{x^3 - 2x^2 - 3x - 4}{x - 2}$

7. $\dfrac{3x^3 - x^2 + 2x + 5}{x - 3}$

8. $\dfrac{2x^3 - 5x^2 + x + 2}{x - 2}$

9. $\dfrac{2x^3 + x - 3}{x - 1}$

10. $\dfrac{3x^3 - 2x + 1}{x - 5}$

Name _____

Class _____

Date _____

Answers

1. _____

2. _____

3. _____

4. _____

5. _____

6. _____

7. _____

8. _____

9. _____

10. _____

Answers

11. _____

12. _____

13. _____

14. _____

15. _____

16. _____

17. _____

18. _____

19. _____

20. _____

11. $\dfrac{x^4 + 2x^2 + 1}{x + 4}$

12. $\dfrac{x^4 - 3x^2 + 1}{x - 4}$

13. $\dfrac{x^5 - 2x^4 + x^3 - 3x^2 - x + 1}{x - 2}$

14. $\dfrac{2x^5 - 3x^4 + x^3 - x^2 + 2x + 1}{x + 2}$

15. $\dfrac{x^2 + x + 1}{x - 1}$

16. $\dfrac{x^2 + x + 1}{x + 1}$

17. $\dfrac{x^4 - 1}{x + 1}$

18. $\dfrac{x^4 + 1}{x - 1}$

19. $\dfrac{x^3 - 1}{x - 1}$

20. $\dfrac{x^3 - 1}{x + 1}$

Appendix B: Another Method of Factoring Trinomials

In Section 3.8 we factored trinomials of the form $ax^2 + bx + c$ by trial and error, or by listing all the possible factors. In this appendix we will give an alternate method of factoring trinomials of the form $ax^2 + bx + c$ that does not require as much trial and error. To use this new method we must rewrite our original trinomial in such a way that the factoring by grouping method (Section 3.7) can be applied.

Here are the steps we use.

Step 1: Form the product ac.
Step 2: Find a pair of numbers whose product is ac and whose sum is b.
Step 3: Write the polynomial to be factored again so that the middle term bx is written as the sum of two terms whose coefficients are the two numbers found in step 2.
Step 4: Factor by grouping.

▼ **Example 1** Factor $3x^2 - 10x - 8$ using these steps.

Solution The trinomial $3x^2 - 10x - 8$ has the form $ax^2 + bx + c$, where $a = 3$, $b = -10$, and $c = -8$.

Step 1: The product ac is $3(-8) = -24$.
Step 2: We need to find two numbers whose product is -24 and whose sum is -10. Let's list all the pairs of numbers whose product is -24 to find the pair whose sum is -10.

Product		Sum	
$1(-24)$	$= -24$	$1 + (-24)$	$= -23$
$-1(24)$	$= -24$	$-1 + 24$	$= 23$
$2(-12)$	$= -24$	$2 + (-12)$	$= -10$
$-2(12)$	$= -24$	$-2 + 12$	$= 10$
$3(-8)$	$= -24$	$3 + (-8)$	$= -5$
$-3(8)$	$= -24$	$-3 + 8$	$= 5$
$4(-6)$	$= -24$	$4 + (-6)$	$= -2$
$-4(6)$	$= -24$	$-4 + 6$	$= 2$

As you can see, of all the pairs of numbers whose product is -24, only 2 and -12 have a sum of -10.

565

Step 3: We now rewrite our original trinomial so the middle term $-10x$ is written as the sum of $-12x$ and $2x$:

$$3x^2 - 10x - 8 = 3x^2 - 12x + 2x - 8$$

Step 4: Factoring by grouping we have

$$3x^2 - 12x + 2x - 8 = 3x(x - 4) + 2(x - 4)$$
$$= (x - 4)(3x + 2)$$

You can see that this method works by multiplying $x - 4$ and $3x + 2$ to get

$$3x^2 - 10x - 8 \qquad \blacktriangle$$

2. Factor $4x^2 + 11x + 6$.

▼ **Example 2** Factor $9x^2 + 15x + 4$.

Solution In this case $a = 9$, $b = 15$, and $c = 4$. The product ac is $9 \cdot 4 = 36$. Listing all the pairs of numbers whose product is 36 along with the corresponding sums we have

Product	Sum
$1(36) = 36$	$1 + 36 = 37$
$3(12) = 36$	$3 + 12 = 15$
$4(9) = 36$	$4 + 9 = 13$
$6(6) = 36$	$6 + 6 = 12$

Notice we only list positive numbers since both the sum and product we are looking for are positive. The numbers 3 and 12 are the numbers we are looking for. Their product is 36 and their sum is 15. We now rewrite the original polynomial $9x^2 + 15x + 4$ with the middle term written as $3x + 12x$. We then factor by grouping:

$$9x^2 + 15x + 4 = 9x^2 + 3x + 12x + 4$$
$$= 3x(3x + 1) + 4(3x + 1)$$
$$= (3x + 1)(3x + 4)$$

The polynomial $9x^2 + 15x + 4$ factors into the product $(3x + 1)(3x + 4)$. $\qquad \blacktriangle$

3. Factor $4x^2 - 4x - 15$.

▼ **Example 3** Factor $8x^2 - 2x - 15$.

Solution The product ac is $8(-15) = -120$. There are many pairs of numbers whose product is -120. We are looking for the pair whose sum is also -2. The numbers are -12 and 10. Writing $-2x$ as $-12x + 10x$ and then factoring by grouping we have

$$8x^2 - 2x - 15 = 8x^2 - 12x + 10x - 15$$
$$= 4x(2x - 3) + 5(2x - 3)$$
$$= (2x - 3)(4x + 5)^* \qquad \blacktriangle$$

---

* I would like to thank Professor Hirsch Gottschalk of San Diego Community College for showing me this method of factoring trinomials.

Answers
2. $(x + 2)(4x + 3)$
3. $(2x - 5)(2x + 3)$

Problem Set B

Factor the following trinomials using the method shown in this appendix.

1. $4x^2 - 4x - 3$

2. $4x^2 - 11x - 3$

3. $4x^2 + 4x - 3$

4. $4x^2 - x - 3$

5. $4a^2 + 11a - 3$

6. $4a^2 - 7a + 3$

7. $8x^2 + 10x + 3$

8. $8x^2 + 14x + 3$

9. $5y^2 + y - 6$

10. $5y^2 - 29y - 6$

Name _____

Class _____

Date _____

Answers

1. _____

2. _____

3. _____

4. _____

5. _____

6. _____

7. _____

8. _____

9. _____

10. _____

Answers

11. _____

12. _____

13. _____

14. _____

15. _____

16. _____

17. _____

18. _____

19. _____

20. _____

11. $5x^2 - 17x + 6$

12. $5x^2 - 13x + 6$

13. $6y^2 + 13y + 5$

14. $6y^2 - 7y - 5$

15. $x^2 + 7x + 12$

16. $x^2 + 2x - 8$

17. $10a^2 - 11a - 6$

18. $10a^2 - 7a - 6$

19. $8x^2 + 3x - 5$

20. $8x^2 - 6x - 5$

Appendix C: Venn Diagrams

In Chapter 1 we defined the union of two sets A and B to be the set of all elements that are in A or in B. The intersections of A and B is the set of elements that are common to both A and B.

Venn diagrams are diagrams, or pictures, that represent the union and intersection of sets. Each of the following diagrams is a Venn diagram. The shaded region in the first diagram shows the union of two sets A and B, while the shaded part of the second diagram shows their intersection.

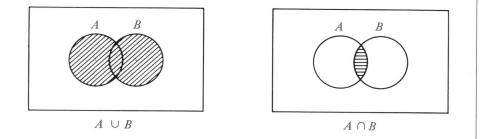

$$A \cup B \qquad\qquad A \cap B$$

In each diagram, we think of the elements of set A as being the points inside the circle labeled A. The elements of set B are the points inside the circle labeled B. We enclose the two sets within a rectangle to indicate that there are still other elements that are neither in A nor in B. The rectangle is sometimes referred to as the *universal set*.

As you might expect, not all sets intersect. Here is the definition we use for nonintersecting sets, along with a Venn diagram that illustrates their relationship.

DEFINITION   Two sets with no elements in common are said to be *disjoint* or *mutually exclusive*. Two sets are disjoint if their intersection is the empty set.

A and B are disjoint if and only if
$$A \cap B = \varnothing$$

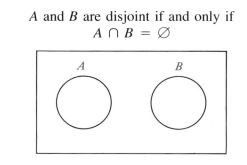

A and *B* are disjoint.

Another relationship between sets that can be represented with Venn diagrams is the subset relationship. The following diagram shows that *A* is a subset of *B*.

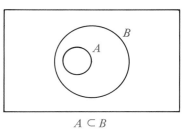

$A \subset B$

Along with giving a graphical representation of union and intersection, Venn diagrams can be used to test the validity of statements involving combinations of sets and operations on sets.

▼ **Example 1**   Use Venn diagrams to check the expression

$$A \cap (B \cup C) = (A \cap B) \cup (A \cap C)$$

(Assume no two sets are disjoint.)

Solution   We begin by making a Venn diagram of the left side with $B \cup C$ shaded in with vertical lines.

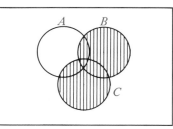

Using the same diagram we now shade in set *A* with horizontal lines.

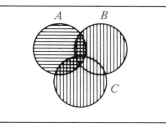

Practice Problems

1. Use Venn diagrams to verify the expression

$$A \cup (B \cup C) = (A \cup B) \cup C$$

assuming no two sets are disjoint.

Answer
1. See Solutions Section.

The region containing both vertical and horizontal lines is the intersection of A with $B \cup C$, or $A \cap (B \cup C)$.

We diagram the right side and shade in $A \cap B$ with horizontaal lines and $A \cap C$ with vertical lines.

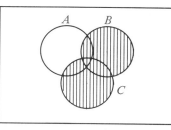

Any region containing vertical or horizontal lines is part of the union of $A \cap B$ and $A \cap C$, or $(A \cap B) \cup (A \cap C)$.

The original statement appears to be true.

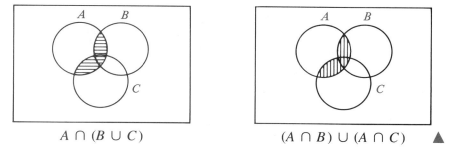

$$A \cap (B \cup C) \qquad\qquad (A \cap B) \cup (A \cap C) \quad \blacktriangle$$

Recall the way we defined the union of two sets using set-builder notation:

$$A \cup B = \{x \mid x \in A \text{ or } x \in B\}$$

The right side of this statement is read "the set of all x such that x is a member of A or x is a member of B." As you can see, the vertical line after the first x is read "such that."

▼ **Example 2** Let A and B be two intersecting sets neither of which is a subset of the other. Use a Venn diagram to illustrate the set

$$\{x \mid x \in A \text{ and } x \notin B\}$$

Solution Using vertical lines to indicate all the elements in A and horizontal lines to show everything that is not in B we have

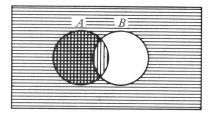

Since the connecting word is "and" we want the region that contains both vertical and horizontal lines.

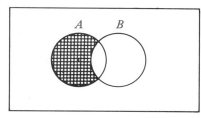

▲

2. Let A and B be two intersecting sets neither of which is a subset of the other. Use a Venn diagram to illustrate the set

$$\{x \mid x \notin A \text{ and } x \in B\}$$

Answer
2. See Solutions Section.

Name _____ Class _____ Date _____

Problem Set C

Use Venn diagrams to show each of the following regions. Assume sets A, B, and C all intersect one another.

1. $(A \cup B) \cup C$

2. $(A \cap B) \cap C$

3. $A \cap (B \cap C)$

4. $A \cup (B \cup C)$

5. $A \cap (B \cup C)$

6. $(A \cap B) \cup C$

7. $A \cup (B \cap C)$

8. $(A \cup B) \cap C$

9. $(A \cup B) \cap (A \cup C)$

10. $(A \cap B) \cup (A \cap C)$

11. Use a Venn diagram to show that if $A \subset B$, then $A \cap B = A$.

12. Use a Venn diagram to show that if $A \subset B$, then $A \cup B = B$.

Let A and B be two intersecting sets neither of which is a subset of the other. Use Venn diagrams to illustrate each of the following sets.

13. $\{x \mid x \in A \text{ and } x \in B\}$

14. $\{x \mid x \in A \text{ or } x \in B\}$

15. $\{x \mid x \notin A \text{ and } x \in B\}$

16. $\{x \mid x \notin A \text{ and } x \notin B\}$

17. $\{x \mid x \notin A \text{ or } x \notin B)$

18. $\{x \mid x \notin A \text{ or } x \in B\}$

19. $\{x \mid x \in A \cap B\}$

20. $\{x \mid x \in A \cup B\}$

Appendix D: Powers, Roots, and Prime Factors

n	n^2	$\sqrt{n}$	n^3	$\sqrt[3]{n}$	Prime factors
1	1	1.000	1	1.000	—
2	4	1.414	8	1.260	prime
3	9	1.732	27	1.442	prime
4	16	2.000	64	1.587	2 · 2
5	25	2.236	125	1.710	prime
6	36	2.449	216	1.817	2 · 3
7	49	2.646	343	1.913	prime
8	64	2.828	512	2.000	2 · 2 · 2
9	81	3.000	729	2.080	3 · 3
10	100	3.162	1,000	2.154	2 · 5
11	121	3.317	1,331	2.224	prime
12	144	3.464	1,728	2.289	2 · 2 · 3
13	169	3.606	2,197	2.351	prime
14	196	3.742	2,744	2.410	2 · 7
15	225	3.873	3,375	2.466	3 · 5
16	256	4.000	4,096	2.520	2 · 2 · 2 · 2
17	289	4.123	4,913	2.571	prime
18	324	4.243	5,832	2.621	2 · 3 · 3
19	361	4.359	6,859	2.668	prime
20	400	4.472	8,000	2.714	2 · 2 · 5
21	441	4.583	9,261	2.759	3 · 7
22	484	4.690	10,648	2.802	2 · 11
23	529	4.796	12,167	2.844	prime
24	576	4.899	13,824	2.884	2 · 2 · 2 · 3
25	625	5.000	15,625	2.924	5 · 5
26	676	5.099	17,576	2.962	2 · 13
27	729	5.196	19,683	3.000	3 · 3 · 3
28	784	5.292	21,952	3.037	2 · 2 · 7
29	841	5.385	24,389	3.072	prime
30	900	5.477	27,000	3.107	2 · 3 · 5
31	961	5.568	29,791	3.141	prime
32	1,024	5.657	32,768	3.175	2 · 2 · 2 · 2 · 2
33	1,089	5.745	35,937	3.208	3 · 11
34	1,156	5.831	39,304	3.240	2 · 17
35	1,225	5.916	42,875	3.271	5 · 7
36	1,296	6.000	46,656	3.302	2 · 2 · 3 · 3
37	1,369	6.083	50,653	3.332	prime
38	1,444	6.164	54,872	3.362	2 · 19
39	1,521	6.245	59,319	3.391	3 · 13
40	1,600	6.325	64,000	3.420	2 · 2 · 2 · 5
41	1,681	6.403	68,921	3.448	prime
42	1,764	6.481	74,088	3.476	2 · 3 · 7
43	1,849	6.557	79,507	3.503	prime
44	1,936	6.633	85,184	3.530	2 · 2 · 11
45	2,025	6.708	91,125	3.557	3 · 3 · 5
46	2,116	6.782	97,336	3.583	2 · 23
47	2,209	6.856	103,823	3.609	prime

Powers, Roots, and Prime Factors (Continued)

n	n^2	$\sqrt{n}$	n^3	$\sqrt[3]{n}$	Prime factors
48	2,304	6.928	110,592	3.634	$2 \cdot 2 \cdot 2 \cdot 2 \cdot 3$
49	2,401	7.000	117,649	3.659	$7 \cdot 7$
50	2,500	7.071	125,000	3.684	$2 \cdot 5 \cdot 5$
51	2,601	7.141	132,651	3.708	$3 \cdot 17$
52	2,704	7.211	140,608	3.733	$2 \cdot 2 \cdot 13$
53	2,809	7.280	148,877	3.756	prime
54	2,916	7.348	157,464	3.780	$2 \cdot 3 \cdot 3 \cdot 3$
55	3,025	7.416	166,375	3.803	$5 \cdot 11$
56	3,136	7.483	175,616	3.826	$2 \cdot 2 \cdot 2 \cdot 7$
57	3,249	7.550	185,193	3.849	$3 \cdot 19$
58	3,364	7.616	195,112	3.871	$2 \cdot 29$
59	3,481	7.681	205,379	3.893	prime
60	3,600	7.746	216,000	3.915	$2 \cdot 2 \cdot 3 \cdot 5$
61	3,721	7.810	226,981	3.936	prime
62	3,844	7.874	238,328	3.958	$2 \cdot 31$
63	3,969	7.937	250,047	3.979	$3 \cdot 3 \cdot 7$
64	4,096	8.000	262,144	4.000	$2 \cdot 2 \cdot 2 \cdot 2 \cdot 2 \cdot 2$
65	4,225	8.062	274,625	4.021	$5 \cdot 13$
66	4,356	8.124	287,496	4.041	$2 \cdot 3 \cdot 11$
67	4,489	8.185	300,763	4.062	prime
68	4,624	8.246	314,432	4.082	$2 \cdot 2 \cdot 17$
69	4,761	8.307	328,509	4.102	$3 \cdot 23$
70	4,900	8.367	343,000	4.121	$2 \cdot 5 \cdot 7$
71	5,041	8.426	357,911	4.141	prime
72	5,184	8.485	373,248	4.160	$2 \cdot 2 \cdot 2 \cdot 3 \cdot 3$
73	5,329	8.544	389,017	4.179	prime
74	5,476	8.602	405,224	4.198	$2 \cdot 37$
75	5,625	8.660	421,875	4.217	$3 \cdot 5 \cdot 5$
76	5,776	8.718	438,976	4.236	$2 \cdot 2 \cdot 19$
77	5,929	8.775	456,533	4.254	$7 \cdot 11$
78	6,084	8.832	474,552	4.273	$2 \cdot 3 \cdot 13$
79	6,241	8.888	493,039	4.291	prime
80	6,400	8.944	512,000	4.309	$2 \cdot 2 \cdot 2 \cdot 2 \cdot 5$
81	6,561	9.000	531,441	4.327	$3 \cdot 3 \cdot 3 \cdot 3$
82	6,724	9.055	551,368	4.344	$2 \cdot 41$
83	6,889	9.110	571,787	4.362	prime
84	7,056	9.165	592,704	4.380	$2 \cdot 2 \cdot 3 \cdot 7$
85	7,225	9.220	614,125	4.397	$5 \cdot 17$
86	7,396	9.274	636,056	4.414	$2 \cdot 43$
87	7,569	9.327	658,503	4.431	$3 \cdot 29$
88	7,744	9.381	681,472	4.448	$2 \cdot 2 \cdot 2 \cdot 11$
89	7,921	9.434	704,969	4.465	prime
90	8,100	9.487	729,000	4.481	$2 \cdot 3 \cdot 3 \cdot 5$
91	8,281	9.539	753,571	4.498	$7 \cdot 13$
92	8,464	9.592	778,688	4.514	$2 \cdot 2 \cdot 23$
93	8,649	9.644	804,357	4.531	$3 \cdot 31$
94	8,836	9.695	830,584	4.547	$2 \cdot 47$
95	9,025	9.747	857,375	4.563	$5 \cdot 19$
96	9,216	9.798	884,736	4.579	$2 \cdot 2 \cdot 2 \cdot 2 \cdot 2 \cdot 3$
97	9,409	9.849	912,673	4.595	prime
98	9,604	9.899	941,192	4.610	$2 \cdot 7 \cdot 7$
99	9,801	9.950	970,299	4.626	$3 \cdot 3 \cdot 11$
100	10,000	10.000	1,000,000	4.642	$2 \cdot 2 \cdot 5 \cdot 5$

Appendix E:
Common Logarithms

x	0	1	2	3	4	5	6	7	8	9
1.0	.0000	.0043	.0086	.0128	.0170	.0212	.0253	.0294	.0334	.0374
1.1	.0414	.0453	.0492	.0531	.0569	.0607	.0645	.0682	.0719	.0755
1.2	.0792	.0828	.0864	.0899	.0934	.0969	.1004	.1038	.1072	.1106
1.3	.1139	.1173	.1206	.1239	.1271	.1303	.1335	.1367	.1399	.1430
1.4	.1461	.1492	.1523	.1553	.1584	.1614	.1644	.1673	.1703	.1732
1.5	.1761	.1790	.1818	.1847	.1875	.1903	.1931	.1959	.1987	.2014
1.6	.2041	.2068	.2095	.2122	.2148	.2175	.2201	.2227	.2253	.2279
1.7	.2304	.2330	.2355	.2380	.2405	.2430	.2455	.2480	.2504	.2529
1.8	.2553	.2577	.2601	.2625	.2648	.2672	.2695	.2718	.2742	.2765
1.9	.2788	.2810	.2833	.2856	.2878	.2900	.2923	.2945	.2967	.2989
2.0	.3010	.3032	.3054	.3075	.3096	.3118	.3139	.3160	.3181	.3201
2.1	.3222	.3243	.3263	.3284	.3304	.3324	.3345	.3365	.3385	.3404
2.2	.3424	.3444	.3464	.3483	.3502	.3522	.3541	.3560	.3579	.3598
2.3	.3617	.3636	.3655	.3674	.3692	.3711	.3729	.3747	.3766	.3784
2.4	.3802	.3820	.3838	.3856	.3874	.3892	.3909	.3927	.3945	.3962
2.5	.3979	.3997	.4014	.4031	.4048	.4065	.4082	.4099	.4116	.4133
2.6	.4150	.4166	.4183	.4200	.4216	.4232	.4249	.4265	.4281	.4298
2.7	.4314	.4330	.4346	.4362	.4378	.4393	.4409	.4425	.4440	.4456
2.8	.4472	.4487	.4502	.4518	.4533	.4548	.4564	.4579	.4594	.4609
2.9	.4624	.4639	.4654	.4669	.4683	.4698	.4713	.4728	.4742	.4757
3.0	.4771	.4786	.4800	.4814	.4829	.4843	.4857	.4871	.4886	.4900
3.1	.4914	.4928	.4942	.4955	.4969	.4983	.4997	.5011	.5024	.5038
3.2	.5051	.5065	.5079	.5092	.5105	.5119	.5132	.5145	.5159	.5172
3.3	.5185	.5198	.5211	.5224	.5237	.5250	.5263	.5276	.5289	.5302
3.4	.5315	.5328	.5340	.5353	.5366	.5378	.5391	.5403	.5416	.5428
3.5	.5441	.5453	.5465	.5478	.5490	.5502	.5514	.5527	.5539	.5551
3.6	.5563	.5575	.5587	.5599	.5611	.5623	.5635	.5647	.5658	.5670
3.7	.5682	.5694	.5705	.5717	.5729	.5740	.5752	.5763	.5775	.5786
3.8	.5798	.5809	.5821	.5832	.5843	.5855	.5866	.5877	.5888	.5899
3.9	.5911	.5922	.5933	.5944	.5955	.5966	.5977	.5988	.5999	.6010
4.0	.6021	.6031	.6042	.6053	.6064	.6075	.6085	.6096	.6107	.6117
4.1	.6128	.6138	.6149	.6160	.6170	.6180	.6191	.6201	.6212	.6222
4.2	.6232	.6243	.6253	.6263	.6274	.6284	.6294	.6304	.6314	.6325
4.3	.6335	.6345	.6355	.6365	.6375	.6385	.6395	.6405	.6415	.6425
4.4	.6435	.6444	.6454	.6464	.6474	.6484	.6493	.6503	.6513	.6522
4.5	.6532	.6542	.6551	.6561	.6571	.6580	.6590	.6599	.6609	.6618
4.6	.6628	.6637	.6646	.6656	.6665	.6675	.6684	.6693	.6702	.6712
4.7	.6721	.6730	.6739	.6749	.6758	.6767	.6776	.6785	.6794	.6803
4.8	.6812	.6821	.6830	.6839	.6848	.6857	.6866	.6875	.6884	.6893
4.9	.6902	.6911	.6920	.6928	.6937	.6946	.6955	.6964	.6972	.6981
5.0	.6990	.6998	.7007	.7016	.7024	.7033	.7042	.7050	.7059	.7067
5.1	.7076	.7084	.7093	.7101	.7110	.7118	.7126	.7135	.7143	.7152
5.2	.7160	.7168	.7177	.7185	.7193	.7202	.7210	.7218	.7226	.7235
5.3	.7243	.7251	.7259	.7267	.7275	.7284	.7292	.7300	.7308	.7316
5.4	.7324	.7332	.7340	.7348	.7356	.7364	.7372	.7380	.7388	.7396
x	0	1	2	3	4	5	6	7	8	9

Common Logarithms (Continued)

x	0	1	2	3	4	5	6	7	8	9
5.5	.7404	.7412	.7419	.7427	.7435	.7443	.7451	.7459	.7466	.7474
5.6	.7482	.7490	.7497	.7505	.7513	.7520	.7528	.7536	.7543	.7551
5.7	.7559	.7566	.7574	.7582	.7589	.7597	.7604	.7612	.7619	.7627
5.8	.7634	.7642	.7649	.7657	.7664	.7672	.7679	.7686	.7694	.7701
5.9	.7709	.7716	.7723	.7731	.7738	.7745	.7752	.7760	.7767	.7774
6.0	.7782	.7789	.7796	.7803	.7810	.7818	.7825	.7832	.7839	.7846
6.1	.7853	.7860	.7868	.7875	.7882	.7889	.7896	.7903	.7910	.7917
6.2	.7924	.7931	.7938	.7945	.7952	.7959	.7966	.7973	.7980	.7987
6.3	.7993	.8000	.8007	.8014	.8021	.8028	.8035	.8041	.8048	.8055
6.4	.8062	.8069	.8075	.8082	.8089	.8096	.8102	.8109	.8116	.8122
6.5	.8129	.8136	.8142	.8149	.8156	.8162	.8169	.8176	.8182	.8189
6.6	.8195	.8202	.8209	.8215	.8222	.8228	.8235	.8241	.8248	.8254
6.7	.8261	.8267	.8274	.8280	.8287	.8293	.8299	.8306	.8312	.8319
6.8	.8325	.8331	.8338	.8344	.8351	.8357	.8363	.8370	.8376	.8382
6.9	.8388	.8395	.8401	.8407	.8414	.8420	.8426	.8432	.8439	.8445
7.0	.8451	.8457	.8463	.8470	.8476	.8482	.8488	.8494	.8500	.8506
7.1	.8513	.8519	.8525	.8531	.8537	.8543	.8549	.8555	.8561	.8567
7.2	.8573	.8579	.8585	.8591	.8597	.8603	.8609	.8615	.8621	.8627
7.3	.8633	.8639	.8645	.8651	.8657	.8663	.8669	.8675	.8681	.8686
7.4	.8692	.8698	.8704	.8710	.8716	.8722	.8727	.8733	.8739	.8745
7.5	.8751	.8756	.8762	.8768	.8774	.8779	.8785	.8791	.8797	.8802
7.6	.8808	.8814	.8820	.8825	.8831	.8837	.8842	.8848	.8854	.8859
7.7	.8865	.8871	.8876	.8882	.8887	.8893	.8899	.8904	.8910	.8915
7.8	.8921	.8927	.8932	.8938	.8943	.8949	.8954	.8960	.8965	.8971
7.9	.8976	.8982	.8987	.8993	.8998	.9004	.9009	.9015	.9020	.9025
8.0	.9031	.9036	.9042	.9047	.9053	.9058	.9063	.9069	.9074	.9079
8.1	.9085	.9090	.9096	.9101	.9106	.9112	.9117	.9122	.9128	.9133
8.2	.9138	.9143	.9149	.9154	.9159	.9165	.9170	.9175	.9180	.9186
8.3	.9191	.9196	.9201	.9206	.9212	.9217	.9222	.9227	.9232	.9238
8.4	.9243	.9248	.9253	.9258	.9263	.9269	.9274	.9279	.9284	.9289
8.5	.9294	.9299	.9304	.9309	.9315	.9320	.9325	.9330	.9335	.9340
8.6	.9345	.9350	.9355	.9360	.9365	.9370	.9375	.9380	.9385	.9390
8.7	.9395	.9400	.9405	.9410	.9415	.9420	.9425	.9430	.9435	.9440
8.8	.9445	.9450	.9455	.9460	.9465	.9469	.9474	.9479	.9484	.9489
8.9	.9494	.9499	.9504	.9509	.9513	.9518	.9523	.9528	.9533	.9538
9.0	.9542	.9547	.9552	.9557	.9562	.9566	.9571	.9576	.9581	.9586
9.1	.9590	.9595	.9600	.9605	.9609	.9614	.9619	.9624	.9628	.9633
9.2	.9638	.9643	.9647	.9652	.9657	.9661	.9666	.9671	.9675	.9680
9.3	.9685	.9689	.9694	.9699	.9703	.9708	.9713	.9717	.9722	.9727
9.4	.9731	.9736	.9741	.9745	.9750	.9754	.9759	.9763	.9768	.9773
9.5	.9777	.9782	.9786	.9791	.9795	.9800	.9805	.9809	.9814	.9818
9.6	.9823	.9827	.9832	.9836	.9841	.9845	.9850	.9854	.9859	.9863
9.7	.9868	.9872	.9877	.9881	.9886	.9890	.9894	.9899	.9903	.9908
9.8	.9912	.9917	.9921	.9926	.9930	.9934	.9939	.9943	.9948	.9952
9.9	.9956	.9961	.9965	.9969	.9974	.9978	.9983	.9987	.9991	.9996
x	0	1	2	3	4	5	6	7	8	9

1. $x + y > xy$

2. $\frac{4}{7}$, $-\frac{7}{4}$, $\frac{4}{7}$

3.

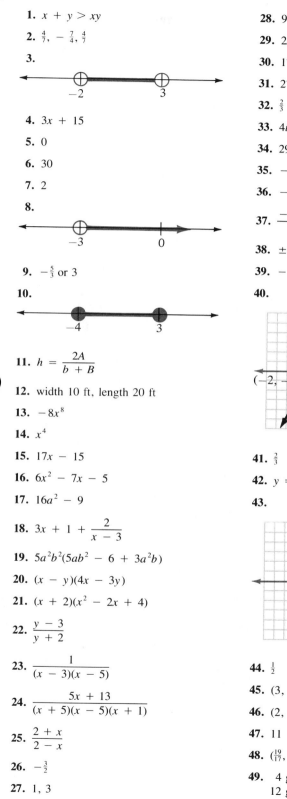

4. $3x + 15$

5. 0

6. 30

7. 2

8.

9. $-\frac{5}{3}$ or 3

10.

11. $h = \dfrac{2A}{b + B}$

12. width 10 ft, length 20 ft

13. $-8x^8$

14. x^4

15. $17x - 15$

16. $6x^2 - 7x - 5$

17. $16a^2 - 9$

18. $3x + 1 + \dfrac{2}{x - 3}$

19. $5a^2b^2(5ab^2 - 6 + 3a^2b)$

20. $(x - y)(4x - 3y)$

21. $(x + 2)(x^2 - 2x + 4)$

22. $\dfrac{y - 3}{y + 2}$

23. $\dfrac{1}{(x - 3)(x - 5)}$

24. $\dfrac{5x + 13}{(x + 5)(x - 5)(x + 1)}$

25. $\dfrac{2 + x}{2 - x}$

26. $-\frac{3}{2}$

27. $1, 3$

28. 9

29. $2x^2y^2\sqrt{3y}$

30. $17\sqrt{5}$

31. $2\sqrt{7} + 2\sqrt{5}$

32. $\frac{2}{3}$

33. $4i\sqrt{3}$

34. 29

35. $-2, 3$

36. $-\frac{4}{3}, \frac{8}{3}$

37. $\dfrac{-3 \pm \sqrt{15}}{3}$

38. ± 10

39. $-5, -4$ or $4, 5$

40.

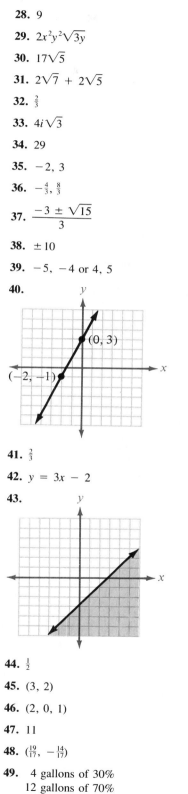

41. $\frac{2}{3}$

42. $y = 3x - 2$

43.

44. $\frac{1}{2}$

45. $(3, 2)$

46. $(2, 0, 1)$

47. 11

48. $\left(\frac{19}{17}, -\frac{14}{17}\right)$

49. 4 gallons of 30%
12 gallons of 70%

50. x-intercepts $= -1$ and 3
vertex $= (1, -4)$

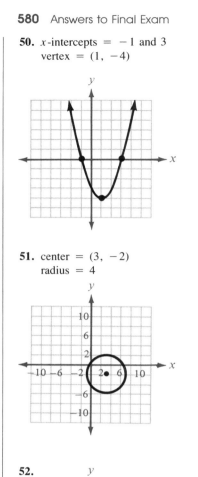

51. center $= (3, -2)$
radius $= 4$

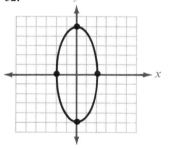

52.

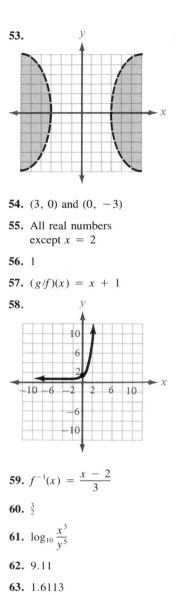

53.

54. $(3, 0)$ and $(0, -3)$

55. All real numbers
except $x = 2$

56. 1

57. $(g/f)(x) = x + 1$

58.

59. $f^{-1}(x) = \dfrac{x - 2}{3}$

60. $\frac{3}{2}$

61. $\log_{10} \dfrac{x^3}{y^5}$

62. 9.11

63. 1.6113

64. 4.38

Solutions to Selected Practice Problems

Solutions to all practice problems that require more than one step are shown here. Before you look back here to see where you have made a mistake, you should try the problem you are working on twice. If you do not get the correct answer the second time you work the problem, then the solution shown here should show you where you went wrong.

CHAPTER 1

SECTION 1.1

2. a. $4^2 = 4 \cdot 4 = 16$
   b. $2^4 = 2 \cdot 2 \cdot 2 \cdot 2 = 16$
   c. $3^3 = 3 \cdot 3 \cdot 3 = 27$
   d. $7^2 = 7 \cdot 7 = 49$

3. a. $6 + 2(3 + 4) = 6 + 2(7)$
$$= 6 + 14$$
$$= 20$$
   b. $5 \cdot 3^2 - 2 \cdot 4^2 = 5 \cdot 9 - 2 \cdot 16$
$$= 45 - 32$$
$$= 13$$
   c. $30 - (2 \cdot 3^2 - 8) = 30 - (2 \cdot 9 - 8)$
$$= 30 - (18 - 8)$$
$$= 30 - 10$$
$$= 20$$

   d. $60 + 20 \div 2 - 40 = 60 + 10 - 40$
$$= 70 - 40$$
$$= 30$$
   e. $3 + 5[2 + (7 \cdot 2 - 10)] = 3 + 5[2 + (14 - 10)]$
$$= 3 + 5(2 + 4)$$
$$= 3 + 5(6)$$
$$= 3 + 30$$
$$= 33$$

SECTION 1.2

3. $\dfrac{3}{7} \cdot \dfrac{2}{5} = \dfrac{3 \cdot 2}{7 \cdot 5} = \dfrac{6}{35}$ **4.** $9 \cdot \dfrac{1}{4} = \dfrac{9}{1} \cdot \dfrac{1}{4} = \dfrac{9}{4}$

SECTION 1.3

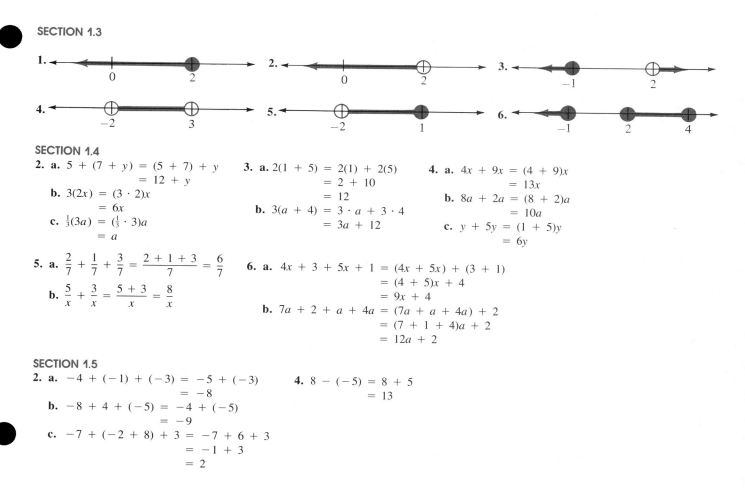

1. 0 2
2. 0 2
3. −1 2
4. −2 3
5. −2 1
6. −1 2 4

SECTION 1.4

2. a. $5 + (7 + y) = (5 + 7) + y$
$$= 12 + y$$
   b. $3(2x) = (3 \cdot 2)x$
$$= 6x$$
   c. $\frac{1}{3}(3a) = (\frac{1}{3} \cdot 3)a$
$$= a$$

3. a. $2(1 + 5) = 2(1) + 2(5)$
$$= 2 + 10$$
$$= 12$$
   b. $3(a + 4) = 3 \cdot a + 3 \cdot 4$
$$= 3a + 12$$

4. a. $4x + 9x = (4 + 9)x$
$$= 13x$$
   b. $8a + 2a = (8 + 2)a$
$$= 10a$$
   c. $y + 5y = (1 + 5)y$
$$= 6y$$

5. a. $\dfrac{2}{7} + \dfrac{1}{7} + \dfrac{3}{7} = \dfrac{2 + 1 + 3}{7} = \dfrac{6}{7}$
   b. $\dfrac{5}{x} + \dfrac{3}{x} = \dfrac{5 + 3}{x} = \dfrac{8}{x}$

6. a. $4x + 3 + 5x + 1 = (4x + 5x) + (3 + 1)$
$$= (4 + 5)x + 4$$
$$= 9x + 4$$
   b. $7a + 2 + a + 4a = (7a + a + 4a) + 2$
$$= (7 + 1 + 4)a + 2$$
$$= 12a + 2$$

SECTION 1.5

2. a. $-4 + (-1) + (-3) = -5 + (-3)$
$$= -8$$
   b. $-8 + 4 + (-5) = -4 + (-5)$
$$= -9$$
   c. $-7 + (-2 + 8) + 3 = -7 + 6 + 3$
$$= -1 + 3$$
$$= 2$$

4. $8 - (-5) = 8 + 5$
$$= 13$$

5. a. $2 - 6 + 4 = 2 + (-6) + 4$
$= -4 + 4$
$= 0$

b. $7 - (-1) + 3 = 7 + 1 + 3$
$= 8 + 3$
$= 11$

c. $-9 - 5 - (-7) = -9 + (-5) + 7$
$= -14 + 7$
$= -7$

d. $6 - |-2| + |-3| = 6 - 2 + 3$
$= 6 + (-2) + 3$
$= 4 + 3$
$= 7$

e. $-3 - (-9) - |-2| = -3 - (-9) - 2$
$= -3 + 9 + (-2)$
$= 6 + (-2)$
$= 4$

7. a. $5x - 3x = (5 - 3)x$
$= 2x$

b. $-5x - 8x = (-5 - 8)x$
$= -13x$

c. $6y - y = (6 - 1)y$
$= 5y$

d. $-8a + 3a = (-8 + 3)a$
$= -5a$

e. $-4x + 9x - 2x = (-4 + 9 - 2)x$
$= 3x$

8. a. $7x - 3 - 4x + 8 = 7x - 4x - 3 + 8$
$= 3x + 5$

b. $10x - x + 5 + 2x = 10x - x + 2x + 5$
$= 11x + 5$

c. $x - 3 - 4 - 3x = x - 3x - 3 - 4$
$= -2x - 7$

SECTION 1.6

1. e. $-2(5)(-1) = -10(-1)$
$= 10$

f. $4(-7 \cdot 2) = 4(-14)$
$= -56$

g. $-3(2x) = (-3 \cdot 2)x$
$= -6x$

h. $-5(4a) = (-5 \cdot 4)a$
$= -20a$

i. $-6(x + 2) = -6 \cdot x + (-6)2$
$= -6x - 12$

j. $-3(4a + 1) = -3(4a) + (-3)(1)$
$= -12a - 3$

3. $\dfrac{3}{4} \div \dfrac{5}{9} = \dfrac{3}{4} \cdot \dfrac{9}{5} = \dfrac{27}{20}$

4. a. $\dfrac{3}{5} \div \dfrac{6}{7} = \dfrac{3}{5} \cdot \dfrac{7}{6}$
$= \dfrac{21}{30}$
$= \dfrac{7}{10}$

b. $12 \div \dfrac{3}{4} = \dfrac{12}{1} \cdot \dfrac{4}{3}$
$= \dfrac{48}{3}$
$= 16$

c. $-\dfrac{5}{6} \div 10 = -\dfrac{5}{6} \cdot \dfrac{1}{10}$
$= -\dfrac{5}{60}$
$= -\dfrac{1}{12}$

5. a. $\dfrac{3(-4) - 8}{12 - 2} = \dfrac{-12 - 8}{12 - 2}$
$= \dfrac{-20}{10}$
$= -2$

b. $4 - 3(2 - 9) - (-1) = 4 - 3(-7) + 1$
$= 4 + 21 + 1$
$= 26$

c. $\dfrac{5(-6) + 3(-2)}{4(-3) + 3} = \dfrac{-30 + (-6)}{-12 + 3}$
$= \dfrac{-36}{-9}$
$= 4$

6. $2(5y - 1) - y = 10y - 2 - y$
$= 9y - 2$

7. $6 - 2(5x + 1) + 4x = 6 - 10x - 2 + 4x$
$= -6x + 4$

8. $4(3a + 1) - (7a - 6) = 12a + 4 - 7a + 6$
$= 5a + 10$

SECTION 1.7

1. 7 $\boxed{-}$ 4 $\boxed{\times}$ 6 $\boxed{=}$ ans: -17

2. 12 $\boxed{\div}$ 4 $\boxed{-}$ 8 $\boxed{\div}$ 2 $\boxed{=}$ ans: -1

3. 8 $\boxed{-}$ $\boxed{(}$ 3 $\boxed{-}$ 7 $\boxed{\times}$ 6 $\boxed{)}$ $\boxed{=}$ ans: 47

4. 3 $\boxed{+/-}$ $\boxed{-}$ 4 $\boxed{+/-}$ $\boxed{=}$ ans: 1

5. 342 $\boxed{+/-}$ $\boxed{-}$ 24 $\boxed{\times}$ 15 $\boxed{+/-}$ $\boxed{-}$ 12 $\boxed{+/-}$ $\boxed{=}$ ans: 30

6. $\boxed{(}$ 34 $\boxed{+/-}$ $\boxed{-}$ 14 $\boxed{+/-}$ $\boxed{)}$ $\boxed{\div}$ $\boxed{(}$ 15 $\boxed{+/-}$ $\boxed{-}$ 5 $\boxed{+/-}$ $\boxed{)}$ $\boxed{=}$ ans: 2

7. 8 $\boxed{x^2}$ $\boxed{-}$ $\boxed{(}$ 4 $\boxed{x^2}$ $\boxed{-}$ 2 $\boxed{x^2}$ $\boxed{)}$ $\boxed{x^2}$ $\boxed{=}$ ans: -80

8. 1.8 $\boxed{\text{STO}}$ 3 $\boxed{\times}$ $\boxed{\text{RCL}}$ $\boxed{y^x}$ 4 $\boxed{=}$ $\boxed{+}$ 2 $\boxed{\times}$ $\boxed{\text{RCL}}$ $\boxed{y^x}$ 3 $\boxed{=}$ ans: 43.1568

CHAPTER 2

SECTION 2.1

1. $4(3) - 2 \stackrel{?}{=} 10$
$12 - 2 = 10$
$10 = 10$

2. $3(5) + 1 \stackrel{?}{=} 16$
$15 + 1 = 16$
$16 = 16$
$4(5) - 6 \stackrel{?}{=} 14$
$20 - 6 = 14$
$14 = 14$

3. $5x - 2 = 33$
$5x - 2 + \mathbf{2} = 33 + \mathbf{2}$
$5x = 35$
$\frac{1}{5}(5x) = \frac{1}{5} \cdot 35$
$x = 7$

4. $\frac{2}{3}x + 4 = -8$
$\frac{2}{3}x + 4 - \mathbf{4} = -8 - \mathbf{4}$
$\frac{2}{3}x = -12$
$\frac{3}{2} \cdot \frac{2}{3}x = \frac{3}{2}(-12)$
$x = -18$

5. $3a - 3 = -5a + 9$
$3a + \mathbf{5a} - 3 = -5a + \mathbf{5a} + 9$
$8a - 3 = 9$
$8a - 3 + \mathbf{3} = 9 + \mathbf{3}$
$8a = 12$
$\frac{1}{8} \cdot 8a = \frac{1}{8} \cdot 12$
$a = \frac{12}{8} = \frac{3}{2}$

SECTION 2.2

1. $4x - 3 + x - 2 = 17 - 3$
$5x - 5 = 14$
$5x - 5 + \mathbf{5} = 14 + \mathbf{5}$
$5x = 19$
$\frac{1}{5}(5x) = \frac{1}{5}(19)$
$x = \frac{19}{5}$

2. $3(4a + 2) - 4 = 7a$
$12a + 6 - 4 = 7a$
$12a + 2 = 7a$
$12a + (\mathbf{-7a}) + 2 = 7a + (\mathbf{-7a})$
$5a + 2 = 0$
$5a + 2 + (\mathbf{-2}) = 0 + (\mathbf{-2})$
$5a = -2$
$\frac{1}{5}(5a) = \frac{1}{5}(-2)$
$a = -\frac{2}{5}$

3. $2(5y - 1) - y = 7y + 2$
$10y - 2 - y = 7y + 2$
$9y - 2 = 7y + 2$
$9y + (\mathbf{-7y}) - 2 = 7y + (\mathbf{-7y}) + 2$
$2y - 2 = 2$
$2y - 2 + \mathbf{2} = 2 + \mathbf{2}$
$2y = 4$
$\frac{1}{2}(2y) = \frac{1}{2}(4)$
$y = 2$

4. $6 - 2(5x - 1) + 4x = 20$
$6 - 10x + 2 + 4x = 20$
$-6x + 8 = 20$
$-6x + 8 + (\mathbf{-8}) = 20 + (\mathbf{-8})$
$-6x = 12$
$-\frac{1}{6}(-6x) = -\frac{1}{6}(12)$
$x = -2$

SECTION 2.3

1. $4x - 2 > 3x + 4$
$4x + (\mathbf{-3x}) - 2 > 3x + (\mathbf{-3x}) + 4$
$x - 2 > 4$
$x - 2 + \mathbf{2} > 4 + \mathbf{2}$
$x > 6$

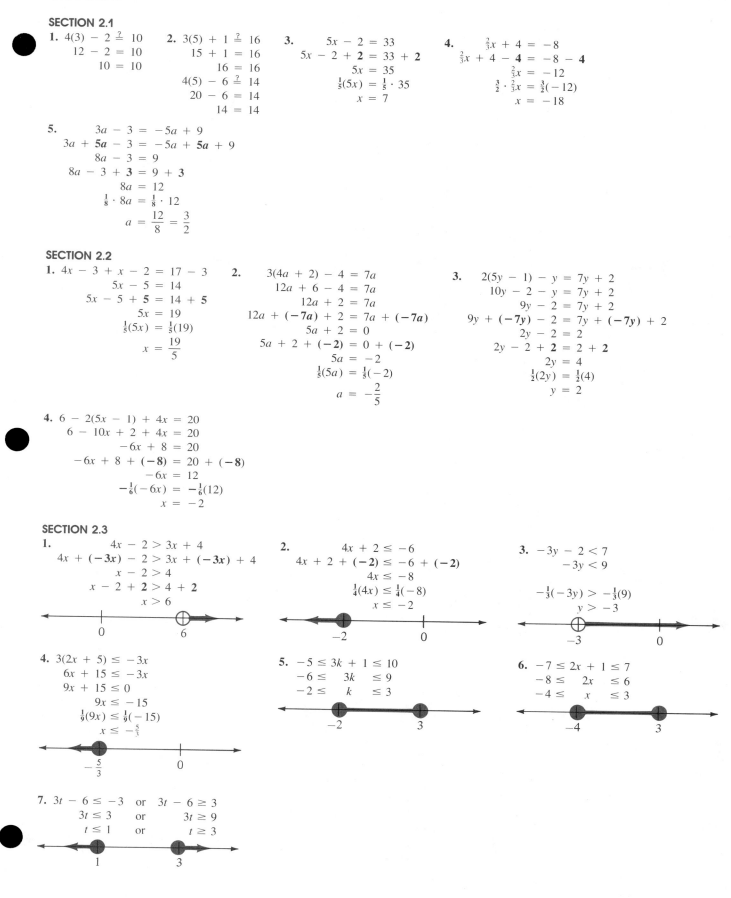

2. $4x + 2 \le -6$
$4x + 2 + (\mathbf{-2}) \le -6 + (\mathbf{-2})$
$4x \le -8$
$\frac{1}{4}(4x) \le \frac{1}{4}(-8)$
$x \le -2$

3. $-3y - 2 < 7$
$-3y < 9$
$-\frac{1}{3}(-3y) > -\frac{1}{3}(9)$
$y > -3$

4. $3(2x + 5) \le -3x$
$6x + 15 \le -3x$
$9x + 15 \le 0$
$9x \le -15$
$\frac{1}{9}(9x) \le \frac{1}{9}(-15)$
$x \le -\frac{5}{3}$

5. $-5 \le 3k + 1 \le 10$
$-6 \le \quad 3k \quad \le 9$
$-2 \le \quad k \quad \le 3$

6. $-7 \le 2x + 1 \le 7$
$-8 \le \quad 2x \quad \le 6$
$-4 \le \quad x \quad \le 3$

7. $3t - 6 \le -3$ or $3t - 6 \ge 3$
$3t \le 3$ or $3t \ge 9$
$t \le 1$ or $t \ge 3$

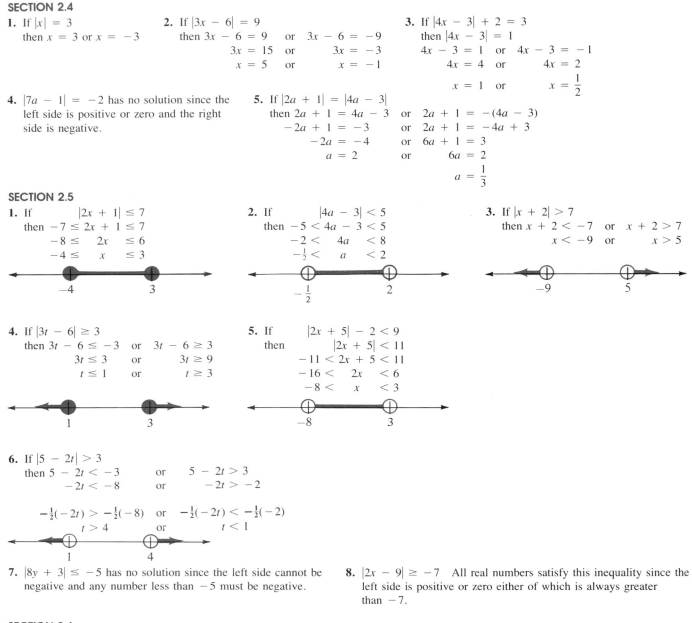

SECTION 2.4

1. If $|x| = 3$
then $x = 3$ or $x = -3$

2. If $|3x - 6| = 9$
then $3x - 6 = 9$ or $3x - 6 = -9$
$3x = 15$ or $3x = -3$
$x = 5$ or $x = -1$

3. If $|4x - 3| + 2 = 3$
then $|4x - 3| = 1$
$4x - 3 = 1$ or $4x - 3 = -1$
$4x = 4$ or $4x = 2$
$x = 1$ or $x = \frac{1}{2}$

4. $|7a - 1| = -2$ has no solution since the left side is positive or zero and the right side is negative.

5. If $|2a + 1| = |4a - 3|$
then $2a + 1 = 4a - 3$ or $2a + 1 = -(4a - 3)$
$-2a + 1 = -3$ or $2a + 1 = -4a + 3$
$-2a = -4$ or $6a + 1 = 3$
$a = 2$ or $6a = 2$
$a = \frac{1}{3}$

SECTION 2.5

1. If $|2x + 1| \le 7$
then $-7 \le 2x + 1 \le 7$
$-8 \le 2x \le 6$
$-4 \le x \le 3$

2. If $|4a - 3| < 5$
then $-5 < 4a - 3 < 5$
$-2 < 4a < 8$
$-\frac{1}{2} < a < 2$

3. If $|x + 2| > 7$
then $x + 2 < -7$ or $x + 2 > 7$
$x < -9$ or $x > 5$

4. If $|3t - 6| \ge 3$
then $3t - 6 \le -3$ or $3t - 6 \ge 3$
$3t \le 3$ or $3t \ge 9$
$t \le 1$ or $t \ge 3$

5. If $|2x + 5| - 2 < 9$
then $|2x + 5| < 11$
$-11 < 2x + 5 < 11$
$-16 < 2x < 6$
$-8 < x < 3$

6. If $|5 - 2t| > 3$
then $5 - 2t < -3$ or $5 - 2t > 3$
$-2t < -8$ or $-2t > -2$
$-\frac{1}{2}(-2t) > -\frac{1}{2}(-8)$ or $-\frac{1}{2}(-2t) < -\frac{1}{2}(-2)$
$t > 4$ or $t < 1$

7. $|8y + 3| \le -5$ has no solution since the left side cannot be negative and any number less than -5 must be negative.

8. $|2x - 9| \ge -7$ All real numbers satisfy this inequality since the left side is positive or zero either of which is always greater than -7.

SECTION 2.6

1. $40 = \frac{1}{2}(b + 5)6$
$40 = 3(b + 5)$
$40 = 3b + 15$
$25 = 3b$
$b = \frac{25}{3}$ ft

2. $P = 2w + 2l$
$P - 2w = 2l$
$\frac{P - 2w}{2} = l$
or $\frac{P}{2} - w = l$

3. $S = 2x^2 + 4xy$
$S - 2x^2 = 4xy$
$\frac{S - 2x^2}{4x} = y$

4. $ax + 5 = cx + 3$
$ax - cx = 3 - 5$
$(a - c)x = -2$
$x = \frac{-2}{a - c}$

SECTION 2.7

1. $2(x - 2) = 28$
$2x - 4 = 28$
$2x = 32$
$x = 16$

2. $2(x + x + 1) = 22$
$2(2x + 1) = 22$
$4x + 2 = 22$
$4x = 20$
$x = 5$
The integers are 5 and 6.

3. $2x + 2(2x) = 36$
$2x + 4x = 36$
$6x = 36$
$x = 6$
Width is 6 inches, length is 12 inches.

4.

	Now	In 5 years
Lloyd	$x + 3$	$x + 8$
Joyce	x	$x + 5$

$x + 8 + x + 5 = 65$
$2x + 13 = 65$
$2x = 52$
$x = 26$
Joyce is 26, Lloyd is 29.

5. $x = .25(74)$ **6.** $x \cdot 84 = 21$ **7.** $35 = .40x$
  $x = 18.5$ $x = \frac{21}{84}$ $\frac{35}{.40} = x$
                      $x = 0.25$ $87.5 = x$
                      $x = 25\%$

SECTION 2.8

1. The two numbers are
  x and $20 - x$.
  $x = 3(20 - x)$
  $x = 60 - 3x$
  $4x = 60$
  $x = 15$
  The numbers are 15 and 5.

2.

	Dimes	Nickels	Total
Number	x	$40 - x$	40
Value	$10x$	$5(40 - x)$	250

$10x + 5(40 - x) = 250$
$10x + 200 - 5x = 250$
$\quad\quad 5x + 200 = 250$
$\quad\quad\quad\quad 5x = 50$
$\quad\quad\quad\quad\ x = 10$
Fred has 10 dimes and 30 nickels.

3.

	Dollars at 8%	Dollars at 10%	Total
Number	x	$8000 - x$	8000
Interest	$.08x$	$.10(8000 - x)$	680

$.08x + .10(8,000 - x) = 680$
$\quad 8x + 10(8,000 - x) = 68,000$
$\quad 8x + 80,000 - 10x = 68,000$
$\quad\quad\quad -2x + 80,000 = 68,000$
$\quad\quad\quad\quad\quad\quad -2x = -12,000$
$\quad\quad\quad\quad\quad\quad\quad\ x = 6,000$
$6,000 at 8\% and \$2,000 at 10\%.$

CHAPTER 3

SECTION 3.1

1. a. $(-2)^3 = (-2)(-2)(-2) = -8$ **2.** $x^5 \cdot x^4 = (x \cdot x \cdot x \cdot x \cdot x)(x \cdot x \cdot x \cdot x)$ **3.** $(4^5)^2 = 4^5 \cdot 4^5 = 4^{10}$
  b. $(-7)^2 = (-7)(-7) = 49$ $= x^9$
  c. $-7^2 = -7 \cdot 7 = -49$
  d. $\left(\frac{3}{5}\right)^3 = \left(\frac{3}{5}\right)\left(\frac{3}{5}\right)\left(\frac{3}{5}\right) = \frac{27}{125}$

4. $(2x)^3 = (2x)(2x)(2x)$ **5. a.** $(-2x^3)(4x^5) = (-2 \cdot 4)(x^3 \cdot x^5)$ **6. a.** $3^{-2} = \frac{1}{3^2} = \frac{1}{9}$
  $= 8x^3$ $= -8x^8$
          b. $(-3y^3)^3(2y^6) = (-27y^9)(2y^6)$ **b.** $(-5)^{-3} = \frac{1}{(-5)^3} = -\frac{1}{125}$
                  $= -54y^{15}$
          c. $(a^2)^3(a^3b^4)^2(b^5)^2 = a^6 \cdot a^6 \cdot b^8 \cdot b^{10}$ **c.** $\left(\frac{2}{3}\right)^{-2} = \frac{1}{\left(\frac{2}{3}\right)^2} = \frac{1}{\frac{4}{9}} = \frac{9}{4}$
                  $= a^{12}b^{18}$

7. a. $(3x^{-4})^2 = 3^2(x^{-4})^2$ **b.** $(3y^{-3})^2(5y^4) = 9y^{-6} \cdot 5y^4$
  $= 9x^{-8}$ $= 45y^{-2}$

  $= 9 \cdot \frac{1}{x^8}$ $= 45 \cdot \frac{1}{y^2}$

  $= \frac{9}{x^8}$ $= \frac{45}{y^2}$

SECTION 3.2

1. a. $\left(\frac{x^3}{y^4}\right)^5 = \frac{(x^3)^5}{(y^4)^5} = \frac{x^{15}}{y^{20}}$ **2. a.** $\frac{3^7}{3^4} = 3^{7-4} = 3^3 = 27$ **3.** $\left(\frac{x^{-4}}{x^7}\right)^{-2} = (x^{-4-7})^{-2} = (x^{-11})^{-2} = x^{22}$

  b. $\left(\frac{2x^{-3}}{y^{-2}}\right)^4 = \frac{(2x^{-3})^4}{(y^{-2})^4}$ **b.** $\frac{x^3}{x^{10}} = x^{3-10} = x^{-7} = \frac{1}{x^7}$

  $= \frac{16x^{-12}}{y^{-8}}$ **c.** $\frac{a^5}{a^{-7}} = a^{5-(-7)} = a^{12}$

  $= \frac{\frac{16}{x^{12}}}{\frac{1}{y^8}}$ **d.** $\frac{m^{-3}}{m^{-5}} = m^{-3-(-5)} = m^{-3+5} = m^2$

  $= \frac{16}{x^{12}} \cdot \frac{y^8}{1}$

  $= \frac{16y^8}{x^{12}}$

5. a. $\dfrac{(3x^3)^2(-2x^{-5})^2}{9x^{-3}(4x^{-2})} = \dfrac{9x^6(4x^{-10})}{9x^{-3}(4x^{-2})}$

$\qquad\qquad = \dfrac{36x^{-4}}{36x^{-5}}$

$\qquad\qquad = x^{-4-(-5)}$

$\qquad\qquad = x$

b. $\left(\dfrac{3x^2y^0z^{-1}}{9x^4y^{-2}z^3}\right)^{-2} = \left(\dfrac{x^{-2}y^2z^{-4}}{3}\right)^{-2}$

$\qquad\qquad = \dfrac{x^4y^{-4}z^8}{\dfrac{1}{9}}$

$\qquad\qquad = \dfrac{9x^4z^8}{y^4}$

6. a. $(3 \times 10^7)(2 \times 10^{-4}) = (3 \cdot 2) \times (10^7)(10^{-4})$

$\qquad\qquad = 6 \times 10^3$

b. $\dfrac{3.9 \times 10^6}{1.3 \times 10^{-4}} = \dfrac{3.9}{1.3} \times \dfrac{10^6}{10^{-4}}$

$\qquad\qquad = 3 \times 10^{10}$

c. $\dfrac{(2.4 \times 10^6)(1.8 \times 10^{-4})}{1.2 \times 10^{-3}} = \dfrac{(2.4)(1.8)}{1.2} \times \dfrac{10^6 \cdot 10^{-4}}{10^{-3}}$

$\qquad\qquad = 3.6 \times 10^5$

SECTION 3.3

2. $8a^2b + 6a^2b - 4a^2b = (8 + 6 - 4)a^2b$

$\qquad\qquad = 10a^2b$

3. $(3x^2 + 2x - 5) + (2x^2 - 7x + 3) = (3x^2 + 2x^2) + (2x - 7x) + (-5 + 3)$

$\qquad\qquad = (3 + 2)x^2 + (2 - 7)x + (-5 + 3)$

$\qquad\qquad = 5x^2 - 5x - 2$

4. $\quad x^3 + 7x^2 + 3x + 2$

$\quad \underline{-3x^3 - 2x^2 + 3x - 1}$

$\quad -2x^3 + 5x^2 + 6x + 1$

5. $(4x^2 - 2x + 7) - (7x^2 - 3x + 1) = 4x^2 - 2x + 7 - 7x^2 + 3x - 1$

$\qquad\qquad = -3x^2 + x + 6$

6. $(7x - 4) - (3x + 5) = 7x - 4 - 3x - 5$

$\qquad\qquad = 4x - 9$

7. $(3x^4 + 2x + 1) - (3x^2 - 5) - (2x^3 - 4x^2 + 2x)$

$\qquad = 3x^4 + 2x + 1 - 3x^2 + 5 - 2x^3 + 4x^2 - 2x$

$\qquad = 3x^4 - 2x^3 + x^2 + 6$

8. $2x - 4[6 - (5x + 3)]$

$\quad = 2x - 4(6 - 5x - 3)$

$\quad = 2x - 4(-5x + 3)$

$\quad = 2x + 20x - 12$

$\quad = 22x - 12$

9. $(9x - 4) - [(2x + 5) - (x + 3)]$

$\quad = 9x - 4 - (2x + 5 - x - 3)$

$\quad = 9x - 4 - (x + 2)$

$\quad = 9x - 4 - x - 2$

$\quad = 8x - 6$

10. $2(-2)^3 - 3(-2)^2 + 4(-2) - 8$

$\quad = 2(-8) - 3(4) + 4(-2) - 8$

$\quad = -16 - 12 - 8 - 8$

$\quad = -44$

SECTION 3.4

1. $5x^2(3x^2 - 4x + 2) = 5x^2(3x^2) + 5x^2(-4x) + 5x^2(2)$

$\qquad\qquad = 15x^4 - 20x^3 + 10x^2$

2. $(4x - 1)(x + 3) = (4x - 1)x + (4x - 1)3$

$\qquad\qquad = 4x^2 - x + 12x - 3$

$\qquad\qquad = 4x^2 + 11x - 3$

3. $\quad x^2 - 5x + 6$

$\quad\quad \underline{3x + 2}$

$\quad 2x^2 - 10x + 12$

$\underline{3x^3 - 15x^2 + 18x}$

$3x^3 - 13x^2 + 8x + 12$

4. $(2a - 3b)(5a - b) = 10a^2 - 2ab - 15ab + 3b^2$

$\qquad\qquad\quad\text{F}\quad\quad\text{O}\quad\quad\text{I}\quad\quad\text{L}$

$\qquad\qquad = 10a^2 - 17ab + 3b^2$

SECTION 3.5

1. $(3x - 2)^2 = (3x - 2)(3x - 2)$

$\qquad\qquad = 9x^2 - 6x - 6x + 4$

$\qquad\qquad = 9x^2 - 12x + 4$

2. a. $(x - y)^2 = x^2 - 2xy + y^2$

b. $(x + 5)^2 = x^2 + 2(x)(5) + 5^2 = x^2 + 10x + 25$

c. $(2x + 5)^2 = (2x)^2 + 2(2x)(5) + 5^2 = 4x^2 + 20x + 25$

d. $(3x - 4y)^2 = (3x)^2 + 2(3x)(-4y) + (-4y)^2 = 9x^2 - 24xy + 16y^2$

3. $(4x - 3)(4x + 3) = 16x^2 + 12x - 12x - 9$

$\qquad\qquad = 16x^2 - 9$

4. a. $(x + 2)(x - 2) = x^2 - 2^2 = x^2 - 4$

b. $(3a + 1)(3a - 1) = (3a)^2 - 1^2 = 9a^2 - 1$

c. $(x^2 + 3)(x^2 - 3) = (x^2)^2 - 3^2 = x^4 - 9$

d. $(5x + 7y)(5x - 7y) = (5x)^2 - (7y)^2 = 25x^2 - 49y^2$

e. $(x^3 - 4a)(x^3 + 4a) = (x^3)^2 - (4a)^2 = x^6 - 16a^2$

SECTION 3.6

1. $\dfrac{12x^4 - 18x^3 + 24x^2}{6x} = \dfrac{12x^4}{6x} - \dfrac{18x^3}{6x} + \dfrac{24x^2}{6x}$

$\qquad\qquad = 2x^3 - 3x^2 + 4x$

2. a. $\dfrac{27x^4y^7 - 81x^5y^3}{-9x^3y^2} = \dfrac{27x^4y^7}{-9x^3y^2} - \dfrac{81x^5y^3}{-9x^3y^2}$

$\qquad\qquad = -3xy^5 + 9x^2y$

b. $\dfrac{12a^5 + 8a^4 + 16a^3 + 4a^2}{8a^4} = \dfrac{12a^5}{8a^4} + \dfrac{8a^4}{8a^4} + \dfrac{16a^3}{8a^4} + \dfrac{4a^2}{8a^4}$

$\qquad\qquad = \dfrac{3a}{2} + 1 + \dfrac{2}{a} + \dfrac{1}{2a^2}$

3.
$$\begin{array}{r} 215 \\ 35\overline{)7546} \\ 70\!\downarrow \\ \hline 54 \\ 35\!\downarrow \\ \hline 196 \\ 175 \\ \hline 21 \end{array}$$

4.
$$\begin{array}{r} 3x + 1 \\ x - 3\overline{)\,3x^2 - 8x - 1} \\ -+ \\ \cancel{}3x^2 \cancel{-} 9x \\ \hline +x - 1 \\ -+ \\ \cancel{}x \cancel{-} 3 \\ \hline 2 \end{array}$$
answer: $3x + 1 + \dfrac{2}{x - 3}$

5.
$$\begin{array}{r} 3x^2 + 6x + 15 \\ x - 2\overline{)\,3x^3 + 0x^2 + 3x + 1} \\ -+ \\ \cancel{}3x^3 \cancel{-} 6x^2 \\ \hline + 6x^2 + 3x \\ -+ \\ \cancel{}6x^2 \cancel{-} 12x \\ \hline + 15x + 1 \\ -+ \\ \cancel{}15x \cancel{-} 30 \\ \hline 31 \end{array}$$
answer: $3x^2 + 6x + 15 + \dfrac{31}{x - 2}$

6.
$$\begin{array}{r} 2x - 3y \\ x - y\overline{)\,2x^2 - 5xy + 3y^2} \\ -+ \\ \cancel{}2x^2 \cancel{-} 2xy \\ \hline - 3xy + 3y^2 \\ +- \\ \cancel{-} 3xy \cancel{+} 3y^2 \\ \hline 0 \end{array}$$
answer: $2x - 3y$

SECTION 3.7

1. $15a^7 - 25a^5 + 30a^3$
$= 5a^3(3a^4) - 5a^3(5a^2) + 5a^3(6)$
$= 5a^3(3a^4 - 5a^2 + 6)$

2. a. $12x^4y^5 - 9x^3y^4 - 15x^5y^3$
$= 3x^3y^3(4xy^2) - 3x^3y^3(3y) - 3x^3y^3(5x^2)$
$= 3x^3y^3(4xy^2 - 3y - 5x^2)$

b. $4(a + b)^4 - 6(a + b)^3 + 16(a + b)^2$
$= 2(a + b)^2 \cdot 2(a + b)^2 - 2(a + b)^2 \cdot 3(a + b) + 2(a + b)^2 \cdot 8$
$= 2(a + b)^2[2(a + b)^2 - 3(a + b) + 8]$

3. $ab^3 + b^3 + 6a + 6 = b^3(a + 1) + 6(a + 1)$
$\qquad\qquad\qquad\qquad = (a + 1)(b^3 + 6)$

4. $12 - 3y^2 - 4x^2 + x^2y^2 = 3(4 - y^2) - x^2(4 - y^2)$
$\qquad\qquad\qquad\qquad = (4 - y^2)(3 - x^2)$

SECTION 3.8

5. $5x^2 + 25x + 30 = 5(x^2 + 5x + 6)$
$\qquad\qquad\qquad = 5(x + 3)(x + 2)$

7. $15x^3y + 25x^2y^2 - 10xy^3 = 5xy(3x^2 + 5xy - 2y^2)$
$\qquad\qquad\qquad\qquad = 5xy(3x - y)(x + 2y)$

9. $3x^2(x - 2) - 7x(x - 2) + 2(x - 2)$
$= (x - 2)(3x^2 - 7x + 2)$
$= (x - 2)(3x - 1)(x - 2)$

SECTION 3.9

5. $x^2 - 6x + 9 - y^2 = (x - 3)^2 - y^2$
$\qquad\qquad\qquad = (x - 3 + y)(x - 3 - y)$

7. $x^3 - 27 = x^3 - 3^3 = (x - 3)(x^2 + 3x + 9)$

8. $8x^3 + y^3 = (2x)^3 + y^3 = (2x + y)(4x^2 - 2xy + y^2)$

9. $x^6 - 1 = (x^3)^2 - 1^2 = (x^3 + 1)(x^3 - 1)$
$\qquad\qquad = (x + 1)(x^2 - x + 1)(x - 1)(x^2 + x + 1)$

SECTION 3.10

1. $3x^8 - 27x^6 = 3x^6(x^2 - 9)$
$\qquad\qquad = 3x^6(x + 3)(x - 3)$

2. $4x^4 + 40x^3 + 100x^2 = 4x^2(x^2 + 10x + 25)$
$\qquad\qquad\qquad\qquad = 4x^2(x + 5)^2$

3. $y^4 + 36y^2 = y^2(y^2 + 36)$

4. $6x^2 - x - 15 = (3x - 5)(2x + 3)$

5. $3x^5 - 81x^2 = 3x^2(x^3 - 27)$
$\qquad\qquad = 3x^2(x - 3)(x^2 + 3x + 9)$

6. $3a^2b^3 + 6a^2b^2 - 3a^2b = 3a^2b(b^2 + 2b - 1)$

7. $x^2 - 10x + 25 - b^2 = (x - 5)^2 - b^2$
$\qquad\qquad\qquad\qquad = (x - 5 + b)(x - 5 - b)$

CHAPTER 4

SECTION 4.1

1. $\dfrac{x^2 - 9}{x + 3} = \dfrac{\cancel{(x + 3)}(x - 3)}{\cancel{x + 3}}$

$\qquad = x - 3$

2. a. $\dfrac{y^2 - y - 6}{y^2 - 4} = \dfrac{(y - 3)\cancel{(y + 2)}}{(y - 2)\cancel{(y + 2)}}$

$\qquad\qquad = \dfrac{y - 3}{y - 2}$

b. $\dfrac{3a^3 + 3}{6a^2 - 6a + 6} = \dfrac{3(a^3 + 1)}{6(a^2 - a + 1)}$

$\qquad\qquad = \dfrac{3(a + 1)\cancel{(a^2 - a + 1)}}{6\cancel{(a^2 - a + 1)}}$

$\qquad\qquad = \dfrac{a + 1}{2}$

c. $\dfrac{x^2 + 4x + ax + 4a}{x^2 + ax + 4x + 4a} = \dfrac{x(x + 4) + a(x + 4)}{x(x + a) + 4(x + a)}$

$\qquad\qquad = \dfrac{\cancel{(x + 4)}\cancel{(x + a)}}{\cancel{(x + a)}\cancel{(x + 4)}}$

$\qquad\qquad = 1$

3. When $a = 7$ and $b = 4$

the expression $\dfrac{a - b}{b - a}$

becomes $\dfrac{7 - 4}{4 - 7} = \dfrac{3}{-3} = -1$

4. $\dfrac{7 - x}{x^2 - 49} = \dfrac{-1\cancel{(x - 7)}}{(x + 7)\cancel{(x - 7)}}$

$\qquad = \dfrac{-1}{x + 7}$

5. $\dfrac{x^2 - 10x + 25}{25 - x^2} = \dfrac{x^2 - 10x + 25}{-1(x^2 - 25)}$

$\qquad = \dfrac{(x - 5)\cancel{(x - 5)}}{-1(x + 5)\cancel{(x - 5)}}$

$\qquad = -\dfrac{x - 5}{x + 5} \quad \text{or} \quad \dfrac{5 - x}{5 + x}$

SECTION 4.2

1. $\dfrac{3}{4} \cdot \dfrac{12}{27} = \dfrac{3 \cdot 12}{4 \cdot 27}$

$\qquad = \dfrac{\cancel{3} \cdot \cancel{2} \cdot \cancel{2} \cdot \cancel{3}}{\cancel{2} \cdot \cancel{2} \cdot \cancel{3} \cdot \cancel{3} \cdot 3}$

$\qquad = \dfrac{1}{3}$

2. $\dfrac{6x^4}{4y^9} \cdot \dfrac{12y^5}{3x^2} = \dfrac{\overset{2}{\cancel{6}} \cdot \overset{3}{\cancel{12}}x^4y^5}{\cancel{3} \cdot \cancel{4}x^2y^9}$

$\qquad = \dfrac{6x^2}{y^4}$

3. $\dfrac{x + 5}{x^2 - 25} \cdot \dfrac{x - 5}{x^2 - 10x + 25} = \dfrac{\cancel{(x + 5)}\cancel{(x - 5)}}{\cancel{(x + 5)}\cancel{(x - 5)}(x - 5)^2}$

$\qquad = \dfrac{1}{(x - 5)^2}$

4. $\dfrac{3y^2 - 3y}{3y - 12} \cdot \dfrac{y^2 - 2y - 8}{y^2 + 3y + 2} = \dfrac{\cancel{3}y(y - 1)\cancel{(y - 4)}\cancel{(y + 2)}}{\cancel{3}\cancel{(y - 4)}(y + 1)\cancel{(y + 2)}}$

$\qquad = \dfrac{y(y - 1)}{y + 1}$

5. $\dfrac{5}{9} \div \dfrac{10}{27} = \dfrac{5}{9} \cdot \dfrac{27}{10}$

$\qquad = \dfrac{\cancel{5} \cdot \cancel{3} \cdot \cancel{3} \cdot 3}{\cancel{3} \cdot \cancel{3} \cdot 2 \cdot \cancel{5}}$

$\qquad = \dfrac{3}{2}$

6. $\dfrac{9x^4}{4y^3} \div \dfrac{3x^2}{8y^5} = \dfrac{9x^4}{4y^3} \cdot \dfrac{8y^5}{3x^2}$

$\qquad = \dfrac{\overset{3}{\cancel{9}} \cdot \overset{2}{\cancel{8}}x^4y^5}{\cancel{3} \cdot \cancel{4}x^2y^3}$

$\qquad = 6x^2y^2$

7. $\dfrac{xy^2 - y^3}{x^2 - y^2} \div \dfrac{x^3 + y^3}{x^2 + 2xy + y^2} = \dfrac{xy^2 - y^3}{x^2 - y^2} \cdot \dfrac{x^2 + 2xy + y^2}{x^3 + y^3}$

$\qquad = \dfrac{y^2\cancel{(x - y)}\cancel{(x + y)}\cancel{(x + y)}}{\cancel{(x + y)}\cancel{(x - y)}\cancel{(x + y)}(x^2 - xy + y^2)}$

$\qquad = \dfrac{y^2}{x^2 - xy + y^2}$

8. $\dfrac{a^2 + 3a - 4}{a - 4} \cdot \dfrac{a + 3}{a^2 - 4a + 3} \div \dfrac{a + 1}{a^2 - 2a - 3}$

$\qquad = \dfrac{(a^2 + 3a - 4)(a + 3)(a^2 - 2a - 3)}{(a - 4)(a^2 - 4a + 3)}$

$\qquad = \dfrac{(a + 4)\cancel{(a - 1)}(a + 3)\cancel{(a - 3)}\cancel{(a + 1)}}{(a - 4)\cancel{(a - 3)}\cancel{(a - 1)}\cancel{(a + 1)}}$

$\qquad = \dfrac{(a + 4)(a + 3)}{a - 4}$

9. $\dfrac{xa + xb - ya - yb}{xa + 2x + ya + 2y} \cdot \dfrac{xa + 2x + ya + 2y}{xa + xb + ya + yb}$

$\qquad = \dfrac{x(a + b) - y(a + b)}{x(a + 2) + y(a + 2)} \cdot \dfrac{x(a + 2) + y(a + 2)}{x(a + b) + y(a + b)}$

$\qquad = \dfrac{\cancel{(a + b)}(x - y)\cancel{(a + 2)}\cancel{(x + y)}}{\cancel{(a + 2)}\cancel{(x + y)}\cancel{(a + b)}(x + y)}$

$\qquad = \dfrac{x - y}{x + y}$

10. $(5x^2 - 45) \cdot \dfrac{3}{5x - 15} = \dfrac{5x^2 - 45}{1} \cdot \dfrac{3}{5x - 15}$

$\qquad = \dfrac{\cancel{5}(x + 3)\cancel{(x - 3)}3}{\cancel{5}\cancel{(x - 3)}}$

$\qquad = 3(x + 3)$

11. $4(x + 3)(x - 3) \cdot \dfrac{x}{x^2 - 9} = \dfrac{4\cancel{(x + 3)}\cancel{(x - 3)}x}{\cancel{(x + 3)}\cancel{(x - 3)}}$

$\qquad = 4x$

SECTION 4.3

1. $\dfrac{3}{8} + \dfrac{1}{8} = \dfrac{3+1}{8}$

$\phantom{\dfrac{3}{8} + \dfrac{1}{8}} = \dfrac{4}{8}$

$\phantom{\dfrac{3}{8} + \dfrac{1}{8}} = \dfrac{1}{2}$

2. $\dfrac{x}{x^2 - 9} + \dfrac{3}{x^2 - 9} = \dfrac{x+3}{x^2 - 9}$

$\phantom{\dfrac{x}{x^2 - 9} + \dfrac{3}{x^2 - 9}} = \dfrac{\cancel{x+3}}{\cancel{(x+3)}(x-3)}$

$\phantom{\dfrac{x}{x^2 - 9} + \dfrac{3}{x^2 - 9}} = \dfrac{1}{x-3}$

3. $\dfrac{2x-7}{x-2} - \dfrac{x-5}{x-2} = \dfrac{2x - 7 - (x-5)}{x-2}$

$\phantom{\dfrac{2x-7}{x-2} - \dfrac{x-5}{x-2}} = \dfrac{2x - 7 - x + 5}{x-2}$

$\phantom{\dfrac{2x-7}{x-2} - \dfrac{x-5}{x-2}} = \dfrac{x-2}{x-2}$

$\phantom{\dfrac{2x-7}{x-2} - \dfrac{x-5}{x-2}} = 1$

4. $\dfrac{3}{10} + \dfrac{11}{42} = \dfrac{3}{2 \cdot 5} + \dfrac{11}{2 \cdot 3 \cdot 7}$

$\phantom{\dfrac{3}{10} + \dfrac{11}{42}} = \dfrac{3}{2 \cdot 5} \cdot \dfrac{\mathbf{3 \cdot 7}}{\mathbf{3 \cdot 7}} + \dfrac{11}{2 \cdot 3 \cdot 7} \cdot \dfrac{\mathbf{5}}{\mathbf{5}}$

$\phantom{\dfrac{3}{10} + \dfrac{11}{42}} = \dfrac{63}{2 \cdot 3 \cdot 5 \cdot 7} + \dfrac{55}{2 \cdot 3 \cdot 5 \cdot 7}$

$\phantom{\dfrac{3}{10} + \dfrac{11}{42}} = \dfrac{118}{2 \cdot 3 \cdot 5 \cdot 7}$

$\phantom{\dfrac{3}{10} + \dfrac{11}{42}} = \dfrac{\cancel{2} \cdot 59}{\cancel{2} \cdot 3 \cdot 5 \cdot 7}$

$\phantom{\dfrac{3}{10} + \dfrac{11}{42}} = \dfrac{59}{105}$

5. $\dfrac{-3}{x^2 - 2x - 8} + \dfrac{4}{x^2 - 16} = \dfrac{-3}{(x-4)(x+2)} + \dfrac{4}{(x-4)(x+4)}$

$\phantom{\dfrac{-3}{x^2 - 2x - 8}} = \dfrac{-3}{(x-4)(x+2)} \cdot \dfrac{\mathbf{x+4}}{\mathbf{x+4}} + \dfrac{4}{(x-4)(x+4)} \cdot \dfrac{\mathbf{x+2}}{\mathbf{x+2}}$

$\phantom{\dfrac{-3}{x^2 - 2x - 8}} = \dfrac{-3x - 12 + 4x + 8}{(x-4)(x+4)(x+2)}$

$\phantom{\dfrac{-3}{x^2 - 2x - 8}} = \dfrac{\cancel{x - 4}}{\cancel{(x-4)}(x+4)(x+2)}$

$\phantom{\dfrac{-3}{x^2 - 2x - 8}} = \dfrac{1}{(x+4)(x+2)}$

6. $\dfrac{x}{x^2 + 5x - 6} - \dfrac{2}{7x - 7} = \dfrac{x}{(x+6)(x-1)} - \dfrac{2}{7(x-1)}$

$\phantom{\dfrac{x}{x^2 + 5x - 6}} = \dfrac{x}{(x+6)(x-1)} \cdot \dfrac{\mathbf{7}}{\mathbf{7}} - \dfrac{2}{7(x-1)} \cdot \dfrac{\mathbf{x+6}}{\mathbf{x+6}}$

$\phantom{\dfrac{x}{x^2 + 5x - 6}} = \dfrac{7x - (2x + 12)}{7(x+6)(x-1)}$

$\phantom{\dfrac{x}{x^2 + 5x - 6}} = \dfrac{7x - 2x - 12}{7(x+6)(x-1)}$

$\phantom{\dfrac{x}{x^2 + 5x - 6}} = \dfrac{5x - 12}{7(x+6)(x-1)}$

7. $\dfrac{x^2}{x-4} + \dfrac{x+12}{4-x} = \dfrac{x^2}{x-4} + \dfrac{x+12}{4-x} \cdot \dfrac{\mathbf{-1}}{\mathbf{-1}}$

$\phantom{\dfrac{x^2}{x-4} + \dfrac{x+12}{4-x}} = \dfrac{x^2}{x-4} + \dfrac{-x - 12}{x-4}$

$\phantom{\dfrac{x^2}{x-4} + \dfrac{x+12}{4-x}} = \dfrac{x^2 - x - 12}{x-4}$

$\phantom{\dfrac{x^2}{x-4} + \dfrac{x+12}{4-x}} = \dfrac{\cancel{(x-4)}(x+3)}{\cancel{x-4}}$

$\phantom{\dfrac{x^2}{x-4} + \dfrac{x+12}{4-x}} = x + 3$

8. $2 + \dfrac{25}{5x - 1} = \dfrac{2}{1} + \dfrac{25}{5x - 1}$

$\phantom{2 + \dfrac{25}{5x-1}} = \dfrac{2}{1} \cdot \dfrac{\mathbf{5x - 1}}{\mathbf{5x - 1}} + \dfrac{25}{5x - 1}$

$\phantom{2 + \dfrac{25}{5x-1}} = \dfrac{10x - 2 + 25}{5x - 1}$

$\phantom{2 + \dfrac{25}{5x-1}} = \dfrac{10x + 23}{5x - 1}$

SECTION 4.4

1. $\dfrac{\frac{2}{3}}{\frac{5}{6}} = \dfrac{2}{3} \cdot \dfrac{6}{5} = \dfrac{12}{15} = \dfrac{4}{5}$

2. $\dfrac{\frac{1}{x} - \frac{1}{3}}{\frac{1}{x} + \frac{1}{3}} = \dfrac{\left(\frac{1}{x} - \frac{1}{3}\right) 3x}{\left(\frac{1}{x} + \frac{1}{3}\right) 3x}$

$\phantom{\dfrac{\frac{1}{x} - \frac{1}{3}}{\frac{1}{x} + \frac{1}{3}}} = \dfrac{\frac{1}{x}(3x) - \frac{1}{3}(3x)}{\frac{1}{x}(3x) + \frac{1}{3}(3x)}$

$\phantom{\dfrac{\frac{1}{x} - \frac{1}{3}}{\frac{1}{x} + \frac{1}{3}}} = \dfrac{3 - x}{3 + x}$

3. $\dfrac{\frac{x+5}{x^2 - 16}}{\frac{x^2 - 25}{x - 4}} = \dfrac{x+5}{x^2 - 16} \cdot \dfrac{x-4}{x^2 - 25}$

$\phantom{\dfrac{\frac{x+5}{x^2-16}}{\frac{x^2-25}{x-4}}} = \dfrac{\cancel{(x+5)}\cancel{(x-4)}}{(x+4)\cancel{(x-4)}\cancel{(x+5)}(x-5)}$

$\phantom{\dfrac{\frac{x+5}{x^2-16}}{\frac{x^2-25}{x-4}}} = \dfrac{1}{(x+4)(x-5)}$

4. $\dfrac{1 - \dfrac{9}{x^2}}{1 - \dfrac{1}{x} - \dfrac{6}{x^2}} = \dfrac{x^2 \cdot \left(1 - \dfrac{9}{x^2}\right)}{x^2 \cdot \left(1 - \dfrac{1}{x} - \dfrac{6}{x^2}\right)}$

$\qquad = \dfrac{x^2 \cdot 1 - x^2 \cdot \dfrac{9}{x^2}}{x^2 \cdot 1 - x^2 \cdot \dfrac{1}{x} - x^2 \cdot \dfrac{6}{x^2}}$

$\qquad = \dfrac{x^2 - 9}{x^2 - x - 6}$

$\qquad = \dfrac{(x + 3)\cancel{(x - 3)}}{\cancel{(x - 3)}(x + 2)}$

$\qquad = \dfrac{x + 3}{x + 2}$

5. $2 + \dfrac{5}{x - \dfrac{1}{5}} = 2 + \dfrac{5}{x - \dfrac{1}{5}} \cdot \dfrac{5}{5}$

$\qquad = \dfrac{2}{1} + \dfrac{25}{5x - 1}$

$\qquad = \dfrac{2}{1} \cdot \dfrac{5x - 1}{5x - 1} + \dfrac{25}{5x - 1}$

$\qquad = \dfrac{10x - 2 + 25}{5x - 1}$

$\qquad = \dfrac{10x + 23}{5x - 1}$

SECTION 4.5

1. $\quad \dfrac{x}{3} + 1 = \dfrac{1}{2} \quad$ LCD $= 6$

$6\left(\dfrac{x}{3} + 1\right) = 6 \cdot \dfrac{1}{2}$

$6 \cdot \dfrac{x}{3} + 6 \cdot 1 = 6 \cdot \dfrac{1}{2}$

$\qquad 2x + 6 = 3$

$\qquad\qquad 2x = -3$

$\qquad\qquad x = -\dfrac{3}{2}$

2. $\quad \dfrac{2}{a + 5} = \dfrac{1}{3} \quad$ LCD $= 3(a + 5)$

$3(a + 5) \cdot \dfrac{2}{a + 5} = 3(a + 5) \cdot \dfrac{1}{3}$

$\qquad 6 = a + 5$

$\qquad 1 = a$

3. $\quad \dfrac{x}{x + 1} - \dfrac{1}{2} = \dfrac{-1}{x + 1} \quad$ LCD $= 2(x + 1)$

$2(x + 1)\left[\dfrac{x}{x + 1} - \dfrac{1}{2}\right] = 2(x + 1) \cdot \dfrac{-1}{x + 1}$

$2(x + 1) \cdot \dfrac{x}{x + 1} - 2(x + 1) \cdot \dfrac{1}{2} = 2(x + 1) \cdot \dfrac{-1}{x + 1}$

$\qquad 2x - (x + 1) = 2(-1)$

$\qquad 2x - x - 1 = -2$

$\qquad x - 1 = -2$

$\qquad x = -1$

The only possible solution is $x = -1$, but when $x = -1$ the original equation has two undefined terms. There is no solution to the equation.

4. $\qquad \dfrac{x}{x^2 - 9} - \dfrac{1}{x + 3} = \dfrac{1}{4x - 12}$

$\dfrac{x}{(x + 3)(x - 3)} - \dfrac{1}{x + 3} = \dfrac{1}{4(x - 3)} \quad$ LCD $= 4(x + 3)(x - 3)$

$4(x + 3)(x - 3) \cdot \dfrac{x}{(x + 3)(x - 3)} - 4(x + 3)(x - 3) \cdot \dfrac{1}{x + 3} = 4(x + 3)(x - 3) \cdot \dfrac{1}{4(x - 3)}$

$\qquad 4x - 4(x - 3) = x + 3$

$\qquad 4x - 4x + 12 = x + 3$

$\qquad 12 = x + 3$

$\qquad 9 = x$

SECTION 4.6

1. Let $x =$ one of the numbers and $3x =$ the other number.

$\dfrac{1}{x} + \dfrac{1}{3x} = \dfrac{4}{3} \quad$ LCD $= 3x$

$3x \cdot \dfrac{1}{x} + 3x \cdot \dfrac{1}{3x} = 3x \cdot \dfrac{4}{3}$

$\qquad 3 + 1 = 4x$

$\qquad 4 = 4x$

$\qquad 1 = x$

The two numbers are 1 and 3.

2.

	d	r	t
Upstream	1	$15 - x$	$\dfrac{1}{15 - x}$
Downstream	2	$15 + x$	$\dfrac{2}{15 + x}$

$\dfrac{1}{15 - x} = \dfrac{2}{15 + x} \quad$ LCD $= (15 - x)(15 + x)$

$1(15 + x) = 2(15 - x)$

$15 + x = 30 - 2x$

$3x = 15$

$x = 5$ mph

3. Let $x =$ the time it takes to do the job when they work together.

$$\frac{1}{8} + \frac{1}{6} = \frac{1}{x} \quad LCD = 24x$$

$$24x \cdot \frac{1}{8} + 24x \cdot \frac{1}{6} = 24x \cdot \frac{1}{x}$$

$$3x + 4x = 24$$
$$7x = 24$$
$$x = \frac{24}{7} \text{ hours}$$

4. Let $x =$ the length of time it takes to fill the sink with both the drain and faucet open.

$$\frac{1}{3} - \frac{1}{4} = \frac{1}{x} \quad LCD = 12x$$

$$4x - 3x = 12$$
$$x = 12 \text{ minutes}$$

CHAPTER 5

SECTION 5.1

2. a. $9^{1/2} = \sqrt{9} = 3$
   b. $27^{1/3} = \sqrt[3]{27} = 3$
   c. $-49^{1/2} = -\sqrt{49} = -7$
   d. $(-49)^{1/2} = \sqrt{-49}$ which is not a real number
   e. $(\frac{16}{25})^{1/2} = \sqrt{\frac{16}{25}} = \frac{4}{5}$
   f. $8^{1/3} \cdot 9^{1/2} = \sqrt[3]{8} \cdot \sqrt{9} = 2 \cdot 3 = 6$
   g. $16^{1/4} + 4^{1/2} = \sqrt[4]{16} + \sqrt{4} = 2 + 2 = 4$

3. a. $9^{3/2} = (9^{1/2})^3 = 3^3 = 27$
   b. $16^{3/4} = (16^{1/4})^3 = 2^3 = 8$
   c. $8^{-2/3} = (8^{1/3})^{-2} = 2^{-2} = \frac{1}{4}$

4. a. $x^{1/2} \cdot x^{1/4} = x^{1/2+1/4} = x^{3/4}$
   b. $(y^{2/5})^{5/3} = y^{(2/5)(5/3)} = y^{2/3}$
   c. $(x^{1/4} \cdot y^{1/2})^8 = x^2 y^4$
   d. $\dfrac{x^{2/3}}{x^{1/4}} = x^{2/3-1/4} = x^{8/12-3/12} = x^{5/12}$

SECTION 5.2

1. $\sqrt{18} = \sqrt{9 \cdot 2}$
$= \sqrt{9}\sqrt{2}$
$= 3\sqrt{2}$

2. $\sqrt{50x^2y^3} = \sqrt{25x^2y^2 \cdot 2y}$
$= \sqrt{25x^2y^2}\sqrt{2y}$
$= 5xy\sqrt{2y}$

3. $\sqrt[3]{27a^4b^3} = \sqrt[3]{27a^3b^3 \cdot a}$
$= \sqrt[3]{27a^3b^3}\sqrt[3]{a}$
$= 3ab\sqrt[3]{a}$

4. a. $\sqrt{75x^5y^8} = \sqrt{25x^4y^8 \cdot 3x}$
$= \sqrt{25x^4y^8}\sqrt{3x}$
$= 5x^2y^4\sqrt{3x}$

b. $\sqrt[4]{48a^8b^5c^4} = \sqrt[4]{16a^8b^4c^4 \cdot 3b}$
$= \sqrt[4]{16a^8b^4c^4}\sqrt[4]{3b}$
$= 2a^2bc\sqrt[4]{3b}$

5. $\sqrt{\dfrac{5}{9}} = \dfrac{\sqrt{5}}{\sqrt{9}}$
$= \dfrac{\sqrt{5}}{3}$

6. $\sqrt{\dfrac{2}{3}} = \dfrac{\sqrt{2}}{\sqrt{3}}$
$= \dfrac{\sqrt{2}}{\sqrt{3}} \cdot \dfrac{\sqrt{3}}{\sqrt{3}}$
$= \dfrac{\sqrt{6}}{3}$

7. a. $\dfrac{5}{\sqrt{2}} = \dfrac{5}{\sqrt{2}} \cdot \dfrac{\sqrt{2}}{\sqrt{2}}$
$= \dfrac{5\sqrt{2}}{2}$

b. $\dfrac{3\sqrt{5x}}{\sqrt{2y}} = \dfrac{3\sqrt{5x}}{\sqrt{2y}} \cdot \dfrac{\sqrt{2y}}{\sqrt{2y}}$
$= \dfrac{3\sqrt{10xy}}{2y}$

8. $\dfrac{5}{\sqrt[3]{9}} = \dfrac{5}{\sqrt[3]{3^2}}$
$= \dfrac{5}{\sqrt[3]{3^2}} \cdot \dfrac{\sqrt[3]{3}}{\sqrt[3]{3}}$
$= \dfrac{5\sqrt[3]{3}}{3}$

9. $\sqrt{\dfrac{48x^3y^4}{7z}} = \dfrac{\sqrt{48x^3y^4}}{\sqrt{7z}}$
$= \dfrac{\sqrt{16x^2y^4}\sqrt{3x}}{\sqrt{7z}}$
$= \dfrac{4xy^2\sqrt{3x}}{\sqrt{7z}}$
$= \dfrac{4xy^2\sqrt{3x}}{\sqrt{7z}} \cdot \dfrac{\sqrt{7z}}{\sqrt{7z}}$
$= \dfrac{4xy^2\sqrt{21xz}}{7z}$

SECTION 5.3

1. $3\sqrt{5} - 2\sqrt{5} + 4\sqrt{5} = (3 - 2 + 4)\sqrt{5}$
$\phantom{3\sqrt{5} - 2\sqrt{5} + 4\sqrt{5}} = 5\sqrt{5}$

2. $4\sqrt{50} + 3\sqrt{8} = 4\sqrt{25 \cdot 2} + 3\sqrt{4 \cdot 2}$
$\phantom{4\sqrt{50} + 3\sqrt{8}} = 4\sqrt{25}\sqrt{2} + 3\sqrt{4}\sqrt{2}$
$\phantom{4\sqrt{50} + 3\sqrt{8}} = 4 \cdot 5\sqrt{2} + 3 \cdot 2\sqrt{2}$
$\phantom{4\sqrt{50} + 3\sqrt{8}} = 20\sqrt{2} + 6\sqrt{2}$
$\phantom{4\sqrt{50} + 3\sqrt{8}} = 26\sqrt{2}$

3. $4\sqrt{18x^2y} - 3x\sqrt{50y} = 4\sqrt{9x^2 \cdot 2y} - 3x\sqrt{25 \cdot 2y}$
$\phantom{4\sqrt{18x^2y} - 3x\sqrt{50y}} = 4\sqrt{9x^2}\sqrt{2y} - 3x\sqrt{25}\sqrt{2y}$
$\phantom{4\sqrt{18x^2y} - 3x\sqrt{50y}} = 4 \cdot 3x\sqrt{2y} - 3x \cdot 5\sqrt{2y}$
$\phantom{4\sqrt{18x^2y} - 3x\sqrt{50y}} = 12x\sqrt{2y} - 15x\sqrt{2y}$
$\phantom{4\sqrt{18x^2y} - 3x\sqrt{50y}} = -3x\sqrt{2y}$

4. $2\sqrt[3]{27a^2b^4} + 3b\sqrt[3]{125a^2b} = 2\sqrt[3]{27b^3 \cdot a^2b} + 3b\sqrt[3]{125 \cdot a^2b}$
$\phantom{2\sqrt[3]{27a^2b^4} + 3b\sqrt[3]{125a^2b}} = 2\sqrt[3]{27b^3}\sqrt[3]{a^2b} + 3b\sqrt[3]{125}\sqrt[3]{a^2b}$
$\phantom{2\sqrt[3]{27a^2b^4} + 3b\sqrt[3]{125a^2b}} = 2 \cdot 3b\sqrt[3]{a^2b} + 3b \cdot 5\sqrt[3]{a^2b}$
$\phantom{2\sqrt[3]{27a^2b^4} + 3b\sqrt[3]{125a^2b}} = 6b\sqrt[3]{a^2b} + 15b\sqrt[3]{a^2b}$
$\phantom{2\sqrt[3]{27a^2b^4} + 3b\sqrt[3]{125a^2b}} = 21b\sqrt[3]{a^2b}$

5. $\dfrac{\sqrt{5}}{3} + \dfrac{1}{\sqrt{5}} = \dfrac{\sqrt{5}}{3} + \dfrac{1}{\sqrt{5}} \cdot \dfrac{\sqrt{5}}{\sqrt{5}}$
$\phantom{\dfrac{\sqrt{5}}{3} + \dfrac{1}{\sqrt{5}}} = \dfrac{\sqrt{5}}{3} + \dfrac{\sqrt{5}}{5}$
$\phantom{\dfrac{\sqrt{5}}{3} + \dfrac{1}{\sqrt{5}}} = \left(\tfrac{1}{3} + \tfrac{1}{5}\right)\sqrt{5}$
$\phantom{\dfrac{\sqrt{5}}{3} + \dfrac{1}{\sqrt{5}}} = \left(\tfrac{5}{15} + \tfrac{3}{15}\right)\sqrt{5}$
$\phantom{\dfrac{\sqrt{5}}{3} + \dfrac{1}{\sqrt{5}}} = \tfrac{8}{15}\sqrt{5}$
$\phantom{\dfrac{\sqrt{5}}{3} + \dfrac{1}{\sqrt{5}}} = \dfrac{8\sqrt{5}}{15}$

SECTION 5.4

1. $\sqrt{2}(3\sqrt{5} - 4\sqrt{2}) = \sqrt{2} \cdot 3\sqrt{5} - \sqrt{2} \cdot 4\sqrt{2}$
$\phantom{\sqrt{2}(3\sqrt{5} - 4\sqrt{2})} = 3\sqrt{10} - 4\sqrt{4}$
$\phantom{\sqrt{2}(3\sqrt{5} - 4\sqrt{2})} = 3\sqrt{10} - 4 \cdot 2$
$\phantom{\sqrt{2}(3\sqrt{5} - 4\sqrt{2})} = 3\sqrt{10} - 8$

2. $(\sqrt{2} + \sqrt{7})(\sqrt{2} - 3\sqrt{7})$
$= \sqrt{2}\sqrt{2} - \sqrt{2} \cdot 3\sqrt{7} + \sqrt{7}\sqrt{2} - \sqrt{7} \cdot 3\sqrt{7}$
$= 2 - 3\sqrt{14} + \sqrt{14} - 21$
$= -19 - 2\sqrt{14}$

3. $(\sqrt{x} + 5)^2 = (\sqrt{x} + 5)(\sqrt{x} + 5)$
$\phantom{(\sqrt{x} + 5)^2} = \sqrt{x}\sqrt{x} + 5\sqrt{x} + 5\sqrt{x} + 25$
$\phantom{(\sqrt{x} + 5)^2} = x + 10\sqrt{x} + 25$

4. $(5\sqrt{a} - 3\sqrt{b})^2 = (5\sqrt{a})^2 - 2 \cdot 5\sqrt{a} \cdot 3\sqrt{b} + (3\sqrt{b})^2$
$\phantom{(5\sqrt{a} - 3\sqrt{b})^2} = 25a - 30\sqrt{ab} + 9b$

5. $(\sqrt{5} + \sqrt{3})(\sqrt{5} - \sqrt{3}) = (\sqrt{5})^2 - (\sqrt{3})^2$
$\phantom{(\sqrt{5} + \sqrt{3})(\sqrt{5} - \sqrt{3})} = 5 - 3$
$\phantom{(\sqrt{5} + \sqrt{3})(\sqrt{5} - \sqrt{3})} = 2$

6. $\dfrac{3}{\sqrt{7} - \sqrt{3}} = \dfrac{3}{\sqrt{7} - \sqrt{3}} \cdot \dfrac{\sqrt{7} + \sqrt{3}}{\sqrt{7} + \sqrt{3}}$
$\phantom{\dfrac{3}{\sqrt{7} - \sqrt{3}}} = \dfrac{3\sqrt{7} + 3\sqrt{3}}{7 - 3}$
$\phantom{\dfrac{3}{\sqrt{7} - \sqrt{3}}} = \dfrac{3\sqrt{7} + 3\sqrt{3}}{4}$

SECTION 5.5

1. $\sqrt{2x + 4} = 4$
$(\sqrt{2x + 4})^2 = 4^2$
$2x + 4 = 16$
$2x = 12$
$x = 6$

2. $\sqrt{7x - 3} = -5$ has no solution since the left side is a positive number or 0 and the right side is a negative number.

3. $\sqrt{4x + 5} + 2 = 7$
$\sqrt{4x + 5} = 5$
$(\sqrt{4x + 5})^2 = 5^2$
$4x + 5 = 25$
$4x = 20$
$x = 5$

4. $\sqrt{2x + 1} - \sqrt{4x - 5} = 0$
$\sqrt{2x + 1} = \sqrt{4x - 5}$
$(\sqrt{2x + 1})^2 = (\sqrt{4x - 5})^2$
$2x + 1 = 4x - 5$
$-2x = -6$
$x = 3$

5. $\sqrt{x - 9} = \sqrt{x} - 3$
$(\sqrt{x - 9})^2 = (\sqrt{x} - 3)^2$
$x - 9 = x - 6\sqrt{x} + 9$
$-9 = -6\sqrt{x} + 9$
$-18 = -6\sqrt{x}$
$3 = \sqrt{x}$
$3^2 = (\sqrt{x})^2$
$9 = x$

6. $\sqrt{x + 2} = \sqrt{x + 3} - 1$
$(\sqrt{x + 2})^2 = (\sqrt{x + 3} - 1)^2$
$x + 2 = x + 3 - 2\sqrt{x + 3} + 1$
$2 = 3 - 2\sqrt{x + 3} + 1$
$2 = 4 - 2\sqrt{x + 3}$
$-2 = -2\sqrt{x + 3}$
$1 = \sqrt{x + 3}$
$1^2 = (\sqrt{x + 3})^2$
$1 = x + 3$
$-2 = x$

7. $\sqrt[3]{3x - 7} = 2$
$(\sqrt[3]{3x - 7})^3 = 2^3$
$3x - 7 = 8$
$3x = 15$
$x = 5$

SECTION 5.6

1. a. $\sqrt{-36} = \sqrt{36}\sqrt{-1} = 6i$
b. $-\sqrt{-64} = -\sqrt{64}\sqrt{-1} = -8i$
c. $\sqrt{-18} = \sqrt{18}\sqrt{-1} = 3\sqrt{2}i = 3i\sqrt{2}$
d. $-\sqrt{-19} = -\sqrt{19}\sqrt{-1} = -\sqrt{19}i = -i\sqrt{19}$

2. a. $i^{20} = (i^2)^{10} = (-1)^{10} = 1$
b. $i^{23} = (i^2)^{11} \cdot i = (-1)^{11}i = -i$
c. $i^{50} = (i^2)^{25} = (-1)^{25} = -1$

3. $4x + 7i = 8 - 14yi$
$\Rightarrow 4x = 8$ and $7 = -14y$
$x = 2$ and $y = -\dfrac{1}{2}$

4. $(2x - 1) + 9i = 5 + (4y + 1)i$
$\Rightarrow 2x - 1 = 5$ and $9 = 4y + 1$
$2x = 6 \qquad 8 = 4y$
$x = 3$ and $2 = y$

5. a. $(2 + 6i) + (3 - 4i) = (2 + 3) + (6i - 4i)$
$= 5 + 2i$
b. $(6 + 5i) - (4 + 3i) = 6 + 5i - 4 - 3i$
$= 2 + 2i$
c. $(7 - i) - (8 - 2i) = 7 - i - 8 + 2i$
$= -1 + i$

SECTION 5.7

1. $(2 + 3i)(1 - 4i) = 2 \cdot 1 - 2 \cdot 4i + 3i \cdot 1 - 3i \cdot 4i$
$= 2 - 8i + 3i - 12i^2$
$= 2 - 5i - 12(-1)$
$= 2 - 5i + 12$
$= 14 - 5i$

2. $-3i(2 + 3i) = -3i \cdot 2 - 3i \cdot 3i$
$= -6i - 9i^2$
$= -6i - 9(-1)$
$= -6i + 9$
$= 9 - 6i$

3. $(2 + 4i)^2 = 2^2 + 2 \cdot 2 \cdot 4i + (4i)^2$
$= 4 + 16i - 16$
$= -12 + 16i$

4. $(3 - 5i)(3 + 5i) = 3^2 - (5i)^2$
$= 9 - 25i^2$
$= 9 + 25$
$= 34$

5. $\dfrac{3 + 2i}{2 - 5i} = \dfrac{3 + 2i}{2 - 5i} \cdot \dfrac{2 + 5i}{2 + 5i}$
$= \dfrac{6 + 15i + 4i + 10i^2}{4 - 25i^2}$
$= \dfrac{6 + 19i - 10}{4 + 25}$
$= \dfrac{-4 + 19i}{29}$
$= -\dfrac{4}{29} + \dfrac{19}{29}i$

6. $\dfrac{3 + 2i}{i} = \dfrac{3 + 2i}{i} \cdot \dfrac{-i}{-i}$
$= \dfrac{-3i - 2i^2}{-i^2}$
$= \dfrac{-3i + 2}{1}$
$= 2 - 3i$

CHAPTER 6

SECTION 6.1

1. $x^2 - x - 6 = 0$
$(x - 3)(x + 2) = 0$
$x - 3 = 0$ or $x + 2 = 0$
$x = 3$ or $x = -2$

2. $3x^2 = 5x + 2$
$3x^2 - 5x - 2 = 0$
$(3x + 1)(x - 2) = 0$
$3x + 1 = 0$ or $x - 2 = 0$
$x = -\dfrac{1}{3}$ or $x = 2$

3. $x^2 = 5x$
$x^2 - 5x = 0$
$x(x - 5) = 0$
$x = 0$ or $x - 5 = 0$
$x = 5$

4. $(x + 1)(x + 2) = 12$
$x^2 + 3x + 2 = 12$
$x^2 + 3x - 10 = 0$
$(x + 5)(x - 2) = 0$
$x + 5 = 0$ or $x - 2 = 0$
$x = -5$ or $x = 2$

5. $1 - \dfrac{2}{x} = \dfrac{8}{x^2}$ LCD $= x^2$
$x^2\left(1 - \dfrac{2}{x}\right) = x^2 \cdot \dfrac{8}{x^2}$
$x^2 \cdot 1 - x^2 \cdot \dfrac{2}{x} = x^2 \cdot \dfrac{8}{x^2}$
$x^2 - 2x = 8$
$x^2 - 2x - 8 = 0$
$(x - 4)(x + 2) = 0$
$x - 4 = 0$ or $x + 2 = 0$
$x = 4$ or $x = -2$

6. $\sqrt{2x^2 - 3x} = 3$
$(\sqrt{2x^2 - 3x})^2 = 3^2$
$2x^2 - 3x = 9$
$2x^2 - 3x - 9 = 0$
$(2x + 3)(x - 3) = 0$
$2x + 3 = 0$ or $x - 3 = 0$
$2x = -3$ or $x = 3$
$x = -\dfrac{3}{2}$

SECTION 6.2

1. $(3x + 2)^2 = 16$

$3x + 2 = \pm 4$

$3x = -2 \pm 4$

$x = \dfrac{-2 \pm 4}{3}$

$x = \dfrac{-2 + 4}{3}$ or $x = \dfrac{-2 - 4}{3}$

$x = \dfrac{2}{3}$ or $x = -2$

2. $(4x - 3)^2 = -50$

$4x - 3 = \pm\sqrt{-50}$

$4x - 3 = \pm 5i\sqrt{2}$

$4x = 3 \pm 5i\sqrt{2}$

$x = \dfrac{3 \pm 5i\sqrt{2}}{4}$

3. $x^2 + 3x - 4 = 0$

$x^2 + 3x = 4$

$x^2 + 3x + \dfrac{9}{4} = 4 + \dfrac{9}{4}$

$\left(x + \dfrac{3}{2}\right)^2 = \dfrac{25}{4}$

$x + \dfrac{3}{2} = \pm\dfrac{5}{2}$

$x = -\dfrac{3}{2} \pm \dfrac{5}{2}$

$x = -\dfrac{3}{2} + \dfrac{5}{2}$ or $x = -\dfrac{3}{2} - \dfrac{5}{2}$

$x = 1$ or $x = -4$

4. $5x^2 - 3x + 2 = 0$

$5x^2 - 3x = -2$

$x^2 - \dfrac{3}{5}x = -\dfrac{2}{5}$

$x^2 - \dfrac{3}{5}x + \dfrac{9}{100} = -\dfrac{2}{5} + \dfrac{9}{100}$

$\left(x - \dfrac{3}{10}\right)^2 = -\dfrac{31}{100}$

$x - \dfrac{3}{10} = \pm\sqrt{-\dfrac{31}{100}}$

$x - \dfrac{3}{10} = \pm\dfrac{i\sqrt{31}}{10}$

$x = \dfrac{3}{10} \pm \dfrac{i\sqrt{31}}{10}$

$x = \dfrac{3 \pm i\sqrt{31}}{10}$

SECTION 6.3

1. $6x^2 + 7x + 2 = 0$

$a = 6,\ b = 7,\ c = 2$

$x = \dfrac{-7 \pm \sqrt{7^2 - 4(6)(2)}}{2(6)}$

$= \dfrac{-7 \pm \sqrt{49 - 48}}{12}$

$= \dfrac{-7 \pm \sqrt{1}}{12}$

$= \dfrac{-7 \pm 1}{12}$

$x = \dfrac{-7 + 1}{12}$ or $x = \dfrac{-7 - 1}{12}$

$x = -\dfrac{1}{2}$ or $x = -\dfrac{2}{3}$

2. $\dfrac{x^2}{2} + x = \dfrac{1}{3}$ LCD $= 6$

$6 \cdot \dfrac{x^2}{2} + 6 \cdot x = 6 \cdot \dfrac{1}{3}$

$3x^2 + 6x = 2$

$3x^2 + 6x - 2 = 0$

$a = 3,\ b = 6,\ c = -2$

$x = \dfrac{-6 \pm \sqrt{6^2 - 4(3)(-2)}}{2(3)}$

$= \dfrac{-6 \pm \sqrt{36 + 24}}{6}$

$= \dfrac{-6 \pm \sqrt{60}}{6}$

$= \dfrac{-6 \pm 2\sqrt{15}}{6}$

$= \dfrac{2(-3 \pm \sqrt{15})}{2 \cdot 3}$

$= \dfrac{-3 \pm \sqrt{15}}{3}$

3. $\dfrac{1}{x + 4} - \dfrac{1}{x} = \dfrac{1}{2}$ LCD $= 2x(x + 4)$

$2x(x + 4)\left(\dfrac{1}{x + 4} - \dfrac{1}{x}\right) = 2x(x + 4) \cdot \dfrac{1}{2}$

$2x(x + 4) \cdot \dfrac{1}{x + 4} - 2x(x + 4) \cdot \dfrac{1}{x} = 2x(x + 4) \cdot \dfrac{1}{2}$

$2x - 2(x + 4) = x(x + 4)$

$2x - 2x - 8 = x^2 + 4x$

$-8 = x^2 + 4x$

$0 = x^2 + 4x + 8$

$$a = 1, b = 4, c = 8$$

$$x = \frac{-4 \pm \sqrt{4^2 - 4(1)(8)}}{2(1)}$$

$$= \frac{-4 \pm \sqrt{16 - 32}}{2}$$

$$= \frac{-4 \pm \sqrt{-16}}{2}$$

$$= \frac{-4 \pm 4i}{2}$$

$$= \frac{\cancel{2}(-2 \pm 2i)}{\cancel{2}}$$

$$= -2 \pm 2i$$

SECTION 6.4

1. a. $x^2 - 3x - 28 = 0$

$b^2 - 4ac = (-3)^2 - 4(1)(-28)$

$\qquad\quad = 9 + 112$

$\qquad\quad = 121$

which is a positive number that is a perfect square. Therefore, our equation has two rational solutions.

b. $x^2 - 6x + 9 = 0$

$b^2 - 4ac = (-6)^2 - 4(1)(9)$

$\qquad\quad = 36 - 36$

$\qquad\quad = 0$

which means our equation has exactly one rational solution.

c. $3x^2 - 2x + 4 = 0$

$b^2 - 4ac = (-2)^2 - 4(3)(4)$

$\qquad\quad = 4 - 48$

$\qquad\quad = -44$

which is a negative number, implying that our equation has two complex solutions.

d. $x^2 + 1 = 4x$

$x^2 - 4x + 1 = 0$

$b^2 - 4ac = (-4)^2 - 4(1)(1)$

$\qquad\quad = 16 - 4$

$\qquad\quad = 12$

which is a positive number but not a perfect square. Our equation, therefore, has two irrational solutions.

2. $9x^2 + kx = -4$

$9x^2 + kx + 4 = 0$

$b^2 - 4ac = k^2 - 4(9)(4) = 0$

$\qquad\qquad\quad k^2 - 144 = 0$

$\qquad\qquad\qquad\quad k^2 = 144$

$\qquad\qquad\qquad\quad\ k = \pm 12$

SECTION 6.5

1. $(x - 2)^2 - 3(x - 2) - 10 = 0$

let $y = x - 2$

$\quad y^2 - 3y - 10 = 0$

$\quad (y - 5)(y + 2) = 0$

$\quad y - 5 = 0$ or $y + 2 = 0$

$\qquad\quad y = 5$ or $\qquad y = -2$

now replace y with $x - 2$

$x - 2 = 5 \qquad x - 2 = -2$

$\quad x = 7 \qquad\qquad x = 0$

2.

$6x^4 - 13x^2 = 5$

$6x^4 - 13x^2 - 5 = 0$

$(3x^2 + 1)(2x^2 - 5) = 0$

$3x^2 + 1 = 0 \quad$ or $\quad 2x^2 - 5 = 0$

$\quad 3x^2 = -1 \quad$ or $\qquad 2x^2 = 5$

$\quad\ x^2 = -\dfrac{1}{3} \quad$ or $\qquad\ x^2 = \dfrac{5}{2}$

$\quad\ x = \pm\dfrac{i\sqrt{3}}{3} \quad$ or $\qquad x = \pm\dfrac{\sqrt{10}}{2}$

3. $x - \sqrt{x} - 12 = 0$

let $y = \sqrt{x}$

$\quad y^2 - y - 12 = 0$

$\quad (y - 4)(y + 3) = 0$

$\quad y - 4 = 0$ or $y + 3 = 0$

$\qquad\quad y = 4$ or $\qquad y = -3$

now replace y with $\sqrt{x}$

$\quad \sqrt{x} = 4$ or $\quad \sqrt{x} = -3$

$\qquad x = 16$ or $\qquad x = 9$

Checking each solution in the original equation will show that 9 is extraneous. The only solution is $x = 16$.

4. $\sqrt{x + 4} + \sqrt{3x} = 2$

$\qquad\quad \sqrt{x + 4} = 2 - \sqrt{3x}$

$\qquad (\sqrt{x + 4})^2 = (2 - \sqrt{3x})^2$

$\qquad\quad\ x + 4 = 4 - 4\sqrt{3x} + 3x$

$\qquad\qquad -2x = -4\sqrt{3x}$

$\qquad\qquad\quad\ x = 2\sqrt{3x}$

$\qquad\qquad\quad x^2 = (2\sqrt{3x})^2$

$\qquad\qquad\quad x^2 = 4 \cdot 3x$

$\qquad\quad x^2 - 12x = 0$

$\qquad\ x(x - 12) = 0$

$x = 0$ or $x - 12 = 0$

$\qquad\qquad\qquad\ x = 12$

Checking each solution in the original equation shows that $x = 12$ is extraneous. The only solution is $x = 0$.

SECTION 6.6

1. Let x = one integer
and $x + 3$ = the other:
$$x^2 + (x + 3)^2 = 29$$
$$x^2 + x^2 + 6x + 9 = 29$$
$$2x^2 + 6x + 9 = 29$$
$$2x^2 + 6x - 20 = 0$$
$$x^2 + 3x - 10 = 0$$
$$(x + 5)(x - 2) = 0$$

$x + 5 = 0$	or	$x - 2 = 0$
$x = -5$	or	$x = 2$
$x + 3 = -5 + 3$		$x + 3 = 2 + 3$
$= -2$		$= 5$

The two integers are -5 and -2 or
2 and 5.

2. $(9 + 2x)(12 + 2x) = 154$
$$108 + 42x + 4x^2 = 154$$
$$54 + 21x + 2x^2 = 77$$
$$2x^2 + 21x + 54 = 77$$
$$2x^2 + 21x - 23 = 0$$
$$(2x + 23)(x - 1) = 0$$

$2x + 23 = 0$	or	$x - 1 = 0$
$x = -\frac{23}{2}$	or	$x = 1$

Since the width of the frame cannot
be negative, the frame is 1 inch wide.

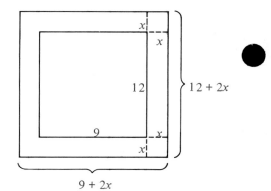

3.

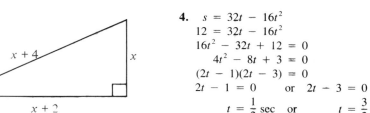

$$(x + 4)^2 = (x + 2)^2 + x^2$$
$$x^2 + 8x + 16 = x^2 + 4x + 4 + x^2$$
$$x^2 + 8x + 16 = 2x^2 + 4x + 4$$
$$0 = x^2 - 4x - 12$$
$$0 = (x - 6)(x + 2)$$

$x - 6 = 0$	or	$x + 2 = 0$
$x = 6$	or	$x = -2$

Since the length of a side cannot be
negative, the shortest side is 6. The
other two sides are $6 + 2 = 8$ and
$6 + 4 = 10$.

4. $s = 32t - 16t^2$
$$12 = 32t - 16t^2$$
$$16t^2 - 32t + 12 = 0$$
$$4t^2 - 8t + 3 = 0$$
$$(2t - 1)(2t - 3) = 0$$

$2t - 1 = 0$	or	$2t - 3 = 0$
$t = \frac{1}{2}$ sec	or	$t = \frac{3}{2}$ sec

5.

	d	r	t
Upstream	8	$x - 2$	$\dfrac{8}{x - 2}$
Downstream	8	$x + 2$	$\dfrac{8}{x + 2}$

$$\frac{8}{x - 2} + \frac{8}{x + 2} = 3 \quad \text{LCD} = (x + 2)(x - 2)$$

$$(x + 2)(x - 2) \cdot \frac{8}{x - 2} + (x + 2)(x - 2) \cdot \frac{8}{x + 2} = (x + 2)(x - 2) \cdot 3$$

$$(x + 2) \cdot 8 + (x - 2) \cdot 8 = (x + 2)(x - 2) \cdot 3$$
$$8x + 16 + 8x - 16 = 3x^2 - 12$$
$$16x = 3x^2 - 12$$
$$0 = 3x^2 - 16x - 12$$
$$0 = (3x + 2)(x - 6)$$

$3x + 2 = 0$	or	$x - 6 = 0$
$x = -\dfrac{2}{3}$	or	$x = 6$

The speed of the boat in still water is 6 mph. (The $-\frac{2}{3}$ cannot be a solution
because it is negative.)

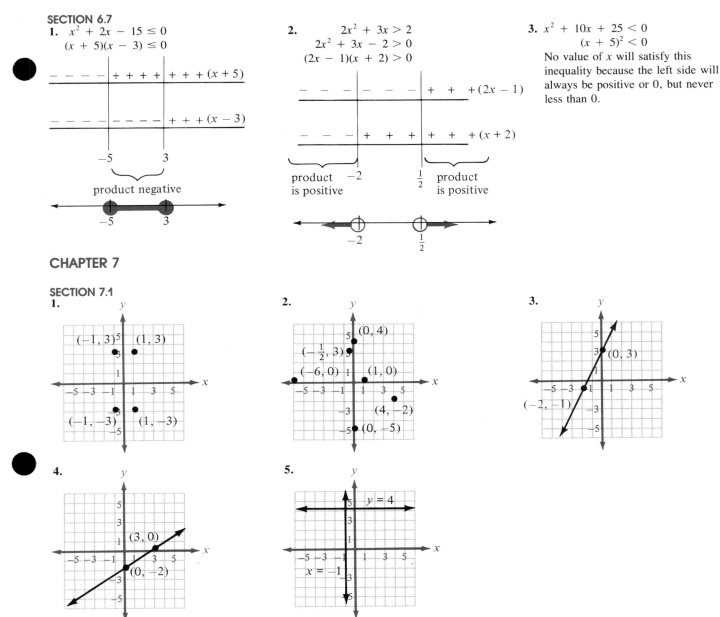

SECTION 6.7

1. $x^2 + 2x - 15 \leq 0$
$(x + 5)(x - 3) \leq 0$

$- - - - - | + + + + | + + + (x + 5)$

$- - - - - | - - - - | + + + (x - 3)$

$-5 \qquad 3$

product negative

$-5 \qquad 3$

2. $2x^2 + 3x > 2$
$2x^2 + 3x - 2 > 0$
$(2x - 1)(x + 2) > 0$

$- - - | - - - | + + + (2x - 1)$

$- - - | + + + | + + + (x + 2)$

product -2 $\frac{1}{2}$ product
is positive   is positive

$-2 \qquad \frac{1}{2}$

3. $x^2 + 10x + 25 < 0$
$(x + 5)^2 < 0$
No value of x will satisfy this inequality because the left side will always be positive or 0, but never less than 0.

CHAPTER 7

SECTION 7.1

1.
$(-1, 3)$ $(1, 3)$
$(-1, -3)$ $(1, -3)$

2.
$(0, 4)$
$(-\frac{1}{2}, 3)$
$(-6, 0)$ $(1, 0)$
$(4, -2)$
$(0, -5)$

3.
$(0, 3)$
$(-2, -1)$

4.
$(3, 0)$
$(0, -2)$

5.
$y = 4$
$x = -1$

SECTION 7.2

1. When $x = 0$, $y = -5$ so the point $(0, -5)$ is on the graph. When $x = 2$, $y = 1$ so the point $(2, 1)$ is a second point on the graph. The ratio of rise to run going from $(0, -5)$ to $(2, 1)$ is $\frac{6}{2} = 3$. The slope of $y = 3x - 5$ is 3.

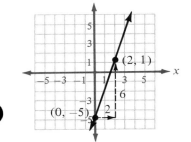

$(2, 1)$
$(0, -5)$

2. $m = \dfrac{4 - (-2)}{3 - 1} = \dfrac{6}{2} = 3$

3. $m = \dfrac{-3 - (-3)}{2 - (-1)} = \dfrac{0}{3} = 0$

4. $\dfrac{a - 3}{-2 - 2} = \dfrac{3}{2}$

$\dfrac{a - 3}{-4} = \dfrac{3}{2}$

$2(a - 3) = 3(-4)$
$2a - 6 = -12$
$2a = -6$
$a = -3$

SECTION 7.3

2. $4x - 5y = 7$
$-5y = -4x + 7$
$y = \frac{4}{5}x - \frac{7}{5}$
slope $= \frac{4}{5}$, y-intercept $= -\frac{7}{5}$

3. $-3x + 2y = -6$
$2y = 3x - 6$
$y = \frac{3}{2}x - 3$

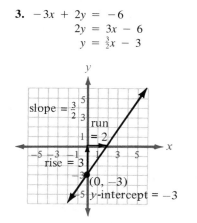

4. $m = 3$, $(x_1, y_1) = (-1, 2)$
$y - y_1 = m(x - x_1)$
$y - 2 = 3(x + 1)$
$y - 2 = 3x + 3$
$y = 3x + 5$

5. $m = \dfrac{5 - (-3)}{2 - 6} = \dfrac{8}{-4} = -2$
let $(x_1, y_1) = (2, 5)$
then $y - 5 = -2(x - 2)$
$y - 5 = -2x + 4$
$y = -2x + 9$

6. $3x - y = 2$
$-y = -3x + 2$
$y = 3x - 2$
The slope of a line perpendicular
to this line is $-\frac{1}{3}$.
Using $m = -\frac{1}{3}$ and $(x_1, y_1) = (3, 2)$
we have
$y - 2 = -\frac{1}{3}(x - 3)$
$y - 2 = -\frac{1}{3}x + 1$
$y = -\frac{1}{3}x + 3$

SECTION 7.4

1.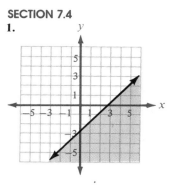

2.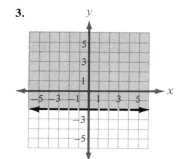

3.

SECTION 7.5

1. $y = kx$
$24 = k \cdot 8$
$\Rightarrow k = 3$
$y = 3x$
$y = 3 \cdot 2$
$= 6$

2. $d = 16t^2$
$= 16(4)^2$
$= 16 \cdot 16$
$= 256$ feet

3. $y = \dfrac{k}{x^3}$
$3 = \dfrac{k}{2^3}$
$3 = \dfrac{k}{8}$
$\Rightarrow k = 24$
$y = \dfrac{24}{x^3}$
$y = \dfrac{24}{3^3}$
$= \dfrac{24}{27}$
$= \dfrac{8}{9}$

4. $V = \dfrac{2400}{P}$
$150 = \dfrac{2400}{P}$
$150P = 2400$
$P = \dfrac{2400}{150}$
$= 16$ lb/sq. in.

5. $y = kx\sqrt{z}$
$30 = k(2)\sqrt{9}$
$30 = 6k$
$\Rightarrow k = 5$
$y = 5x\sqrt{z}$
$= 5(4)\sqrt{4}$
$= 40$

6. $R = \dfrac{0.0005l}{d^2}$
$= \dfrac{0.005(300)}{(0.25)^2}$
$= 2.4$ ohms

CHAPTER 8

SECTION 8.1

1. $2x - y = 7$ $\xrightarrow{\text{4 times each side}}$ $8x - 4y = 28$
$3x + 4y = -6$ $\xrightarrow{\text{no change}}$ $\underline{3x + 4y = -6}$
$\qquad\qquad\qquad\qquad\qquad 11x \quad\;\; = 22$
$\qquad\qquad\qquad\qquad\qquad\qquad\quad x = 2$
Substituting $x = 2$ into $2x - y = 7$ gives us
$y = -3$. The solution is $(2, -3)$.

2. $3x - 2y = -8$ $\xrightarrow{\text{2 times each side}}$ $6x - 4y = -16$
$-2x + 3y = 7$ $\xrightarrow{\text{3 times each side}}$ $\underline{-6x + 9y = \;\;\;21}$
$\qquad\qquad\qquad\qquad\qquad\qquad\qquad 5y = 5$
$\qquad\qquad\qquad\qquad\qquad\qquad\qquad\; y = 1$
Substituting $y = 1$ into $3x - 2y = -8$ gives us
$x = -2$. The solution is $(-2, 1)$.

3. $2x + 7y = 3 \xrightarrow{-2 \text{ times each side}} -4x - 14y = -6$
$\ 4x + 14y = 1 \xrightarrow[\text{no change}]{} \underline{4x + 14y = 1}$
$\phantom{3.\ 4x + 14y = 1 \xrightarrow[\text{no change}]{} } 0 = -5$

We have eliminated both variables and are left with a false statement indicating that the lines are parallel. There is no solution to the system.

4. $2x + 7y = 3 \xrightarrow{-2 \text{ times each side}} -4x - 14y = -6$
$\ 4x + 14y = 6 \xrightarrow[\text{no change}]{} \underline{4x + 14y = 6}$
$\phantom{4.\ 4x + 14y = 6 \xrightarrow[\text{no change}]{} } 0 = 0$

We have eliminated both variables and are left with a true statement. The lines coincide. Any ordered pair that satisfies one of the equations will satisfy the other.

5. $\frac{1}{3}x + \frac{1}{2}y = 4 \xrightarrow{\text{times } 6} 2x + 3y = 24$
$\ \frac{2}{3}x - \frac{1}{4}y = 3 \xrightarrow[\text{times } 12]{} \underline{8x - 3y = 36}$
$\phantom{5.\ \frac{2}{3}x - \frac{1}{4}y = 3 \xrightarrow[]{} 10x } = 60$
$\phantom{5.\ \frac{2}{3}x - \frac{1}{4}y = 3 \xrightarrow[]{} xxxxx} x = 6$

Substituting $x = 6$ into any equation with both variables gives $y = 4$. The solution is $(6, 4)$.

6. $4x - 2y = -2$
$\ y = x + 3$
Substituting $x + 3$ for y in the first equation gives us
$4x - 2(x + 3) = -2$
$4x - 2x - 6 = -2$
$2x - 6 = -2$
$2x = 4$
$x = 2$
When $x = 2$, $y = 2 + 3 = 5$. The solution is $(2, 5)$.

7. $5x - 3y = -4$
$\ x + 2y = 7$
Solving the second equation for x gives $x = -2y + 7$. Substituting this for x in the first equation we have
$5(-2y + 7) - 3y = -4$
$-10y + 35 - 3y = -4$
$-13y + 35 = -4$
$-13y = -39$
$y = 3$
Putting $y = 3$ into either of the first two equations gives $x = 1$. The solution is $(1, 3)$.

SECTION 8.2

1. $x + 2y + z = 2$ (1)
$\ x + y - z = 6$ (2)
$\ x - y + 2z = -7$ (3)
Adding equations (1) and (2) yields
$2x + 3y = 8$ (4)
Adding twice (2) to (3) yields
$3x + y = 5$ (5)
We solve the system made up of equations (4) and (5) as follows.
$2x + 3y = 8 \xrightarrow{\text{no change}} 2x + 3y = 8$
$3x + y = 5 \xrightarrow[\text{times } -3]{} \underline{-9x - 3y = -15}$
$\phantom{3x + y = 5 \xrightarrow[]{} -7x} = -7$
$\phantom{3x + y = 5 \xrightarrow[]{} xxxx} x = 1$
Substituting $x = 1$ into equation (5) gives us $y = 2$. Substituting $x = 1$ and $y = 2$ into equation (1) gives us $z = -3$. The solution is $(1, 2, -3)$.

2. $3x - 2y + z = 2$ (1)
$\ 3x + y + 3z = 7$ (2)
$\ x + 4y - z = 4$ (3)
Adding (1) and (3) yields
$4x + 2y = 6$ (4)
Adding three times (3) to (2) yields
$6x + 13y = 19$ (5)
We solve the system made up of (4) and (5) as follows:
$4x + 2y = 6 \xrightarrow{\text{times } 6} 24x + 12y = 36$
$6x + 13y = 19 \xrightarrow[\text{times } -4]{} \underline{-24x - 52y = -76}$
$\phantom{6x + 13y = 19 \xrightarrow[]{} -40y} = -40$
$\phantom{6x + 13y = 19 \xrightarrow[]{} xxxx} y = 1$
Putting $y = 1$ into equation (4) gives us $x = 1$. When x is 1 and y is 1 in equation (1), then $z = 1$. The solution is $(1, 1, 1)$.

3. $3x + 5y - 2z = 1$ (1)
$\ 6x + 10y - 4z = 2$ (2)
$\ x - 8y + z = 4$ (3)
Equation (2) is twice equation (1) indicating that the planes they represent coincide with one another. There is either no solution to the system, or an infinite number of solutions.

4. $3x - y + 2z = 4$ (1)
$\ 6x - 2y + 4z = 2$ (2)
$\ 5x - 3y + 7z = 5$ (3)
If we add -2 times equation (1) to equation (2) we are left with the false statement $0 = -6$. This means that the planes represented by these equations are parallel. Therefore, there is no solution to the system.

5. $x + 2y = 0$ (1)
$\ 3y + z = -3$ (2)
$\ 2x - z = 5$ (3)
Adding equations (2) and (3) gives us equation (4) which is
$2x + 3y = 2$ (4)
This equation, together with equation (1) form a system in two variables.
$x + 2y = 0 \xrightarrow{\text{times } -2} -2x - 4y = 0$
$2x + 3y = 2 \xrightarrow[\text{no change}]{} \underline{2x + 3y = 2}$
$\phantom{2x + 3y = 2 \xrightarrow[]{} -y} = 2$
$\phantom{2x + 3y = 2 \xrightarrow[]{} xx} y = -2$
When $y = -2$ in equation (1), x becomes 4. When we substitute -2 for y in equation (2), z is 3. The solution is $(4, -2, 3)$.

SECTION 8.3

1. a. $\begin{vmatrix} 2 & 1 \\ 4 & 3 \end{vmatrix} = 6 - 4 = 2$

2. $\begin{vmatrix} -3 & x \\ 2 & x \end{vmatrix} = 20$

$-3x - 2x = 20$
$-5x = 20$
$x = -4$

3. $\begin{vmatrix} 2 & 0 & 1 \\ 3 & 1 & 2 \\ 5 & -2 & 1 \end{vmatrix} = 2 + 0 + 6 - (-5 - 8 + 0) = 8 - (-13)$
$= 21$

b. $\begin{vmatrix} 4 & -2 \\ 0 & 3 \end{vmatrix} = 12 - 0 = 12$

4. $\begin{vmatrix} 2 & 0 & -1 \\ 3 & 1 & 2 \\ 5 & -2 & 1 \end{vmatrix} = 2\begin{vmatrix} 1 & 2 \\ -2 & 1 \end{vmatrix} - 0\begin{vmatrix} 3 & 2 \\ 5 & 1 \end{vmatrix} - 1\begin{vmatrix} 3 & 1 \\ 5 & -2 \end{vmatrix}$

$= 2(1 + 4) - 0(3 - 10) - 1(-6 - 5)$
$= 2(5) - 0 - 1(-11)$
$= 10 + 11$
$= 21$

5. $\begin{vmatrix} 0 & 4 & -2 \\ 3 & 1 & 1 \\ 1 & -2 & 0 \end{vmatrix} = -4\begin{vmatrix} 3 & 1 \\ 1 & 0 \end{vmatrix} + 1\begin{vmatrix} 0 & -2 \\ 1 & 0 \end{vmatrix} + 2\begin{vmatrix} 0 & -2 \\ 3 & 1 \end{vmatrix}$

$= -4(0 - 1) + 1(0 + 2) + 2(0 + 6)$
$= -4(-1) + 1(2) + 2(6)$
$= 4 + 2 + 12$
$= 18$

SECTION 8.4

1. $3x - 5y = 2$
$2x + 4y = 1$

$D = \begin{vmatrix} 3 & -5 \\ 2 & 4 \end{vmatrix} = 22$

$D_x = \begin{vmatrix} 2 & -5 \\ 1 & 4 \end{vmatrix} = 13$

$D_y = \begin{vmatrix} 3 & 2 \\ 2 & 1 \end{vmatrix} = -1$

$x = \dfrac{D_x}{D} = \dfrac{13}{22}$

$\left(\dfrac{13}{22}, -\dfrac{1}{22}\right)$

$y = \dfrac{D_y}{D} = -\dfrac{1}{22}$

2. $x + 2y + z = 2$
$x + y - z = 6$
$x - y + z = -4$

$D = \begin{vmatrix} 1 & 2 & 1 \\ 1 & 1 & -1 \\ 1 & -1 & 1 \end{vmatrix} = -6$

$D_x = \begin{vmatrix} 2 & 2 & 1 \\ 6 & 1 & -1 \\ -4 & -1 & 1 \end{vmatrix} = -6$

$D_y = \begin{vmatrix} 1 & 2 & 1 \\ 1 & 6 & -1 \\ 1 & -4 & 1 \end{vmatrix} = -12$

$D_z = \begin{vmatrix} 1 & 2 & 2 \\ 1 & 1 & 6 \\ 1 & -1 & -4 \end{vmatrix} = 18$

$x = \dfrac{D_x}{D} = \dfrac{-6}{-6} = 1$

$y = \dfrac{D_y}{D} = \dfrac{-12}{-6} = 2$

$z = \dfrac{D_z}{D} = \dfrac{18}{-6} = -3$

The solution is $(1, 2, -3)$.

3. $x + y = 3$
$2x - z = 3$
$y + 2z = 9$

$D = \begin{vmatrix} 1 & 1 & 0 \\ 2 & 0 & -1 \\ 0 & 1 & 2 \end{vmatrix} = -3$

$D_x = \begin{vmatrix} 3 & 1 & 0 \\ 3 & 0 & -1 \\ 9 & 1 & 2 \end{vmatrix} = -12$

$D_y = \begin{vmatrix} 1 & 3 & 0 \\ 2 & 3 & -1 \\ 0 & 9 & 2 \end{vmatrix} = 3$

$D_z = \begin{vmatrix} 1 & 1 & 3 \\ 2 & 0 & 3 \\ 0 & 1 & 9 \end{vmatrix} = -15$

$x = \dfrac{D_x}{D} = \dfrac{-12}{-3} = 4$

$y = \dfrac{D_y}{D} = \dfrac{3}{-3} = -1$

$z = \dfrac{D_z}{D} = \dfrac{-15}{-3} = 5$

The solution is $(4, -1, 5)$.

SECTION 8.5

1. Let x and y represent the two numbers. Then,
$x + y = 14$
$y = 2x - 1$
The two numbers are 5 and 9.

2. Let $x =$ the number of adult tickets sold and $y =$ the number of children's tickets sold.
$x + y = 750$
$2x + 1y = 1{,}090$
The number of adult tickets is 340 and the number of children's tickets is 410.

3. Let $x =$ the amount invested at 6% and $y =$ the amount invested at 7%.
$x + y = 12{,}000$
$.06x + .07y = 790$
To solve this system, multiply the top equation by -6, and the bottom equation by 100 to get
$-6x - 6y = -72{,}000$
$6x + 7y = 79{,}000$
The amount invested at 6% is $5,000 and the amount invested at 7% is $7,000.

4. Let $x =$ the number of gallons of 30% solution and $y =$ the number of gallons of 70% solution.
$x + y = 16$
$.30x + .70y = .60(16) = 9.6$
Multiply the top equation by -3 and the bottom equation by 10 to get
$-3x - 3y = -48$
$3x + 7y = 96$
Which yields 4 gallons of 30% solution and 12 gallons of 70% solution.

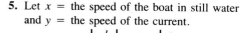

5. Let x = the speed of the boat in still water and y = the speed of the current.

	d	r	t
Upstream	18	$x - y$	3
Downstream	20	$x + y$	2

$$18 = 3(x - y)$$
$$20 = 2(x + y)$$
or $\quad 3x - 3y = 18$
$$\quad 2x + 2y = 20$$

The speed of the boat in still water is 8 mph, while the speed of the current is 2 mph.

6. Let x = the number of nickels,
 y = the number of dimes,
and z = the number of quarters.
$$x + y + z = 15$$
$$5x + 10y + 25z = 110$$
$$x = 4y - 1$$
Rewriting the third equation, the system can be written as
$$x + y + z = 15$$
$$5x + 10y + 25z = 110$$
$$x - 4y = -1$$
There are 11 nickels, 3 dimes, and 1 quarter.

CHAPTER 9

SECTION 9.1

1. To find the x-intercepts we let $y = 0$
$$x^2 - 2x - 3 = 0$$
$$(x - 3)(x + 1) = 0$$
$$x = 3, x = -1$$
The x-coordinate of the vertex is
$$x = \frac{-b}{2a} = \frac{-(-2)}{2(1)} = 1$$
The y-coordinate of the vertex is
$$y = 1^2 - 2(1) - 3 = -4$$

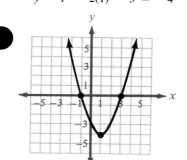

2. x-intercepts:
$$-x^2 + 2x + 8 = 0$$
$$x^2 - 2x - 8 = 0$$
$$(x - 4)(x + 2) = 0$$
$$x = 4, x = -2$$
Vertex:
$$x = \frac{-b}{2a} = \frac{-2}{2(-1)} = 1$$
$$y = -(1)^2 + 2(1) + 8 = 9$$

3. The x-intercepts are found by using the quadratic formula on $2x^2 - 4x + 1 = 0$. They are irrational numbers, approximately .3 and 1.7. Two other points on the graph are $(0, 1)$ and $(2, 1)$.
Vertex:
$$x = \frac{-b}{2a} = \frac{-(-4)}{2(2)} = 1$$
$$y = 2(1)^2 - 4(1) + 1 = -1$$

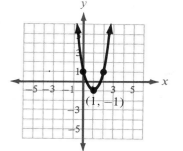

4. The graph does not cross the x-axis because the equation $-x^2 + 4x - 5 = 0$ does not have real solutions. Two points on the graph are $(0, -5)$ and $(4, -5)$.
Vertex:
$$x = \frac{-b}{2a} = \frac{-4}{2(-1)} = 2$$
$$y = -(2)^2 + 4(2) - 5 = -1$$

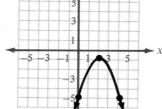

SECTION 9.2

1. $d = \sqrt{(-4-2)^2 + (1-5)^2}$
$= \sqrt{36 + 16}$
$= \sqrt{52}$
$= 2\sqrt{13}$

2. $\sqrt{(x-3)^2 + (2+1)^2} = \sqrt{10}$
$(x-3)^2 + 9 = 10$
$(x-3)^2 = 1$
$x - 3 = \pm 1$
$x = 3 \pm 1$
$x = 3 + 1 \quad \text{or} \quad x = 3 - 1$
$\quad = 4 \qquad\qquad = 2$
Both solutions check.

3. $(x-4)^2 + (y+3)^2 = 2^2$

4. Center $= (0, 0)$, radius $= 5$
$(x-0)^2 + (y-0)^2 = 5^2$
$x^2 + y^2 = 25$

5.

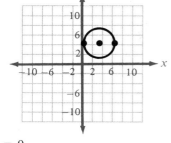

6.

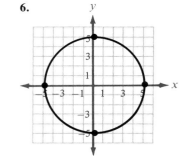

7. $x^2 + y^2 - 6x + 4y - 3 = 0$
$x^2 - 6x \qquad + y^2 + 4y = 3$
$x^2 - 6x + \mathbf{9} + y^2 + 4y + \mathbf{4} = 3 + \mathbf{9} + \mathbf{4}$
$(x-3)^2 + (y+2)^2 = 16$

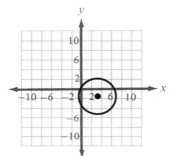

SECTION 9.3

1.

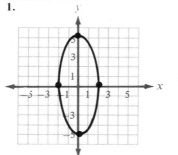

2.

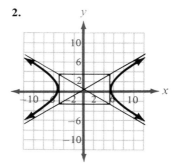

SECTION 9.4

1.

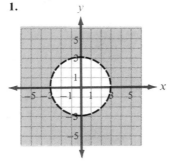

2.

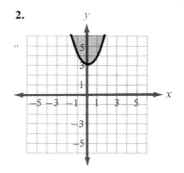

3.   *y*

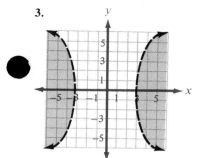

4.   *y*

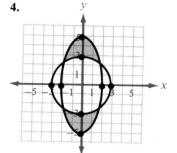

SECTION 9.5

1. $x^2 + y^2 = 9$
$x - y = 3$

Solving the bottom equation for x gives $x = y + 3$. Substituting $y + 3$ for x in the top equation we have
$$(y + 3)^2 + y^2 = 9$$
$$y^2 + 6y + 9 + y^2 = 9$$
$$2y^2 + 6y = 0$$
$$2y(y + 3) = 0$$
$$y = 0 \quad \text{or} \quad y = -3$$
Substituting these values of y into $x = y + 3$ gives $x = 3$ and $x = 0$, respectively. The two solutions are $(3, 0)$ and $(0, -3)$.

2. $16x^2 - 4y^2 = 64 \xrightarrow{\text{no change}} 16x^2 - 4y^2 = 64$
$x^2 + y^2 = 4 \xrightarrow[\text{times 4}]{} \underline{4x^2 + 4y^2 = 16}$
$$20x^2 = 80$$
$$x^2 = 4$$
$$x = \pm 2$$
Using the second equation in the original system, we have
When $x = 2$ $\qquad 2^2 + y^2 = 4 \Rightarrow y = 0$
When $x = -2$ $\quad (-2)^2 + y^2 = 4 \Rightarrow y = 0$
The two solutions are $(2, 0)$ and $(-2, 0)$.

3. $x^2 + y^2 = 4$
$y = x^2 - 4$

Substituting $x^2 - 4$ from the second equation in for y in the first equation yields
$$x^2 + (x^2 - 4)^2 = 4$$
$$x^2 + x^4 - 8x^2 + 16 = 4$$
$$x^4 - 7x^2 + 16 = 4$$
$$x^4 - 7x^2 + 12 = 0$$
$$(x^2 - 4)(x^2 - 3) = 0$$
$$x^2 = 4 \quad \text{or} \quad x^2 = 3$$
$$x = \pm 2 \quad \text{or} \quad x = \pm\sqrt{3}$$
Substituting these four values of x into the second equation in our system gives us four solutions: $(2, 0)$, $(-2, 0)$, $(\sqrt{3}, -1)$, $(-\sqrt{3}, -1)$.

4. Let x and y represent the two numbers.
$x^2 + y^2 = 58$
$y = x^2 - 2$
Substituting $x^2 - 2$ into the first equation in place of y gives us
$$x^2 + (x^2 - 2)^2 = 58$$
$$x^2 + x^4 - 4x^2 + 4 = 58$$
$$x^4 - 3x^2 - 54 = 0$$
$$(x^2 - 9)(x^2 + 6) = 0$$
$$x^2 = 9 \quad \text{or} \quad x^2 = -6$$
$$x = \pm 3 \quad \text{or} \quad x = \pm i\sqrt{6}$$
When $x = \pm 3, y = 7$
When $x = \pm i\sqrt{6}, y = -8$,
but since we have no way of comparing the size of a complex number like $i\sqrt{6}$ with a real number like -8, we cannot check the complex solutions. The only solutions are 3 and 1 and -3 and 1.

CHAPTER 10

SECTION 10.1

2. $(0, -3), (1, -1), (2, 1)$
$(\frac{1}{2}, -2), (-2, -7), (-10, -23)$

3. Relation a is also a function because no two different ordered pairs have the same first coordinates.

6. $x + 5 \geq 0$
$x \geq -5$

SECTION 10.2

1. a. $f(0) = 4(0)^2 - 3 = -3$
 b. $f(3) = 4(3)^2 - 3$
 $= 4 \cdot 9 - 3$
 $= 36 - 3$
 $= 33$
 c. $f(5) = 4(5)^2 - 3$
 $= 4 \cdot 25 - 3$
 $= 97$
 d. $f(-2) = 4(-2)^2 - 3$
 $= 4 \cdot 4 - 3$
 $= 13$

3. a. $f(5) = 2 \cdot 5 + 1 = 11$
 b. $g(5) = (5)^2 - 3 = 22$
 c. $f(-2) = 2(-2) + 1 = -3$
 d. $g(-2) = (-2)^2 - 3 = 1$
 e. $f(a) = 2a + 1$
 f. $g(a) = a^2 - 3$

4. a. $f[g(2)] = f[4 \cdot 2 + 1]$
 $= f(9)$
 $= 3(9)^2$
 $= 243$
 b. $g[f(2)] = g[3 \cdot 2^2]$
 $= g(12)$
 $= 4(12) + 1$
 $= 49$
 c. $f[g(x)] = f(4x + 1)$
 $= 3(4x + 1)^2$
 $= 48x^2 + 24x + 3$
 d. $g[f(x)] = g(3x^2)$
 $= 4(3x^2) + 1$
 $= 12x^2 + 1$

5.
$$\frac{f(x + h) - f(x)}{h} = \frac{5(x + h) - 2 - (5x - 2)}{h}$$
$$= \frac{5x + 5h - 2 - 5x + 2}{h}$$
$$= \frac{5h}{h}$$
$$= 5$$

6.
$$\frac{f(x) - f(a)}{x - a} = \frac{3x + 2 - (3a + 2)}{x - a}$$
$$= \frac{3x + 2 - 3a - 2}{x - a}$$
$$= \frac{3x - 3a}{x - a}$$
$$= \frac{3(x - a)}{x - a}$$
$$= 3$$

SECTION 10.3

1. a. $(f + g)(x) = f(x) + g(x)$
 $= 3x^2 + 4 + 2x - 1$
 $= 3x^2 + 2x + 3$
 b. $(f - g)(x) = f(x) - g(x)$
 $= 3x^2 + 4 - (2x - 1)$
 $= 3x^2 - 2x + 5$
 c. $(fg)(x) = f(x)\, g(x)$
 $= (3x^2 + 4)(2x - 1)$
 $= 6x^3 - 3x^2 + 8x - 4$
 d. $(f/g)(x) = \dfrac{f(x)}{g(x)}$
 $= \dfrac{3x^2 + 4}{2x - 1}$

2. a. $(f + g)(x) = f(x) + g(x)$
 $= 3x + 2 + 3x^2 - 10x - 8$
 $= 3x^2 - 7x - 6$
 b. $(fh)(x) = f(x)\, h(x)$
 $= (3x + 2)(x - 4)$
 $= 3x^2 - 10x - 8$
 $= g(x)$
 c. $(fg)(x) = f(x)\, g(x)$
 $= (3x + 2)(3x^2 - 10x - 8)$
 $= 9x^3 - 24x^2 - 44x - 16$
 d. $(g/f)(x) = \dfrac{g(x)}{f(x)}$
 $= \dfrac{3x^2 - 10x - 8}{3x + 2}$
 $= \dfrac{(3x + 2)(x - 4)}{3x + 2}$
 $= x - 4$
 $= h(x)$

3. a. $(f + g)(2) = 3(2)^2 - 7(2) - 6$
 $= 12 - 14 - 6$
 $= -8$
 b. $(fh)(-1) = 3(-1)^2 - 10(-1) - 8$
 $= 3 + 10 - 8$
 $= 5$
 c. $(fg)(0) = 9(0)^3 - 24(0)^2 - 44(0) - 16$
 $= -16$
 d. $\left(\dfrac{f}{g}\right)(5) = 5 - 4$
 $= 1$

SECTION 10.4

1.

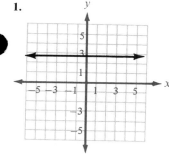

2.

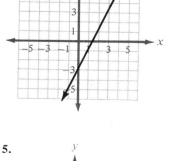

3.

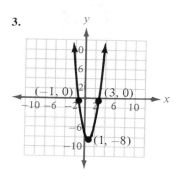

4. a. $f(0) = 4^0 = 1$
b. $f(1) = 4^1 = 4$
c. $f(2) = 4^2 = 16$
d. $f(3) = 4^3 = 64$

e. $f(-1) = 4^{-1} = \dfrac{1}{4}$

f. $f(-2) = 4^{-2} = \dfrac{1}{4^2} = \dfrac{1}{16}$

5.

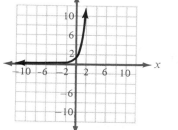

6.

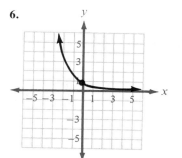

SECTION 10.5

1. The inverse of $y = 4x + 1$ is $x = 4y + 1$. Solving for y we have

$$4y + 1 = x$$
$$4y = x - 1$$
$$y = \frac{x - 1}{4}$$
$$f^{-1}(x) = \frac{x - 1}{4}$$

2. The equation of the inverse is
$$x = y^2 + 1 \text{ or } f^{-1}(x) = \pm\sqrt{x - 1}.$$

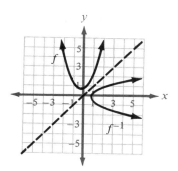

3. The equation of the inverse is
$$\frac{y^2}{4} + \frac{x^2}{16} = 1$$

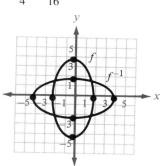

4.

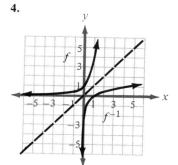

CHAPTER 11

SECTION 11.1

1. $\log_2 x = 3$ is equivalent to $x = 2^3 = 8$

2. $\log_x 5 = 2$ is equivalent to $x^2 = 5$
$x = \sqrt{5}$ only, since the base in a logarithmic statement cannot be negative.

3. $\log_9 27 = x$ is equivalent
to $\quad 9^x = 27$
$(3^2)^x = 3^3$
$3^{2x} = 3^3$
so $\quad 2x = 3$
$x = \dfrac{3}{2}$

4. First graph $y = 3^x$ and then reflect it about the line $y = x$ to obtain the graph of $y = \log_3 x$.

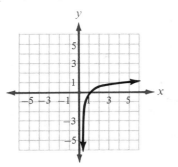

5. $\log_3 27 = \log_3 3^3$
$= 3$

6. $\log_{10} 1000 = \log_{10} 10^3$
$= 3$

7. $\log_6 6 = \log_6 6^1$
$= 1$

8. $\log_3 1 = \log_3 3^0$
$= 0$

9. $\log_2 (\log_8 8) = \log_2 1$
$= 0$

SECTION 11.2

1. $\log_3 \dfrac{5a}{b} = \log_3 5a - \log_3 b$
$= \log_3 5 + \log_3 a - \log_3 b$

2. $\log_{10} \dfrac{x^2}{\sqrt[3]{y}} = \log_{10} \dfrac{x^2}{y^{1/3}}$
$= \log_{10} x^2 - \log_{10} y^{1/3}$
$= 2 \log_{10} x - \tfrac{1}{3}\log_{10} y$

3. $3 \log_4 x + \log_4 y - 2 \log_4 z$
$= \log_4 x^3 + \log_4 y - \log_4 z^2$
$= \log_4 x^3 y - \log_4 z^2$
$= \log_4 \dfrac{x^3 y}{z^2}$

4. $\log_2 (x + 3) + \log_2 x = 2$
$\log_2 (x + 3)x = 2$
$(x + 3)x = 2^2$
$x^2 + 3x = 4$
$x^2 + 3x - 4 = 0$
$(x - 1)(x + 4) = 0$
$x = 1 \quad \text{or} \quad x = -4$
Since $x = -4$ would make the second term of our original equation undefined, the only solution is $x = 1$.

SECTION 11.3

1. $\log 27{,}600 = \log (2.76 \times 10^4)$
$= \log 2.76 + \log 10^4$
$= .4409 + 4$
$= 4.4409$

2. $\log 952 = \log (9.52 \times 10^2)$
$= \log 9.52 + \log 10^2$
$= .9786 + 2$
$= 2.9786$

3. $\log .00391 = \log (3.91 \times 10^{-3})$
$= \log 3.91 + \log 10^{-3}$
$= .5922 + (-3)$
$= 7.5922 - 10$

4. $\log .00952 = \log (9.52 \times 10^{-3})$
$= \log 9.52 + \log 10^{-3}$
$= .9786 + (-3)$
$= 7.9786 - 10$

5. The mantissa is .9786 which is the logarithm of 9.52. The characteristic is 3, so
$x = 9.52 \times 10^3$
or $x = 9520$

6. The mantissa is .4099 which is the logarithm of 2.57. The characteristic is $8 - 10 = -2$.
$x = 2.57 \times 10^{-2}$
or $x = .0257$

7. $n = (952)(39{,}100)$
$\log n = \log (952)(39{,}100)$
$= \log 952 + \log 39{,}100$
$= 2.9786 + 4.5922$
$\log n = 7.5708$
so $n = 3.72 \times 10^7$

8. $n = \sqrt{3780}$
$= (3780)^{1/2}$
$\log n = \log (3780)^{1/2}$
$= \tfrac{1}{2} \log 3780$
$= \tfrac{1}{2} (3.5775)$
$\log n = 1.7888$
so $n = 6.15 \times 10^1$
or $n = 61.5$

9. $n = \dfrac{(478)^3(5.62)}{\sqrt{9050}}$
$\log n = \log \dfrac{(478)^3(5.62)}{(9050)^{1/2}}$
$= 3 \log 478 + \log 5.62 - \tfrac{1}{2} \log 9050$
$= 3(2.6794) + (.7497) - \tfrac{1}{2}(3.9566)$
$= 8.0382 + .7497 - 1.9783$
$\log n = 6.8096$
so $n = 6.45 \times 10^6$

SECTION 11.4

1.
$$12^{x+2} = 20$$
$$\log 12^{x+2} = \log 20$$
$$(x+2)\log 12 = \log 20$$
$$x + 2 = \frac{\log 20}{\log 12}$$
$$x = \frac{\log 20}{\log 12} - 2$$
$$= \frac{1.3010}{1.0792} - 2$$
$$= -.7945$$

2. $\log_6 14 = \dfrac{\log 14}{\log 6}$
$$= \frac{1.1461}{.7782}$$
$$= 1.4728$$

3. $\log_{12} 478 = \dfrac{\log 478}{\log 12}$
$$= \frac{2.6794}{1.0792}$$
$$= 2.4828$$

SECTION 11.5

1. $-\log (4.8 \times 10^{-3})$
$$= -[.6812 + (-3)]$$
$$= -.6812 + 3$$
$$\cong 2.32$$

2. $-\log (H_2O^+) = 8.1$
$$\log (H_2O^+) = -8.1$$
$$= -8.1 + 10 - 10$$
$$= 1.9 - 10$$
$$(H_2O^+) = 7.94 \times 10^{-9}$$

3.
$$A = (3)2^{-1000/5600}$$
$$A = (3)2^{-5/28}$$
$$\log A = \log 3 - \tfrac{5}{28} \log 2$$
$$\log A = .4234$$
$$A = 2.65 \text{ grams}$$

4.
$$A = 5000 (1 + .08)^{10}$$
$$A = 5000 (1.08)^{10}$$
$$\log A = \log 5000 + 10 \log 1.08$$
$$= 3.6990 + 10(0.0334)$$
$$\log A = 4.0330$$
$$A = 1.08 \times 10^4$$
$$= \$10,800$$

5.
$$10,000 = 5,000(1 + .11)^t$$
$$10,000 = 5,000(1.11)^t$$
$$2 = (1.11)^t$$
$$\log 2 = t \log 1.11$$
$$t = \frac{\log 2}{\log 1.11}$$
$$= \frac{.3010}{.0453}$$
$$= 6.64 \text{ years}$$

APPENDIX A

1.
$$\begin{array}{r|rrrr}
-2 & 1 & 2 & -8 & 1 \\
 & \downarrow & -2 & 0 & 16 \\
\hline
 & 1 & 0 & -8 & 17
\end{array}$$
Answer: $x^2 - 8 + \dfrac{17}{x+2}$

2.
$$\begin{array}{r|rrrr}
3 & 2 & -5 & 0 & 3 \\
 & \downarrow & 6 & 3 & 9 \\
\hline
 & 2 & 1 & 3 & 12
\end{array}$$
Answer: $2x^2 + x + 3 + \dfrac{12}{x-3}$

3.
$$\begin{array}{r|rrrr}
-2 & 1 & 0 & 0 & 8 \\
 & \downarrow & -2 & 4 & -8 \\
\hline
 & 1 & -2 & 4 & 0
\end{array}$$
Answer: $x^2 - 2x + 4$

APPENDIX B

1. $ac = -24$
$b = -5$
Two numbers whose product is -24 and whose sum is -5 are -8 and 3.
$$8x^2 - 5x - 3 = 8x^2 - 8x + 3x - 3$$
$$= 8x(x - 1) + 3(x - 1)$$
$$= (x - 1)(8x + 3)$$

2. $ac = 24$
$b = 11$
Two numbers whose product is 24 and whose sum is 11 are 8 and 3.
$$4x^2 + 11x + 6 = 4x^2 + 8x + 3x + 6$$
$$= 4x(x + 2) + 3(x + 2)$$
$$= (x + 2)(4x + 3)$$

3. $ac = -60$
$b = -4$
Two numbers whose product is -60 and whose sum is -4 are -10 and 6.
$$4x^2 - 4x - 15 = 4x^2 - 10x + 6x - 15$$
$$= 2x(2x - 5) + 3(2x - 5)$$
$$= (2x - 5)(2x + 3)$$

APPENDIX C

1.

$A \cup (B \cup C)$

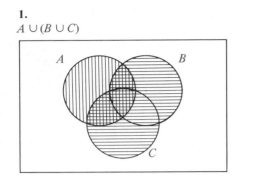

2.

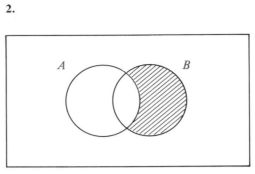

$(A \cup B) \cup C$

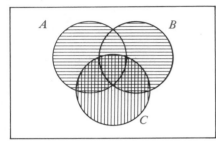

Answers to Odd-Numbered Exercises and Chapter Tests

CHAPTER 1

PROBLEM SET 1.1

1. $x + 5$ **3.** $6 - x$ **5.** $2t < y$ **7.** $\frac{3x}{2y} > 6$ **9.** $x + y < x - y$ **11.** $3(x - 5) > y$ **13.** $s - t \neq s + t$

15. $2(t + 3) \not> t - 6$ **17.** 36   **19.** 100   **21.** 8   **23.** 16   **25.** 10,000   **27.** 121   **29.** 19   **31.** 42   **33.** 55
35. 56   **37.** 21   **39.** 56   **41.** 41   **43.** 22   **45.** 2   **47.** 5,431   **49.** 50   **51.** 6   **53.** 2   **55.** 41   **57.** 138
59. {0, 1, 2, 3, 4, 5, 6}   **61.** {2, 4}   **63.** {−2, −1, 0, 1, 2, 3, 5, 7}   **65.** {1}   **67.** {−2, −1, 0, 1, 2, 4, 6}   **69.** {0, 2}
71. {0, 1, 2, 3, 4, 5, 6}   **73.** {2, 4}   **75.** {0, 2}   **77.** {0, 6}   **79.** {0, 1, 2, 3, 4, 5, 6, 7}   **81.** {1, 2, 4, 5}

PROBLEM SET 1.2

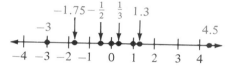

3. $4, -4, \frac{1}{4}$ **5.** $-\frac{1}{2}, \frac{1}{2}, -2$ **7.** $5, -5, \frac{1}{5}$ **9.** $\frac{3}{8}, -\frac{3}{8}, \frac{8}{3}$ **11.** $-\frac{1}{6}, \frac{1}{6}, -6$ **13.** $3, -3, \frac{1}{3}$ **15.** $\sqrt{3}, -\sqrt{3}, 1/\sqrt{3}$
17. $-1/\sqrt{2}, 1/\sqrt{2}, -\sqrt{2}$ **19.** $x, -x, 1/x$ **21.** $1, -1$ **23.** 0   **25.** 2   **27.** $\frac{3}{4}$ **29.** π **31.** -4 **33.** -2
35. $-\frac{3}{4}$ **37.** 2   **39.** $-\frac{1}{3}$ **41.** 5   **43.** 8   **45.** 5   **47.** 6   **49.** 0   **51.** {1, 2}   **53.** $\{-6, -5.2, 0, 1, 2, 2.3, \frac{9}{2}\}$
55. $\{-\sqrt{7}, -\pi, \sqrt{17}\}$ **57.** {0, 1, 2}   **59.** False; 1/0 undefined   **61.** True   **63.** True   **65.** False; 0/1 = 0, 0 is rational
67. True   **69.** True   **71.** $\frac{21}{40}$ **73.** $\frac{12}{5}$ **75.** $\frac{120}{17}$ **77.** $\frac{280}{9}$ **79.** $\frac{72}{385}$ **81.** 1   **83.** 1   **85.** 2   **87.** 1
89. -3 and 7   **91.** $1 = 0.999\ldots$ **93.** $0.282828\ldots$ **95.** $-\$15$ **97.** -6 and 6

PROBLEM SET 1.3

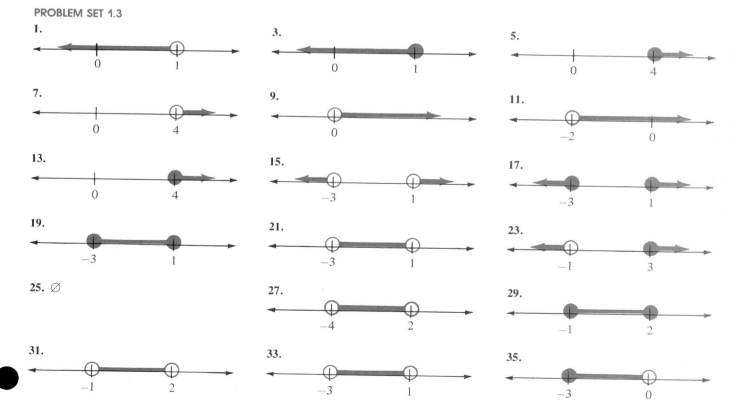

37.

39.

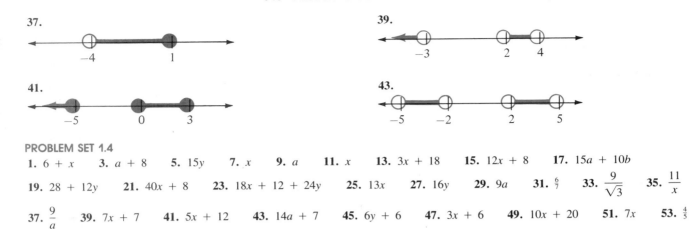

41.

43.

PROBLEM SET 1.4

1. $6 + x$ **3.** $a + 8$ **5.** $15y$ **7.** x **9.** a **11.** x **13.** $3x + 18$ **15.** $12x + 8$ **17.** $15a + 10b$

19. $28 + 12y$ **21.** $40x + 8$ **23.** $18x + 12 + 24y$ **25.** $13x$ **27.** $16y$ **29.** $9a$ **31.** $\frac{6}{7}$ **33.** $\frac{9}{\sqrt{3}}$ **35.** $\frac{11}{x}$

37. $\frac{9}{a}$ **39.** $7x + 7$ **41.** $5x + 12$ **43.** $14a + 7$ **45.** $6y + 6$ **47.** $3x + 6$ **49.** $10x + 20$ **51.** $7x$ **53.** $\frac{4}{5}$

55. Commutative **57.** Commutative **59.** Additive inverse **61.** Commutative **63.** Associative and commutative

65. Associative and commutative **67.** Distributive **69.** $y \cdot 5$ **71.** $a + 3$ **73.** 7 **75.** $(2 + x) + 6$ **77.** $xy + 2y$

79. 11

PROBLEM SET 1.5

1. 4 **3.** -4 **5.** -8 **7.** -5 **9.** 5 **11.** -13 **13.** -14 **15.** 4 **17.** -10 **19.** -4 **21.** 10

23. -35 **25.** 16 **27.** 3 **29.** -5 **31.** 1 **33.** 19 **35.** -14 **37.** 10 **39.** -1 **41.** 11 **43.** -4

45. -3 **47.** 8 **49.** 16 **51.** $2x - 8$ **53.** $5y - 15$ **55.** $7x - 28$ **57.** $4a - 8 + 4b$ **59.** $5x - 5y - 20$

61. $3x$ **63.** $-13x$ **65.** $4y$ **67.** a **69.** $-6x$ **71.** $-11a$ **73.** $2x$ **75.** $7x - 14$ **77.** $x + 7$

79. $-3a + 2$ **81.** 13 **83.** $2t - 1$ **85.** -8 **87.** $-7x$ **89.** 13 **91.** $6a$ **93.** $15x - 20$ **95.** $3y + 8$

PROBLEM SET 1.6

1. -15 **3.** 15 **5.** -24 **7.** 20 **9.** -12 **11.** -24 **13.** -24 **15.** 24 **17.** $-10x$ **19.** $-21a$

21. $-32y$ **23.** $15x$ **25.** $-5x - 40$ **27.** $-8x - 6$ **29.** $-12x + 30$ **31.** -2 **33.** 2 **35.** $-\frac{2}{3}$ **37.** 32

39. 64 **41.** $-\frac{1}{18}$ **43.** $\frac{4}{3}$ **45.** -14 **47.** -7 **49.** 18 **51.** -44 **53.** -30 **55.** 18 **57.** 4 **59.** $\frac{5}{3}$

61. 11 **63.** 12 **65.** $14x + 12$ **67.** $-a - 12$ **69.** $3x + 13$ **71.** $-7m + 27$ **73.** $-2x + 9$ **75.** $y + 6$

77. $7y + 10$ **79.** $-11x + 10$ **81.** -3 **83.** -11 **85.** $2x$

PROBLEM SET 1.7

1. 17 **3.** 14 **5.** 37 **7.** 13 **9.** 12 **11.** 14 **13.** -2 **15.** 50 **17.** 64 **19.** 625 **21.** 28 **23.** $\frac{1}{27}$

25. 2 **27.** 3.6 **29.** 39.98 **31.** 44.7083 **33.** 11.46 **35.** 31.95 **37.** -59.9298 **39.** -675 **41.** 141

43. 146.41 **45.** 3,844 **47.** 2 **49.** 0.4345238

CHAPTER 1 TEST

1. $2(3x + 4y)$ **2.** $(2a - 3b) < (2a + 3b)$ **3.** 57 **4.** 10 **5.** 16 **6.** 0 **7.** $\{1, 3\}$ **8.** $\varnothing$ **9.** $3, -\frac{1}{3}$

10. $-\frac{4}{3}, \frac{3}{4}$ **11.** 3 **12.** -2 **13.** $\{-5, 0, 1, 4\}$ **14.** $\{-5, -4.1, -3.75, -\frac{5}{6}, 0, 1, 1.8, 4\}$ **15.** $\{-\sqrt{2}, \sqrt{3}\}$

16. All of them

17.

18.

19. Commutative property of addition **20.** Multiplicative identity property

21. Associative and commutative property of multiplication **22.** Associative and commutative property of addition **23.** -19

24. 14 **25.** -19 **26.** 14 **27.** -26 **28.** $\frac{5}{2}$ **29.** 2 **30.** 1 **31.** 0 **32.** 1 **33.** $24x$ **34.** $-10x$

35. $5x + 15$ **36.** $-2x - 18$ **37.** $-6x - 12$ **38.** $-12x - 8$ **39.** $-6x + 10y - 8$ **40.** $7x$ **41.** $4x$

42. $-4x$ **43.** $2x$ **44.** $-6x - 4$ **45.** $4y - 10$ **46.** $3x - 17$ **47.** $11a - 10$ **48.** $-\frac{7}{3}$ **49.** $-\frac{5}{2}$ **50.** 16

CHAPTER 2

PROBLEM SET 2.1

1. 8 **3.** 5 **5.** 2 **7.** -7 **9.** -4 **11.** $\frac{7}{2}$ **13.** $-\frac{11}{5}$ **15.** 12 **17.** -10 **19.** 7 **21.** -7 **23.** 3

25. 3 **27.** $\frac{4}{5}$ **29.** 3 **31.** No **33.** $12x - 7$ **35.** $7y - 3$ **37.** $-12x + 14$

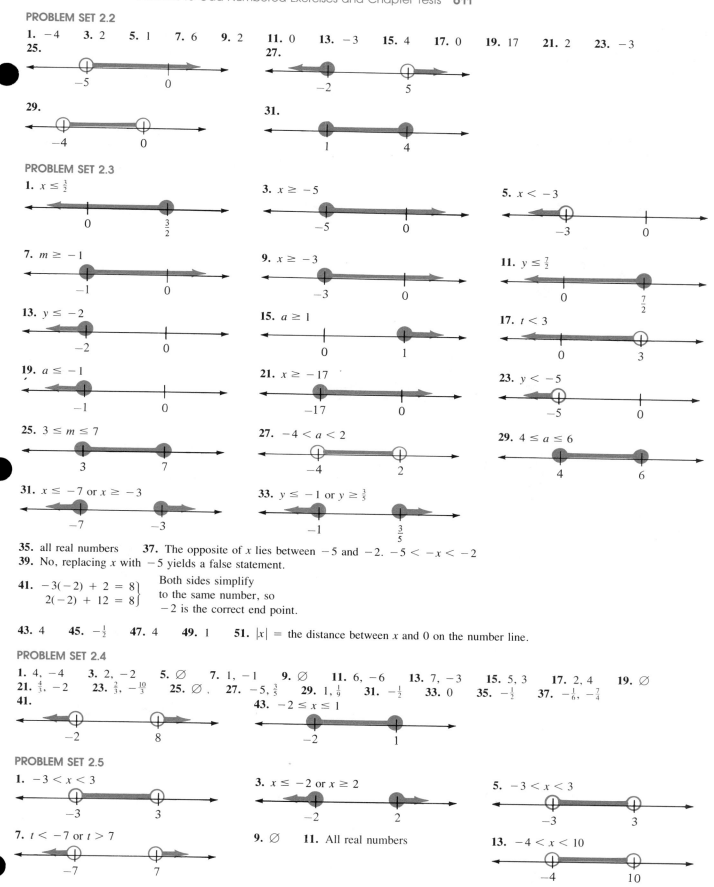

PROBLEM SET 2.2

1. -4 **3.** 2 **5.** 1 **7.** 6 **9.** 2 **11.** 0 **13.** -3 **15.** 4 **17.** 0 **19.** 17 **21.** 2 **23.** -3
25.
27.

29.
31.

PROBLEM SET 2.3

1. $x \leq \frac{3}{2}$

3. $x \geq -5$

5. $x < -3$

7. $m \geq -1$

9. $x \geq -3$

11. $y \leq \frac{7}{2}$

13. $y \leq -2$

15. $a \geq 1$

17. $t < 3$

19. $a \leq -1$

21. $x \geq -17$

23. $y < -5$

25. $3 \leq m \leq 7$

27. $-4 < a < 2$

29. $4 \leq a \leq 6$

31. $x \leq -7$ or $x \geq -3$

33. $y \leq -1$ or $y \geq \frac{3}{5}$

35. all real numbers   **37.** The opposite of x lies between -5 and -2. $-5 < -x < -2$
39. No, replacing x with -5 yields a false statement.

41. $\left.\begin{array}{r} -3(-2) + 2 = 8 \\ 2(-2) + 12 = 8 \end{array}\right\}$ Both sides simplify to the same number, so -2 is the correct end point.

43. 4 **45.** $-\frac{1}{2}$ **47.** 4 **49.** 1 **51.** $|x| =$ the distance between x and 0 on the number line.

PROBLEM SET 2.4

1. $4, -4$ **3.** $2, -2$ **5.** $\varnothing$ **7.** $1, -1$ **9.** $\varnothing$ **11.** $6, -6$ **13.** $7, -3$ **15.** $5, 3$ **17.** $2, 4$ **19.** $\varnothing$
21. $\frac{4}{3}, -2$ **23.** $\frac{2}{3}, -\frac{10}{3}$ **25.** $\varnothing$ **27.** $-5, \frac{3}{5}$ **29.** $1, \frac{1}{9}$ **31.** $-\frac{1}{2}$ **33.** 0 **35.** $-\frac{1}{2}$ **37.** $-\frac{1}{6}, -\frac{7}{4}$
41.
43. $-2 \leq x \leq 1$

PROBLEM SET 2.5

1. $-3 < x < 3$

3. $x \leq -2$ or $x \geq 2$

5. $-3 < x < 3$

7. $t < -7$ or $t > 7$

9. $\varnothing$ **11.** All real numbers

13. $-4 < x < 10$

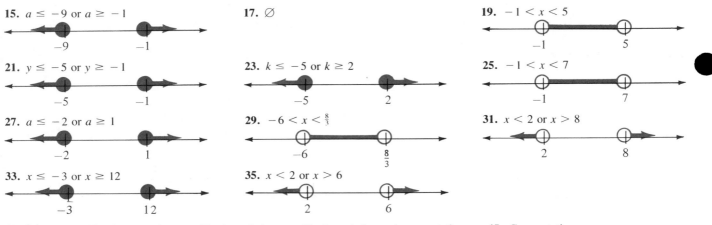

15. $a \leq -9$ or $a \geq -1$ **17.** $\varnothing$ **19.** $-1 < x < 5$

21. $y \leq -5$ or $y \geq -1$ **23.** $k \leq -5$ or $k \geq 2$ **25.** $-1 < x < 7$

27. $a \leq -2$ or $a \geq 1$ **29.** $-6 < x < \frac{8}{3}$ **31.** $x < 2$ or $x > 8$

33. $x \leq -3$ or $x \geq 12$ **35.** $x < 2$ or $x > 6$

37. $|x| \leq 4$ **39.** Commutative   **41.** Associative   **43.** Associative and commutative   **45.** Commutative

PROBLEM SET 2.6

1. 6   **3.** 4   **5.** 5   **7.** 1   **9.** 8   **11.** 21   **13.** $l = \dfrac{A}{w}$ **15.** $t = \dfrac{I}{pr}$ **17.** $T = \dfrac{PV}{nR}$ **19.** $b = y - mx$

21. $c = 2s - a - b$ **23.** $r = \dfrac{A - P}{Pt}$ **25.** $F = \dfrac{9}{5}C + 32$ **27.** $d = \dfrac{A - a}{n - 1}$ **29.** $y = 3x - 2$ **31.** $x = zs + \mu$

33. $x = \dfrac{5}{a - b}$ **35.** $P = \dfrac{A}{1 + rt}$ **37.** $x = \dfrac{d - b}{a - c}$ **39.** $\mu - 2.5s < x < \mu + 2.5s$ **41.** $30° \leq C \leq 40°$

43. $2(x + 3)$ **45.** $5(x - 3)$ **47.** $3x + 2 = x - 4$

PROBLEM SET 2.7

Along with the answers to the odd-numbered problems in this problem set we are including the equations used to solve each problem. Be sure that you try the problems on your own before looking here to see what the correct equations are.

1. $x + 2 = 2x - 5$; 7   **3.** $3(x + 4) = 3$; -3 **5.** $2(2x + 1) = 3(x - 5)$; -17 **7.** $5x + 2 = 3x + 8$; 3

9. $x + (x + 2) = 18$; 8 and 10   **11.** $x + (x + 1) = 3x - 1$; 2 and 3   **13.** $2x + (x + 1) = 7$; 2

15. $2x - (x + 2) = 5$; 7 and 9   **17.** The width is x, the length is $2x$; $2x + 4x = 60$; 10 ft by 20 ft

19. The length of a side is x; $4x = 28$; 7 ft   **21.** The shortest side is x, the medium side is $x + 3$, the longest side is $2x$;

$x + (x + 3) + 2x = 23$; 5 inches   **23.** The width is x, the length is $2x - 3$; $2(2x - 3) + 2x = 18$; 4 meters

25. Amy's age is x, Patrick's age is $x + 4$; $x + 10 + x + 14 = 36$; Amy is 6, Patrick is 10

27. Kate's age is x, Jane's age is $3x$; $3x + 5 = 2(x + 5) - 2$; Kate is 3, Jane is 9   **29.** $x = .54(38) = 20.52$

31. $x \cdot 36 = 9$; 25%   **33.** $37 = .04x$; 925   **35.** 18   **37.** 24   **39.** 10

PROBLEM SET 2.8

1. $x = 2(24 - x)$; 16 and 8   **3.** $x = 2(16 - x) - 2$; 10 and 6   **5.** $5x + 10(36 - x) = 280$; 16 nickels, 20 dimes

7. $5x + 25(26 - x) = 250$; 20 nickels, 6 quarters   **9.** $.08x + .09(9,000 - x) = 750$; $6,000 at 8%, $3,000 at 9%

11. $5,000 at 12%, $10,000 at 10%   **13.** $.08x + .09(6,000 - x) = 500$; $4,000 at 8%, $2,000 at 9%

15. $x < 4$ **17.** $x \geq -6$ **19.** $-2 < x < 1$

CHAPTER 2 TEST

1. 12   **2.** $-\frac{4}{3}$ **3.** $\frac{17}{3}$ **4.** -3 **5.** $-\frac{7}{4}$ **6.** 2   **7.** $t \geq -6$

8. $x \leq 1$ **9.** $x < 6$ **10.** $y \geq -52$

11. 6, 2   **12.** $-1, -6$ **13.** $x < -1$ or $x > \frac{4}{3}$ **14.** $-\frac{2}{3} \leq x \leq 4$

15. $w = \dfrac{A - 2l}{2}$ **16.** $B = \dfrac{2A}{h} - b$ **17.** $x + (x + 2) = 18$; 8 and 10   **18.** $x + 9 = 2x$; 9 and 13

19. $x = 2(19 - x) + 4$; 14 and 5   **20.** $5x + 10(14 - x) = 110$; 6 nickels, 8 dimes

CHAPTER 3

PROBLEM SET 3.1

1. 16 **3.** -16 **5.** -27 **7.** 32 **9.** $\frac{1}{8}$ **11.** $\frac{25}{36}$ **13.** x^9 **15.** 64 **17.** $-8x^6$ **19.** $-6a^6$ **21.** $-36x^{11}$
23. $324n^{34}$ **25.** $\frac{1}{9}$ **27.** $-\frac{1}{32}$ **29.** $\frac{1}{9}$ **31.** $\frac{16}{9}$ **33.** 17 **35.** -4 **37.** x^3 **39.** $\frac{a^6}{b^{15}}$ **41.** $\frac{48}{x^5}$ **43.** $\frac{8}{125y^{18}}$

45. $\frac{1}{x^3}$ **47.** y^3 **49.** 3.78×10^5 **51.** 4.9×10^3 **53.** 3.7×10^{-4} **55.** 4.95×10^{-3} **57.** 5.62×10^{-1}

59. 5,340 **61.** 7,800,000 **63.** 0.00344 **65.** 0.49 **67.** $(2 + 4)^{-1} = 6^{-1} = \frac{1}{6}, 2^{-1} + 4^{-1} = \frac{1}{2} + \frac{1}{4} = \frac{3}{4}$
69. 22 **71.** 14 **73.** 14 **75.** -1 **77.** 5

PROBLEM SET 3.2

1. $\frac{x^6}{y^4}$ **3.** $\frac{4b^2}{a^4}$ **5.** $\frac{1}{9}$ **7.** 8 **9.** $\frac{1}{x^{10}}$ **11.** $2a$ **13.** $\frac{1}{81}$ **15.** x^6 **17.** $\frac{b^7}{a}$ **19.** x^4y^6 **21.** $\frac{4n^5}{m^2}$ **23.** $\frac{x^5}{3}$

25. $\frac{4x^{18}}{y^{10}}$ **27.** $\frac{b^3}{a^4c^3}$ **29.** $\frac{x^{10}}{y^{15}}$ **31.** x^5 **33.** a **35.** 1 **37.** 8×10^4 **39.** 9×10^{10} **41.** 2×10^9

43. 2×10^{-4} **45.** 2.5×10^{-6} **47.** 1.8×10^{-7} **49.** 4.98×10^1 **51.** 2×10^8 **53.** 2×10^4 **55.** 2.78×10^7
57. 6 **59.** 9 **61.** -7 **63.** 1.003×10^{19} **65.** $2x + 12$ **67.** 3 **69.** $6y - 3$ **71.** $-4x + 38$

PROBLEM SET 3.3

1. Trinomial 2 5 **3.** Binomial 1 3 **5.** Trinomial 2 8 **7.** Polynomial 3 4 **9.** Monomial 0 $-\frac{3}{4}$
11. Trinomial 3 6 **13.** $7x + 1$ **15.** $2x^2 + 7x - 15$ **17.** $12a^2 - 7ab - 10b^2$ **19.** $x^2 - 13x + 3$
21. $3x^2 - 7x - 3$ **23.** $-y^3 - y^2 - 4y + 7$ **25.** $2x^3 + x^2 - 3x - 17$ **27.** $x^2 + 2xy + 10y^2$
29. $-3a^3 + 6a^2b - 5ab^2$ **31.** $-3x$ **33.** $3x^2 - 12xy$ **35.** $17x^5 - 12$ **37.** $14a^2 - 2ab + 8b^2$ **39.** $2 - x$
41. $10x - 5$ **43.** $9x - 35$ **45.** $9y - 4x$ **47.** $9a + 2$ **49.** -2 **51.** 5 **53.** -15
55. $(3 + 4)^2 = 49; 3^2 + 16 = 25; 3^2 + 8 \cdot 3 + 16 = 49$ **57.** 240 feet **59.** The sum of the first n odd numbers is n^2.
61. $20x^5$ **63.** $2a^3b^3$ **65.** $6x^3$ **67.** $-2x^2y$

PROBLEM SET 3.4

1. $12x^3 - 10x^2 + 8x$ **3.** $-3a^5 + 18a^4 - 21a^2$ **5.** $2a^5b - 2a^3b^2 + 2a^2b^4$ **7.** $x^2 - 2x - 15$ **9.** $6x^2 - 19x + 15$
11. $x^3 + 9x^2 + 23x + 15$ **13.** $a^3 - b^3$ **15.** $8x^3 + y^3$ **17.** $2a^3 - a^2b - ab^2 - 3b^3$ **19.** $6x^4 - 44x^3 + 70x^2$
21. $x^2 + x - 6$ **23.** $x^2 - 5x + 6$ **25.** $6a^2 + 13a + 6$ **27.** $6x^2 + 2x - 20$ **29.** $5x^2 - 29x + 20$
31. $20a^2 + 9a + 1$ **33.** $20x^2 - 9xy - 18y^2$ **35.** $8x^2 - 22xy + 15y^2$ **37.** $28a^2 - ab - 2b^2$ **39.** $x^4 + 3x^2 + 2$
41. $x^4 - 3x^2 - 10$ **43.** $x^2 + ax + bx + ab$ **45.** $x^2 - 25$ **47.** $4x^2 - 9y^2$ **49.** $x^4 - 9$
51. $(2 + 3)^2 = 25, 2^2 + 2(2)(3) + 3^2 = 25, 2^2 + 3^2 = 13$ **53.** 4 **55.** $\frac{5}{3}$

PROBLEM SET 3.5

1. $x^2 + 10x + 25$ **3.** $x^2 - 6x + 9$ **5.** $a^2 - 2a + 1$ **7.** $a^2 + 8a + 16$ **9.** $y^2 - 12y + 36$ **11.** $x^2 + 4x + 4$
13. $4a^2 - 12a + 9$ **15.** $25x^2 + 20xy + 4y^2$ **17.** $25x^2 - 20xy + 4y^2$ **19.** $x^2 - 9$ **21.** $a^2 - 1$ **23.** $y^2 - 64$
25. $x^4 - 36$ **27.** $4a^2 - 9b^2$ **29.** $9r^2 - 49s^2$ **31.** $25x^2 - 16y^2$ **33.** $x^4 + 4x^2 + 4$ **35.** $x^4 - 2x^2y^2 + y^4$
37. $x^2 - \frac{1}{4}$ **39.** $a^2 + a + \frac{1}{4}$ **41.** $x^3 + 6x^2 + 12x + 8$ **43.** $a^3 - 3a^2 + 3a - 1$ **45.** $x^4 - 81$ **47.** 2, -4
49. 0, -14

PROBLEM SET 3.6

1. $2x^2 - 4x + 3$ **3.** $-2x^2 - 3x + 4$ **5.** $2y^2 + \frac{5}{2} - \frac{3}{2y^2}$ **7.** $-\frac{5}{2}x + 4 + \frac{3}{x}$ **9.** $4ab^3 + 6a^2b$

11. $-xy + 2y^2 + 3xy^2$ **13.** $\frac{4x^2}{y} - 3x + 5y + \frac{2y^2}{x}$ **15.** $a^{6N} - a^{3N}$ **17.** $4x^{5m} - 3x^{2m} + 2$ **19.** $x - 7 + \frac{7}{x + 2}$

21. $2x + 5 + \frac{2}{3x - 4}$ **23.** $2x^2 - 5x + 1 + \frac{4}{x + 1}$ **25.** $4x + 3y + \frac{18y^2}{2x - 3y}$ **27.** $x^3 + 2x^2 + 4x + 6 + \frac{17}{x - 2}$
29. $y^3 + 2y^2 + 4y + 8$ **31.** $x^2 + xy + y^2$ **33.** $25x^5 + 20x^4 - 30x^3$ **35.** $x^2 + 5x + xy + 5y$

PROBLEM SET 3.7

1. $5x^2(2x - 3)$ **3.** $9y^3(y^3 + 2)$ **5.** $3ab(3a - 2b)$ **7.** $7xy^2(3y^2 + x)$ **9.** $3(a^2 - 7a + 10)$ **11.** $4x(x^2 - 4x - 5)$
13. $10x^2y^2(x^2 + 2xy - 3y^2)$ **15.** $xy(-x + y - xy)$ **17.** $2xy^2z(2x^2 - 4xz + 3z^2)$ **19.** $5abc(4abc - 6b + 5ac)$
21. $(a - 2b)(5x - 3y)$ **23.** $3(x + y)^2(x^2 - 2y^2)$ **25.** $(x + 5)(2x^2 + 7x + 6)$ **27.** $(x + 1)(3y + 2a)$
29. $(x + 3)(xy + 1)$ **31.** $(a + b)(1 + 5x)$ **33.** $3(3x - 2y)$ **35.** $(x - 2)(3y^2 + 4)$ **37.** $(x - 4)(2y^3 + 1)$
39. $(x - a)(x - b)$ **41.** $(b + 5)(a - 1)$ **43.** $(b^2 + 1)(a^4 - 5)$ **45.** 6 **47.** $x^2 + 5x + 6$ **49.** $x^2 - x - 6$
51. $x^2 - 7x + 6$

PROBLEM SET 3.8

1. $(x + 3)(x + 4)$ **3.** $(x + 3)(x - 4)$ **5.** $(y + 3)(y - 2)$ **7.** $(x + 2)(x - 8)$ **9.** $(x + 2)(x + 6)$
11. $3(a - 2)(a - 5)$ **13.** $4x(x - 5)(x + 1)$ **15.** $(x + 2y)(x + y)$ **17.** $(a + 6b)(a - 3b)$ **19.** $(x - 8a)(x + 6a)$
21. $(x - 6b)^2$ **23.** $3(x - 3y)(x + y)$ **25.** $2a^3(a^2 + 2ab + 2b^2)$ **27.** $10x^2y^2(x + 3y)(x - y)$ **29.** $(2x - 3)(x + 5)$
31. $(2x - 5)(x + 3)$ **33.** $(2x - 3)(x - 5)$ **35.** $(2x - 5)(x - 3)$ **37.** prime   **39.** $(2a + 1)(3a + 2)$
41. $(4y + 3)(y - 1)$ **43.** $(3x - 2)(2x + 1)$ **45.** $(2r - 3)^2$ **47.** $(4x + y)(x - 3y)$ **49.** $(2x - 3a)(5x + 6a)$
51. $(3a + 4b)(6a - 7b)$ **53.** $2(2x - 1)(2x + 3)$ **55.** $y^2(3y - 2)(3y + 5)$ **57.** $2a^2(2a - 3)(3a + 4)$
59. $2x^2y^2(4x + 3y)(x - y)$ **61.** $(3x^2 + 1)(x^2 + 3)$ **63.** $(5a^2 + 3)(4a^2 + 5)$ **65.** $3(4r^2 - 3)(r^2 + 1)$
67. $(x + 5)(2x + 3)(x + 2)$ **69.** $(2x + 3)(x + 5)(x + 2)$ **71.** $9x^2 - 25y^2$ **73.** $a + 250$ **75.** $x^2 + 6x + 9$
77. $4x^2 - 20x + 25$ **79.** $x^3 + 8$

PROBLEM SET 3.9

1. $(x - 3)^2$ **3.** $(a - 6)^2$ **5.** $(3x + 4)^2$ **7.** $(4a + 5b)^2$ **9.** $4(2x - 3)^2$ **11.** $3a(5a + 1)^2$ **13.** $(x + 3)(x - 3)$
15. $(2a + 1)(2a - 1)$ **17.** $(3x + 4y)(3x - 4y)$ **19.** $(x - 3)(x + 3)(x^2 + 9)$ **21.** $(2a - 3)(2a + 3)(4a^2 + 9)$
23. $(x - y)(x + y)(x^2 + xy + y^2)(x^2 - xy + y^2)$ **25.** $(a - 2)(a + 2)(a^2 + 2a + 4)(a^2 - 2a + 4)$ **27.** $5(x - 5)(x + 5)$
29. $3(a^2 + 4)(a - 2)(a + 2)$ **31.** $(x - 5)(x + 1)$ **33.** $y(y + 8)$ **35.** $(2 - a)(8 + a)$ **37.** $(x - 5 + y)(x - 5 - y)$
39. $(a + 4 + b)(a + 4 - b)$ **41.** $(x + y + a)(x + y - a)$ **43.** $(x - y)(x^2 + xy + y^2)$ **45.** $(a + 2)(a^2 - 2a + 4)$
47. $(y - 1)(y^2 + y + 1)$ **49.** $(r - 5)(r^2 + 5r + 25)$ **51.** $(2x - 3y)(4x^2 + 6xy + 9y^2)$ **53.** $x \geq -7$ **55.** $a < 6$
57. $x > 2$

PROBLEM SET 3.10

1. $(x + 9)(x - 9)$ **3.** $(x - 3)(x + 5)$ **5.** $(x + 2)(x + 3)^2$ **7.** $(x^2 + 2)(y^2 + 1)$ **9.** $2ab(a^2 + 3a + 1)$
11. Does not factor   **13.** $3(2a + 5)(2a - 5)$ **15.** $(3x - 2y)^2$ **17.** $4x(x^2 + 4y^2)$ **19.** $2y(y + 5)^2$
21. $a^4(a + 2b)(a^2 - 2ab + 4b^2)$ **23.** $(x^2 + 4)(x + 2)(x - 2)$ **25.** $5(a + b)^2$ **27.** Does not factor
29. $3(x + 2y)(x + 3y)$ **31.** $(x - 3)(x - 7)^2$ **33.** $(x + 8)(x - 8)$ **35.** $a^5(7a + 3)(7a - 3)$ **37.** Does not factor
39. $a(5a + 3)(5a + 1)$ **41.** $3a^2b(2a - 1)(4a^2 + 2a + 1)$ **43.** $5x^2(2x + 3)(2x - 3)$ **45.** $2x^3(4x - 5)(2x - 3)$
47. $(y + 1)(y^2 - y + 1)(y - 1)(y^2 + y + 1)$ **49.** $3x^2y^2(2x + 3y)^2$ **51.** $(x - 2 - y)(x - 2 + y)$
53. $-5 < x < 1$ **55.** $x \leq -1$ or $x \geq 2$

CHAPTER 3 TEST

1. x^8 **2.** $\frac{1}{32}$ **3.** $\frac{16}{9}$ **4.** $32x^{12}y^{11}$ **5.** a^2 **6.** x^6 **7.** $\frac{2a^{12}}{b^{15}}$ **8.** 6.53×10^6 **9.** 8.7×10^{-4} **10.** 8.7×10^7

11. 3×10^8 **12.** $3x^3 - 5x^2 - 8x - 4$ **13.** $4x + 75$ **14.** $6y^2 + y - 35$ **15.** $2x^3 + 3x^2 - 26x + 15$

16. $16a^2 - 24ab + 9b^2$ **17.** $36y^2 - 1$ **18.** $4x^3 - 2x^2 - 30x$ **19.** $3x^4 - \frac{3x}{2y} + 2x^2y^2$ **20.** $x^2 - 4x - 2 + \frac{8}{2x - 1}$

21. $(x + 4)(x - 3)$ **22.** $2(3x - 1)(2x + 5)$ **23.** $(4a^2 + 9y^2)(2a + 3y)(2a - 3y)$ **24.** $(7a - b^2)(x^2 - 2y)$
25. $(x + 3)(x^2 - 3x + 9)$ **26.** $4a^3b(a - 8b)(a + 2b)$ **27.** $(x - 5 + b)(x - 5 - b)$ **28.** $(x^2 + 9)(x + 3)(x - 3)$
29. $(x + 2)(x - 2)^2$ **30.** $4a^2(a - 2)(a^2 + 2a + 4)$

CHAPTER 4

PROBLEM SET 4.1

1. $\frac{x - 4}{6}$ **3.** $\frac{4x - 3y}{x(x + y)}$ **5.** $(a^2 + 9)(a + 3)$ **7.** $y + 3$ **9.** $\frac{a - 6}{a + 6}$ **11.** $\frac{2y + 3}{y + 1}$ **13.** $\frac{x - 2}{x - 1}$ **15.** $\frac{x - 3}{x + 2}$

17. $\frac{a^2 - ab + b^2}{a - b}$ **19.** $\frac{2x + 3y}{2x + y}$ **21.** $\frac{x + 3}{y - 4}$ **23.** $\frac{x + b}{x - 2b}$ **25.** -1 **27.** $-(y + 6)$ **29.** $\frac{-(3a + 1)}{3a - 1}$ **31.** -1

39. $\frac{21}{10}$ **41.** $\frac{11}{8}$ **43.** $\frac{1}{18}$ **45.** 32

PROBLEM SET 4.2

1. $\frac{1}{6}$ **3.** $\frac{9}{4}$ **5.** $\frac{1}{2}$ **7.** $\frac{15y}{x^2}$ **9.** $\frac{b}{a}$ **11.** $\frac{2y^5}{z^3}$ **13.** $\frac{x + 3}{x + 2}$ **15.** $y + 1$ **17.** $\frac{3(x + 4)}{x - 2}$ **19.** $\frac{(a - 2)(a + 2)}{a - 5}$

21. $\frac{x + 3}{x + 4}$ **23.** 1 **25.** $\frac{x - 1}{x^2 + 1}$ **27.** $\frac{(a + 4)(a - 3)}{(a - 4)(a + 5)}$ **29.** $\frac{(y - 2)(y + 1)}{(y + 2)(y - 1)}$ **31.** $\frac{x - 1}{x + 1}$ **33.** $3x$ **35.** $2(x + 5)$

37. $x - 2$ **39.** $-(y - 4)$ **41.** $(a - 5)(a + 1)$

43. $x < -2$ or $x > 8$ **45.** $1 < x < 4$ **47.** $-2 \leq x \leq 1$

PROBLEM SET 4.3

1. $\frac{5}{4}$ **3.** $\frac{1}{3}$ **5.** $\frac{41}{24}$ **7.** $\frac{19}{144}$ **9.** $\frac{31}{24}$ **11.** 1   **13.** -1 **15.** $\frac{1}{x + y}$ **17.** 1   **19.** 1   **21.** $(x + $.'

23. $\frac{6x + 5}{(x + 1)(x - 1)}$ **25.** $\frac{2(2x - 3)}{(x - 3)(x - 2)}$ **27.** $\frac{4}{(a - 3)(a + 1)}$ **29.** $\frac{1}{(y + 4)(y + 3)}$ **31.** $\frac{a}{(a + 4)(a + 5)}$.

33. $\frac{x + 1}{(x - 2)(x + 3)}$ **35.** $\frac{1}{(x + 2)(x + 1)}$ **37.** $\frac{4x + 5}{2x + 1}$ **39.** $\frac{2x - 3}{2x}$ **41.** $\frac{1}{2}$ **43.** $\frac{51}{10}$ **45.** y **47.** $2x - 1$

49. $\frac{1}{(x - 1)(x - 2)}$

PROBLEM SET 4.4

1. $\frac{9}{8}$ **3.** $\frac{2}{15}$ **5.** $\frac{119}{20}$ **7.** $\frac{1}{x + 1}$ **9.** $\frac{a + 1}{a - 1}$ **11.** $\frac{y - x}{y + x}$ **13.** $\frac{1}{(x + 5)(x - 2)}$ **15.** $\frac{1}{a^2 - a + 1}$ **17.** $\frac{x + 3}{x + 2}$

19. $\frac{a + 3}{a - 2}$ **21.** $\frac{a - 1}{a + 1}$ **23.** 1   **25.** $\frac{-x^2 + x - 1}{x - 1}$ **27.** $\frac{5}{3}$ **29.** $\frac{2x - 1}{2x + 3}$

31. $(a^{-1} + b^{-1})^{-1} = \left(\frac{1}{a} + \frac{1}{b}\right)^{-1} = \left(\frac{a + b}{ab}\right)^{-1} = \frac{ab}{a + b}$ **33.** $\frac{1 - x^{-1}}{1 + x^{-1}} = \frac{1 - \frac{1}{x}}{1 + \frac{1}{x}} = \frac{\frac{x - 1}{x}}{\frac{x + 1}{x}} = \frac{x - 1}{x + 1}$ **35.** -15 **37.** 20

39. 5   **41.** 1

PROBLEM SET 4.5

1. $-\frac{35}{3}$ **3.** $-\frac{18}{5}$ **5.** $\frac{36}{11}$ **7.** 2   **9.** 5   **11.** 2   **13.** Possible solution -1 which does not check; $\varnothing$ **15.** 5   **17.** $\frac{2}{3}$
19. 18   **21.** Possible solution 4 which does not check; $\varnothing$ **23.** -6 **25.** -5 **27.** $\frac{53}{17}$
29. Possible solution 3 which does not check; $\varnothing$ **31.** $\frac{22}{3}$ **33.** $\frac{15}{8}$ ohms   **35.** 2   **37.** $2(x + 3) = 16; 5$
39. $2x + 2(2x - 3) = 42$; width is 8 meters, length is 13 meters.

PROBLEM SET 4.6

As you can see, in addition to the answers to the problems we have included some of the equations used to solve the problems. Remember, you should attempt the problems on your own before looking here to check your answers or equations.

1. $\frac{1}{x} + \frac{1}{3x} = \frac{20}{3}$; $\frac{1}{5}$ and $\frac{3}{5}$.   **3.** $\frac{7 + x}{9 + x} = \frac{5}{6}$; 3   **5.** Let $x = $ speed of current; $\frac{1.5}{5 - x} = \frac{3}{5 + x}$; $\frac{5}{3}$ mi/hr

7. Train A—75 mi/hr, Train B—60 mi/hr   **9.** Let $x = $ time it takes them together; $\frac{1}{3} + \frac{1}{6} = \frac{1}{x}$; 2 days   **11.** 9 hours

13. Let $x = $ time to fill with both open; $\frac{1}{8} - \frac{1}{16} = \frac{1}{x}$; 16 hours   **15.** 15 hours   **17.** $l = \frac{A - 2w}{2}$ **19.** $m = \frac{y - b}{x}$

21. $n = \frac{A - a + d}{d}$

CHAPTER 4 TEST

1. $x + y$ **2.** $\frac{x - 1}{x + 1}$ **3.** $2(a + 4)$ **4.** $4(a + 3)$ **5.** $x + 3$ **6.** $\frac{38}{105}$ **7.** $\frac{7}{8}$ **8.** $\frac{1}{a - 3}$ **9.** $\frac{3(x - 1)}{x(x - 3)}$

10. $\frac{x}{(x + 4)(x + 5)}$ **11.** $\frac{5}{2}$ **12.** $\frac{3a + 8}{3a + 10}$ **13.** $\frac{x - 3}{x - 2}$ **14.** $-\frac{3}{5}$ **15.** Possible solution 3, which does not check; $\varnothing$
16. $\frac{3}{13}$ **17.** -7 **18.** 15 hours

CHAPTER 5

PROBLEM SET 5.1

1. 6   **3.** -3 **5.** 2   **7.** -2 **9.** 2   **11.** $\frac{9}{5}$ **13.** $\frac{4}{5}$ **15.** 9   **17.** 125   **19.** 8   **21.** $\frac{1}{3}$ **23.** $\frac{1}{27}$ **25.** $\frac{6}{5}$

27. $\frac{8}{27}$ **29.** 7   **31.** $\frac{3}{4}$ **33.** $x^{4/5}$ **35.** a **37.** $\frac{1}{x^{2/5}}$ **39.** $a^{3/2}b^{2/3}$ **41.** $x^{16/15}$ **43.** $x^{1/6}$ **45.** $x^{9/25}y^{1/2}z^{1/5}$

47. $x^{1/2}y^{1/3}$ **49.** $\frac{b^{7/4}}{a^{1/8}}$ **51.** $y^{3/10}$ **53.** $(9^{1/2} + 4^{1/2})^2 = (3 + 2)^2 = 5^2 = 25$ **55.** $\sqrt{\sqrt{a}} = (a^{1/2})^{1/2} = a^{1/4} = \sqrt[4]{a}$

57. 25 mi/hr   **59.** x^2 **61.** $54a^6b^2c^4$ **63.** $-36x^{11}$ **65.** $\frac{8}{125y^{18}}$

PROBLEM SET 5.2

1. $2\sqrt{2}$ **3.** $3\sqrt{2}$ **5.** $5\sqrt{3}$ **7.** $12\sqrt{2}$ **9.** $4\sqrt{3}$ **11.** $3\sqrt{5}$ **13.** $3\sqrt[3]{2}$ **15.** $4\sqrt[3]{2}$ **17.** $2\sqrt[5]{2}$ **19.** $3\sqrt{6}$

21. $2\sqrt[3]{5}$ **23.** $3\sqrt{11}$ **25.** $3x\sqrt{2x}$ **27.** $4y^3\sqrt{2y}$ **29.** $2xy^2\sqrt[3]{5xy}$ **31.** $4abc^2\sqrt{3b}$ **33.** $2bc\sqrt[3]{6a^2c}$

35. $2xy^2\sqrt[5]{2x^3y^2}$ **37.** $\dfrac{2\sqrt{3}}{3}$ **39.** $\dfrac{5\sqrt{6}}{6}$ **41.** $\dfrac{\sqrt{2}}{2}$ **43.** $\dfrac{\sqrt{5}}{5}$ **45.** $2\sqrt[3]{4}$ **47.** $\dfrac{2\sqrt[3]{3}}{3}$ **49.** $\dfrac{\sqrt{6x}}{2x}$ **51.** $\dfrac{\sqrt[3]{36xy^2}}{3y}$

53. $\dfrac{3x\sqrt{15xy}}{5y}$ **55.** $\dfrac{5xy\sqrt{6xz}}{2z}$ **57.** $\dfrac{2ab\sqrt[3]{6ac^2}}{3c}$ **59.** $x+3$ **61.** $5\sqrt{13}$ ft   **63.** $7x^2$ **65.** $7a^3$

67. x^2-2x-4

PROBLEM SET 5.3

1. $7\sqrt{5}$ **3.** $16\sqrt{6}$ **5.** $-x\sqrt{7}$ **7.** $\sqrt[3]{10}$ **9.** $9\sqrt{6}$ **11.** 0 **13.** $4\sqrt{2}$ **15.** $\sqrt{5}$ **17.** $-32\sqrt{2}$ **19.** $-3x\sqrt{2}$

21. $-2\sqrt[3]{2}$ **23.** $8x\sqrt[3]{xy^2}$ **25.** $3a^2b\sqrt{3ab}$ **27.** $11ab\sqrt[3]{3a^2b}$ **29.** $\sqrt{2}$ **31.** $\dfrac{8\sqrt{5}}{15}$ **33.** $\dfrac{2\sqrt{3}}{3}$ **35.** $\dfrac{3\sqrt{2}}{2}$

37. $\dfrac{2\sqrt{6}}{3}$ **39.** $\sqrt{12}=3.464;\ 2\sqrt{3}=2(1.732)=3.464$ **41.** $\sqrt{8}+\sqrt{18}=2.828+4.243=7.071;\ \sqrt{50}=7.071;$

$\sqrt{26}=5.099$ **43.** $8\sqrt{2x}$ **45.** 5 **47.** $6x^2-10x$ **49.** $2a^2+5a-25$ **51.** $9x^2-12xy+4y^2$ **53.** x^2-4

PROBLEM SET 5.4

1. $\sqrt{6}-9$ **3.** $24\sqrt{3}+6\sqrt{6}$ **5.** $7+2\sqrt{6}$ **7.** $x+2\sqrt{x}-15$ **9.** $34+20\sqrt{3}$ **11.** $19+8\sqrt{3}$

13. $x-6\sqrt{x}+9$ **15.** $4a-12\sqrt{ab}+9b$ **17.** 1 **19.** 15 **21.** $a-49$ **23.** $2\sqrt{3}-2\sqrt{2}$ **25.** $\dfrac{\sqrt{3}+1}{2}$

27. $\dfrac{x+3\sqrt{x}}{x-9}$ **29.** $\dfrac{10+3\sqrt{5}}{11}$ **31.** $\dfrac{3\sqrt{x}+3\sqrt{y}}{x-y}$ **33.** $-2-\sqrt{3}$ **35.** $\dfrac{a+2\sqrt{ab}+b}{a-b}$ **37.** $\dfrac{5-\sqrt{21}}{4}$

39. $\dfrac{\sqrt{x}-3x+2}{1-x}$ **43.** $10\sqrt{3}$ **45.** $x+6\sqrt{x}+9$ **47.** 75 **49. a.** $\dfrac{5\sqrt{2}}{4}$ sec **b.** $\tfrac{5}{2}$ sec   **51.** 7 **53.** 5 **55.** 3

PROBLEM SET 5.5

1. 4 **3.** $\varnothing$ **5.** 5 **7.** $\varnothing$ **9.** $\tfrac{39}{2}$ **11.** $\varnothing$ **13.** 5 **15.** 3 **17.** $-\tfrac{32}{3}$ **19.** -1 **21.** $\varnothing$ **23.** 7 **25.** 8

27. 0 **29.** 9 **31.** 0 **33.** 8 **35.** $\varnothing$ **37.** $h=100-16t^2$ **39.** x^5 **41.** x^{40} **43.** x^{30}

PROBLEM SET 5.6

1. $6i$ **3.** $-5i$ **5.** $6i\sqrt{2}$ **7.** $-2i\sqrt{3}$ **9.** 1 **11.** -1 **13.** $-i$ **15.** $x=3,\ y=-1$ **17.** $x=-2,\ y=-\tfrac{1}{2}$

19. $x=-8,\ y=-5$ **21.** $x=7,\ y=\tfrac{1}{2}$ **23.** $x=\tfrac{3}{7},\ y=\tfrac{2}{5}$ **25.** $5+9i$ **27.** $5-i$ **29.** $2-4i$ **31.** $1-6i$

33. $2+2i$ **35.** $-1-7i$ **37.** $6+8i$ **39.** $2-24i$ **41.** $\sqrt{6}-2$ **43.** $x+10\sqrt{x}+25$ **45.** $\dfrac{x-3\sqrt{x}}{x-9}$

PROBLEM SET 5.7

1. $-15+12i$ **3.** $7-7i$ **5.** $18+24i$ **7.** $10+11i$ **9.** $21+23i$ **11.** $-26+7i$ **13.** $-21+20i$

15. $-2i$ **17.** $-7-24i$ **19.** 5 **21.** 40 **23.** 13 **25.** 164 **27.** $-3-2i$ **29.** $-2+5i$ **31.** $\tfrac{8}{13}+\tfrac{12}{13}i$

33. $-\tfrac{18}{13}-\tfrac{12}{13}i$ **35.** $-\tfrac{5}{13}+\tfrac{12}{13}i$ **37.** $\tfrac{13}{15}-\tfrac{2}{5}i$ **39.** $\tfrac{31}{53}-\tfrac{24}{53}i$ **41.** $x+3$ **43.** $\dfrac{x-6}{x+6}$ **45.** $\dfrac{x^2-xy+y^2}{x-y}$

CHAPTER 5 TEST

1. $\tfrac{1}{9}$ **2.** $\tfrac{7}{5}$ **3.** $a^{5/12}$ **4.** $\dfrac{x^{13/12}}{y}$ **5.** $5xy^2\sqrt{5xy}$ **6.** $2x^2y^2\sqrt[3]{5xy^2}$ **7.** $\sqrt{6}/3$ **8.** $\dfrac{2a^2b\sqrt{15bc}}{5c}$ **9.** $-6\sqrt{3}$

10. $-ab\sqrt[3]{3}$ **11.** $x+3\sqrt{x}-28$ **12.** $21-6\sqrt{6}$ **13.** $\dfrac{5+5\sqrt{3}}{2}$ **14.** $\dfrac{x-2\sqrt{2x}+2}{x-2}$ **15.** 10 **16.** $\varnothing$

17. -4 **18.** -3 **19.** $x=\tfrac{2}{3},\ y=\tfrac{1}{2}$ **20.** $x=\tfrac{1}{2},\ y=7$ **21.** $-1-9i$ **22.** $6i$ **23.** $17-6i$ **24.** $9-40i$

25. $2-3i$ **26.** $\tfrac{10}{13}+\tfrac{15}{13}i$ **27.** $-\tfrac{5}{13}-\tfrac{12}{13}i$ **28.** $i^{38}=(i^4)^9\cdot i^2$
$=1(-1)$
$=-1$

CHAPTER 6

PROBLEM SET 6.1

1. $6,-1$ **3.** $\tfrac{1}{3},-4$ **5.** $\tfrac{2}{3},\tfrac{3}{2}$ **7.** $5,-5$ **9.** $-3,7$ **11.** $-4,\tfrac{5}{2}$ **13.** $-\tfrac{1}{5},\tfrac{1}{3}$ **15.** $-\tfrac{4}{3},\tfrac{4}{3}$ **17.** $-10,0$

19. $-5,1$ **21.** $1,2$ **23.** $-2,3$ **25.** $-2,\tfrac{1}{4}$ **27.** $-3,4$ **29.** $-\tfrac{4}{3},1$ **31.** $-3,3$ **33.** $\tfrac{5}{3},-\tfrac{1}{2}$ **35.** $-\tfrac{4}{3},\tfrac{1}{2}$

37. Possible solutions 2 and 7; only 7 checks   **39.** Possible solutions 3 and $\tfrac{8}{5}$; only $\tfrac{8}{5}$ checks   **41.** $-2,\tfrac{2}{3}$ **43.** $t=2$ seconds

45. x^2+6x+9 **47.** $x^2-8x+16$ **49.** $(x-3)^2$ **51.** $(x+2)^2$

PROBLEM SET 6.2

1. ± 5 **3.** $\pm 3i$ **5.** 2, 8 **7.** $-2, 3$ **9.** $\dfrac{-3 \pm 3i}{2}$ **11.** $x^2 + 12x + 36 = (x + 6)^2$ **13.** $x^2 - 4x + 4 = (x - 2)^2$

15. $a^2 - 10a + 25 = (a - 5)^2$ **17.** $x^2 + 5x + \frac{25}{4} = (x + \frac{5}{2})^2$ **19.** $-6, 2$ **21.** $-3, -9$ **23.** $1 \pm 2i$

25. $4 \pm \sqrt{15}$ **27.** $\dfrac{5 \pm \sqrt{37}}{2}$ **29.** $1 \pm \sqrt{5}$ **31.** $\dfrac{4 \pm \sqrt{13}}{3}$ **37.** $\dfrac{2 + \sqrt{5}}{2} = 2.118; \dfrac{2 - \sqrt{5}}{2} = -0.118$ **39.** 9

41. 17 **43.** $3 + \sqrt{17}$

PROBLEM SET 6.3

1. $-2, -3$ **3.** $2 \pm \sqrt{3}$ **5.** 1, 2 **7.** $\dfrac{2 \pm i\sqrt{14}}{3}$ **9.** $\dfrac{3 \pm \sqrt{5}}{4}$ **11.** $-3 \pm \sqrt{17}$ **13.** $\dfrac{-1 \pm i\sqrt{5}}{2}$ **15.** 1

17. $\dfrac{1 \pm i\sqrt{47}}{6}$ **19.** $-\frac{1}{2}, 3$ **21.** $\dfrac{-1 \pm i\sqrt{7}}{2}$ **23.** $1 \pm \sqrt{2}$ **25.** $\dfrac{-3 \pm \sqrt{5}}{2}$ **27.** 3, -5 **29.** 0, $\dfrac{-1 \pm i\sqrt{5}}{2}$

31. $\dfrac{-3 - 2i}{5}$ **33.** 0 or 29 **35.** 5 **37.** 27 **39.** $\frac{1}{4}$

PROBLEM SET 6.4

1. $D = 16$, two rational **3.** $D = 0$, one rational **5.** $D = 5$, two irrational **7.** $D = 17$, two irrational

9. $D = 36$, two rational **11.** $D = 116$, two irrational **13.** ± 10 **15.** ± 12 **17.** 9 **19.** -16 **21.** $\pm 2\sqrt{6}$

23. 9 **25.** $\dfrac{2}{x^7}$ **27.** $\dfrac{1}{x^{20}}$

PROBLEM SET 6.5

1. 1, 2 **3.** $-\frac{5}{2}, -8$ **5.** $\pm 3, \pm i\sqrt{3}$ **7.** $-\frac{9}{8}, \frac{1}{2}$ **9.** $\pm \dfrac{\sqrt{30}}{6}, \pm i$ **11.** 4, 25 **13.** Possible solutions 25 and 9; only 25 checks

15. Possible solutions $\frac{25}{9}$ and $\frac{49}{4}$; only $\frac{25}{9}$ checks **17.** 27, 38 **19.** 4 **21.** Possible solutions 0 and 32; only 0 checks **23.** 4

25. 7 **27.** 2, $-1 \pm i\sqrt{3}$ **29.** Boots are $5; a suit is $18 **31.** $18 and $26

PROBLEM SET 6.6

1. $x^2 + (x + 2)^2 = 34$; 3, 5 or $-5, -3$ **3.** 4, 5 or $-5, -4$ **5.** $x + \dfrac{1}{x} = \dfrac{10}{3}$; 3 or $\frac{1}{3}$ **7.** $x + \sqrt{x} = 6$; 4

9. 2 ft **11.** 6, 8, 10 **13.** $x^2 + (3x)^2 = (2\sqrt{10})^2$; 2 cm, 6 cm **15.** $74 = 5t + 16t^2$; 2 sec **17.** $\frac{1}{4}$ sec and 1 sec

19. $\dfrac{8}{x - 2} + \dfrac{8}{x + 2} = 3$; 6 mi/hr

21. $x < -\frac{1}{2}$ or $x > \frac{2}{3}$

23. $x \geq -2$ and $x \leq 4$

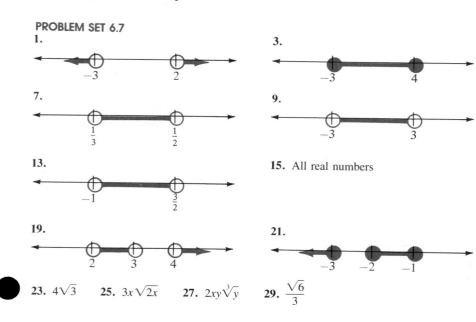

PROBLEM SET 6.7

1.

3.

5.

7.

9.

11.

13.

15. All real numbers

17. No solution, $\varnothing$

19.

21.

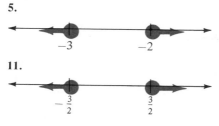

23. $4\sqrt{3}$ **25.** $3x\sqrt{2x}$ **27.** $2xy\sqrt[3]{y}$ **29.** $\dfrac{\sqrt{6}}{3}$

CHAPTER 6 TEST

1. $7, -3$ **2.** $\pm\frac{9}{5}$ **3.** $1, 2$ **4.** 2 **5.** $-2 \pm i\sqrt{2}$ **6.** $2 \pm \sqrt{2}$ **7.** $\frac{3}{2}, -1$ **8.** $\frac{8}{5}, 5$ **9.** 9

10. $D = 81$, two rational   **11.** $\pm\frac{i}{2}, \pm\sqrt{2}$ **12.** $0, 4$ **13.** $\frac{1}{2}, 1$ **14.** $\frac{1}{4}, 9$ **15.** $3, 5$ **16.** 2 mph

17.

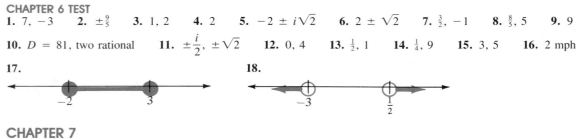

18.

CHAPTER 7

PROBLEM SET 7.1

1-15 (odd).

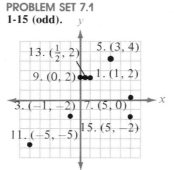

13. $(\frac{1}{2}, 2)$ 5. $(3, 4)$ 9. $(0, 2)$ 1. $(1, 2)$ 3. $(-1, -2)$ 7. $(5, 0)$ 11. $(-5, -5)$ 15. $(5, -2)$

17. $(-\frac{5}{2}, \frac{9}{2})$ **19.** $(-3, \frac{5}{2})$ **21.** $(-2, 0)$ **23.** $(-3, -2)$ **25.** $(-3, -3)$ **27.** $(3, -4)$

29.

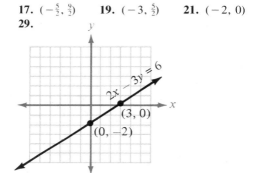

$2x - 3y = 6$
$(3, 0)$
$(0, -2)$

31.

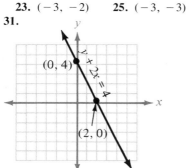

$(0, 4)$
$y + 2x = 4$
$(2, 0)$

33.

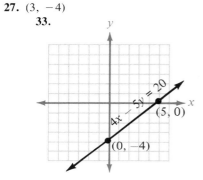

$4x - 5y = 20$
$(5, 0)$
$(0, -4)$

35.

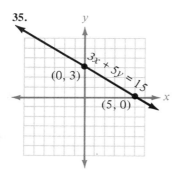

$(0, 3)$
$3x + 5y = 15$
$(5, 0)$

37.

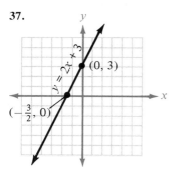

$y = 2x + 3$
$(0, 3)$
$(-\frac{3}{2}, 0)$

39.

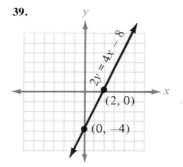

$2y = 4x - 8$
$(2, 0)$
$(0, -4)$

41.

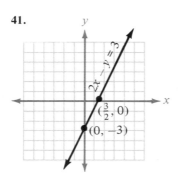

$2x - y = 3$
$(\frac{3}{2}, 0)$
$(0, -3)$

43.

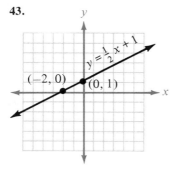

$y = \frac{1}{2}x + 1$
$(-2, 0)$
$(0, 1)$

45.

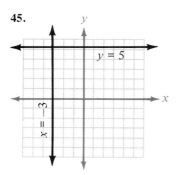

$y = 5$
$x = -3$

47.

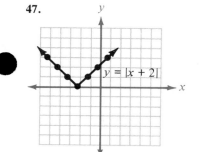

49. $-\frac{7}{4}$ **51.** -5 **53.** 2, 4

PROBLEM SET 7.2

1. 1   **3.** no slope   **5.** -1 **7.** -2 **9.** -4 **11.** $-\frac{3}{2}$ **13.** no slope   **15.** 0   **17.** $-\frac{39}{2}$ **19.** 5   **21.** -1
23. -5 **25.** -8 **27.** $\sqrt{2}/3$ **29.** 0   **31.** 8   **33.** $-2, 3$ **35.** 24 feet   **37.** $y = \frac{3}{2}x - 3$ **39.** $y = -\frac{2}{3}x + \frac{5}{3}$
41. $y = 5x - 17$

PROBLEM SET 7.3

1. $y = 2x + 3$ **3.** $y = x - 5$ **5.** $y = \frac{x}{2} + \frac{3}{2}$ **7.** $y = 4$

9. $m = 3$,
y-intercept $= -2$
perpendicular slope $= -\frac{1}{3}$

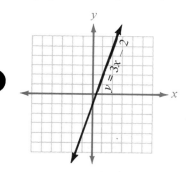

11. $m = \frac{2}{3}$,
y-intercept $= -4$,
perpendicular slope $= -\frac{3}{2}$

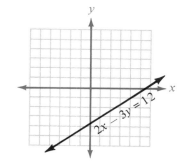

13. $m = -\frac{4}{5}$,
y-intercept $= 4$,
perpendicular slope $= \frac{5}{4}$

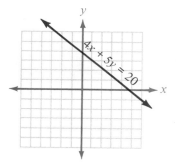

15. $y = 2x + 1$ **17.** $y = -3x + 14$ **19.** $y = -\frac{1}{2}x + 2$ **21.** $y = \frac{2}{3}x - \frac{11}{6}$ **23.** $y = -2x + 7$ **25.** $y = -\frac{7}{2}x + \frac{17}{2}$
27. $y = \frac{5}{3}x + 5$ **29.** $y = 5$
31. slope $= 0$,
y-intercept $= -2$

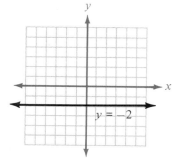

33. $y = 3x + 7$ **35.** $y = -\frac{5}{2}x - 13$ **37.** $y = \frac{1}{4}x + \frac{1}{4}$ **39.** $y = \frac{2}{3}x - 2$ **41.** $x + 2\sqrt{x} - 15$
43. $9 - 4\sqrt{5}$ **45.** $\dfrac{x - 2\sqrt{x}}{x - 4}$

PROBLEM SET 7.4

1.
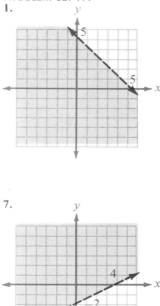

3.
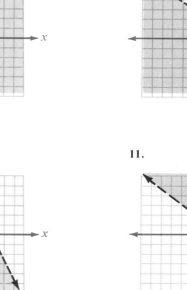

5.

7.
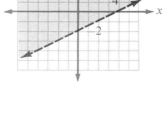

9.
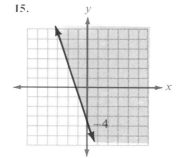

11.
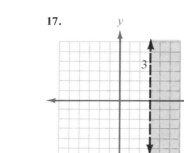

13.
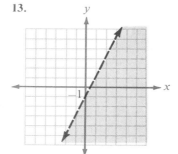

15.

17.

19.
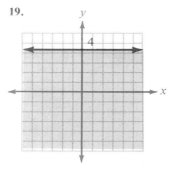

21.
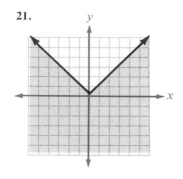

23. 7   **25.** 13   **27.** Possible solutions -6 and 1; only 1 checks.   **29.** -4

PROBLEM SET 7.5

1. 30   **3.** 5   **5.** -6 **7.** $\frac{1}{2}$ **9.** 8   **11.** $4\sqrt{2}$ **13.** $\frac{81}{5}$ **15.** $\pm 3\sqrt{2}$ **17.** 64   **19.** 8   **21.** $\frac{50}{3}$ lb   **23.** 12 lb

25. $\frac{1504}{15}$ sq. in.   **27.** 1.5 ohms   **29.** $9 - 2i$ **31.** $11 + 10i$ **33.** $5 - 12i$ **35.** $\dfrac{-5 + 12i}{13}$

CHAPTER 7 TEST

1. x-intercept $= 3$,
y-intercept $= 6$,
slope $= -2$

2. x-intercept $= -\frac{3}{2}$,
y-intercept $= -3$,
slope $= -2$

3. x-intercept $= -\frac{8}{3}$,
y-intercept $= 4$,
slope $= \frac{3}{2}$

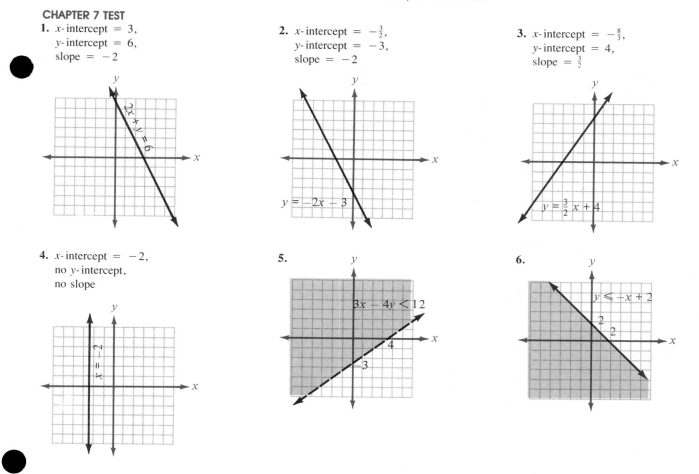

4. x-intercept $= -2$,
no y-intercept,
no slope

5.

6.

7. $y = 2x + 5$ **8.** $y = -\frac{3}{7}x + \frac{5}{7}$ **9.** $y = \frac{2}{5}x - 5$ **10.** $y = -\frac{1}{3}x - \frac{7}{3}$ **11.** $x = 4$ **12.** 18   **13.** 5   **14.** $\frac{2000}{3}$ lb

CHAPTER 8

PROBLEM SET 8.1
1. $(2, 3)$ **3.** $(1, 1)$ **5.** lines coincide $\{(x, y)|3x - 2y = 6\}$ **7.** $(1, -\frac{1}{2})$ **9.** $(4, -3)$ **11.** $(2, 2)$ **13.** parallel lines; $\varnothing$
15. $(10, 24)$ **17.** $(4, \frac{10}{3})$ **19.** $(0, 3)$ **21.** $(6, 2)$ **23.** $(2, 4)$ **25.** $(3, -3)$ **27.** lines coincide $\{(x, y)|2x - y = 5\}$
29. $(6,000, 4,000)$ **31. a.** $y = 16x + 22$ **b.** 3 min   **33.** $7\sqrt{3}$ **35.** $-5x\sqrt{5}$ **37.** $21\sqrt{2}$

PROBLEM SET 8.2
1. $(1, 2, 1)$ **3.** $(2, 1, 3)$ **5.** $(2, 0, 1)$ **7.** dependent system   **9.** $(1, 1, 1)$ **11.** dependent system   **13.** $(\frac{1}{2}, 1, 2)$
15. $(1, 3, 1)$ **17.** $(-1, 2, -2)$ **19.** 4 amp, 3 amp, 1 amp   **21.** $-2, 4$ **23.** $\frac{2}{3}, \frac{3}{2}$ **25.** $\dfrac{-1 \pm i\sqrt{3}}{2}$ **27.** $\dfrac{3 \pm \sqrt{3}}{2}$

PROBLEM SET 8.3
1. 3   **3.** 5   **5.** -1 **7.** 0   **9.** -3 **11.** -2 **13.** $-2, 5$ **15.** 3   **17.** 0   **19.** 3   **21.** 8   **23.** 6
25. -228 **27.** $\begin{vmatrix} y & x \\ m & 1 \end{vmatrix} = y - mx = b; y = mx + b$ **29.** $\pm 2, \pm i\sqrt{2}$ **31.** $\frac{9}{4}, 1$ **33.** 4

PROBLEM SET 8.4
1. $(3, 1)$ **3.** parallel lines, $\varnothing$ **5.** $(-\frac{15}{43}, -\frac{27}{43})$ **7.** $(\frac{60}{43}, \frac{46}{43})$ **9.** $(\frac{1}{2}, \frac{5}{2}, 1)$ **11.** $(3, -1, 2)$ **13.** dependent system
15. $\left(-\dfrac{10}{91}, -\dfrac{63}{91}, \dfrac{107}{91}\right)$ **17.** $(3, -2, 4)$ **19.** $(3, 1, 2)$ **21.** $x = 50$ items   **23.** $\dfrac{x}{x + 15} = \dfrac{4}{7}; \dfrac{20}{35}$
25. $\dfrac{1}{5} + \dfrac{1}{6} + \dfrac{1}{10} = \dfrac{1}{x}; \dfrac{15}{7}$ hours

PROBLEM SET 8.5
1. $y = 2x + 3$, $x + y = 18$ The two numbers are 5 and 13   **3.** 10, 16   **5.** 1, 3, 4
7. Let x = the number of adult tickets and y = the number of children's tickets.
   $x + y = 925$ 225 adult and
   $2x + y = 1150$ 700 children's tickets
9. Let x = the amount invested at 6% and y = the amount invested at 7%.
      $x + y = 20{,}000$ He has $12,000 at 6%
   $.06x + .07y = 1280$ and $8,000 at 7%
11. $4000 at 6%, $8,000 at 7.5%   **13.** 3 gal of 50%, 6 gal of 20%   **15.** 5 gal of 20%, 10 gal of 14%
17. Let x = the speed of the boat and y = the speed of the current.
   $3(x - y) = 18$ The speed of the boat is 9 mph
   $2(x + y) = 24$ The speed of the current is 3 mph
19. 270 mph airplane, 30 mph wind   **21.** 3 of each

23. $-2 \leq x \leq 4$ **25.** $x < -3$ or $x > \frac{1}{2}$

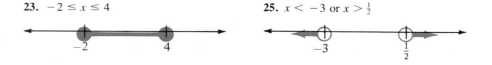

CHAPTER 8 TEST
1. $(1, 2)$ **2.** $(3, 2)$ **3.** $\left(-\frac{54}{13}, -\frac{58}{13}\right)$ **4.** $(1, 2)$ **5.** $(3, -2, 1)$ **6.** -14 **7.** -26 **8.** $\left(-\frac{14}{3}, -\frac{19}{3}\right)$
9. lines coincide $\{(x, y) \mid 2x + 4y = 3\}$ **10.** $\left(\frac{5}{11}, -\frac{15}{11}, -\frac{1}{11}\right)$ **11.** $4000 at 5%, $8000 at 6%
12. 3 oz of cereal I, 1 oz of cereal II

CHAPTER 9

PROBLEM SET 9.1
1. x-intercepts $= -3, 1$;   **3.** x-intercepts $= -5, 1$;   **5.** x-intercepts $= -1, 1$;
   vertex $= (-1, -4)$ vertex $= (-2, 9)$ vertex $= (0, -1)$

7. x-intercepts $= 3, -3$;   **9.** x-intercepts $= -1, 3$ **11.** x-intercepts $= (1 + \sqrt{5}, 0), (1 - \sqrt{5}, 0)$;
   vertex $= (0, 9)$ vertex $= (1, -8)$ vertex $= (1, -5)$

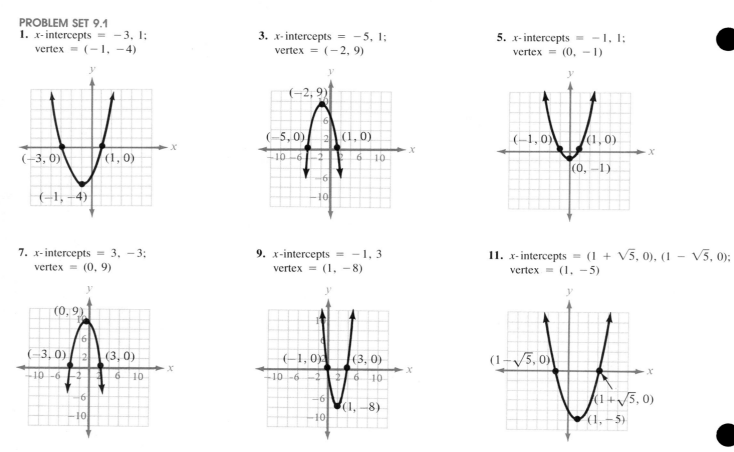

13. vertex = (2, −8)

15. vertex = (1, −4)

17. vertex = (0, 1)

19. vertex = (0, −3)

21. vertex = $(-\frac{2}{3}, -\frac{1}{3})$

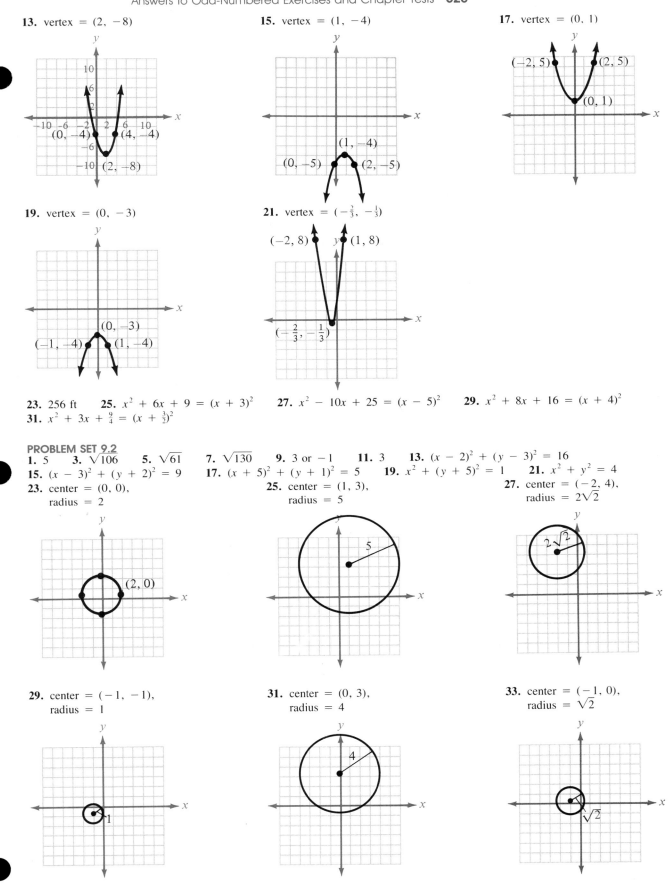

23. 256 ft   **25.** $x^2 + 6x + 9 = (x + 3)^2$ **27.** $x^2 - 10x + 25 = (x - 5)^2$ **29.** $x^2 + 8x + 16 = (x + 4)^2$
31. $x^2 + 3x + \frac{9}{4} = (x + \frac{3}{2})^2$

PROBLEM SET 9.2
1. 5   **3.** $\sqrt{106}$ **5.** $\sqrt{61}$ **7.** $\sqrt{130}$ **9.** 3 or −1   **11.** 3   **13.** $(x - 2)^2 + (y - 3)^2 = 16$
15. $(x - 3)^2 + (y + 2)^2 = 9$ **17.** $(x + 5)^2 + (y + 1)^2 = 5$ **19.** $x^2 + (y + 5)^2 = 1$ **21.** $x^2 + y^2 = 4$
23. center = (0, 0),
radius = 2

25. center = (1, 3),
radius = 5

27. center = (−2, 4),
radius = $2\sqrt{2}$

29. center = (−1, −1),
radius = 1

31. center = (0, 3),
radius = 4

33. center = (−1, 0),
radius = $\sqrt{2}$

35. center = (2, 3),
radius = 3

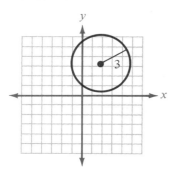

37. center = $(-1, -\frac{1}{2})$,
radius = 2

39. $x^2 + y^2 = 25$ **41.** $x^2 + y^2 = 16$ **43.** $(x - 2)^2 + (y - 5)^2 = 10$ **45.** 3   **47.** 5   **49.** $\frac{2}{3}$

PROBLEM SET 9.3

1.

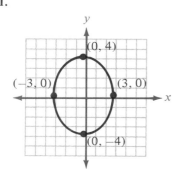

3.

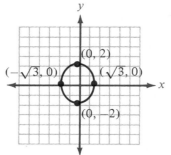

5.

7.

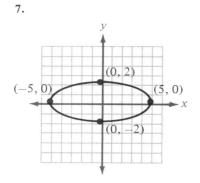

9.

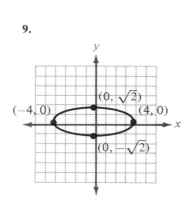

11.

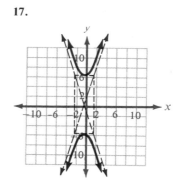

13.

15.

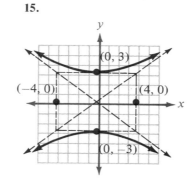

17.

19.

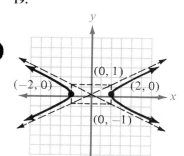

21.

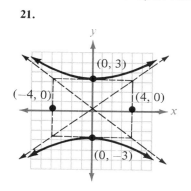

23. $y = \frac{3}{4}x$; $y = -\frac{3}{4}x$

25. 8

27.

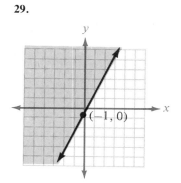

29.

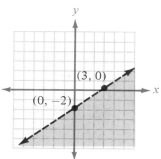

31.

PROBLEM SET 9.4

1.

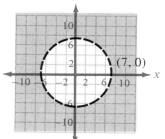

3.

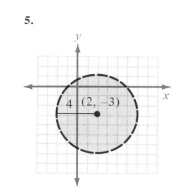

5.

7.

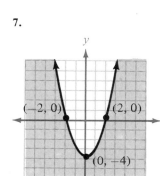

9.

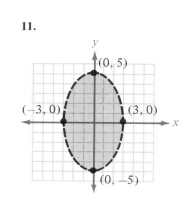

11.

13.

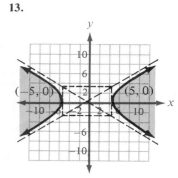

15.

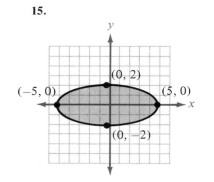

17.

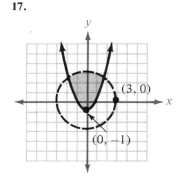

19.

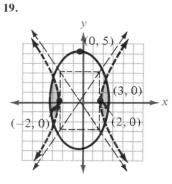

21.

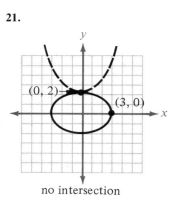

no intersection

23. $(1, 2)$ **25.** $(0, 3)$ **27.** $(3, 4)$

PROBLEM SET 9.5

1. $(0, 3), (\frac{12}{5}, -\frac{9}{5})$ **3.** $(0, 4), (\frac{16}{5}, \frac{12}{5})$ **5.** $(5, 0), (-5, 0)$ **7.** $(0, -3), (\sqrt{5}, 2), (-\sqrt{5}, 2)$
9. $(0, -4), (\sqrt{7}, 3), (-\sqrt{7}, 3)$ **11.** $(-4, 11), (\frac{5}{2}, \frac{5}{4})$ **13.** $(3, 0), (-3, 0)$ **15.** $(4, 0), (0, -4)$ **17.** $(8, 5)$ or $(-8, -5)$
19. $(6, 3)$ or $(13, -4)$ **21.** $y = -3x + 5$ **23.** $y = 5x - 17$ **25.** $y = \frac{2}{3}x - 2$

CHAPTER 9 TEST

1.
(a)

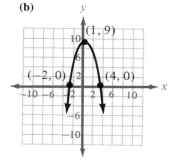

(b)

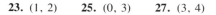

2. $\sqrt{82}$ **3.** -5 and 3 **4.** $(x + 2)^2 + (y - 4)^2 = 9$ **5.** $x^2 + y^2 = 25$ **6.** center $= (5, -3)$,
radius $= \sqrt{39}$

7.

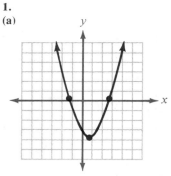

8.

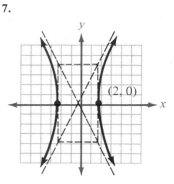

9. center = (2, −1),
radius = 3

10.

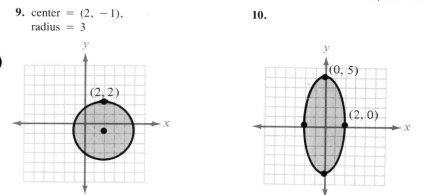

(2, 2)

(0, 5)

(2, 0)

11. (0, 5), (4, −3)   **12.** (0, −4), ($\sqrt{7}$, 3), (−$\sqrt{7}$, 3)

CHAPTER 10

PROBLEM SET 10.1

1. $D = \{1, 2, 4\}$, $R = \{3, 5, 1\}$, yes   **3.** $D = \{-1, 1, 2\}$, $R = \{3, -5\}$, yes   **5.** $D = \{7, 3\}$, $R = \{-1, 4\}$, no
7. $D = \{4, 3\}$, $R = \{3, 4, 5\}$, no   **9.** $D = \{5, -3, 2\}$, $R = \{-3, 2\}$, yes   **11.** yes   **13.** no   **15.** no   **17.** yes
19. yes   **21.** $\{x|x \geq -3\}$ **23.** $\{x|x \geq \frac{1}{2}\}$ **25.** $\{x|x \leq \frac{1}{4}\}$ **27.** $\{x|x \neq 5\}$ **29.** $\{x|x \neq \frac{1}{2}, x \neq -3\}$
31. $\{x|x \neq -2, x \neq 3\}$ **33.** $\{x|x \neq -2, x \neq 2\}$

35.

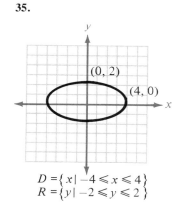

(0, 2)

(4, 0)

$D = \{x| -4 \leqslant x \leqslant 4\}$
$R = \{y| -2 \leqslant y \leqslant 2\}$

37.

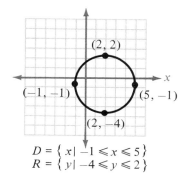

(2, 2)

(−1, −1)

(5, −1)

(2, −4)

$D = \{x| -1 \leqslant x \leqslant 5\}$
$R = \{y| -4 \leqslant y \leqslant 2\}$

39.

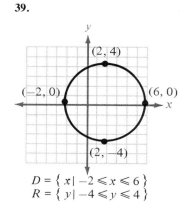

(2, 4)

(−2, 0)

(6, 0)

(2, −4)

$D = \{x| -2 \leqslant x \leqslant 6\}$
$R = \{y| -4 \leqslant y \leqslant 4\}$

41.

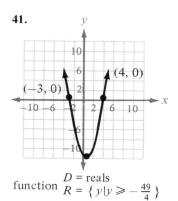

(4, 0)

(−3, 0)

function
D = reals
$R = \{y|y \geqslant -\frac{49}{4}\}$

43.

$D = \{x|x \leqslant -2 \text{ or } x \geqslant 2\}$
R = reals

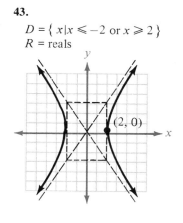

(2, 0)

45. a. yes
b. $D = \{t|0 \leq t \leq 6\}$
$R = \{h|0 \leq h \leq 60\}$
c. 3   **d.** 60   **e.** 0 and 6

47. (1, 2, 3)   **49.** (1, 3, 1)

PROBLEM SET 10.2

1. -1 **3.** -11 **5.** -5 **7.** 2 **9.** 4 **11.** 35 **13.** -13 **15.** 4 **17.** 0 **19.** 2 **21.** 2 **23.** $-\frac{1}{2}$
25. 1 **27.** -9 **29.** $3a^2 - 4a + 1$ **31.** $3a^2 + 14a + 16$ **33.** 16 **35.** 15 **37.** 1 **39.** $12x^2 - 20x + 8$
41. 2 **43.** $2x + h$ **45.** -4 **47.** $3(2x + h)$ **49.** $4x + 2h + 3$ **51.** 3 **53.** 4 **55.** $x + a$ **57.** 5
59. $x + a$ **61.** \$107, \$175, \$1000 **63.** 2 and 3 **65.** $-\frac{3}{2}$ **67.** -13 **69.** 31 **71.** -14

PROBLEM SET 10.3

1. $6x + 2$ **3.** $-2x + 8$ **5.** $8x^2 + 14x - 15$ **7.** $(2x + 5)/(4x - 3)$ **9.** $4x - 7$ **11.** $3x^2 - 10x + 8$
13. $-2x + 3$ **15.** $3x^2 - 11x + 10$ **17.** $9x^3 - 48x^2 + 85x - 50$ **19.** $x - 2$ **21.** $1/(x - 2)$ **23.** $3x^2 - 7x + 3$
25. $6x^2 - 22x + 20$ **27.** 15 **29.** 98 **31.** $\frac{3}{2}$ **33.** 1 **35.** 40 **37.** 147 **39. a.** \$2.49 **b.** \$1.53 **c.** 5 min
41. $\left(-\frac{15}{43}, -\frac{27}{43}\right)$ **43.** $(1, 3, 1)$

PROBLEM SET 10.4

1.
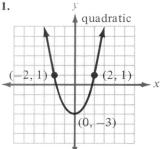

3.

5.
constant

7.
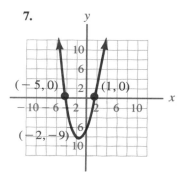

9. $\frac{1}{9}$ **11.** $\frac{1}{4}$ **13.** 1 **15.** 2 **17.** $\frac{1}{27}$ **19.** 13 **21.** 17 **23.** 2 **25.** $\frac{17}{72}$

27.
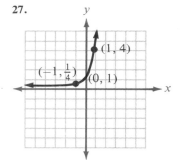

29.
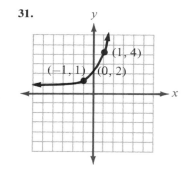

31.
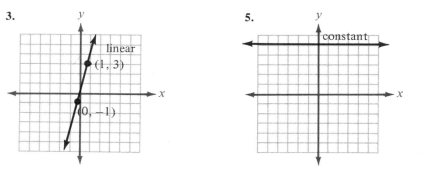

33.
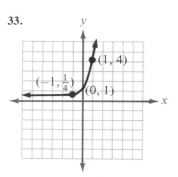

35.

39. 200, 400, 800, 1600, 10 days **41.** 5
43. 3 or -1 **45.** Center $(0, 0)$, $r = 5$
47. Center $(-3, 2)$, $r = 4$

PROBLEM SET 10.5

1. $f^{-1}(x) = \dfrac{x+1}{3}$ **3.** $f^{-1}(x) = \dfrac{1-x}{3}$ **5.** $f^{-1}(x) = \pm\sqrt{x-4}$ **7.** $f^{-1}(x) = 4x+3$ **9.** $f^{-1}(x) = 2(x+3)$

11. $f^{-1}(x) = \pm\sqrt{3-x}$

13.

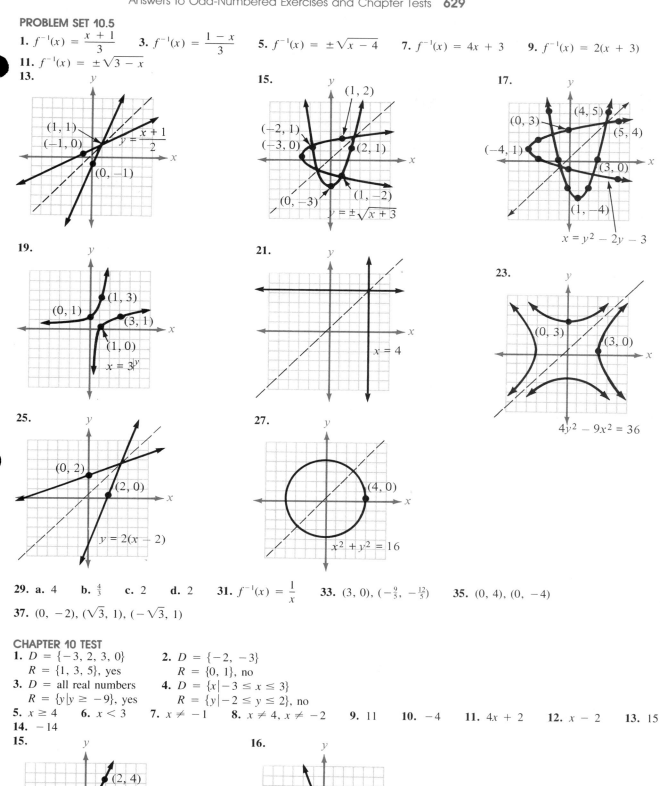

15.

17.

19.

21.

23.

25.

27.

29. a. 4   **b.** $\frac{4}{3}$ **c.** 2   **d.** 2   **31.** $f^{-1}(x) = \dfrac{1}{x}$ **33.** $(3, 0), \left(-\frac{9}{5}, -\frac{12}{5}\right)$ **35.** $(0, 4), (0, -4)$

37. $(0, -2), (\sqrt{3}, 1), (-\sqrt{3}, 1)$

CHAPTER 10 TEST

1. $D = \{-3, 2, 3, 0\}$ **2.** $D = \{-2, -3\}$
    $R = \{1, 3, 5\}$, yes $R = \{0, 1\}$, no
3. D = all real numbers   **4.** $D = \{x \mid -3 \le x \le 3\}$
    $R = \{y \mid y \ge -9\}$, yes $R = \{y \mid -2 \le y \le 2\}$, no
5. $x \ge 4$ **6.** $x < 3$ **7.** $x \ne -1$ **8.** $x \ne 4, x \ne -2$ **9.** 11   **10.** -4 **11.** $4x + 2$ **12.** $x - 2$ **13.** 15
14. -14

15.

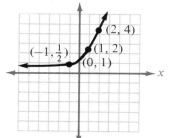

16.

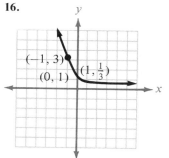

17.

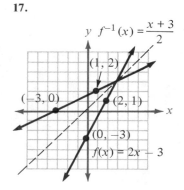

18.

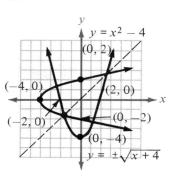

CHAPTER 11

PROBLEM SET 11.1

1. $\log_2 16 = 4$ **3.** $\log_5 125 = 3$ **5.** $\log_{10} .01 = -2$ **7.** $\log_2 \frac{1}{32} = -5$ **9.** $\log_{1/2} 8 = -3$ **11.** $\log_3 27 = 3$
13. $10^2 = 100$ **15.** $2^6 = 64$ **17.** $8^0 = 1$ **19.** $10^{-3} = .001$ **21.** $6^2 = 36$ **23.** $5^{-2} = \frac{1}{25}$ **25.** 9   **27.** $\frac{1}{125}$
29. 4   **31.** $\frac{1}{3}$ **33.** 2   **35.** $\sqrt[3]{5}$

37.

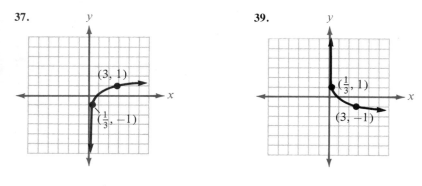

39.

41.

43.

45. 4   **47.** $\frac{3}{2}$ **49.** 3   **51.** 1   **53.** 0   **55.** 0   **57.** $\frac{1}{2}$ **59.** 2.52 min   **61.** -2 **63.** -5 **65.** 2, -4
67. $\frac{1}{2}$, -3

PROBLEM SET 11.2

1. $\log_3 4 + \log_3 x$ **3.** $\log_6 5 - \log_6 x$ **5.** $5 \log_2 y$ **7.** $\frac{1}{3} \log_9 z$ **9.** $2 \log_6 x + 3 \log_6 y$ **11.** $\frac{1}{2} \log_5 x + 4 \log_5 y$
13. $\log_b x + \log_b y - \log_b z$ **15.** $\log_{10} 4 - \log_{10} x - \log_{10} y$ **17.** $2 \log_{10} x + \log_{10} y - \frac{1}{2} \log_{10} z$

19. $3 \log_{10} x + \frac{1}{2} \log_{10} y - 4 \log_{10} z$ **21.** $\frac{2}{3} \log_b x + \frac{1}{3} \log_b y - \frac{4}{3} \log_b z$ **23.** $\log_b xz$ **25.** $\log_3 \frac{x^2}{y^3}$ **27.** $\log_{10} \sqrt{x} \sqrt[3]{y}$

29. $\log_2 \frac{x^3 \sqrt{y}}{z}$ **31.** $\log_2 \frac{\sqrt{x}}{y^3 z^4}$ **33.** $\log_{10} \frac{x^{3/2}}{y^{3/4} z^{4/5}}$ **35.** $\frac{2}{3}$ **37.** 18   **39.** Possible solutions -1 and 3; only 3 checks
41. 3   **43.** Possible solutions -2 and 4; only 4 checks   **45.** Possible solutions -1 and 4; only 4 checks   **47.** Possible solutions
$-\frac{5}{2}$ and $\frac{5}{3}$; only $\frac{5}{3}$ checks   **49.** 3.94×10^8 **51.** 3.91×10^{-2} **53.** 0.00523   **55.** 50,300

PROBLEM SET 11.3

1. 2.5775   **3.** 1.5775   **5.** 3.5775   **7.** 8.5775 − 10   **9.** 4.5775   **11.** 2.7782   **13.** 3.3032   **15.** 7.9872 − 10
17. 8.4969 − 10   **19.** 9.6010 − 10   **21.** 759   **23.** .00759   **25.** 1430   **27.** .00000447   **29.** .0000000918
31. 9260   **33.** 1.27   **35.** 20   **37.** 10.1   **39.** 386   **41.** 40,200,000   **43.** 24,800   **45.** 133,000   **47.** 258,000,000
49. 42 lb   **51.** 3.3×10^4 **53.** $x > -7$ **55.** $x \leq 1$ **57.** $x < -4$ or $x > \frac{3}{2}$ **59.** $3 \leq x \leq 5$

PROBLEM SET 11.4

1. 1.4651   **3.** .6825   **5.** −1.5439   **7.** −.6477   **9.** −.3333   **11.** 2.0000   **13.** −.1846   **15.** .1846   **17.** 1.6168
19. 2.1131   **21.** 1.3333   **23.** .7500   **25.** 1.3917   **27.** .7186   **29.** .9650   **31.** 1.0363   **33.** 2.6356   **35.** 4.1629

37. $n = \dfrac{\log A - \log P}{\log(1 + r)}$ **39.** 60 geese, 48 ducks

41. Let x = number of oranges and y = number of apples

$$\frac{10x}{3} + \frac{5y}{4} = 680 \quad \text{He bought 150 oranges and 144 apples.}$$

$$\frac{50x}{3} + \frac{5y}{16} = 2545$$

PROBLEM SET 11.5

1. 2.40   **3.** 5.30   **5.** 4.38   **7.** 1.07   **9.** 3.98×10^{-4} **11.** 3.16×10^{-7} **13. a.** 1.62   **b.** .87   **c.** .00293
d. 2.86×10^{-6} **15.** 5600   **17.** $8950   **19.** $4120   **21.** 14.2 years   **23.** 11.9 years   **25.** $\frac{7}{3}$, 1   **27.** $\varnothing$
29. $x < -1$ or $x > 9$ **31.** $-1 \leq x \leq 2$

CHAPTER 11 TEST

1. 64   **2.** $\sqrt{5}$

3.

4.

5. $\frac{2}{3}$ **6.** 1.5645   **7.** 4.3692   **8.** 8.0899 − 10   **9.** 7.04×10^4 **10.** 2.25×10^{-3} **11.** 14,200   **12.** 15.6   **13.** 2.19
14. 1.47   **15.** 1.4651   **16.** $\frac{5}{4}$ **17.** 15   **18.** 8   **19.** $5110   **20.** 3.52

APPENDIX A

1. $x - 7 + \dfrac{20}{x + 2}$ **3.** $3x - 1$ **5.** $x^2 + 4x + 11 + \dfrac{26}{x - 2}$ **7.** $3x^2 + 8x + 26 + \dfrac{83}{x - 3}$ **9.** $2x^2 + 2x + 3$

11. $x^3 - 4x^2 + 18x - 72 + \dfrac{289}{x + 4}$ **13.** $x^4 + x^2 - x - 3 - \dfrac{5}{x - 2}$ **15.** $x + 2 + \dfrac{3}{x - 1}$ **17.** $x^3 - x^2 + x - 1$
19. $x^2 + x + 1$

APPENDIX B

1. $(2x + 1)(2x - 3)$ **3.** $(2x - 1)(2x + 3)$ **5.** $(4a - 1)(a + 3)$ **7.** $(2x + 1)(4x + 3)$ **9.** $(5y + 6)(y - 1)$
11. $(5x - 2)(x - 3)$ **13.** $(3y + 5)(2y + 1)$ **15.** $(x + 4)(x + 3)$ **17.** $(5a + 2)(2a - 3)$ **19.** $(8x - 5)(x + 1)$

APPENDIX C

1.

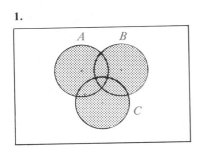

3.

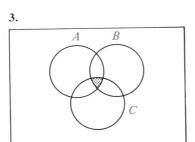

5.

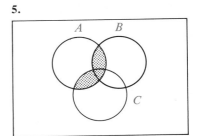

7.

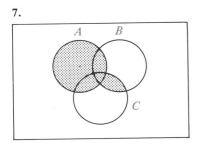

9.

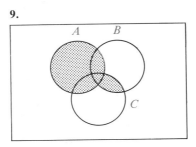

11.

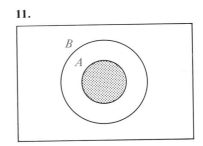

13.

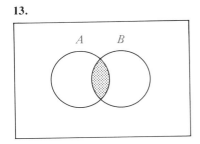

15.

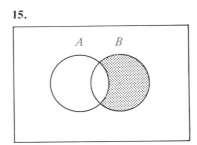

17.

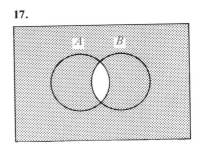

19.

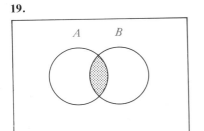

Index